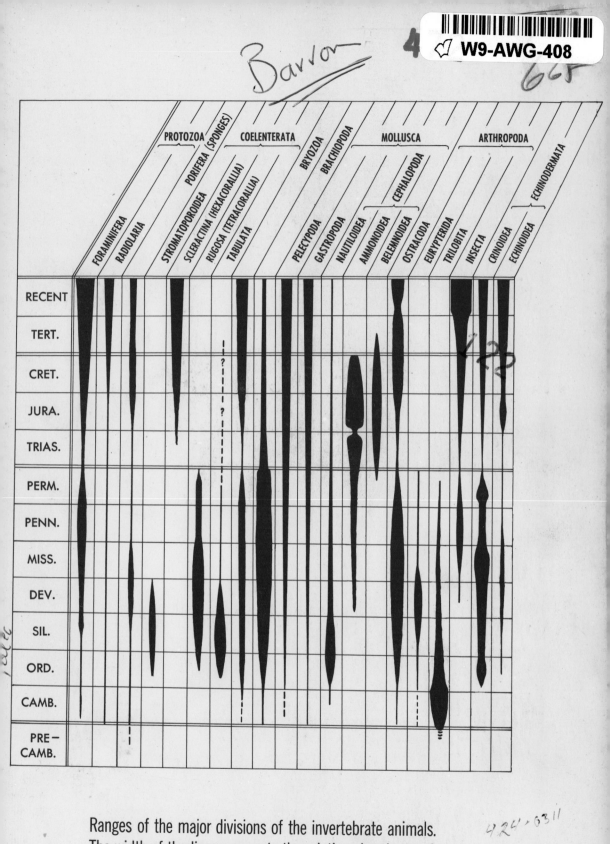

Ranges of the major divisions of the invertebrate animals.
The width of the line represents the relative abundance of
members of the groups during the geological past.

THOMAS H. CLARK, Ph.D., Harvard University, was for many years Logan Professor of Paleontology and Chairman of the Department of Geological Sciences at McGill University, where he is now Professor Emeritus and Advisor in Geology to the Redpath Museum. He has been for several years Consultant to the Quebec Department of Natural Resources. He previously taught at Harvard University. Professor Clark is a Fellow of the Geological Society of America and of the Royal Society of Canada. He has served as President of the Geological Association of Canada.

COLIN W. STEARN, Ph.D., Yale University, is Logan Professor of Geological Sciences at McGill University, where he has also served as Assistant Dean of the Graduate Faculty. He has participated in field surveys for the Geological Survey of Canada, British American Oil Company, and the Quebec Department of Natural Resources. Professor Stearn is a Fellow of the Geological Society of America and of the Royal Society of Canada.

GEOLOGICAL
EVOLUTION
OF
NORTH AMERICA

THOMAS H. CLARK

COLIN W. STEARN

BOTH OF McGILL UNIVERSITY

SECOND EDITION

THE RONALD PRESS COMPANY • NEW YORK

Library of Congress Catalog Card Number: 68–21648

PRINTED IN THE UNITED STATES OF AMERICA

Preface

We set out to write a historical geology textbook for first-year geology students with the conviction, borne out by several years of teaching the subject, that a regional approach is the most effective. We believed that the student could gain a knowledge of the regional geology of North America while learning the methods by which the stratigrapher and paleontologist interpret the record of the rocks. This remains the goal of the Second Edition.

The historical development of the continent is presented in terms of its major structural units: the bordering geosynclines, the platform, and the Canadian Shield. A greater unity of treatment is achieved by considering the development of these great structural units through a major part of geological time. The student is led to a clear recognition of the similarities and equally important differences in the patterns of behavior of the various structural elements.

Throughout, emphasis has been placed on the presentation of principles. The aim of the book is to illustrate to the elementary student the many methods used by the historical geologist. Some of the examples are discussed in considerable detail, so that the student will appreciate the nature of the materials that are the basis for the geologist's interpretation of the stratigraphic and paleontologic record. To reinforce the principles that the student has learned in each chapter, a summary has been added along with a few questions designed to stimulate him to think about the material.

This book incorporates recent advances in historical geology, such as the extensive use of potassium–argon and rubidium–strontium dating. The new evidence of paleomagnetism which has forced a reappraisal of theories of continental drift and polar wandering is extensively discussed. Part II, on cratonic sedimentation, is organized on the basis of the sequences in cratonic rocks proposed by L. L. Sloss.

The evolution of life, as shown by fossils, is an integral part of historical geology. A close relationship between biological material and the evolution of geological structures is maintained through the book. In Part VI, where life is described through the major divisions of geological time, the periods are grouped so as to highlight some of the salient points in earth history. Throughout this portion of the book, there is a clear dependence upon illustrations of habitats to emphasize the interrelationships between animals and plants of any particular time.

In addition to qualitative facies maps of the continent, there are several kinds of quantitative facies maps and isopach maps. From these the student learns that stratigraphy is not purely a descriptive subject, but that the geometry and facies variations of sedimentary deposits can be described and analyzed mathematically.

All the new drawings and maps for this edition are the work of Mary Joan Stearn, to whom the authors wish to express their gratitude here for her devoted and skillful work. The new photographs of specimens from the McGill Museums have been taken by Harold Coletta, whose assistance is gratefully acknowledged. We are grateful also to the officers of the Peter Redpath and McCord Museums at McGill for permission to use the specimens from their collections.

We acknowledge with gratitude also the assistance of our colleagues at McGill who read and criticized parts of the manuscript: Professors Ronald Doig, O. Denstedt, J. A. Elson, J. E. Gill, T. E. Morris, E. W. Mountjoy, A. R. Philpotts, V. A. Saull, and A. L. Thompson. We are especially grateful to Dr. Robert Carroll of the Redpath Museum for his advice on the preparation of the sixth part of the book. Our thanks also go to Dr. J. W. Kerr of the Geological Survey of Canada, who critically reviewed the chapter on the Arctic Islands. The kindness of the many geologists and institutions who have sent us photographs or allowed us to reproduce their own illustrations is acknowledged beneath the individual figures.

Although both of us participated in the writing of the whole book, the senior author prepared the sections on life history and the junior author the sections on the physical evolution of the continent.

Thomas H. Clark
Colin W. Stearn

Montreal, Quebec
March, 1968

Contents

IV · THE APPALACHIAN GEOSYNCLINE

V · CONTINENTAL NUCLEUS AND NORTHLAND

VI · THE EVOLUTION OF LIFE

APPENDIXES

I

THE METHODS AND PROBLEMS OF HISTORICAL GEOLOGY

Stratigraphy

INTRODUCTION

Scope

The archeologist Heinrich Schliemann, long obsessed with a desire to find the site of ancient Troy, began excavations in 1872 on a low hill in Asia Minor on the plain overlooking the Dardanelles, gateway to the Black Sea (Fig. 1–1). The siege of Troy, made famous in the Homeric poems the *Iliad* and the *Odyssey*, could have been fact or fiction; only by finding the remains of the city that the Greeks besieged and won with a wooden horse 3000 years ago could the question be settled. Schliemann excavated the rubble of civilizations that covered the rocky hill, removing layer after layer, and distinguishing stage after stage in the occupation of this strategic site. The topmost layers revealed implements, architecture, and art of a city of the Roman empire; the basal one had neolithic stone artifacts of an age before man worked with metal. Several layers, or strata, above the base, a citadel of "cyclopean" architecture—the "topless towers" of poets— built of huge, crudely shaped stones, showed evidence of having been destroyed by fire.

Subsequent research has shown that this was the Troy of which the Homeric bards sang, the home of Helen whose face "launched a thousand ships," the Troy whose siege Odysseus attended and from which he set out on a ten-year voyage home.

The archeologist reads the history of man's civilization by digging into such sites as Troy, carefully recording the contents of each layer, relating the artifacts of one layer to those of another to discover how man's skill in fashioning materials progressed, tracing the path of trade goods from one site to another, plotting the migrations of nomadic peoples bringing their culture from afar. Similarly, the historical geologist reads the record of the earth's history in the layers of sedimentary rocks. Like the archeologist, he finds evidence of the conditions of the past in the inorganic constituents of each layer, such as the sedimentary particles, and in the organic constituents, the fossils. These are analogous to the building stones and the burials of archeological excavations. The archeologist uses the same methods as the historical geologist, but while the archeologist is concerned with tracing the history of man's culture

Fig. 1–1. The mound of Troy, excavated by Schliemann and many later archeologists, stands on the Trojan Plain in Turkey. (Courtesy of the Department of Classics, University of Cincinnati.)

through the thousands of years since he first made tools, the geologist's scope of investigation stretches back through the hundreds of millions of years during which life has existed on earth to the time billions of years ago when the earth was formed and electrons, protons, and neutrons first came together to form the elements. Formidable though the task of the archeologist may be, the greater task of the historical geologist can be measured in terms of the 5 billion years since the origin of our planet as compared to its inhabitation by man a million years ago.

Schliemann extended his investigations to Crete and Greece, and in excavations at Mycenae and Tiryns he found architecture, weapons, and implements similar to those of the cyclopean level at Troy. Levels at different sites were matched, and a regional picture of civilization around the Aegean Sea was built up for the Homeric period of about 1200 B.C. Similarly, the historical geologist attempts a synthesis of conditions of the past

by matching or correlating layers of rocks at different localities to build a regional picture. Some of the recording rocks have been removed by erosion since they were deposited and will never tell their story; others have been so metamorphosed in mountain building that the evidence for their origin has become obscure; still others are deeply buried beneath younger layers and have not yet been penetrated by drilling. The farther back the geologist tries to trace the history of the world, the more difficult his work becomes for, in general, older rocks have been subjected to more episodes of erosion and metamorphism and are more deeply buried than younger ones. To picture the earth, or part of it, at some particular time in the past, he must take account of conditions revealed by whatever rocks may be present in small, separated areas, and fit them together as one fits together the pieces of a jigsaw puzzle. Many pieces of the puzzle have not yet been found; some have been destroyed or damaged beyond recognition; and some have confusing patterns that do not seem to fit into the parts of the picture that have already been assembled. To the historical geologist, the earth's history seems at times like a story recorded in a book each page of which is torn into small pieces. Many of the pages and some of the pieces of each page are missing, and at least a quarter of those missing will never be found.

Yet even from such a book the outlines of the story may be read. The major features of the history of North America have been known for many years, and as new information is assembled more and more details of the puzzles are filled in. Many branches of geology contribute to the synthesis that is historical geology. Stratigraphy and sedimentology are the most important of these because they are concerned with sedimentary rocks, which constitute the best available record of conditions in the past. Paleontology makes an important contribution, for the fossils found in sedimentary rocks give us the best means of dating the events of the past (see Chapter 2). Also, much can be deduced from fossils concerning the conditions under which early organisms lived. The interpretation of relatively recent events and processes that have left their mark upon the landscape is made by **geomorphology,** the study of land forms and surficial deposits. Through the studies of structural geologists we understand the architecture of mountain ranges, resolve the forces that formed them, and recognize the sequence of events that raised them from the ocean floor. Each of the geological sciences contributes something to our knowledge of the earth's past.

This book is an introduction to the methods by which the record of the rocks is interpreted to form a picture of the history of a single continent. The history of North America thus portrayed should demonstrate to the student the guiding principles by which the pieces of the geological jigsaw puzzle are fitted together, so that he may learn to read the record of the rocks for himself.

Incentives

Although the interpretation of the geological history of a region may be treated as an intellectual exercise only, it may also be a profitable one. Many geologists are employed by oil companies to reconstruct conditions in ancient sedimentary basins from information collected during the drilling of oil wells or as part of the field work of the company's geologists. The practical value of geological studies lies in their ability to aid in the discovery of mineral wealth. The historical geologist or the stratigrapher, in making this type of scientific prediction, works like other scientists. He collects information from the rocks of an area and tabulates it or plots it on a map. He then tries to discover in his compilation some arrangement, system, or relationship that will logically explain the facts. For the stratigrapher the process involves a recognition of the conditions of the past that determined the type of sediment deposited. He tries to refer each kind of rock to the environment in which it was deposited, in order to construct a logical pattern of land and sea, rivers and mountains, bays and estuaries. When the geography of an earlier period has been recreated in the mind and on the maps of the geologist, he may be able to predict where certain types of rock will be found. If the petroleum geologist is looking for oil-bearing sandstone lenses formed millions of years ago as offshore bars and now buried deep beneath younger sedimentary layers, he must first reconstruct the position of the ancient shoreline. If he wishes to find coal seams, a reconstruction of the unique conditions of sedimentation that cause coal formation will be essential. These same principles may be applied to exploration for any mineral resource, such as limestone, gypsum, or rock salt, whose occurrence is controlled by sedimentation.

Many deposits of metals occur in and around the igneous intrusions that accompany mountain making. A detailed knowledge of the historical sequence of events of mountain formation is a great help in prospecting for and developing such deposits. Similarly, deposits of asbestos, slate, marble, and chromite are related to episodes of metamorphism that must be understood before an intelligent search for such materials can be undertaken. Although historical geology had its origins in man's curiosity, the knowledge gained has many practical applications.

INTERPRETATION OF SEDIMENTARY ROCKS

In the northern part of New York State and in southern Quebec the stratigrapher may find that the surfaces of bedding planes are covered with irregular merging and diverging ridges and that the beds themselves are penetrated by small U-shaped tubes (Fig. 1–2). He may measure the size and mineralogy of the grains, the nature of the bedding, the di-

Fig. 1–2. Modern and ancient ripple marks, a lesson in uniformitarianism. *Top:* A modern beach. *Bottom:* The bedding plane of Lower Ordovician sandstone deposited on a similar beach 500 million years ago. (Courtesy of the Geological Survey of Canada.)

mensions of the corrugated ridges, the porosity, and many other parameters, but no one of these by itself nor even all taken together will tell him about the origin of the sandstone unless he continues his investigation in the shallow waters and beaches of modern oceans and lakes. There he will find the sand under the shallow water moved into ridges, or ripple marks, by the oscillatory motion of the waves. He will find that the grain size of the sand is dependent on the strength of the waves and currents, that the mineralogy of the sand is dependent on the rock of the source area from which it is being eroded, and that the small tubes are the burrows of worms characteristic of this particular environment. By a comparison of the ancient sedimentary rock with its modern counterpart the geologist can reconstruct in some detail the environment of the past.

In western Pennsylvania a geologist may collect dark carbonaceous shales with impressions of ferns thickly strewn on their bedding planes. He will base his interpretation of them on a comparison with the black mud accumulating in swamps of the present day, where ferns fall in and are buried. If fossil ferns are similar to some growing today, they may help him to determine the climate of that past period.

The principle involved in making these interpretations was first clearly stated by James Hutton almost two centuries ago. At a time when many geologists believed that the earth's history was a rapid series of catastrophies such as earthquakes, volcanic eruptions, floods, and mass extinctions of life, Hutton insisted that it could be better explained in terms of the slow processes observed every day, acting over a great length of time. His doctrine has long been known as uniformitarianism and is summed up in the phrase: the present is the key to the past.

Some caution must be exercised in the application of the principle of uniformitarianism. The earth today has much greater relief than it seems to have had at many times in the past and therefore the current rates of erosion and deposition are not likely to be typical of the earth's history as a whole. Conditions at the beginning of its history, when the earth was cooling from a hot stage, were certainly much different from those of today.

Even a casual observer applying uniformitarianism can conclude that much of the dry land of the earth was once covered by the sea. Large areas of all the continents are covered with layers of sedimentary rocks whose structures, textures, and fossils show that they are of marine origin. In mapping the shorelines of these continental seas of the past, the historical geologist must be careful to distinguish sedimentary rocks of marine origin from those laid down in lakes, swamps, rivers, and deserts.

Sediments deposited in non-marine environments have features characteristic of their specific environment. Lake deposits are fine-grained and minutely layered, stream deposits are sandy or gravelly and show cross-bedding, and glacial deposits consist of boulders and cobbles of various lithologies embedded in a claylike matrix. Most of the ancient non-marine deposits are of the deltaic type formed on an alluvial plain by rivers emerging from a growing mountain range. Unfortunately, these textures and structures, typical of certain non-marine sedimentary rocks, can also be formed in the sea.

Geologists have relied on color to distinguish non-marine from marine sediments, but this criterion can be misleading. Many non-marine sediments are colored pale yellow, red, or brown by a small content of hematite (ferric oxide) or "limonite" (hydrous iron oxides). These oxides result from the weathering of iron-rich minerals in the presence of atmospheric oxygen. If, however, the sediments bearing the ferric oxides are brought by rivers to the sea, they lose their color because the iron is reduced on the sea floor to the colorless ferrous state by bacteria that use up all the available oxygen as they decompose waste organic matter. Because of this reducing action on the sea floor, most marine sediments are gray; but sometimes ferric oxides will slip through the reducing barrier and color marine sediments red. The reducing action of bacteria is not limited to the ocean; in lakes and swamps also, iron compounds oxidized in weathering are reduced and lose their color. Though many, and probably most, red sediments are non-marine, a few are marine; most gray sediments are marine, but many non-marine sediments are also gray.

If color is an unreliable guide, how does the geologist distinguish marine from non-marine beds? Geochemists have suggested that the proportion in which certain key elements, such as boron and strontium, occur in sediments may be a help. The most reliable indicators of the environment of deposition are the fossils contained in a sedimentary rock. Certain groups of marine animals today cannot live in fresh water, or out of water. Among such animals are corals, sea stars and sea urchins, lamp shells, barnacles, and squids. The principle of uniformitarianism indicates that sedimentary rocks containing the fossils of such animals are surely marine. The marine or non-marine origin of many sedimentary rocks that lack both fossils and distinctive structures must remain undecided until new methods are developed.

INTERPRETATION OF A STRATIGRAPHIC SECTION

At Niagara Falls the drainage of the Great Lakes plunges over an escarpment of sedimentary rocks which can be traced from northern New York State northwestward into southern Ontario. The rocks of this escarpment, or cuesta, exposed at Niagara are illustrated in Fig. 1–3. At the base of the escarpment is a distinctive red shale. It is overlain successively by 12 feet of white sandstone, 50 feet of gray-green shale, 40 feet of red and green shale and sandstone, and so on. Each set of beds consisting of a single rock type such as sandstone, shale, or limestone, or some uniform combination of these types, is called a formation. Each sedimentary formation represents a past episode of deposition in a particular environment. A significant

change in the environment of deposition or in the source area was reflected in the nature of the sediments being laid down and induced the accumulation of a new formation. The boundaries of formations are drawn where the lithology changes and are usually arranged so that the formation can be easily plotted on a geological map.

Formations are named after a geographical locality. The locality is designated by the geologist who originally describes the formation as the site of the type section, which is usually the best exposure of the formation known to him. This type section serves as a standard for those who wish to ascertain the nature and boundaries of the formation. Because the type section of the red shale at the base of the Niagara Gorge is at the town of Queenston, the shale is called the Queenston Shale. The sandstone above it is well exposed at the Whirlpool on the Niagara River and it has therefore been called the Whirlpool Sandstone. If a formation consists of a single rock type, that rock name may follow the geographic name in the designation of the formation as, for example, Whirlpool Sandstone. If the formation is composed of two or more rock types that are interbedded, the term "formation" follows the geographic name, as in Grimsby Formation. Formations may be divided into smaller units called members, and several formations showing some lithologic similarity may be united into groups, such as the Cataract Group and the Niagara Group at Niagara.

The succession of formations at Niagara Falls represents a succession of conditions in an ancient basin of deposition. When the Queenston Shale was being deposited, red muds were washed into the area by rivers. The overlying Whirlpool Sandstone reflects the submergence of the basin beneath a shallow sea where the waves sifted a clean white sand. Apparently the water deepened when the Cabot Head Shale was deposited and the fossils in these beds record a rich marine fauna of invertebrates. The red shales and sandstones of the Grimsby Formation indicate the onset of non-marine deltaic condi-

FORMATIONS

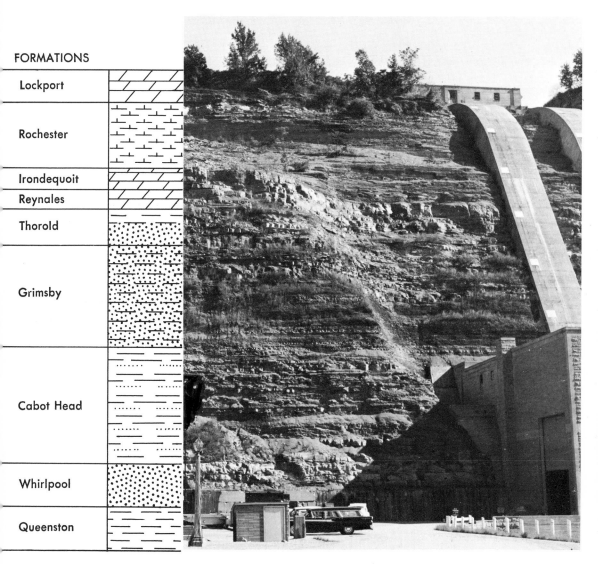

| Lockport |
| Rochester |
| Irondequoit |
| Reynales |
| Thorold |
| Grimsby |
| Cabot Head |
| Whirlpool |
| Queenston |

Fig. 1–3. Formations of the Niagara escarpment as exposed at Decew Falls, near Niagara Falls, Ontario. (M. J. Copeland, courtesy of the Geological Survey of Canada.)

tions and complete the sedimentary cycle from emergence, through submergence, and back to emergence. By interpreting the conditions of deposition of each of the formations in such a section the geologist can read the record of the rocks chapter by chapter.

CORRELATION OF SURFACE SECTIONS

Let us return to our comparison of the discovery of the Homeric world. To reveal the history of Troy, Schliemann excavated a single site. His work can be compared to that of a geologist reconstructing the history of the sedimentary rocks at Niagara Falls. To reconstruct the regional civilization of which Troy was a part, archeologists had to excavate other citadels, such as Tiryns and Mycenae, and identify in these ruins the layers contemporary with those at Troy. This was accomplished by comparing utensils, architectural styles, weapons—in short, all evidences of civilization. To reconstruct the past environment of a large area, the geologist must bring together the sequences of events recorded by successive formations in many parts of the area and determine which formations are contemporaneous. This process of tracing the lateral interrelationships to determine contemporaneity or other time relationships between formations is called **correlation.**

The methods of correlation can be illustrated by the sedimentary rocks of the Niagara escarpment discussed above. The geologist measures successions, or sections, of rocks exposed in this escarpment at several places along its 200-mile length and then tries to deduce the mutual relationships of the rocks and to join the sections together to produce a continuous picture of the regional variations. Figure 1–4 illustrates graphically three sections that have been measured in these rocks and the correlation of their component parts.

The top of the section at Niagara Falls and the crest of the escarpment are formed by thick-bedded Lockport Dolomite. Beds similar in lithology and of the same thickness may be found at the top of the other two sections. This sequence of beds in the three sections may reasonably be assumed to represent the same formation, but if any doubt remained, it so happens that in this area the geologist can trace the outcrop of the dolomite almost continuously by walking along the top of the escarpment from one section to another.

The Reynales Dolomite does not change in lithology along the escarpment. This formation may be identified easily for it has near its base in all sections a thin layer packed with the shells of the brachiopod * *Pentamerus laevis.* Although the Reynales Dolomite presents no problems in correlation, the beds above and below it are not the same in the different sections. Below it at Niagara Falls are, in descending order, a white sandstone (Thorold), a red sandstone and shale (Grimsby), a gray shale (Cabot Head), and

* Short summaries of the main groups of fossils are contained in Appendix A.

another white sandstone (Whirlpool) (Fig. 1–5). At c, this interval of the section consists of a reddish silty shale (Cabot Head), a dolomite (Manitoulin), and a white sandstone (Whirlpool). Questions that must be answered in correlation include:

1. What happens to the Grimsby and Thorold formations between a and c?
2. How much of the formation called the Cabot Head Shale at c was deposited at the same time as the Cabot Head Shale at a?
3. To what part of the section at Niagara Falls is the Manitoulin Dolomite equivalent?

The stratigraphic interval whose correlation is under discussion is bounded below by the Whirlpool Sandstone and above by the Reynales Dolomite in all sections. Because these two formations act as markers we can be reasonably sure that the rocks between them at the different sections were deposited within the same interval of time. Several alternative explanations of the disappearance of the Thorold and Grimsby formations between a and c can be considered:

1. These formations were never deposited at c; that is, the border of their basin of deposition lay between a and c (Fig. 1–5A).
2. These formations were deposited at c but were eroded before the Reynales Dolomite was deposited (Fig. 1–5B).
3. The deposition of the Grimsby and Thorold formations at Niagara Falls was contemporaneous with the deposition of the upper part of the Cabot Head at c (Fig. 1–5C).

Explanations 1 and 2 require that an erosion surface exist at c above the Cabot Head Shale. An erosion surface in the geological record is called an **unconformity.** If the beds above and below the surface are not parallel, the surface is called an **angular unconformity** and records a period of deformation followed by an interval of erosion. If the beds above and below the surface are parallel, it is called a **disconformity** and records only an interruption of deposition by erosion. Disconform-

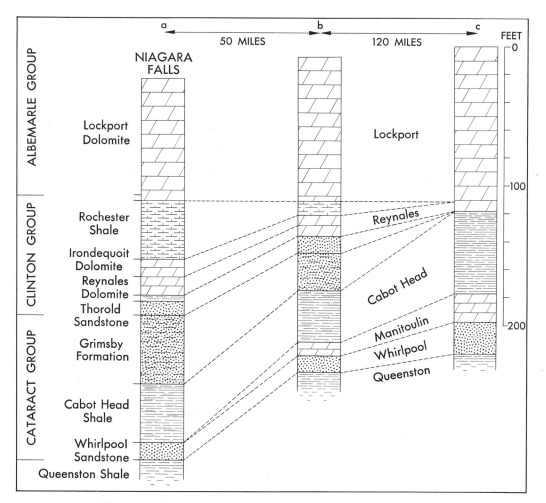

Fig. 1–4. Stratigraphic sections of the Silurian rocks measured at three places along the Niagara escarpment west of Niagara Falls.

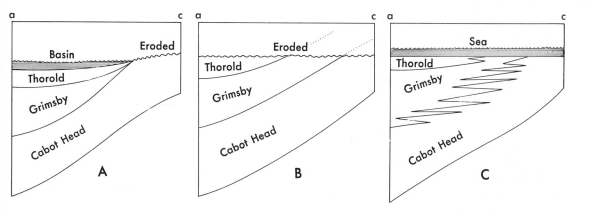

Fig. 1–5. Three possibilities in the correlation of the Grimsby and Thorold formations with the Cabot Head Formation between sections *a* and *c* of the Niagara escarpment. A. The edge of the basin of deposition of the Grimsby and Thorold formations was between *a* and *c*. B. The two formations have been eroded beneath an unconformity. C. The two formations pass laterally into the Cabot Head Formation.

ities may be recognized by channels eroded in the lower formation, by soil developed during the episode of erosion, or by a change in conditions of sedimentation introduced in the new depositional episode. Some disconformities show none of these features and are therefore difficult to detect.

In order to decide between these three alternatives, the geologist must investigate the escarpment between sections *a* and *c* to see whether the Grimsby and Thorold formations are truncated by erosion or whether they grade into the upper part of the Cabot Head Shale. At *b* the geologist might measure another section between *a* and *c*. The Thorold, Grimsby, and Cabot Head formations are present but the Grimsby is considerably thinner than at *a*. The zone of contact between the Cabot Head Shale and the Grimsby shaly sandstone at *b* is marked by alternating beds of the two rock types. Beds of sandstone in this contact zone traced from *b* toward *c* along the escarpment become thinner and eventually die out in the shale. A shale bed traced from *b* toward *a* dies out in the sandstone (Fig. 1–5C). The beds of the two formations interpenetrate like fingers of one hand placed between those of the other. This interfingering of lithologies is proof that the two formations were deposited during one interval of time. Along the escarpment the basal beds of the Grimsby Formation pass toward *c* laterally into the Cabot Head Shale until at *c* none of the Grimsby Formation is left. The purer sandstones of the Thorold Formation interfinger with the shaly sandstones of the Grimsby.

A similar relationship can be demonstrated between the Cabot Head Shale and the Manitoulin Dolomite at its base. Toward Niagara the beds of dolomite interfinger with, and die out in, the basal part of the shale until none is left.

We have now established a correlation between columns *a* and *c* and have shown that the Grimsby and Thorold formations at *a* are correlatives of the upper part of the Cabot Head Shale at *c*, and also that the Manitoulin Dolomite at *c* is a correlative of the lower part

of the Cabot Head Shale at *a*. The time during which the Cabot Head Shale was deposited at *a* is quite different from that at *c*. The difference in age illustrates the general principle that sedimentary formations are defined not with reference to time but on the basis of lithology alone.

The principles that have governed our correlation of the Cataract Group and the base of the Clinton Group may be summarized as follows:

1. Position in a sequence. The group of beds that changes is bounded by the Whirlpool and Reynales formations.
2. Relationship to key beds. The Reynales Dolomite, with its distinctive *Pentamerus* band, forms an easily traceable bed which does not change. Such persistent beds which indicate a horizon of correlation are called key beds.
3. Interfingering of formations.
4. Thickness relationships. Even though the lithology changes, the thickness of the strata between the Reynales and Whirlpool formations is essentially constant from *a* to *c*. This relationship suggests, but does not prove, that the strata in the two sections represent the same time interval.

To complete the list we can add to these four the principles by which the correlation of the Lockport and Reynales dolomites was established:

5. Similarity of lithology.
6. Continuity of outcrop, established by "walking it out."

These six principles are dependent only on the lithology of the formations.

The stratigraphy between the three sections can now be filled in to show the interrelationship of the sedimentary formations (Fig. 1–6). The gradation of the Grimsby Formation into the Cabot Head Shale is called a facies change, and Fig. 1–6 is said to be a facies diagram. The term **facies** refers to the total aspect of a sequence of strata, including lithologic characters, bedding, fossils, structures, and any other primary feature that makes the sequence distinctive. A **facies**

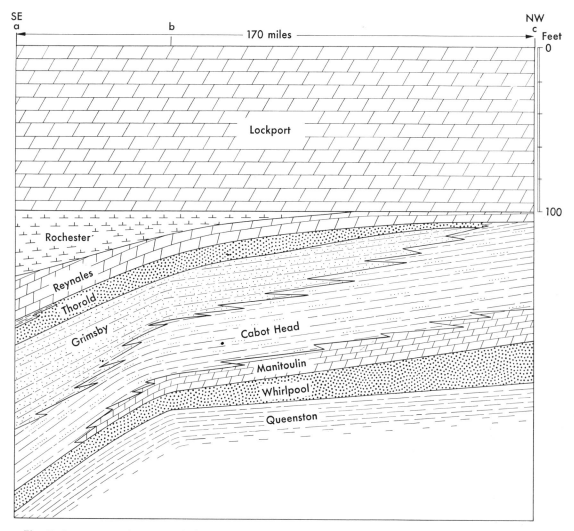

Fig. 1–6. Facies diagram of the Silurian rocks of the Niagara escarpment west of Niagara Falls.

change is any regional change in these characters and is a reflection of changing conditions in the basin where the sedimentary rocks were laid down.

So far we have considered the information given by individual rocks, by isolated sections, and by cross-sections constructed from sections of rocks exposed at the surface. Sedimentary formations are not one-, nor two-, but three-dimensional, tabular bodies. The rocks of the Niagara escarpment dip southward at less than 1 degree toward a basin-like structure called the Michigan

basin (see Fig. 5–10). As their dip carries them deeper these rocks are overlain by younger layers until, 100 miles south of the escarpment, they are thousands of feet below the surface. A far greater volume of this tabular body of rocks is buried than is exposed along the escarpment. These buried rocks can be identified in the cores or cuttings of holes drilled down to them through the overlying sedimentary rocks. Drilling is expensive but if the chances of finding petroleum are high, it is justified by the prospect of profit. The sandstones of the Cataract

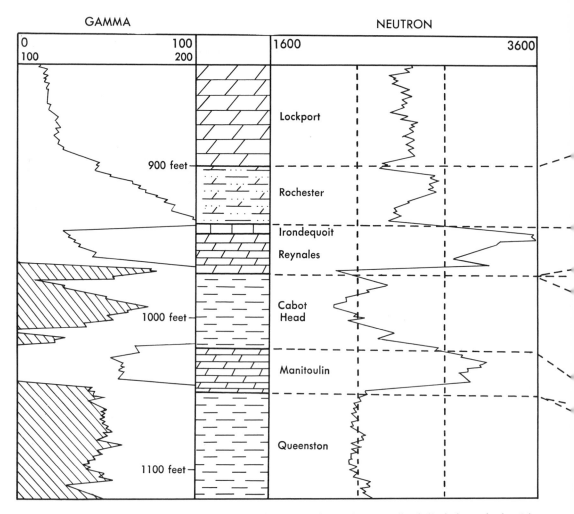

GAMMA | NEUTRON

| 0 | 100 | 1600 | 3600 |
| 100 | 200 | | |

Lockport

900 feet —

Rochester

Irondequoit

Reynales

1000 feet —
Cabot Head

Manitoulin

Queenston

1100 feet —

Fig. 1–7. Radioactivity logs of two wells drilled through the Silurian rocks of southwestern Ontario. The graph on the right side of the lithologic symbols represents the measure of the response of the rocks to bombardment by a source of neutrons. The graph on the left is a measure of the natural radioactivity of the various formations. Where

Group trap gas in many fields a few tens of miles south of the escarpment, and limestones of the Niagara Group contain both oil and gas 100 miles south of it. A three-dimensional picture of the rocks whose edges are exposed at the escarpment can be constructed with information gained by drilling for this gas and oil.

The geologist gets stratigraphic information from an oil well in several ways. The drilling bit shaves and chips fragments of rock from the sedimentary layers, and the drilling mud that is pumped through the bit brings these samples to the surface where they can be recovered. By identifying the samples the geologist can make a log, or section, of the rocks through which the bit has passed. After the hole has been drilled, the rock that forms its walls may be investigated by a variety of instruments lowered into the hole. The records of instruments which measure the resistivity of the rock and the natural electric currents flowing in them are called **electric logs**. Other instruments measure the radioactivity of the sedimentary layers, their reaction to neutron bombardment,

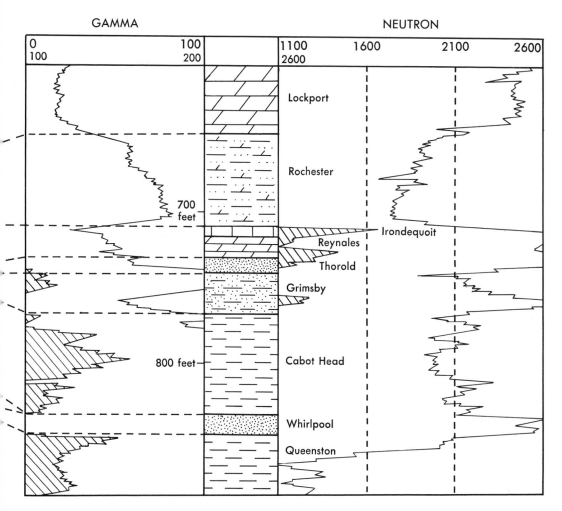

GAMMA NEUTRON

the graphs go off scale on the right, they are continued in shaded form on the left of the scale. Note the similar graphs of similar lithologies, the accuracy with which the depths of the formational contacts can be determined, and the correlations that can be drawn between the formations.

the velocity of sound in them, and other properties. Each of these can be interpreted by the expert in terms of the lithology, porosity, or fluid content of the rocks tested (Fig. 1–7). From these mechanical logs the geologist interprets the succession of sedimentary rocks in the well and correlates the formations from well to well, and from well to outcrop section. The amount of information on the sedimentary rocks of North America revealed by such subsurface methods now far exceeds that derived from the study of surface exposures.

STRATIGRAPHIC MAPS

A geological map records the distribution of stratigraphic formations and other rock bodies on the surface of the land. The three dimensions of sedimentary formations are best illustrated by other maps. The stratigrapher uses many different kinds of maps to interpret the history of a basin of deposition; here we can mention only a few.

Regional variations in the thickness of a formation or other stratigraphic unit are shown on an **isopach map**. The word "isopach" is derived from Greek words meaning equal thickness. The lines on an isopach map connect points at which the formation, bed, or other sedimentary unit is of the same thickness. On his base map the geologist plots the thickness of the unit intersected in the wells or measured in the surface sections. The regional pattern of "thicks" or "thins" is emphasized by contour lines like the contour lines on a topographic map which show hills and valleys. Where the value of the contours increases in a topographic map, a hill is indicated; but where the value increases in an isopach map, the sediments thicken (Fig. 1–8).

Figure 1–9 is an isopach map of the Cataract Group of the Niagara escarpment. It shows that this set of beds thins from about 200 feet to less than 100 feet along a broad arch trending northeast between Lakes Huron and Erie.

Variations in the lithology of a formation or other stratigraphic unit may also be expressed on a map. Figure 1–10 is a map showing variations in lithology within the Clinton Group of New York, Michigan, and Ontario. Methods of correlation are not precise enough to allow the construction of a map that shows the distribution of the various lithologies or facies at some particular in-

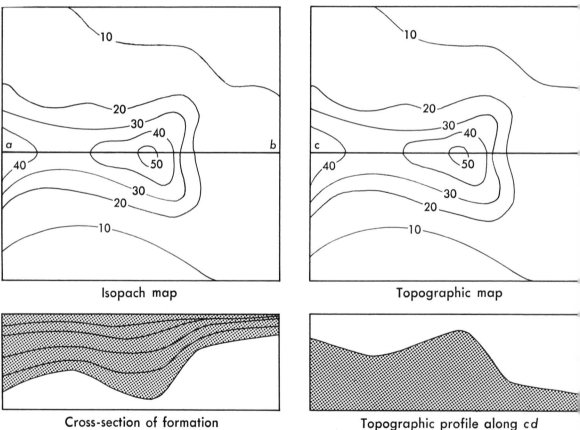

Isopach map   Topographic map

Cross-section of formation   Topographic profile along cd
along ab at close of deposition

Fig. 1–8. Comparison of an isopach and a topographic map. In an isopach map the datum from which the measurements of thickness are made is the upper surface of the formation. In a topographic map the altitudes are measured from the datum of sea level.

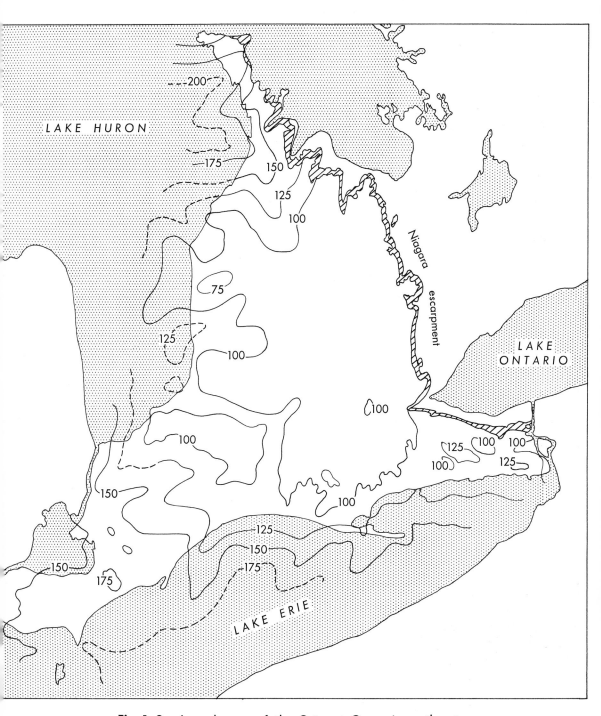

Fig. 1–9. Isopach map of the Cataract Group in southwestern Ontario. The belt of outcrop of the group along the Niagara escarpment is shown by the cross-hatched zone. Note how the group thins over a broad arch in the center of the map. (After B. F. Sanford, courtesy of the Geological Survey of Canada.)

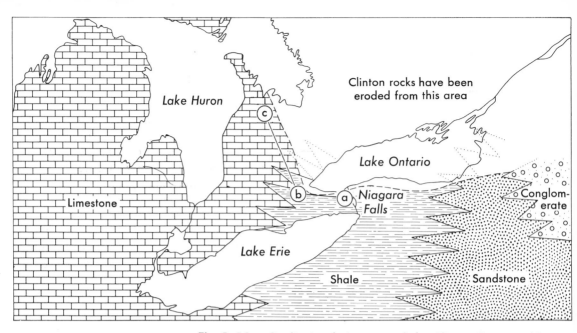

Fig. 1–10. Qualitative facies map of the Clinton Group in New York, Michigan, and Ontario. The line of the facies diagram (Fig. 1–6) is indicated by the line a–b–c.

stant in the past. However, the average position of the areas of sandstone, limestone, and shale deposition can be reconstructed for the interval of time during which a set of beds such as the Clinton Group was deposited. In this book the boundaries between the facies are plotted as zigzag lines embracing the belt in which two facies interfinger. The map (Fig. 1–10) shows the influence of an eastern source of clastics on sedimentation in New York and Ontario and the position of the limestone sea in the clear water beyond the influence of the clastics. Other such facies maps will be found throughout this book.

Such a map gives only a qualitative impression of the lithologic variation in a stratigraphic interval; other types of maps give quantitative information. From the interval to be mapped the geologist measures the aggregate thickness of the beds of a given lithology, such as sandstone, in all the wells

and surface sections of a given area. These values are then plotted on a map at the location of each section, and contours joining points of equal thickness of the lithology are drawn. Instead of the thickness of the lithology, the map may show the proportion of the interval that is represented by the original lithology. The contour lines on these maps are called **isoliths** because they join points of equal lithology. Figure 1–11 is an isolith map showing the percentage of sandstone beds in the Cataract Group in southwestern Ontario. An isolith map may be constructed for each of the lithologies of the interval being studied.

Aggregate thicknesses measured from surface and subsurface stratigraphic sections may be used to make maps showing the proportions of two or three types of rock in an interval. If the geologist wants to illustrate the areal variation of the proportion of sand to shale he plots and contours the ratio of the aggregate thicknesses of the two lithologies:

$$\text{sand–shale ratio} = \frac{\text{aggregate thickness of sandstone beds}}{\text{aggregate thickness of shale beds}}$$

Two ratios may be contoured on the same map to show the variation of three rock types in an area.

The facies of a stratigraphic unit can be shown quantitatively in many ways on a map by the use of ratios and patterns. Figure 1–12 is a map of the facies of the Cataract Group south and west of the Niagara escarpment showing the proportions of sandstone, shale, and limestone encountered in wells and surface sections of this group. The patterns illustrate the occurrence of the limestone and dolomite facies along the arch defined by the isopachs (compare Fig. 1–9) and the greater proportion of shale on its flanks. The increase in the proportion of sandstone toward the east is also shown, as in Fig. 1–11, but this map includes much more information about other lithologies in the section than the simpler isolith map. Figure 1–12 is called a **lithofacies map** and may be constructed for any set of lithologic components. A lithofacies map shows quantitatively the areal variation in the proportion of two or more sedimentary rocks in the stratigraphic interval being mapped. If the lithology of the sections is recorded on punched cards and introduced into a computer and plotter, the machine can be programmed to draw a lithofacies map. Many oil companies and government agencies now record the stratigraphic information from wells in a form that can be used by computers, and some geologists even make their field notes by punching cards instead of giving written descriptions.

Petroleum geologists have invented a wide variety of stratigraphic maps such as these to serve their individual needs. **Facies departure maps** show the degree by which sections at a given locality differ from a particular facies; **entropy maps** show the degree of mixing of the lithologies in sections; and **vertical variation maps** may show the number of beds of a given lithology within a stratigraphic interval. These maps are the tools the geologist uses, wherever appropriate, to interpret conditions of the past.

PALEOGEOGRAPHY

The final product of the geologist's reconstruction of conditions in the past is a paleogeographic map representing his interpretation of the geography of an interval of time. **Paleogeographic maps** show the past positions of mountains and plains, rivers and lakes, and, most important of all, the shoreline. Figure 5–1 (p. 84) is an example of such a map. In locating the shoreline the geologist faces the difficulties, already discussed, of distinguishing marine from nonmarine sediments.

Although the position of the shoreline is important geologically, it cannot be exactly or confidently shown on any paleogeographic map because it is constantly shifting. The movement of the shoreline is clearly evident in Europe, where surveys of the coast have been made over a longer period of time than in North America, and ancient structures built on the coast show its former position. The castle at Harlech, Wales, was built in 1285 at the sea's edge but now stands half a mile inland. In certain other places the waves are eroding the shoreline several feet a year. Even if the shore moves only a few feet a year, it would shift hundreds of miles in a million years, which is a relatively small part of geological time.

Some sedimentary structures in ancient sediments may help in locating the shorelines of the past, but many of these features formed on the beach are ephemeral and are destroyed by the next advancing tide or the next storm. Marine sediments are coarser near the shore because currents and wave action cannot carry the large particles farther out. Some structures in sediments, such as oscillation ripple marks, sun cracks, and swash marks, are commonly associated with shallow water near the shore. If fossils of animals similar to those that now live near the shore are found in sedimentary rocks, they also help to locate the old shoreline.

In reconstructing the distribution of ancient seas and continents the geologist con-

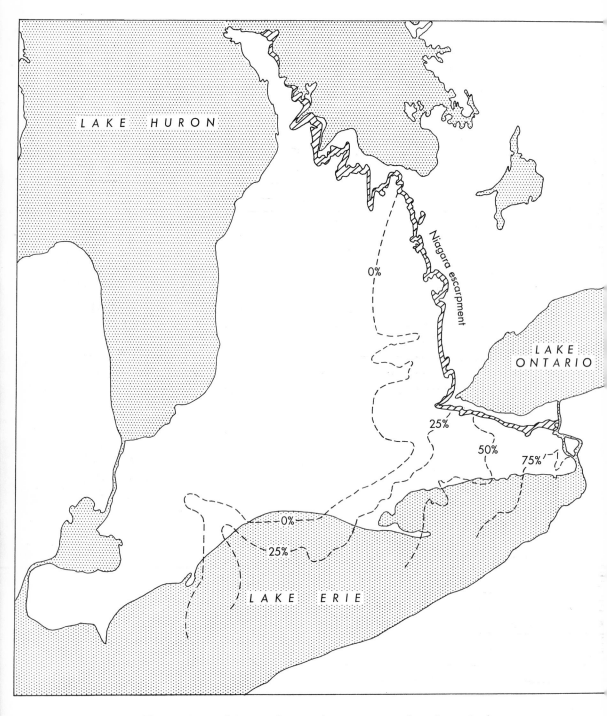

Fig. 1–11.   Isolith map showing the percentage of sandstone in the Cataract Group of southwestern Ontario. Beds of this age have been eroded from the area east of the Niagara escarpment, whose trace is indicated by the cross-hatching. (Modified from B. F. Sanford, courtesy of the Geological Survey of Canada.)

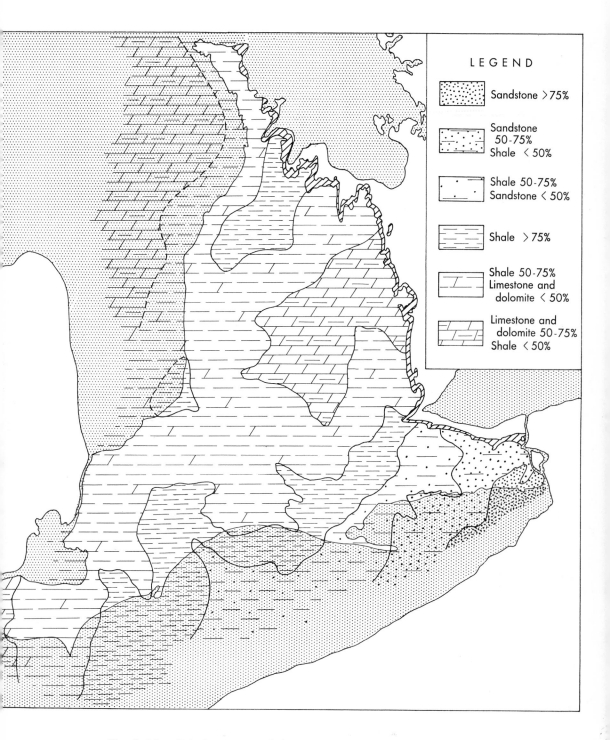

Fig. 1–12. Lithofacies map of the Cataract Group in southwestern Ontario. The patterns show the proportions of sandstone, shale, and carbonate rocks in the Cataract Group in various regions of the area. (After B. F. Sanford, courtesy of the Geological Survey of Canada.)

siders not only the structures, lithology, and distribution of sedimentary rocks but the regional distribution of the fossils, which records the life of the ancient seas. Today each of the oceans is inhabited by a distinct fauna the members of which are said to constitute a faunal realm. Even though environments in the Pacific Ocean are duplicated in the Atlantic, the land barrier of the American continents prevents the mixing of the organisms and preserves the contrast. The contrast is most evident at Panama, where, of the 805 species of shelled invertebrates collected on the Pacific side of the isthmus and the 517 species collected on the Atlantic side, only 24 are common to both shores. Paleontologists can detect similar faunal realms in the distribution of fossils. Where major discontinuities in the geographic distribution of fossil faunas are found, the paleontologist may postulate that a barrier separated two seaways. Similar discontinuities in faunas are caused by the adaptations of animals to differing environments (see Chapter 2), and the paleontologist must beware that the land barrier he postulates was not merely a boundary between different environments.

SUMMARY

The historical geologist reads the story of the earth in layers of sedimentary rock, each of which records an episode of deposition.

Only incomplete reconstructions are possible, for much of the sedimentary record of the earth's past has been destroyed by erosion, buried beneath younger sedimentary layers, or transformed by metamorphism.

The environment of deposition of each sedimentary rock may be interpreted by the principle of uniformitarianism; the changing conditions in one locality are revealed by a succession of different beds.

Stratigraphers classify sedimentary rock sequences into groups, formations, and members on the basis of lithologic differences.

By correlating stratigraphic sections from one surface exposure to another, and from well to well, the geologist is able to interpret regional changes in facies.

Quantitative attributes of sedimentary rock bodies can be plotted on isopach, isolith, ratio, lithofacies, and other types of stratigraphic maps to express changes in the lithology of the units in three dimensions.

QUESTIONS

1. What are the similarities and differences between the work of the historical geologist and that of the historian writing a history of, for example, New York City in the nineteenth century?

2. What features that you have seen along a modern shoreline might be preserved to help the geologist find ancient shorelines?

3. By using reference works, find out who James Hutton was, when he lived, and the nature of his disagreement with Abraham Gottlieb Werner.

4. Compare and contrast in as many ways as possible an isopach and a topographic contour map.

REFERENCES AND SUGGESTED READINGS

American Commission on Stratigraphic Nomenclature. "Code of Stratigraphic Nomenclature," *American Association of Petroleum Geologists Bulletin*, 45: 645–65, 1961. This paper, usually called the "stratigraphic code," formally establishes the recommended usage of stratigraphic terms such as *formation, member, series, period*, etc., for North American geologists.

DUNBAR, C. O., and RODGERS, J. *Principles of Stratigraphy*. New York: John Wiley & Sons, Inc., 1957. This book is a standard text in stratigraphy, as are the books by Krumbein and Sloss, and Weller (see below), and discusses problems of correlating strata and interpreting the stratigraphic record.

HAUN, J. D., and LeRoy, L. W. *Subsurface Geology in Petroleum Exploration*. Golden: Colorado School of Mines, 1958. This text, and the one by Moore (below), is concerned with the methods by which the petroleum geologist obtains information from the sedimentary rocks penetrated in drilling and the methods of analyzing these data in maps, charts, and sections.

KRUMBEIN, W. C., and SLOSS, L. L. *Stratigraphy and Sedimentation*, 2d ed. San Francisco: W. H. Freeman and Co., 1963.

MOORE, C. A. *Handbook of Subsurface Geology*. New York: Harper & Row, 1963.

SLOSS, L. L., DAPPLES, E. C., and KRUMBEIN, W. C. *Lithofacies Maps*. New York: John Wiley & Sons, Inc., 1960. This book is a compilation of many lithofacies maps of parts of the United States and Canada. A map of the United States for each geological period is included.

WELLER, J. M. *Stratigraphic Principles and Practice*. New York: Harper & Row, 1960.

2

Paleontology

In the previous chapter the science of stratigraphy and the way in which sedimentary rocks are used in compiling a history of the earth were described. Much has been deduced from sedimentary rocks alone, and as a result we have a fair understanding of the succession of events leading up to the present condition of the earth. In solving stratigraphic problems, fossils, if found, play an important and sometimes invaluable part, and no stratigraphic discussion is complete unless their description and occurrence are considered.

FOSSILS

Definition

Paleontology, the study of fossils, is that part of the geological and biological sciences that is concerned with ancient life. Fossils can be defined as the remains of organisms, or traces of their existence, preserved in rocks. Attempts to better what is given above have led some definers to add the restrictive phrases "by natural causes" and "in

prehistoric time." These phrases would justly disqualify such objects as a bird's nest left by a tourist in a hot spring overnight and taken out the next morning thinly encrusted with "stone." Prehistoric time means one thing in North America, another in Spain, and still another in Mesopotamia. Strict application of either phrase leads to difficulties, and neither should be rigorously enforced.

Fossils, according to the definition, are the remains of an organism, i.e., something that was once actually part of a living animal or plant before death and fossilization, or a trace of the existence of an organism, such as a footprint or a painting on a prehistoric cave wall. A few examples will show the common kinds of fossils.

Direct Evidences

Organisms are composed of protoplasm, a soft jelly-like substance which decomposes almost instantly upon the death of the organism, protected or supported by a more or less hard shell, covering, or internal skeleton. One class of fossils comprises all organisms that have been preserved entire, unchanged.

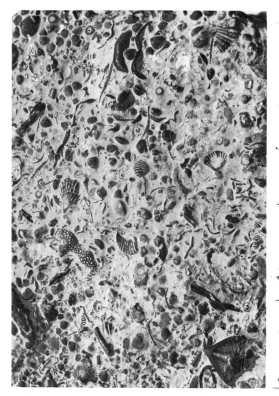

Fig. 2–1. Silurian limestone containing a wealth of small brachiopods and bryozoans, all of which have been reinforced by calcium carbonate. The relatively soft and porous limestone matrix has been weathered, leaving the fossils in relief. (Courtesy of the Redpath Museum.)

These are the rarest of fossils, exemplified by the carcasses of the woolly mammoth from the frozen gravels of Siberia preserved by the cold so perfectly that in one specimen the last meal remained undigested in the stomach, and the flesh, after several thousand years, remained edible.

Preservation of only the hard parts of an organism is far more common. Shells and bones, the chitinous exoskeletons of insects, and woody matter are all relatively enduring compared with protoplasm, yet all are subject to decay by bacteria or disintegration by waves, currents, and carnivores unless buried quickly enough. Most invertebrate shells are made of calcium carbonate, a few of calcium phosphate, and a few of silica, all of which are resistant to the agents of disintegration

and decay. On the other hand, the commonest fossils of vertebrates are bones, teeth, and scales, all of which eventually decay under natural conditions; they are therefore most common in younger rocks and become progressively rare in older beds.

A third kind of fossil consists of the original material of the organism infiltrated by mineral matter. All shells and bones contain organic matter distributed as layers or tubes within the hard parts. Upon the death of the organism this organic matter decomposes, and its place may be taken by minerals, deposited from groundwater, of much the same chemical composition as the shell. This filling process is known as **permineralization** or **reinforcement** (Fig. 2–1). A permineralized clam shell contains all of the calcium carbonate that was in the original shell, plus enough newly deposited calcium carbonate to fill the areas vacated by the organic matter. Probably the majority of invertebrate fossils belong in this category. Bone, consisting largely of calcium carbonate and calcium phosphate, may be reinforced by either or both of these substances (Fig. 2–2).

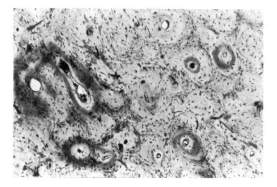

Fig. 2–2. Section of bone (probably of a Tertiary whale) reinforced by calcium carbonate, showing the preservation in minute detail of the haversian systems and interstitial lamellae. (Courtesy of M. A. Gibson.)

The protective shell of insects and other arthropods (chitin), the outer cellulose layer of leaves (cutase), and the woody parts of plants (cellulose) provide good examples of preservation by **distillation or carbon con-**

Fig. 2–4. A graptolite (*Tetragraptus,* Ordovician) preserved by carbonization of the original chitinous skeleton. (Courtesy of the Smithsonian Institution.)

Fig. 2–3. Fernlike leaves (*Pecopteris,* Pennsylvanian) preserved by carbonization of the original plant material. (Courtesy of the Redpath Museum.)

centration. If such materials are buried and so pass beyond the reach of bacteria, they may come into conditions of high enough temperature to lose by distillation all of their volatile materials—oxygen, hydrogen, nitrogen, and hydrocarbons—leaving a residue of almost pure carbon (which makes up about one half of wood, chitin, etc.). Thus, a fossil leaf consisting of a thin film of carbon on the surface of shale is in effect a tiny film of coal (Fig. 2–3). Coal is, after all, the remains of plant matter that has lost most of its gaseous constituents as a result of increased temperature. Chitin is affected in much the same way, so that trilobites, insects, graptolites (Fig. 2–4), and many other groups of animals are typically preserved as thin, black, carbonaceous or even graphitic films. In such specimens every part of the fossil was at the time of death part of the organism. Nothing has been added, and only the volatile components have disappeared.

Indirect Evidences

The second phrase in our definition of a fossil is "trace of the existence of an organism." Many clam shells are buried in sedimentary beds porous enough for percolating groundwater to dissolve the shell material completely, leaving a vacant space in the rock (Fig. 2–5). When such a rock is broken open and the cavity revealed, the surfaces against which the shell once rested will preserve the size and shape of the shell and the ornamentation of its surface. Such a fossil is called a mold or impression. If we now pour plaster of Paris on these molds, or knead in some modeling clay, these substances when removed will show the actual appearance of the outside of the shell. These are casts, replicas, in this case, of the exterior of the shell. Insects, flowers, etc., preserved in Tertiary amber (Fig. 2–6) rarely possess any organic substance, and are, therefore, molds of the exterior of the organism. The cavities left after the decomposition of the humans, dogs, fruit on store shelves, etc., buried by ash and mud at Pompeii might be included as natural molds, but the artificially made casts to be seen in museums do not fulfill either of the two restrictive clauses discussed

Fig. 2–6. Mold of caddis fly preserved in Tertiary amber from the Baltic region. (Courtesy of the Smithsonian Institution.)

Fig. 2–5. *Top:* Mold of the interior of a clam shell. The black space indicates the thickness of the original shell. A natural or an artificial filling of this space would provide a cast (replica) of the original shell. *Bottom:* Molds of gastropod (*Turritella,* Tertiary) shells. The smooth parts are fillings, i.e., molds, of the interior of the shells. The long, incomplete impression is a mold of the exterior. (Courtesy of the Redpath Museum.)

above in defining a fossil. The cast of a two-horned rhinoceros, overrun in Washington by a lava flow which congealed just in time to allow the animal's outline to be preserved, somewhat imperfectly, is quite admissible as a natural cast.

Another large group of fossils includes tracks, trails, and burrows. These are molds of the exterior surfaces of feet, tails, etc., and are valuable indicators of the impressibility of the sediment in which they were made, the number and nature of the impressing structures, and, in many cases, the mode of progression of the animal concerned (Fig. 2–7). Burrows are progressive molds of the exterior of the animal that made them (Fig. 2–8). They may be naturally or artificially filled with mud or plaster, forming a cast of the animal's foot or some measure of the cross-section of its body. Burrows which are excavated far beyond body width are artifacts, discussed below.

A clam shell may, upon burial, come in contact with a solution of silica under chemical

Fig. 2–7. Trackways. *Left: Laoporus,* an amphibian. *Right: Paleo-helcura,* an invertebrate, probably an arthropod. Both from the Permian beds of the Grand Canyon. (Courtesy of the Smithsonian Institution.)

Fig. 2–8. Worm(?) borings (*Scolithus,* Upper Cambrian). *Top:* View of what was once the sea floor. *Bottom:* Vertical face of the same specimen (about ½ actual size).

conditions which favor the dissolution of calcium carbonate and the simultaneous deposition of silica. When this takes place, no part of the resulting fossil is organic, yet it is just as much a proof of the prior existence of the organism as would be the original shell.

So faithfully is this transfer or **replacement** accomplished that the cellular structure of wood and bones (Fig. 2–9) may be reproduced in minutest detail, and the delicate exterior surfaces of calcareous shells of clams may be preserved. Pyrite and, rarely, hematite are other notable replacing materials, but are scarcely more durable than the original calcium carbonate. A fossil replaced by silica becomes very much more resistant to weathering (Fig. 2–10). Silicified fossils removed from limestone by dissolving the matrix in acid may show exquisite preservation of delicate spines and fine ornamentation (see Fig. 20–16).

Fig. 2–9. Polished surface of a silicified tree (genus and period unknown). Note the faithful reproduction of both radial and concentric structures of the original wood.

Fig. 2–10. Silicified coral (*Halysites*, Silurian). The coral colony, originally composed of calcium carbonate, has been completely replaced by silica, the superior hardness and resistance to weathering of which allow it to stand out in prominent relief to the limestone in which it is embedded. (Courtesy of the Redpath Museum.)

Fossils which cannot be classified in the categories described above include coprolites, petroleum, lithographic limestone, certain markings, and others. Coprolites, the fossilized excrement of animals, often betray by undigested remains the diet of the animal concerned. Petroleum is almost universally considered an organic distillate, and, if so, is a trace of the previous existence of organisms. However, the connection is so tenuous that few people today would classify petroleum as a fossil, although it is commonly referred to as a "fossil fuel." Some very fine-grained limestones, such as the lithographic limestone of Bavaria, are considered to be the natural product of a series of chemical reactions resulting from the decay of soft-bodied organisms. If this could be proved for any particular limestone, such a limestone would by strict application of the definition be considered a fossil. Certain markings on bed-

Fig. 2–11. Markings on the upper surface of a ripple-marked bed of Precambrian quartzite (Huronian of Ontario). The curved spindles meet at approximately right angles and show peculiar, symmetrically disposed flutings, leading to the presumption, but not proof, of their organic origin. (Courtesy of H. J. Hofmann and the Geological Survey of Canada.)

Fig. 2–12. *Daimonelix* (Miocene of Nebraska). Spiral forms, 5–6 feet in length, believed to be the fillings of burrows of small beaver-like animals. The spirals almost invariably lead downward to upward-inclined chambers, in which there are found, as shown in the cut section, skeletons of the Miocene mammal *Paleocastor*. (Courtesy of the Nebraska State Museum.)

ding planes are interpreted as the trace of a fish fin or some other part of an organism being brushed over the bottom mud. Inasmuch as we never know what animal or plant was responsible, such markings qualify as problematica (Fig. 2–11).

One last group of indirect evidences is known as artifacts. Many animals manufacture structures apart from the results of their physiological processes (shells, bones, etc.). Birds build nests, ants construct hills, man early in his career made stone implements. All of these things definitely qualify as fossils, and the human artifacts are of supreme importance in unraveling human prehistory. Two other kinds of artifacts are excavations and constructions. To the first belong those puzzling spiral structures called *Daimonelix* (Fig. 2–12), made, it is thought, by a small, extinct species of beaver; but because the animal must fit in the burrow loosely, it cannot be considered a mold of the exterior. Examples of the second are the tubes of certain Foraminifera and worms formed partly of organic matter (chitin, etc.) and partly of sand and other grains, presumably to form a protective integument, and hence molds of the exterior of the animal which built them.

Pseudofossils

Lastly, in any collection of fossil-like rocks the paleontologist is forced to recognize and discard the non-fossils, or, as they are better called, pseudofossils. These are inorganically formed structures which look like fossils, such as concretions, cone-in-cone structures or layers, current marks, raindrop impressions, etc. Weathering and metamorphism contribute their action to the creation of structures resembling organisms. *Eozoon canadense* (Fig. 2–13), a metamorphic structure with a banded appearance, is reminiscent of many algal fossils.

Nature of the Paleontological Record

Only under the rarest conditions is an organism in the modern seas fated to become fossilized, and some modern soft-bodied groups may not leave behind a single representative for future paleontologists to collect. Fossilization has been one of the rarest acci-

dents of the geological past, and in all probability not one in a million of the organisms that have ever lived has left a trace behind. In the sea or on land, hosts of predators, scavengers, and bacteria are ready to devour or decompose the soft parts of dying and dead organisms and to crush and scatter the hard parts. The cleanness of the shallow sea floor or the open forest where thousands or millions of animals die each year is an indication of the efficiency of the scavengers and predators of the marine and non-marine environments. If organisms escape these organic agents of destruction, they still may be destroyed by mechanical agents of their environment such as currents, abrasion, and dissolution.

Although an individual organism has little chance of becoming fossilized, we must remember that many modern species, and presumably many extinct ones also, are represented by millions of individuals. Many fossil

Fig. 2–13. *Eozoon,* a Precambrian structure once considered to be a fossil, now generally agreed to be a result of the metamorphism of limestone. (Courtesy of the Redpath Museum.)

species had ranges of millions of years and must have been represented during this span of time by astronomical numbers of individuals. The chances that one of such a long-lived, abundant species will be preserved are good. Still, George G. Simpson of Harvard has estimated that perhaps 300 million species of animals have lived in geological time, of which from 1 to 10 per cent have been preserved in the paleontological record; of these we have discovered and described so far only 91,000. The challenge of these figures to the paleontologist who wishes to discover as much as possible about ancient life is obvious. In biological classification (see Appendix B) species are grouped into genera, genera into families, families into orders, and so on. Although only a small proportion of the species that ever lived has so far been described, a much greater proportion of the number of genera is known, and for the more abundant groups of macrofossils we probably have a record of all the families. Simpson considers it unlikely that any groups of ancient life of the rank of order are as yet undiscovered in the paleontological record. This means that we have an accurate description of the major outlines of ancient life and detailed knowledge of some parts of it.

Much has been written of the inadequacy or imperfection of the fossil record. Paleontologists prefer not to use these terms because for many purposes the record is adequate; they prefer to discuss the chances of preservation of various kinds of life as the bias of the record. In many ways the paleontological record is not a representative sample of the life of the past; that is, the sample is biased in many directions. Most important to the paleontologist is its bias against soft-bodied organisms. The representation of modern invertebrate phyla in the fossil record is directly proportional to their ability to secrete a hard shell or skeleton. Of some groups, such as the jellyfish, worms, and many protozoans, we have practically no fossil record except vague impressions on bedding planes. Possibly, orders or classes of soft-bodied animals may have existed in the past and may have left no paleontological

record. The resulting incompleteness of the record is less of an obstacle to the geologist than to the biologist, for the geologist can use the preserved fossils for dating and correlation, but the biologist, who is likely to be more interested in phylogenies than in guide fossils, commonly finds that the expected earliest members of the major taxa are missing from the fossil record, presumably because they were without shells.

The record is biased in several other ways which can be mentioned only briefly here. Most of our fossiliferous rocks were deposited in shallow marine waters along continental shelves; few deep-sea sediments are available to the paleontologist for collecting because the record of this environment remains at the bottom of the ocean basins and has not, like the record of the continental shelves, been lifted onto dry land where it can be studied in detail. The record of terrestrial animals and plants is biased in favor of the lowland, swamp species. Organisms that lived on higher ground lived in an area of erosion, where no sediments were being laid down in which they could become buried. To interpret the record of life correctly the paleontologist must keep these biases in mind.

Fossils are found predominantly in sedimentary rocks. They are most abundant in limestone, less so in shale, and relatively rare in sandstone. Because most shells are composed of calcium carbonate, an accumulation of such materials would automatically qualify as a limestone. In each of these rock types fossils may be so abundant as to form most of the rock, or they may be only a minor constituent.

Among the less common sedimentary rocks, conglomerate rarely contains any fossils except bones and shells too large or too tough to be destroyed by the processes that brought the pebbles and boulders together. Coal is made up wholly of fossilized vegetation, and in many places shows an abundance of fern-like or leaflike remains (Fig. 2–3). Evaporites are practically without fossils, and of the iron ores only the Clinton hematite beds (see p. 291)—replacements of fossiliferous limestone—are fossil bearing. Cherts are commonly well supplied with fossils but their sum total is small. Diatomaceous and radiolarian oozes are made up almost completely of microfossils.

PALEONTOLOGICAL CORRELATION

William Smith

William Smith (1769–1837), an English civil engineer, spent much of his life surveying for and supervising the digging of canals. The sedimentary rocks in England had already been differentiated and named, and much work had been done on British fossils, which had been described and named according to the Linnean system of nomenclature.* To this stage of development Smith added two others of great importance. First, in studying the formations cut through in the construction of his canals, he noticed that the beds all dipped toward the southeast, and that, as one traveled in that direction one passed over the edges of successively younger beds. Smith was able to develop a stratigraphic column of formations and to predict for the first time what kind of rock would be found in a water well or in the next village to the northwest. This stratigraphic and structural synthesis would have been enough to place Smith among the founders of stratigraphic geology (he is commonly referred to as "Strata Smith"), but his second discovery was of even greater importance. He noticed that wherever he dug into a certain formation, the fossils that turned up were always the same, and that those fossils did not occur in any other formation. This, he discovered, was true for the entire country. Here, then, was a way of identifying the presence of a certain formation from fossils picked up and brought to him by his assistants, or from the study of fossils in the cabinets of local collectors.

For a dozen years Smith accumulated a tremendous amount of information, undeniably linking certain fossils to certain formations, and discussed his findings freely

* See Appendix A.

with interested persons. In 1815, he published a hand-colored map of England and Wales, showing with surprising accuracy of detail the geological formations then known. There followed the next year an explanatory pamphlet entitled "Strata Identified by Organized Fossils." Fortunately, Smith lived to see his revolutionary innovation accepted and respected and his map made the prototype of geological maps of other localities. To these intangibles were added a Royal Society gold medal and a modest pension from the Crown.

Cuvier and Brogniart

While William Smith was laying the foundations of biostratigraphy, two scientists in France were coming to the same conclusions concerning stratigraphic succession and diagnostic fossils. Both were well established in Paris—Georges Cuvier (1769–1832) first as professor of comparative anatomy at the University of Paris and later as Perpetual Secretary of the Institute of France, and Alexandre Brogniart (1770–1847) as professor of mineralogy at the Museum of Natural History in Paris. Together these two men, zoologist and geologist, scoured the countryside around Paris and accumulated enough information so that by 1808 they were able to publish their conclusions: that the strata of the Paris basin were arranged in a definite succession, and that each subdivision contained its own peculiar assemblage of fossils. (Although this publication antedated Smith's map and report, it must be remembered that for a decade before, Smith had distributed to anyone interested an account of his labors and results.) A translation of their own words will illustrate their methods: "The means which we have employed . . . for the recognition of a bed already observed in a distant quarter, has been taken from the nature of the fossils contained in each bed. The fossils . . . present tolerably marked differences of species from one group of beds to another."

The principles worked out independently by Smith in England and by Cuvier and Brogniart in France became a secure foundation for stratigraphic paleontology, upon which practically all post-Precambrian correlations have depended. Cuvier's contribution is likely to be obscured by his brilliant accomplishments in vertebrate paleontology and his other endeavors as a high government official, but to these three men historical geology owes a lasting debt.

Biostratigraphy

In correlating formations by means of fossils, Smith and Cuvier were using the principle that like fossils found in different beds indicate like times of deposition of those beds. This principle is valid because the life of the past was not static but constantly evolving. Each division of time in the past was characterized by distinctive organisms, by which it can be identified in different places and in different kinds of rocks.

In Chapter 1 the principles by which the stratigrapher determines the equivalency of beds on the basis of their lithology were considered. Some of these methods allow the stratigrapher to establish the contemporaneity of two sequences of rocks, but most of them merely establish the physical relationships (continuity, interfingering, etc.) between formations. To reconstruct the history of an area the stratigrapher must have a method of establishing the time at which certain events recorded in the rocks occurred; such a measure is provided by the paleontological record. A detailed study of the succession of fossil faunas in a sedimentary sequence will allow the paleontologist to construct a time framework which ideally will be independent of the lithologic framework of sedimentation.

Although the total biota of the world changed from moment to moment, this constant flux was made up of plant and animal species each of which had a definite time span of existence during which it was able to colonize any hospitable environment. In a sedimentary section this time span is expressed in a thickness of strata within which the organism is found as a fossil. This thickness is known as the zone of the particular fossil and is the fundamental unit of bio-

stratigraphy. A **zone** is defined in the stratigraphic code as "a stratum or body of strata characterized by the occurrence of a fossil taxon or taxa from one or more of which it received its name." This definition implies that in some sequences of rocks where no single species has a range convenient for correlation purposes, zones may be recognized on the basis of the combined ranges of groups of species. A zone is not limited in thickness. The dinosaur zone includes most of the rocks deposited during the Mesozoic Era, but such zones are not as valuable in correlation as those based on animals or plants that lived for a relatively short time. To avoid confusion with the use of the word "zone" in other contexts, the biostratigraphic unit is sometimes called a **biozone.**

To illustrate that the zone and formation are part of separate systems of stratigraphic classification, let us take an example. In Fig. 2–14, A and B are two sections that have been described lithologically and whose fossils have been collected by the stratigrapher. Each includes a shale formation overlain and underlain by sandstone. The locus of occurrence of the species X is indicated in the two sections. At A the zone of fossil X is partly in the shale formation and partly in the overlying sandstone; at B it is partly in the underlying sandstone and partly in the shale. On the assumption that the life span of species X was the same at both localities, the paleontologist concludes that the deposition of the shale began earlier at locality A than at locality B.

Just as formations are brought together into groups and subdivided into members, zones are united into **stages** and **series** to form a hierarchy of biostratigraphic subdivisions of rock strata. A stage is a succession of beds characterized by one or more zones and a series is a succession of beds which includes several stages.

In dividing a stratigraphic section into biostratigraphic units, the paleontologist first collects as many fossils as possible throughout the region and plots their overlapping ranges on a chart such as that in Fig. 2–15.

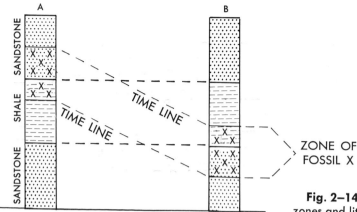

Fig. 2–14. The relationship between fossil zones and lithic units.

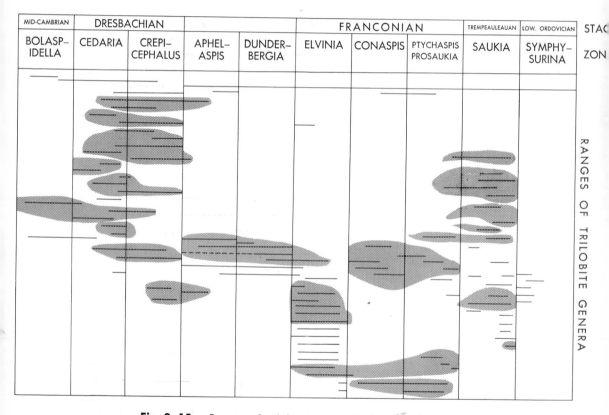

Fig. 2–15. Ranges of trilobite genera in the Upper Cambrian, or Croixan Series of the Llano region, Texas. The vertical lines represent the ranges of genera, the shaded areas families. The horizontal lines not enclosed within an area of shading represent genera which are not grouped into families on this chart. A zone is named after a prominent member of the fossil fauna, and its lower boundary is defined by the first appearance of the fossils concerned. (Courtesy of C. Lochman-Balk and the Paleontological Society.)

He then selects from the mass of ranges those fossils which are abundant and short-lived enough to define easily recognizable zones. These zones, such as the *Cedaria, Crepicephalus,* and *Aphelaspis* zones in the illustration, must be sequential (with no time gaps left) and relatively thin if they are to be used to make a precise determination of events in the past. They are then assembled into stages such as Dresbachian, Franconian, and Trempealeauan, all of which belong in the Croixan Series. Once such a set of zones has been set up it is a valuable point of reference for placing in their stratigraphic position isolated fossil-bearing sections whose relationship to other stratigraphic sections cannot be determined on a lithologic basis.

Index and Guide Fossils

Neither Smith nor Cuvier considered a special designation for those fossils which were most useful in identifying rock units. Two terms are in use today for such fossils—guide fossils and index fossils. These are species or, in a wider sense, assemblages of species, that characterize a rock unit over a particular interval of deposition. Because the value of index fossils is to point to the age equivalency of a stratum with some part of a reference section, species that occur in only one locality are useless. Let us assume that we have a plateau cut by five streams yielding canyon-wall sections of 50 feet each (Fig. 2–16). The paleontologist will identify as far as possible all species taken from these sections. Some, such as species *b* and *e*, may be found throughout the entire section in each locality, and therefore will have no value for dividing the sections into zones or for matching zones from section to section. Others, for instance species *a*, may be restricted to bed *A*, making up the lowest 10 feet; or, like species *c*, may be restricted to the upper beds *C, D,* and *E*. Species *d* climbs stratigraphically from left to right through beds *B* and *C*, and may even yield information concerning migration. Its range may, with caution, be extrapolated beyond the limits of the diagram.

One of the assumptions of paleontological correlation is that dispersal of organisms is, when compared with the vast length of geological time, essentially instantaneous. If an organism were to take several million years to migrate from point *X* to point *Y*, then it would appear in the stratigraphic sections at *X* and *Y* at different times. Unless he finds evidence to the contrary, the paleontologist must assume that the appearance of a fossil is contemporaneous over the area of its distribution. This assumption is based on studies of the dispersal of modern animals similar to those used in correlation. A good example is the movement of the slipper-shell *Crepidula* along the south coast of England from the Thames to the Isle of Wight between 1891 and 1916. During this 25-year period this snail species spread through 200 miles, even

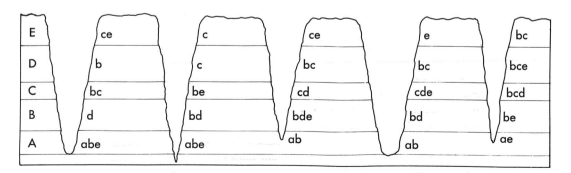

Fig. 2–16. A possible method of selecting index fossils.

though the adult scarcely moves at all during its lifetime. At this rate of dispersal, *Crepidula* would be carried once around the world in 3,000 years—geologically speaking, an instant. In choosing fossils for zonation and correlation paleontologists try to pick those whose occurrence in many different rock types shows that they were carried by wind and water currents widely and quickly over the world.

Not all fossils are suitable to be used as index fossils and to establish zones. Some, like the genus *Lingula, s.l.** (Ordovician–Recent), range through several periods (see Fig. 19–3). Others, restricted to a few feet or even inches of beds, may be of local occurrence only.* There are four characteristics of a good index fossil: (1) it must have a narrow stratigraphic range; (2) it must have a wide geographic distribution; (3) it must be easy to recognize; and (4) it must be common. Such index fossils are, then, the tools with which the paleontologist works to aid the stratigrapher in the age determination of rocks, so that a section of limestone in Ohio can be correlated with rocks in Kentucky or in Ontario.

Among marine fossils, pelagic forms, i.e., surface swimmers or floaters such as graptolites (Fig. 2–4), are the most useful. Because they evolved rapidly and were dispersed instantly (in the geological sense) over the entire surface of the oceans, their fossils are excellent time markers. Ammonoid cephalopods (see Figs. 21–21 and 21–23), which lived on the ocean floor but moved actively, are equally good for correlation and subdivision of Mesozoic strata. Foraminifera are extensively used as guide fossils for Mesozoic and Cenozoic strata. Figure 2–17 indicates the usefulness of the genera of the family ALVEOLINIDAE. The species of these genera make possible a much greater refinement of ranges. Terrestrial organisms, both plants and animals, should theoretically be of great value, the former because of seed dispersal by wind, and the latter because of an ability

* See Appendix A for explanation.

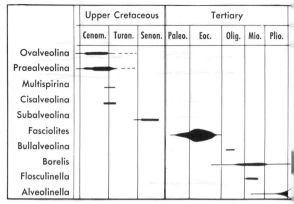

Fig. 2–17. The time ranges of the genera of the family Alveolinidae, each of which could serve the purpose of an index fossil. Most of the species of each genus have shorter ranges and are therefore of greater value than the genera. The family is world-wide in distribution. (From *Treatise on Invertebrate Paleontology*, courtesy of the Geological Society of America and the University of Kansas Press.)

to move about relatively rapidly and to extend their range widely. Such value is, however, lessened by the rarity of terrestrial deposits. Spores and pollen grains (Fig. 2–18) have in the last decade or two become intensely important, for, being blown by the wind, they may fall into the sea, lakes, swamps, etc., and be preserved.

PALEONTOLOGY AND EVOLUTION

William Smith had proved that the strata of Britain could be arranged in a chronological sequence and that each formation was marked by its own characteristic fossils, but the idea that the fossils might be arranged in lines of descent did not occur to him. For fifty years prior to Darwin's *Origin of Species* the theory was being developed that the resemblance of the representative fossil fauna and flora to the modern biota decreased as investigations proceeded into older and older rocks; as a natural consequence the suggestion was being entertained that this situation might be due to the descent of one fossil species from another, with continuous improvements leading to the

Fig. 2–18. Spores from Mesozoic rocks of Canada. The study of these minute fossils and of pollen grains is a branch of micropaleontology called palynology. (Courtesy of the Geological Survey of Canada.)

developed the concept of the survival of the fittest of nature's chance variants and the elimination of the unfit, thus antedating A. R. Wallace and Charles Darwin by 2300 years. The most influential of the Greek evolutionists was Aristotle (384–322 B.C.), whose animal and plant garden (a private zoo) afforded him abundant opportunities to study similarities and differences among organisms. Guided by his observations he supposed that an internal perfecting tendency (entelechy) was responsible for the improvement generation by generation along various lines of descent, ending in the present biota. Despite the great respect in which Aristotle was held throughout the early Christian era, the Dark Ages, and the early Middle Ages, his ideas on evolution were completely neglected.

Special Creation

Prior to Aristotle the theory of special creation had become crystallized in the religious writings of the Jews, and the account of the creation of plants and animals on the third, fifth, and sixth days of Creation came to hold a dominating place in Christian theology. In this view species were immutable; some might become extinct, but no new ones could be created. The Bible stated that "God saw everything that he had made, and, behold, it was very good." The introduction of a new kind of animal or plant would be an impious denial of that statement. To this view Carl Linneus (1707–1778) was an adherent, but he held to it less inflexibly than did most of his contemporaries, allowing that interspecific breeding may have produced hybrids and thus increased the number of species.

Lamarck and Cuvier

After tentative gropings along the right path in the middle of the eighteenth century by men like Erasmus Darwin (1731–1802) and Georges Buffon (1709–1788), a new and important step forward was made by Jean-Baptiste Lamarck (1744–1829), the first modern scientist to assert clearly that species have

modern biota. In this speculative atmosphere Darwin grew up, and not only transformed this incipient concept of evolution into what has come to be considered fact, but offered, in the theory of natural selection, by far the most satisfactory mechanism to explain its gross operation.

Early Views

Scientists today almost unanimously accept the theory of **organic evolution.** We find in the writings of Greek philosophers between 550 and 325 B.C. the idea that animals and plants were the end products of a long series of changes over many generations and had developed from fewer and simpler forms into the modern complexity of species. Of these philosophers Anaximander (611–546 B.C.) was the earliest. Empedocles (ca. 450 B.C.)

arisen in the passage of time by the accumulation of gradual changes. He postulated that these changes had been induced in the organism indirectly by its environment, that organs that were used tended to develop, whereas disuse of organs led to their disappearance. This led him to formulate the doctrine of the inheritance of acquired characteristics, now largely discredited. In spite of his championship of a false cause, his work as a naturalist could have been of immense value had it not been for the implacable opposition to his ideas taken by Cuvier, whose researches into the vertebrate fossils of the Paris basin had earned him great renown. Cuvier was a member of the ruling establishment in Paris, and anyone whose views were opposed to his was mercilessly crushed. He championed the theory of the successive annihilation of faunas in parts of the earth by crustal revolutions, such as vast inundations of land areas or upheavals of the sea floor, and the replacement of the lost fauna by an immigration of species from other localities. Cuvier, like Lamarck, believed that life was continuous, but he exaggerated the influence of his "revolutions." Because he recognized that life of the past was arranged in an order of ascending complexity he was to that extent an evolutionist. His followers distorted what might have been a cornerstone of evolutionary progress by crystallizing this distorted view into the bizarre theory of catastrophism, in which each successive fauna was thought to have been catastrophically and completely eliminated, thus preventing the continuity of life. The struggle between the disciples of Lamarck and of Cuvier lasted throughout the first half of the nineteenth century, and though we no longer hear of Cuvier's views, Lamarck's ideas are still upheld in modified form by those who call themselves Neo-Lamarckians.

Darwin and Natural Selection

Although many abortive attempts to establish the truth of the doctrine of evolution were made in the first half of the nineteenth century, Charles Darwin (1809–1882) was the first to amass sufficient evidence to support the view that the present diversity of animals and plants has resulted from a continuous descent from earlier and simpler forms by a long process of progressive, small modifications. This view was simultaneously promulgated by A. R. Wallace (1822–1913) without, however, the massive supporting data gathered by Darwin. With the possible exception of Aristotle, none of Darwin's predecessors had accumulated so convincing an array of facts and observations: he lifted the question of the validity of the theory of evolution from the realm of speculation and set it squarely upon a firm basis of fact and deduction.

Darwin (and later Wallace, too) received his first impetus to delve into the course and causes of evolution by reading Malthus' "Essay on the Principle of Population as it affects the future Improvement of Society" (sixth edition, 1826), in which the author showed that, unless curbed, the human population would soon outgrow its static food supply. Some factor must operate to keep the population within bounds. What was that factor? Both Darwin and Wallace had come to the conclusion that the hazards of existence, the search for food, success or failure in obtaining a mate, escape from enemies, etc., provided a means of giving some individuals an advantage over others. Among animals, for example, those with longer legs than the average could develop greater speed, while those with protective coloring could escape enemies; in the end, those with greater speed would be the ones which would escape, and those with superior protective coloration would avoid detection by predators. Hence, said Darwin, the next generation would carry forward those characteristics favorable to survival. Darwin called this process natural selection, but he confessed that he was almost completely ignorant of the basic cause of the variations. Darwin did not know about the work of his contemporary Gregor Mendel (1822–1884), whose discovery of laws governing the role of heredity lay unnoticed for 35 years, or of August Weismann (1834–1914), whose demonstrations of the mechanism of heredity signified the end of the doctrine of the inheritance of acquired characteristics. Nor, of course, could he know of the modern work of the schools of genetics where experimentation with environmentally controlled variants among animals (especially *Drosophila*) have led to an understanding of the roles of chromosomes and genes in controlling heredity and variation.

Evidences of Evolution

Although Darwin's exposition of natural selection in his *Origin of Species* (1859 *et seq.*) was sufficient to place organic evolution on a firm basis, corroborative evidence came from other sources. Studies in comparative anatomy show that each group of organisms has a common plan of structure. All placental mammalian teeth are developed in accordance with the basic dental formula shown below (see p. 494):

$$\frac{3\text{-}1\text{-}4\text{-}3}{3\text{-}1\text{-}4\text{-}3}$$

The anatomy of almost all land vertebrates shows the fore and hind limbs built on the same basic plan of bones (see Fig. 21–15). All echinoderms have a test and water-vascular system disposed according to a pentameral symmetry (see Fig. A–23). These similarities suggest descent of the individuals and species of the group from a common ancestor. Common ancestry may also be shown in similar physiological features, such as blood types.

Evidence that evolution has taken place comes from the study of the faunas of oceanic islands. The Galapagos Islands, separated by 600 miles of ocean from the South American mainland, have a biota of birds, turtles, lizards, and plants resembling that of the mainland but containing distinct species. The Cape Verde Islands in the Atlantic also have their own biota resembling, but distinct from, that of neighboring Africa 400 miles distant. That migration from the mainland took place in each set of islands, and that geographic isolation has led to the observed differences, is an undeniable conclusion. The faunas of oceanic islands also illustrate the diversification of a group of migrant animals in occupying the habitats available in a new land. Although many groups of birds are present on the South American mainland, only a few migrated to the Galapagos Islands. There the habitats which were occupied by other families of birds on the mainland were unfilled. The finches, which made the migration without competition, evolved to fill niches such as woodpecking, insect eating, and cactus eating, and adapted to them by modifications of body, particularly beaks. This phenomenon is known as adaptive radiation.

A dozen other lines of investigation have so cemented the idea of degree of close relationship that doubt no longer exists concerning the unity of the animal kingdom. For instance, there are in many animals vestigial organs, structures which once served useful purposes but which, through perhaps countless generations, have lost their importance but have not been eliminated by nature. Our own body has been called a museum of relics. The ear muscles, for instance, are vestiges of a once advantageous structure and indicate our descent from animals with active ears that allow them to determine the direction of sound and therefore of a possible enemy. Our appendix is a relic of a digestive system long since modified, and is today a distinct disadvantage to some of us.

Phylogenies

With few exceptions the above evidences supporting the theory of organic evolution are taken from living animals and plants. Only paleontology provides this historical perspective and comes as close as possible to being proof of evolution. A series of brachiopods, foraminifers, or horses in a succession of sedimentary beds can be arranged in chronological order of existence to illustrate the directions that evolution has followed. Such a sequence is known as a phylogeny and tells the history of a taxon, in contrast to ontogeny, which lists the changes undergone by an individual organism from birth to death. The phylogeny of the horse will provide an example of this kind of evidence and is given here in barest outline, leaving a fuller treatment for Chapter 22. Horse fossils are common throughout the Cenozoic beds of western North America. The earliest fossil horse was about the size of a fox terrier. It had four toes on the fore feet and three on the hind feet; high-crowned, short-rooted teeth characteristic of browsers (eaters of leaves and other soft vegetation); and a skull in which the eye socket was situated midway along the length. In the Oligocene representative of the horse family, the toes had been reduced to three on both fore and hind feet and the teeth and eye socket remained about the same, but the height of the animal had about doubled. By Miocene times the side toes were largely non-functional, so that the weight was carried almost wholly on the middle toe; the teeth were flat-crowned with longer roots, characteristic of grazers (grass eaters); the eye socket lay somewhat posterior of the midpoint of the skull; and the size had increased to that of a modern pony. In Pliocene times fossil horses show only remnants of the side toes, or these are represented by mere splints, so that the animal walked upon his middle toe. The teeth were flat-crowned with infolded enamel and had become very long-rooted. The eye had migrated to a point about one-third the distance from the posterior end of the skull. With only inconsequential changes, mostly in size, Pleistocene horses grade into the modern species, *Equus caballus*. Here is a definite succession of changes in feet, teeth, size, and eye socket position. This phylogeny, and the biological information gathered from a study of living horses, is close to absolute proof of the evolution of the horse from primitive forebears; it is not absolute proof, for nowhere in paleontology can we be sure that one fossil is the direct descendant of another. That the group to which one belonged was descended from the group to which the other belonged is, however, a logical and meaningful conclusion.

In a visit to any geological museum today one thing that must strike an intelligent ob-

server is the primitiveness and paucity of the fossils collected from early formations, and the gradual but marked increase in number, variety, and organization of animals in collections from the succeeding formations. Two of the most important changes as time progressed are the introduction of new animals and plants and the dying off of others. The history of any group of fossils (brachiopod, fish, cycad, trilobite) shows progress from primitive forms to more and more complex, or, one might say, more advanced forms, and usually ends in extinction. Moreover, the new kinds are introduced in time in order of their complexity. Let one simple example suffice for the present. Show a zoologist a fish, an amphibian, a reptile, and a mammal, and ask him to arrange them in order of their zoological complexity. He will follow the order given above. Now ask a paleontologist when these four types of life were first introduced, and the answer will be in the same order. One example may not be convincing, but in nearly all groups that might be selected, newer, more complex forms follow the simpler, earlier ones with such regularity as to suggest the working of a law. In fact this is the doctrine of organic evolution, according to which life began on earth as a simple single-celled organism, and by descent with modification all the multiplicity of modern forms arose. This is the essence of the doctrine to which there is no scientific dissent today.

PALEOECOLOGY

Ecology and Paleoecology

The ecologist studies the relationships between plants and animals of the modern world and their environment. He is concerned not only with the interactions between the various members of plant and animal communities but with the influence of physical factors in the environment on the community. Each environment is characterized by animals and plants which are adapted to the particular conditions, both physical and biological, under which they exist, and

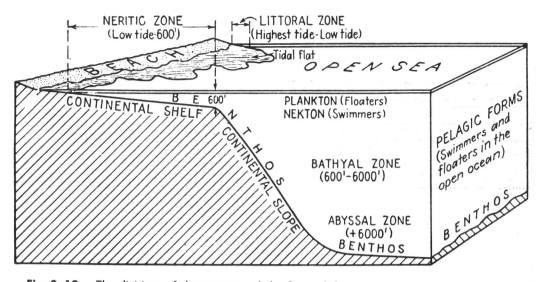

Fig. 2–19.   The divisions of the waters and the floor of the ocean into life zones. (Courtesy of R. R. Shrock, from Shrock and Twenhofel, *Principles of Invertebrate Paleontology.* New York: McGraw-Hill Book Co., 1953. Used by permission.)

which react to changes in these factors. The classification of environments is the beginning of the study of ecological relationships. The ecologist classifies the environments of the sea largely on the basis of depth: the littoral zone between high and low tides, the neritic zone of the continental shelves, the bathyal zone of the continental slopes, and the abyssal zone of the ocean deeps (Fig. 2–19). The animals and plants that live on the ocean floor are said to be **benthonic** or part of the benthos; those that swim in the water above are **nectonic;** and those that float passively are **planktonic.** Each of these broad environments can be further divided many times into habitats each of which is characterized by its own community of animals and plants.

We are not surprised that different environments or habitats on land and in the sea support different animals and plants, for these differences are a familiar part of our world. The plants which grow in marshes are not found on dry hillsides, nor do the

birds that live in the pine woods frequent the meadowlands. The mussels that cling to rocky, wave-washed shores are not found in the shifting sands of beaches. In the past, as at present, each animal had its own habitat and this environment was reflected in the sediment laid down where the animal lived. Animals and plants of the non-marine marshlands were entombed and fossilized in dark, non-marine shales. Clams of the beach were enclosed in quartz sandstones. The study of the relationship of fossil animals to the environments in which they lived and the sediments in which they were buried is the science of **paleoecology.**

Facies Faunas

In Chapter 1 the total aspect of the primary features of a sedimentary rock was referred to as a facies. Each facies, such as the quartz sand facies, or the black shale facies, is the result of a set of depositional conditions, and each may be associated with a fauna also characteristic of these conditions. Quartz sandstones commonly contain worm burrows and the molds of clams that lived in shallow water. Gray siltstones are characterized by a fossil fauna of clams that lived in estuarine conditions. These are facies faunas, groups of animals associated with a particular lithology. All fossils are to a greater or lesser degree facies fossils, but some are found in a greater range of lithologies than others; that is, during life they inhabited a greater variety of environments than others. The fossils of animals that floated or swam in marine environments are found in many different kinds of bottom deposits, for their existence at the sea surface was independent of the material deposited on the bottom. Graptolites, floating Paleozoic animals, although particularly abundant in the black shale facies, are also found in limestones, siltstones, and even sandstones, where they were deposited from the water above when they died.

Fossils which are strictly restricted to a single lithology are useful only for correlating sections in which that lithology is found. Two contemporaneous sections of sediments might have no fossils in common if one of them was gray siltstone and the other quartz sandstone, because no animals living at that time were common to the two environments in which the rocks were deposited. Obviously, the fossils that will be of greatest use in correlation will be those which lived in a variety of environments in the past or were drifted by winds, waves, or currents into a variety of environments after death. The fossils which the paleontologist chooses for establishing zones are ideally of the kind which is insensitive to facies control or floated and swam during life. The paradox of paleontological correlation is that, although like fossils indicate like time, unlike fossils do not necessarily indicate unlike time. They may merely indicate that the beds were laid down in different environments.

Paleoecological Interpretation

The interpretation of past environments is one of the aims of the historical geologist. From the physical characteristics of sedimentary rocks much can be deduced about the environment in which they were deposited by applying the principle of uniformitarianism as explained in Chapter 1. The fossils contained in the rocks can be used in a similar manner to aid the reconstruction of past conditions. By comparing the animal communities found in modern seas with fossil communities, the paleontologist can deduce the physical factors that controlled the ancient environment. The division of a modern reef into ecological zones on the basis of animals adapted to the various environments (fore-reef, surf, reef flat, lagoon) can be duplicated in the fossils preserved in ancient reefs. The different faunas of corals and stromatoporoids found in reefs millions of years old can be interpreted in terms of the conditions in modern reefs on the basis of a comparison of the fossils with modern communities. Such paleoecological interpretations are further examined in Chapters 7 and 8.

SUMMARY

Fossils may be the remains of organisms or indications of the previous existence of organisms. Fossilization is a natural rarity, but provides a satisfactory outline of the progress of life. Soft-bodied organisms and animals and plants of the highlands of the earth have rarely been preserved. Fossils are commonest in limestone and shale.

Early in the nineteenth century William Smith of England and Cuvier and Brogniart in France independently recognized that there was a regional uniformity of the succession of strata, and that each formation was characterized by its own set of fossils. The time during which a certain animal lived is called a zone, and fossils used to identify zones are called index fossils.

The concept of organic evolution grew from early ideas to the statement of the theory by Darwin in 1859. Three names stand out—Lamarck, Cuvier, and Darwin—among the founders of the doctrine. Evolution is supported by studies in comparative anatomy, geographic isolation, vestigial structures, and phylogenies.

The ecologist is concerned with the adaptation of organisms to their environment: marine or non-marine, shallow water, deep water, etc. Facies faunas are those limited to a certain type of environment, and are important in working out lithological developments but may have limited significance for purposes of time correlation. The paleoecologist has only a fraction of the biota to work with but uses that fraction to deduce the details of the physical environment under which it lived.

QUESTIONS

1. Under what environmental conditions can a complete organism be preserved? Of what use is the cavity from which a shell or a bone has been removed by solution?

2. Why are some silicified fossils superior to the original object?

3. Why are Smith, Cuvier, and Brogniart considered important, and what kind of geology did their researches advance? Contrast the state of geological knowledge in William Smith's time with that of our own.

4. What is a zone? How precisely can zonation be carried out? Define an index fossil. Give the characteristics of a good index fossil.

5. What were the points of agreement and disagreement between Cuvier and Lamarck? What theories did each support that are abandoned today? What was Darwin's major contribution to evolution?

6. Why is the study of paleoecology more complicated than that of ecology?

7. What are facies fossils? Are they the best kind of fossil for establishing zones? Give reasons for your answer.

REFERENCES AND SUGGESTED READINGS

ADAMS, F. D. *The Birth and the Development of the Geological Sciences.* Baltimore: The Williams & Wilkins Co., 1938. A good account of early progress in geology though rather short on paleontology and stratigraphy. Also available in paperback (Dover Books, 1954).

FENTON, C. L., and FENTON, M. A. *Giants of Geology.* Garden City, N.Y.: Doubleday and Co., Inc., 1952. A series of interesting sketches of more than a score of early geologists, including William Smith and Georges Cuvier.

GEIKIE, SIR ARCHIBALD. *The Founders of Geology.* London: The Macmillan Co., 1905.

HIMMELFARB, G. *Darwin and the Darwinian Revolution.* Garden City, N.Y.: Doubleday and Co., Inc., 1959. A highly readable and authoritative history of the main personalities and ideas involved in the conflicts set off by the publication of the *Origin of Species.* Available in paperback (Anchor Books, 1962).

LADD, H. S. (Ed.). *Treatise on Marine Ecology and Paleoecology,* 2 vols. New York: Geological Society of America, 1957. A collection of papers by recognized authorities on generalities concerning paleoecology, the conditions surrounding the origin of marine life, the classification of marine environments, and a score of special topics. A considerable section of Volume 2 is devoted to an annotated bibliography of marine paleoecology, arranged according to biological taxa.

SHIMER, H. W., and SHROCK, R. R. *Index Fossils of North America.* New York: John Wiley & Sons, Inc., 1944. An invaluable book for the working stratigrapher and paleontologist that describes and illustrates thousands of species of fossils used in solving problems of correlation and paleontology.

SIMPSON, G. G. *The Meaning of Evolution.* New Haven: Yale University Press, 1949. A semipopular but thoroughly scientific treatment of evolution, including such topics as racial life and death, the concept of progress in evolution, the history of evolutionary thought, and the future of man and life. Paperback edition available (Mentor Books, 1951).

SIMPSON, G. G. "The History of Life," in *The Evolution of Life,* Sol Tax (ed.). Chicago: University of Chicago Press, 1960. An essay concerned largely with philosophical comments on the Darwinian theory and statistical data relative to the development of fossil vertebrate groups.

Geochronology

3

Hutton: uniformitarianism

THE LENGTH OF GEOLOGICAL TIME

In 1650 Bishop Ussher calculated from biblical records that the year of the creation of the earth was 4004 B.C. Although the intellectual atmosphere of the seventeenth century seems strange to us now and the bishop's calculations misguided, the inclusion of his dates in the Authorized Version of the Bible molded for two hundred years the thinking of all but a handful of men on the length of the earth's history. Until the nineteenth century, it was the custom of natural scientists to believe that all the events they were beginning to read in the record of the rocks had to be crowded into a few thousand years. No wonder many of the geologists of the late eighteenth and early nineteenth centuries belonged to what is now called the catastrophist school. They believed that the earth's history was a series of extraordinary catastrophic events such as volcanic eruptions, earthquakes that tore open the canyons of river valleys, floods which overwhelmed the land, and mass extinctions and recreations of life. Not until the geologists' perspective of geological time had been deepened could they be sure of the validity of the concept of uniformitarianism, first set forth by James Hutton at a time when there was no evidence to support his hypothesis of the great vista of the history of the earth.

A more realistic attitude toward the processes of erosion and sedimentation and of astrophysics convinced many geologists and astronomers that such a limited span was inadequate, and by the middle of the nineteenth century the earth's age was estimated in terms of a few tens of millions of years. Only within the last 30 years have geologists discovered that the age of the earth must be measured in billions and not millions of years.

The concept of the length of geological time is the most important contribution geology has made in this century both to the other sciences and to culture. Astronomy and cosmogony have been greatly affected by the time scale of the earth's history proposed by geochronologists. The time of the origin of the earth, of meteorites, and even of the elements themselves can be suggested or determined by methods of geochronology. Through the joint studies of paleontologists and geochronologists, the rates at which animals evolved and the time elapsed during the upward progression of life from the first

46

living cell have been measured. Comparison of man's short span on earth with the length of time that life has existed, or with the span of time since the earth was formed, must shape our viewpoint of his place in the system of nature. The evidence that geology presents for the length of the earth's history has already had a profound effect on the Judeo-Christian viewpoint of the creation of the world.

RELATIVE AND ABSOLUTE TIME SCALES

In the excavations at Troy, used as an example of stratigraphic principles in the first chapter, many superimposed settlements were discovered, each characterized by a different assemblage of tools, weapons, and architecture. At the top were the ruins of a city of the early Christian era, below this the remnants of the Hellenistic town established by Alexander the Great, and below that the smoke-stained walls of the citadel of the Homeric Period. "Early Christian," "Hellenistic," and "Homeric" are stages of civilization but they also form a time scale against which events in other areas can be compared. Although it is the aim of historians and archeologists to date these episodes of culture in years, they would be just as real and could be used almost as effectively to classify man's progress whether or not their span in years could be measured. Indeed many divisions of time such as "Old Stone Age" and "New Stone Age" had been used by archeologists long before they were dated by modern methods. The cultural chronology is a relative one. Archeologists have, however, by reference to ancient records determined that Homeric Troy fell to the besieging Greeks around 1200 B.C. This date is absolute, not relative, and refers to a time scale based on the number of years before or after the birth of Christ. In dating events of the past the geologist also uses both relative and absolute time scales. His absolute time scale is divided into years before the present; his relative time scale is divided into periods and eras on the basis of the changes in life recorded in fossils.

THE RELATIVE GEOLOGICAL CALENDAR

The early chapters of the story of man are obscure because the fossil record of the primates during his period of emergence is scant, but from the time that man learned to write, our knowledge of his progress is much more detailed. The time during which primitive man left no written records is commonly referred to as the prehistoric period. The history of the earth may be similarly divided into a younger part, of which we have a record preserved in the rocks, and an older part, for which some events may be inferred but for which no record exists in the rocks of the crust. Like the time of the origin of man, the time at which the earth became a separate celestial body is lost in the obscurity of the formation of the universe, but the best modern estimates place this time at 4–5 billion years ago (see Chapter 4). We can call the time elapsed since the earth was formed earth time. What happened during the first hundreds of millions of years of earth time we can only guess. The oldest dated rocks are about 3½ billion years old but they bear evidence of former cycles of erosion and deposition about 4 billion years old. These oldest rocks mark the beginning of the geological record. Earth time can therefore be divided into pregeological time, that part of earth time before a permanent record in the rocks was formed, and geological time, the time elapsed since the beginning of the rock record. The condition of the earth in pregeological time will be discussed in the next chapter; here we are concerned with the further division of geological time.

The establishment of the eras and periods of the relative geological time scale is an interesting story (Table 3–1). The names of divisions of this scale were not at first applied to divisions of time but to sequences of sedimentary rocks that could be distinguished by their lithology, their occurrence in a given area, or their separation from other such sequences by unconformities. Some of these names were descriptive, such as Cretaceous (chalky) and Carboniferous (coal bearing); others, such as Devonian or Jurassic, were named from the geographical locality where the rocks were first found. As geologists extended their observations, the divisions that were at first purely lithologic came to have a time connotation. Beds in North America that could be shown by paleontological correlation to have been deposited at the same time as the folded shales and limestones of Devon, England, were said to be deposited during the Devonian Period. Sandstones in Asia that contain the same fossil ammonites as the limestones of the Jura Mountains in France were said to be of Jurassic age. Thus terms that were originally descriptive of local groups of rocks became applied to world-wide divisions of geological time. By this process the span of geological time has been subdivided into a number of eras and periods which are as convenient and conventional subdivisions as hours and minutes are as subdivisions of the day.

Development of the Geological Timetable

The first practical geological timetable was proposed by Abraham Werner, late in the eighteenth century. Building upon earlier

Table 3–1
Development of the Relative Time Scale

EARLY SUBDIVISIONS				MODERN USAGE		
Arduino 1760	Lehmann 1756 Füchsel 1760–1773	Werner ca. 1800	English Equivalents	Eras	Periods	Epochs
Volcanic Tertiary	Angeschwemmt-gebirge	Angeschwemmt-gebirge Neues Flötzge-birge	Alluvium Tertiary	CENOZOIC Phillips 1841	NEOGENE PALEOGENE	Pleistocene Pliocene Miocene Oligocene Eocene Paleocene
Secondary		Flötzgebirge	Secondary	MESOZOIC Phillips 1841	CRETACEOUS d'Halloy 1822 JURASSIC von Humboldt 1795 TRIASSIC von Alberti 1834	
Primitive	Flötzgebirge	Übergangs-gebirge	Transition	PALEOZOIC Sedgwick 1838	PERMIAN Murchison 1841 PENNSYLVANIAN Williams 1891 MISSISSIPPIAN Winchell 1870 DEVONIAN Murchison, Sedgwick 1837 SILURIAN Murchison 1835 ORDOVICIAN Lapworth 1879 CAMBRIAN Sedgwick 1835	
	Urgebirge	Urgebirge	Primary	PRECAMBRIAN°		

° For details see Chapter 16.

work by Johann Lehmann, George Füchsel, and Giovanni Arduino, he noticed in Germany that everywhere beneath the sedimentary rocks there lay a basement of crystalline rocks (Fig. 3–1). These rocks, he supposed, represented the original crust of the earth, and therefore he called them Urgebirge (Primitive, or Primary Series). Directly above these was a series of essentially horizontal limestones, shales, and other sedimentary rocks. These Werner called the Flötzgebirge (Flat-lying Series, later called Secondary). Above these he found a thin veneer of sands and gravels to which he gave the

rock formations recognized at the beginning of the nineteenth century, together with their approximate modern equivalents, is as follows:

Alluvium ⎫	
Tertiary ⎬	Cenozoic
Secondary	Mesozoic
Transition	Paleozoic
Primary	Precambrian

Among the many fundamental differences between the Primary and Transition series is the lack of fossils in the former and their abundance in Transition and later strata.

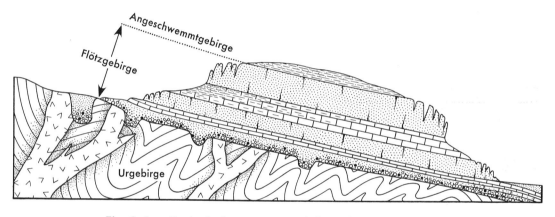

Fig. 3–1. Geological cross-section of the rocks studied by Werner in Saxony showing the relationship between his three major divisions of the stratigraphic record. A major unconformity exists between the Urgebirge and the Flötzgebirge. (After A. W. Grabau, courtesy of D. C. Heath & Co.)

name Angeschwemmtgebirge (Alluvium). Nearby it was later found that sedimentary rocks thousands of feet thick lay upon the Primary rocks and yet were covered by Secondary strata. As these in many ways were transitional between the two series, Werner named them the Übergangsgebirge (Transition Series).

Other observers later discovered that there was a great sequence of sedimentary rocks lying between the Secondary and the Alluvium. For these beds the obvious name Tertiary suggested itself, and the Alluvium later became the Quaternary. The order of

The fossils that occur in post-Primary strata show a progressively greater resemblance to organisms now living. This evolution of life has given rise to a new set of terms replacing the Wernerian divisions, terms indicative of the kind of life in existence during those times. Thus the earliest, or Transition, was named the time of old life, or Paleozoic; the Secondary, the era of middle life, or Mesozoic; and the Tertiary and Alluvium became the era of recent life, or Cenozoic. The names Primary and Primitive have been discarded and for convenience have been replaced by the term Precambrian.

The **principle of superposition,** which states that in any normal succession of sedimentary rocks younger beds overlie older beds, is fundamental in stratigraphy. Although Werner's classification was primarily a structural one, the application of this principle allows it to assume chronological significance; that is, the beds lowest in his section (Primary) were laid down in his oldest division of geological time, and those at the top in his youngest division. Such a broad classification could not long remain undivided, and within the century the five divisions were destined to be broken up into scores of shorter time intervals.

On the Continent and in England, where historical geology and stratigraphy grew up, seams of coal are interstratified with the rocks at the top of the Transition series. Because the series includes the coal-bearing beds, the English geologist William Conybeare proposed (in 1832) to call them the "Carboniferous order."

In the early 1830's the oldest Transition rocks recognized were slates, quartzites, and limestones, occurring mostly in Wales and southwestern England. Two friends, Roderick Murchison and Adam Sedgwick, the first a retired officer of Wellington's army and the second a Cambridge don, undertook the task of unraveling the complex geology of that region. They were successful in reducing the strata to some sort of order, and each was convinced that he had recognized a subdivision of the Transition rocks older than anything then known. Murchison, who had been working in south Wales, a region inhabited in early days by a tribe known as the Silures, christened his rocks the Silurian System. Sedgwick had discovered what seemed to him to be a still older assemblage, one that rested directly upon the Primary rocks. He named his assemblage the Cambrian series, taking the name from the ancient name of Wales. Unfortunately, upon further investigation, there appeared to be a thickness of rocks common to both. These Murchison claimed for his Silurian, and Sedgwick for his Cambrian. Neither would

yield, and the partnership in geological research that had proved so fruitful was dissolved. For 40 years the controversy concerning the overlapping systems divided geologists over the world into two camps, even after Charles Lapworth of Edinburgh proposed as a compromise that the controversial strata should be made into a separate system which he designated the Ordovician from the name of an ancient British tribe. The Ordovician System was not recognized immediately in Great Britain or on the Continent but gained wide acceptance in North America. Even now in some parts of Europe the Silurian System is used in the sense of Murchison's definition and is considered to consist of a lower Ordovician division and an upper Gotlandian division. The latter is named after the Island of Gotland in the Baltic Sea where Silurian limestones are well exposed.

While still friends, Murchison and Sedgwick spent one season in Devon where they found folded and faulted limestones and slates containing fossils that were recognized to be older than those in the Carboniferous System and younger than those in the Silurian. They jointly proposed the euphonious name Devonian for this new system. After this proposal the subdivision of the Transition group was as follows:

> Carboniferous
> Devonian
> Silurian
> Cambrian

In 1840 and 1841, Murchison, who had become internationally famous for his books on the Silurian System, spent two seasons investigating coal resources of Russia and found there, in the province of Perm, strata which he named the Permian System. In England the rocks overlying the Carboniferous System consist of an unfossiliferous red sandstone and a magnesian limestone. Murchison's reasons for founding the Permian System, quoted below, illustrate the concept held by the founders of these units that the system was primarily a lithologic division but had some time connotation:

The Carboniferous system is surmounted east of the Volga by a vast series of beds of marls, schists, limestones, sandstones, and conglomerates to which I propose to give the name "Permian system" because, although this series represents as a whole the lower red sandstone . . . and the magnesian limestone . . . yet it cannot be classified exactly (whether by the succession of strata or their contents) with either of the German or British subdivisions of this age. Moreover, the British lithological term of new red sandstone is inapplicable to the great masses of marls, white and yellow sandstones . . . . (*Philosophical Magazine*, 1841.)

In North America a striking unconformity in the sedimentary rocks of the Carboniferous System has allowed geologists to distinguish an upper (Pennsylvanian) system and a lower (Mississippian) system. These subdivisions are not in common use outside North America.

The Secondary rocks were studied in great detail in Europe in the early part of the nineteenth century. There they had long been divided into three parts, the youngest of which contained the chalk of the English Channel and was therefore conveniently called the Cretaceous System. The lowest part, because of the ease with which it could be divided into three units, chiefly on the basis of color, came to be called the Triassic; the middle part, well exposed in the Jura Mountains, was called the Jurassic System.

By reference to the sections in the Paris basin, southwestern France, and Italy, the Tertiary rocks were divided into groups largely on the basis of the percentage of living mollusks contained in them. Charles Lyell coined the terms Pliocene (more recent), Miocene (less recent), and Eocene (dawn of recent) for Tertiary beds that contain more than 35 per cent, 17–18 per cent, and 3½ per cent modern mollusks, respectively. Lyell later added the term Pleistocene (most recent), and others suggested Oligocene (few recent) and Paleocene (ancient recent). The terms Tertiary and Quaternary are part of the ordinal system long out of use for older rocks and should be discarded. However, they are both in use today and refer to pre-Pleistocene and post-Pliocene Cenozoic rocks, respectively. Little need has been felt by geologists for a division of the Tertiary and Quaternary rocks into systems. If systems are recognized they are usually the Paleogene for the first three series and the Neogene for the last three.

In this way a composite section of sedimentary rocks was built up for northern Europe, the component parts of which were taken from local sequences of rocks. Where the boundaries between systems are gradational and not lithologically distinct, disputes arose concerning their positions that had to be settled by arbitration. By paleontological correlation between the sections geologists found that some of the systems as originally established overlapped in time on others. Because the systems were coming to be used as divisions of a time scale, their overlap in time was undesirable.

Each system has a type section, the area from which it was first described, but by paleontological correlation the system can be recognized on other continents. The rocks of the Niagara escarpment can be shown by means of fossils to be of the same age as the typical Silurian rocks of Wales and are therefore said to represent the Silurian System of New York and Ontario. The term **system** is now used to refer to any set of rocks that contains fossils which allow a correlation to be made with a particular type section. The term **period** was introduced to designate the time taken to deposit the system at its type locality and represents basically the duration of those organisms found as fossils in the system at its type locality. The succession of periods forms the relative time scale. In subdividing systems and periods two sets of terms are used, one referring to divisions of time purely, called time or **chronologic** terms, and the other referring to successions of rocks characterized by a particular set of fossils, called **biostratigraphic** terms. Some geologists consider the biostratigraphic terms **time-stratigraphic** terms, that is, terms that refer to a succession of strata laid down during a certain interval of time. They would define a system as the succession of rocks laid down at various places around the world during the time represented by the system at its type locality. If, as most paleontologists believe, fossils are reliable indicators of time equivalence, then biostratigraphic divisions will eventually be confirmed as time-stratigraphic divisions. Until a method of dating sedimentary strata in years has been perfected, however, we must remember that systems and their subdivisions are recognized almost without exception by their fossils (Table 3–2).

Table 3–2
Comparative Terminology

Time Terms	Biostratigraphic Terms (Time-stratigraphic of some geologists)	Lithological Terms		
Era	Erathem			
Period	System	Group	Formation	Member
Epoch	Series			
Age	Stage			

Systems are divided into **series;** the corresponding time term is an **epoch.** Most systems can be divided into three series: lower, middle, and upper. The Lower, Middle, and Upper Cambrian series were deposited in the Early, Middle, and Late Cambrian epochs respectively. Similarly, series and epochs are divided into **stages** and **ages.**

Dating Sedimentary Rocks by the Relative Scale

Because they are standards for comparison, the type sections of the systems in Europe have received intensive study. Their fossil faunas have been collected foot by foot and the rocks have been subdivided into a succession of zones. Recall that a zone is a set of beds which contains an index fossil or group of fossils from which the age of the beds can be identified. These zones are gathered into stages and the stages grouped into series to form a detailed time-stratigraphic division of the type section.

Unfortunately, not all type sections are suitable for such intensive study. The rocks of the type section of the Devonian System are folded, faulted, metamorphosed, and not well exposed. Only recently have geologists been able to unravel the stratigraphic succession in this difficult area. For these reasons the standard used for the Devonian System is the much better exposure of these rocks in southern Belgium and western Germany.

Sedimentary rocks far from the type sections are placed in the relative time scale by comparing their fossils with those of the type sections. The paleontologist collects fossils from the rocks, divides the rocks into zones on the basis of the fossils, and then tries to correlate the zones with those of the European type sections. If the characteristic fossils of the European zones appear in his rocks, correlation is easy. More commonly, no species of fossils is common to both sets of rocks, and the paleontologist must compare his collections with the fauna of the type section on the basis of over-all similarity and stage of evolution. If he finds that his paleontological evidence is not good enough to establish a reliable correlation with the European zones and stages, he may create a local set of biostratigraphic divisions to aid in correlating sections within his basin of deposition. The most important set of zones and stages refers to the type section, but regional standards may be established in each basin of deposition for the convenience of the stratigrapher. The ages of Devonian rocks of eastern North America, for example, are commonly referred to a succession of stages whose type sections are in New York. The Devonian rocks of western Canada, however, are rarely referred to these stages because paleontologists in this area find reference to the stages of the European standard section more convenient.

The fossil faunas of most sedimentary rocks bear sufficient similarity to those of the European type sections to be placed at least approximately in the standard relative time scale. The type sections are largely composed of marine rocks whose paleontological zonation is based on invertebrate fossils. In central and southern Africa marine sedimentary rocks are rare except at the edges of the continent, and the interior is covered with thick sequences of non-marine sediments containing vertebrate fossils. Because these fossils cannot be directly compared with the European marine invertebrate faunas, they cannot be dated accurately in terms of the European systems, so another set of systems has been set up in Africa. For example, the Karoo System of South Africa seems to include beds which range in age from late Carboniferous to early Jurassic on the standard time scale. Similarly, vertebrate paleontologists, in dating the Cenozoic continental sedimentary rocks of the western United States by means of mammalian fossils, use a time scale of 20 divisions that is largely independent of the Cenozoic divisions based on marine invertebrates in Table 3–1.

Time and biostratigraphic terms, such as system, period, stage, epoch, etc., should not be confused with the terms used to divide sedimentary rocks on the basis of lithology. These terms, such as formation, group, and member, are independent of time and are based on the type of rock only (Table 3–2). Hence, stratigraphers use three sets of terms: lithological, for dividing a sequence of rocks on the basis of lithology (e.g., Grimsby Formation); biostratigraphic, for dividing a sequence of rocks on the basis of fossils (e.g., Lower Silurian Series); and time, for dividing geological time (e.g., Early Silurian Epoch).

ABSOLUTE AGE DETERMINATIONS

While the relative geological time scale was being developed, no one had any idea how long a period was in terms of years or whether the periods were of equal length. It was naturally a subject of considerable speculation, and attempts were made to relate the duration of the periods to the age of the earth by calculations of the rate of sedimentation and erosion. Unfortunately, none of the methods used up to the end of the nineteenth century is valid, and they now have only historical interest. One of the most influen-

tial of these discarded estimates was made by Lord Kelvin and was based on the rate of cooling of the sun. He believed that the earth could not have been inhabited by life for more than 20 million years, but his calculations depended on a misconception concerning the source of energy of the sun.

Other estimates of the lengths of geological time were based on assumed rates of deposition, erosion, and addition of salt to the sea. None of these rates is constant, so they cannot supply accurate figures for the absolute dating of rocks.

Early Methods Based on Radioactivity

Certain atoms, said to be radioactive, are unstable; they decay either directly or through a long series of intermediate products to stable atoms. The rate of this decay can be accurately measured and is not affected by changes in temperature, pressure, or any known environmental factor. The rate at which a radioactive element is transformed into another element is called its half life. Thorium, as an example, has a half life of 1.38×10^{10} years. After the passing of this immense period of time only half the thorium in a given sample will remain; and, in another like period, half of that half will have decayed, and so on. The phenomenon of radioactivity was discovered near the end of the nineteenth century by Antoine Becquerel, but Bertram Boltwood was the first (1907) to see its application to the dating of rocks. Boltwood worked with uranium, which decays, with a very long half life (4.5×10^9 years), through several intermediate stages to a stable type of lead. He analyzed samples of the mineral uraninite, a uranium oxide, for uranium and lead, and by a simple calculation determined how long the lead had been accumulating from the breakdown of uranium, or, in other words, how long ago the uranium and its enclosing rock were emplaced.

During the complex pattern of disintegration of uranium and thorium to lead, at several stages the gas helium is given off (an alpha particle is a helium nucleus). If the

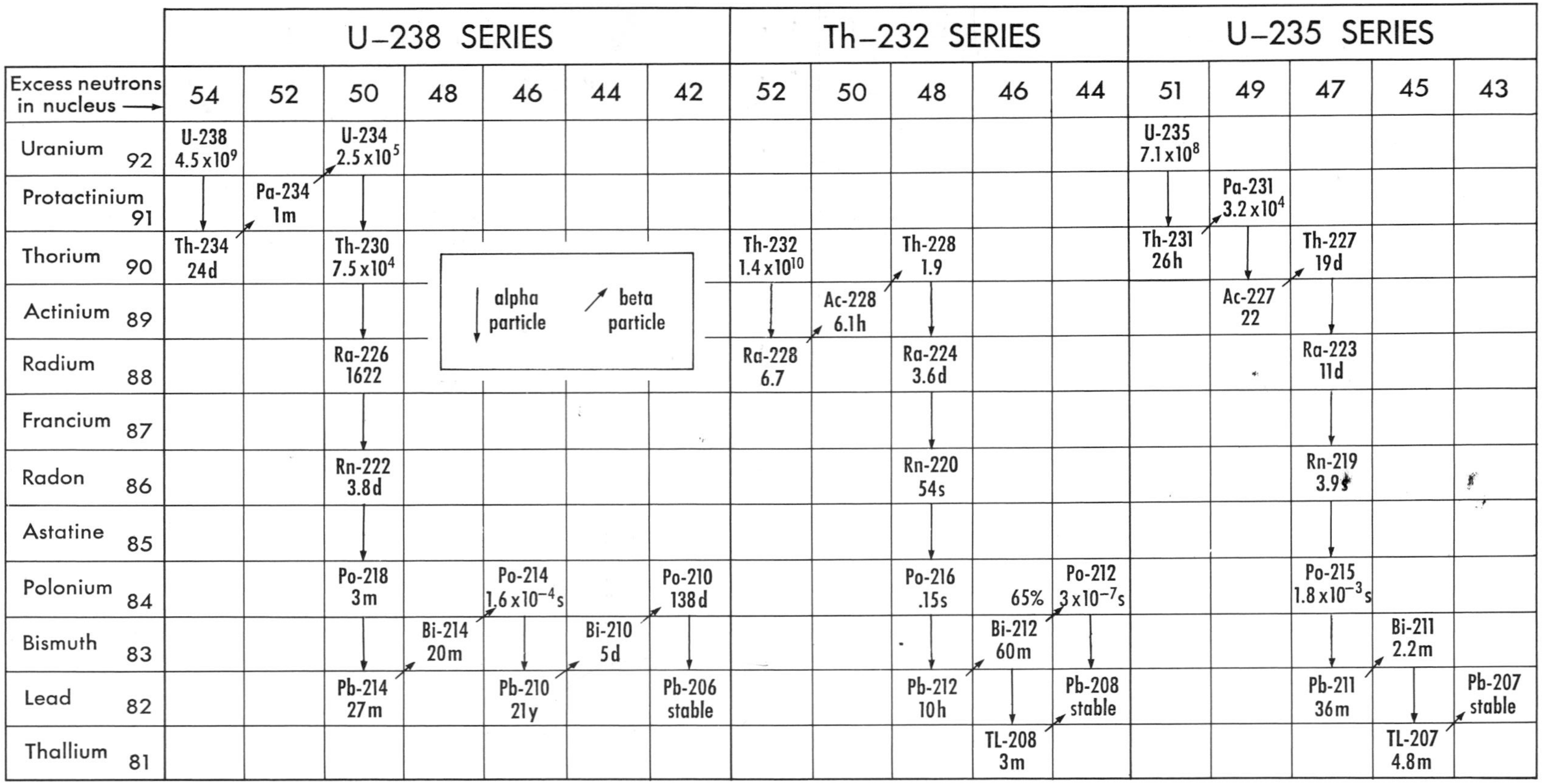

U-238 SERIES

Excess neutrons in nucleus →	54	52	50	48	46	44	42
Uranium 92	U-238 4.5×10⁹		U-234 2.5×10⁵				
Protactinium 91		Pa-234 1m					
Thorium 90	Th-234 24d		Th-230 7.5×10⁴				
Actinium 89							
Radium 88			Ra-226 1622				
Francium 87							
Radon 86			Rn-222 3.8d				
Astatine 85							
Polonium 84			Po-218 3m		Po-214 1.6×10⁻⁴ s		Po-210 138d
Bismuth 83				Bi-214 20m		Bi-210 5d	
Lead 82			Pb-214 27m		Pb-210 21y		Pb-206 stable
Thallium 81							

Legend: alpha particle (vertical arrow ↑), beta particle (diagonal arrow ↗)

Th-232 SERIES

	52	50	48	46	44
Uranium 92					
Thorium 90	Th-232 1.4×10¹⁰		Th-228 1.9		
Actinium 89		Ac-228 6.1h			
Radium 88	Ra-228 6.7		Ra-224 3.6d		
Radon 86			Rn-220 54s		
Polonium 84			Po-216 .15s	65%	Po-212 3×10⁻⁷s
Bismuth 83				Bi-212 60m	
Lead 82			Pb-212 10h		Pb-208 stable
Thallium 81				Tl-208 3m	

U-235 SERIES

	51	49	47	45	43
Uranium 92	U-235 7.1×10⁸				
Protactinium 91		Pa-231 3.2×10⁴			
Thorium 90	Th-231 26h		Th-227 19d		
Actinium 89		Ac-227 22			
Radium 88			Ra-223 11d		
Radon 86			Rn-219 3.9s		
Polonium 84			Po-215 1.8×10⁻³ s		
Bismuth 83				Bi-211 2.2m	
Lead 82			Pb-211 36m		Pb-207 stable
Thallium 81				Tl-207 4.8m	

Fig. 3-2. Decay series of the long-lived uranium and thorium isotopes. The elements with their atomic numbers (number of protons in the nucleus) are plotted along the left margin, and the number of excess neutrons in the nucleus along the top. Vertical arrows indicate the release of an alpha particle in the passage of one element to another and diagonal arrows show the release of a beta particle. The approximate half lives of the isotopes are indicated in the boxes in years, unless noted as follows: s, seconds; m, minutes; h, hours; d, days.

Jo good, now.

helium were retained in the rock or mineral containing the uranium then the amount that had accumulated relative to the uranium content would be a measure of the age of the sample. The helium method was used extensively in the 1930's until it was shown that analyses made on the separated mineral constituents of a rock gave very different ages. With the possible exception of magnetite, minerals vary in their ability to retain helium; therefore, this method of dating was discarded. Although now of historical interest only, the helium method is discussed here as an illustration that not all techniques for dating rocks have proved to be reliable. Many ages that were formerly considered accurate have subsequently been revised; the absolute time scale is under constant revision.

While the helium method was gaining and then losing popularity, new refinements were made in the uranium–lead method first used by Boltwood. Both lead and uranium were found to consist of several kinds of atoms (Fig. 3–2). The nuclei of atoms are composed of **protons** and **neutrons**. A proton is a nuclear particle of unit mass with a positive charge; a neutron has the same mass as a proton but carries no charge. The number of protons in the nucleus, designated by the **atomic number** of the element, determines its chemical properties. The number of neutrons and protons together determines its atomic weight. The **atomic weight** is a number which represents the weight of one atom of an element compared with the number 16, which represents the weight of an atom of oxygen. **Isotopes** of an element have the same number of protons in the nucleus, the same atomic number, and the same chemical properties, but they have different atomic weights because they have different numbers of neutrons in their nuclei.

Thorium and the two isotopes of uranium which are important in dating rocks decay to three different isotopes of lead in accordance with the following scheme:

U^{238} through several steps → Pb^{206}
half life 4.5×10^9 years

U^{235} through several steps → Pb^{207}
half life 0.7×10^9 years

Th^{232} through several steps → Pb^{208}
half life 14×10^9 years

The isotopes in a sample containing both uranium and thorium can be determined by means of an instrument called a **mass spectrometer**. This instrument measures the curvatures of the paths of charged atoms (which are proportional to their masses) as they travel through a magnetic field. From a single uranium-bearing sample three ages can be calculated by using the two ratios of daughter to parent isotopes (U^{238}/Pb^{206}, U^{235}/Pb^{207}) and the ratio between the two daughter isotopes (Pb^{207}/Pb^{206}), which also varies with time.

Not uncommonly, the three ages determined by the uranium–lead method are discordant; that is, they do not agree on the age of the sample. One of the most thoroughly analyzed occurrences of uranium is in the nodules in an Upper Cambrian shale in Sweden. The range of ages given by the three ratios for the many samples analyzed is as follows:

Pb^{206}/U^{238} 355–455 million years
Pb^{207}/Pb^{206} 650–945 million years
Pb^{207}/U^{235} 420–430 million years

The discrepancy between these ages has been explained as due to the leaching of lead from the sample by weathering and groundwater and to the escape from the sample of radon, a radioactive gas which is one of the intermediate stages in the sequence from uranium to lead. Geologists are pressing efforts to estimate these processes and to clear the discordant ages that have plagued the uranium–lead method.

A variant of the uranium–lead method is based on the relatively high content of uranium and its daughter product, lead, in crystals of **zircon**, a mineral that is composed of zirconium silicate and is widely scattered in igneous rocks. Zircon crystallizes in igneous rocks but is highly resistant to weathering and may remain after less stable minerals have been reduced to clay. It may then be incorporated in sedimentary rocks and subjected to metamorphism, and may persist in schists and gneisses, retaining undisturbed its radioactive clock. Zircon found in sedimentary or metamorphic rocks may therefore give evidence as to the age of its source rocks.

Gneisses in the eastern United States have feldspar with absolute ages indicative of Paleozoic metamorphism, but the zircons are much older and show that the gneisses were ultimately derived from the metamorphism of Precambrian rocks or the metamorphism of Paleozoic sediments whose zircons were eroded from Precambrian rocks. Originally, the radioactivity of the zircon crystals was measured by a counter and the method was called the lead–alpha (Pb/α) method, but now the parent and daughter products are measured by sophisticated analytical techniques.

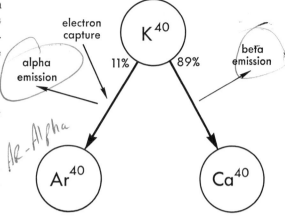

Fig. 3–3. Disintegration of potassium 40 to argon 40 and calcium 40.

The Potassium–Argon Method.

The method of absolute dating most widely employed today uses an isotope of potassium, K^{40}, which is present to the extent of .01 per cent in all potassium. Although this is a small proportion, potassium, unlike uranium, is a common element in the rocks and minerals of the earth's crust and the radioactivity of this isotope accounts for a large part of the normal background radiation that can be detected at the earth's surface. The radioactive decay of K^{40} (Fig. 3–3) yields both an isotope of argon (Ar^{40}) and an isotope of calcium (Ca^{40}). Although only 10 per cent of the K^{40} changes to Ar^{40}, it is easier to measure this branch of the disintegration than the one that gives rise to Ca^{40} because ordinary Ca^{40} is abundant and difficult to separate from that derived from K^{40}. However, the disintegration of K^{40} to Ca^{40} has been used for dating sediments rich in potassium and lacking calcium. The half life of the disintegration to argon is 1.3×10^9 years. The potassium content is determined chemically or by the mass spectrometer; the sample is fused in a vacuum; and the amount of Ar^{40} is measured in the mass spectrometer. Measurements and calculations must be made to

eliminate the more abundant isotopes of both potassium and argon which do not take part in the disintegration.

Argon is a gas and will easily escape from a mineral if the mineral is heated, weathered, or crushed. As the accuracy of the method depends on the retention of all the argon generated by K^{40} in the mineral, the minerals to be dated should be fresh, unfractured, unweathered, and rich in potassium. Muscovite, biotite, and the potassium feldspars, such as orthoclase, are the minerals most commonly used. Minerals, such as glauconite and feldspar, that grow in sedimentary rocks during their deposition and consolidation on the sea floor may be used to date these rocks. Glauconite is a complex silicate mineral related to the clay minerals and rich in iron and potassium. Ages determined from glauconite may be 10–20 per cent lower than those obtained by other methods, as a result of argon loss from this mineral. Such ages are, therefore, minimum ages only, but even these are valuable in constructing a time scale. Analyses can also be made by the potassium–argon method using whole rocks in which the minerals are not separated. A discussion on the significance in dating episodes of metamorphism by this method is reserved for Chapter 12.

The Rubidium–Strontium Method

Rubidium is one of the rarer elements but as it has about the same ionic radius as potassium, it substitutes for this element in the crystal structures of potassium minerals and does not form minerals of its own. Twenty-eight per cent of common rubidium is composed of the radioactive isotope rubidium 87, which, through electron emission, changes to strontium 87. Both isotopes are measured in the mass spectrometer and a calculation of the age of the sample is made with the knowledge that the half life of the transition is about 5×10^{10} years. The proportion of strontium that was originally present in the rock and not derived from rubidium can be calculated by also measuring the amount of strontium 86, an isotope that is not of radioactive origin. Rubidium occurs in sufficient quantity in the same minerals that are used in the potassium–argon method—various micas (notably lepidolite, a lithium mica), feldspars, and glauconite. Whereas the potassium–argon method is highly susceptible to interference by the reheating of the sample in metamorphism, the rubidium–strontium method allows the geochronologist, by means of a complex interpretation, to look through stages of metamorphism to the original age of the rock.

Radiocarbon Dating

Carbon 14 is a radioactive isotope formed in the atmosphere by cosmic ray bombardment of nitrogen. Hence it is present in a small percentage of the carbon dioxide of the air, in plants that extract carbon dioxide from the air to build tissues, and consequently also in animals. Carbon 14 begins to decay as soon as it is formed and has a half life of 5730 years. The constant proportion of carbon 14 to ordinary carbon (C^{12}) in the atmosphere is the result of an equilibrium between its rate of creation and rate of decay. A living organism retains this equilibrium proportion by constant interchange, through respiration, of its carbon with that of the atmosphere. When the organism dies this exchange ceases and its content of C^{14} steadily decreases as the isotope decays. After about 70,000 years so little C^{14} is left in plant and animal fossils that even our most sensitive equipment can barely detect it. Any objects containing organic carbon can be dated, but wood, charcoal, peat, shells, and carbonates precipitated in lakes are most commonly used. Unfortunately, the method can be used only for events that occurred relatively recently in geological time, during the last part of the Pleistocene.

Other Methods

Geologists, in their search for other methods of dating rocks, have discovered numerous techniques which are not in general use. Tritium, an isotope of hydrogen, and beryllium 10 are, like carbon 14, unstable products of the cosmic ray bombardment of the atmosphere which have been applied to dating problems. Chlorine 36 is an unstable isotope produced by the cosmic ray bombardment of rocks near the surface and may be of use in determining how long a rock has been exposed at the earth's surface. The light given off by carbonate rocks when heated (thermoluminescence) has been thought to be roughly proportional to their age. These and many other methods have their special uses and their drawbacks. Many discoveries remain to be made in this field, which has revolutionized historical geology within the last two decades.

Dating the Geological Time Scale

Events of the earth's history have been largely dated by fossils and referred to the relative time scale. Now that the dates of rocks in years can be determined, the historical geologist can be supplied with the answers to such questions as: How long ago was the beginning of the Paleozoic? For how long did the Middle Silurian sea occupy the continent? For how long have the mammals inhabited the earth?

Through the work of the geochronologist and the paleontologist a correlation of the absolute and relative time scales has been

GEOLOGICAL TIME SCALE

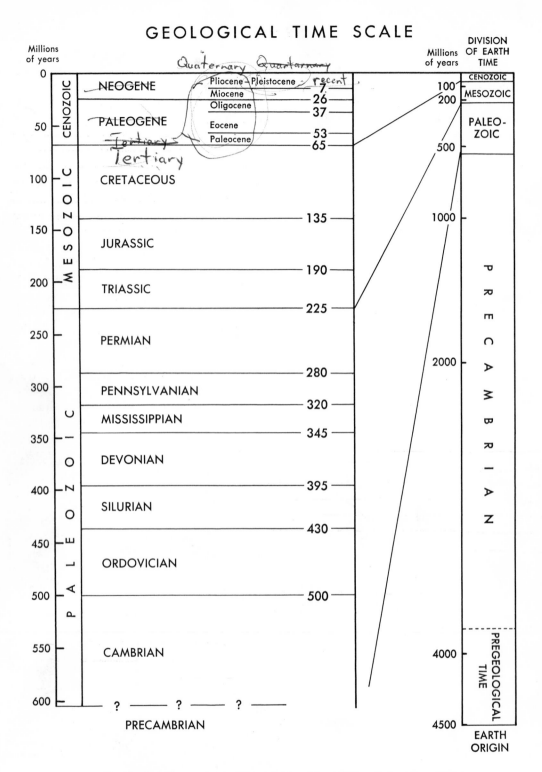

Fig. 3–4. The geological time scale. The height of the boxes representing the periods on the left is proportional to their duration. The Pleistocene Epoch is too short to be represented on this scale. On the right the division of earth time into eras is illustrated to show the large proportion of time occupied by the Precambrian eras.

achieved (see Fig. 3–4). Because time scales such as these are continually under revision as new rocks are dated, the scales in older reference works will differ from those in newer ones. Not all the samples that have been dated in years are useful in compiling such scales, for unless the sample can be accurately placed in the relative time scale also, it contributes little to the correlation of the two scales.

One group of minerals that can be reliably dated on both scales occurs in igneous intrusions. **Uraninite** and **pitchblende,** the principal sources of uranium, occur in dikelike bodies that are offshoots of batholiths. Intrusions are younger than the rocks they penetrate and older than the rocks that overlie them unconformably (Fig. 3–5). If the ages of these bounding strata are close together, such as Late Ordovician and Early Silurian, then the time of intrusion is precisely dated. More commonly their ages are

as widely separated as Late Ordovician and Permian, so that the time of the intrusion can be placed in the time scale only between these wide limits. For example, a pitchblende from Colorado which geological evidence indicates accompanied a granite stock intruded at the end of the Paleocene supplies a good point of correlation between the two scales at 59 million years. In contrast, igneous rocks of New England that intrude early Paleozoic metamorphic rocks of indefinite age and are overlain by Triassic rocks, although they can be determined to be 230 million years old by the potassium–argon method, do not tell us anything about the absolute age of any part of the relative time scale. From other intrusions more precisely dated in the relative time scale we know that 230 million years ago was late in the Permian Period and can therefore determine the relative age of the New England granites by their absolute age.

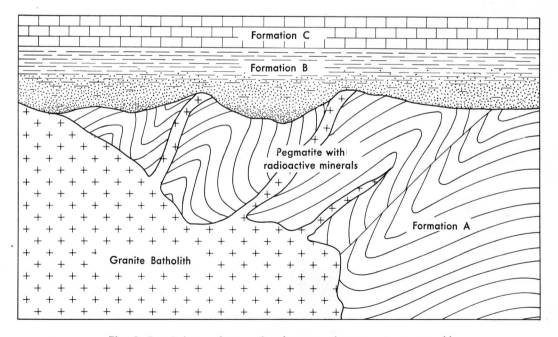

Fig. 3–5. Relative dating of radioactive deposits. Pegmatite dikes intruding formation A carry radioactive minerals that can be dated in years. These minerals are younger than formation A, in which they are emplaced, and older than formations B and C, which overlie the intrusives unconformably.

Lavas may also be dated by the potassium–argon and rubidium–strontium methods. If they are enclosed in fossiliferous sedimentary rocks which give their relative ages, such occurrences can be valuable points of correlation between the two scales. The flows in the upper Triassic rocks of the northern Appalachians (see page 312) were extruded at the same time as the Palisades sill. The 195-million-year age given by potassium–argon analysis of this sill supplies an excellent dating of the Late Triassic.

Metamorphic rocks can also be dated by the potassium–argon and rubidium–strontium methods. Such rocks are commonly devoid of fossils and difficult to place in the relative time scale, but studies of them may yield valuable evidence concerning the thermal and metamorphic history of an area.

As most of the time scale is based on sequences of fossil-bearing sedimentary rocks, the most useful methods for establishing the duration of the periods and epochs are those which can be applied to sedimentary rocks. The lead methods have been used on a few uranium-rich shales such as the Chattanooga Shale of Tennessee at the Devonian–Mississippian boundary (350 million years). As mentioned above, the potassium–argon and rubidium–strontium methods have been applied to date glauconite, which is common in sandstones deposited in relatively shallow, aerated waters. As an example, glauconite from Early Cambrian sandstones of Russia has indicated that a minimum age for the beginning of Cambrian time is 570 million years. The middle part of the Permian type section at Solikarnsk in Russia can be dated as 240 million years by potassium–calcium analysis of the potassium salts in the evaporite deposits.

Volcanic ash from an eruption may settle in the sea or a lake, forming a bed rich in potassium feldspar. Such beds make excellent points of calibration for the relative time scale for they can be dated by the potassium–argon method and are commonly closely associated with fossil-bearing sedimentary rocks. The latest Cretaceous rocks of Alberta, dated by volcanic ash associated with coal as 63 million years old, give us an estimate of the time of the Cenozoic–Mesozoic boundary. The potassium–argon method for dating volcanic ash beds has been extensively used in the Cenozoic mammal-bearing sequences of the western United States. Analysis of the many tuffaceous beds has resulted in a detailed correlation of the ages established by fossils with those established by the geochronologist (Fig. 3–6). Such detailed dating of sedimentary rocks may yield answers to many problems that have troubled paleontologists, such as whether the difference between faunas from separate localities is due to different conditions of life rather than their different ages, and whether migration is relatively instantaneous when compared to the length of geological time or a slow process which may make the migrating organisms appear at different places at different times (see Chapter 2).

Numerous studies such as these have been summarized in the time scale presented in Fig. 3–4. Although many dates are now available from the Precambrian of North America, none of the divisions of geological time based on these is yet accepted on a world-wide basis. The subdivision of the rocks of the Canadian Shield by age determinations is considered further in Chapter 16.

The length of geological time indicated by the geochronologist is so great that, like astronomical distances, it taxes the imagination. The figures are given more realism by means of an analogy. If we condense time by a factor of a million so that one year represents a million years, we can compare the four billion years of geological time to the four thousand years since 2000 B.C. (Fig. 3–7). The oldest rocks of the earth's crust would be forming at a time equivalent on our condensed scale to the period of the Middle Kingdom of Egyptian civilization. The Precambrian eras would then, following this analogy, include the Egyptian, Greek, and Roman empires, and the Dark and Middle Ages, up to the beginning of the Renaissance or about 1370. The time of the Hundred

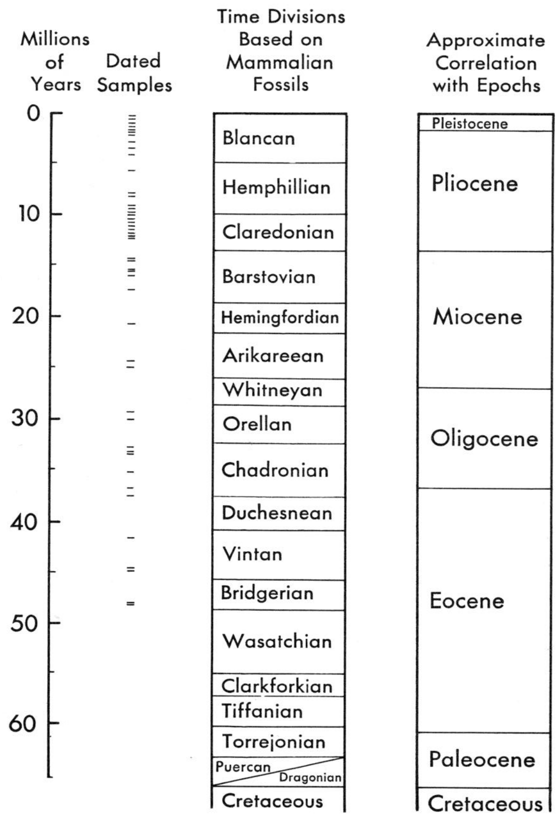

Millions of Years | Since 2000 B.C.

| CENOZOIC |
| MESOZOIC |
| PALEOZOIC |

P R E C A M B R I A N

100
200
300
400
500
1000
2000
3000
4000

World Wars
Civil War
American Revolution
Cartier
Columbus
Joan of Arc
Renaissance
Charlemagne
Dark Ages
Roman Empire
Hellenistic Period
Persian Empire
Greek City States
Assyrian Empire
Egyptian New Kingdom
Egyptian Middle Kingdom

1900 A.D.
1800 A.D.
1700 A.D.
1600 A.D.
1500 A.D.
1000 A.D.
A.D.
B.C.
1000 B.C.
2000 B.C.

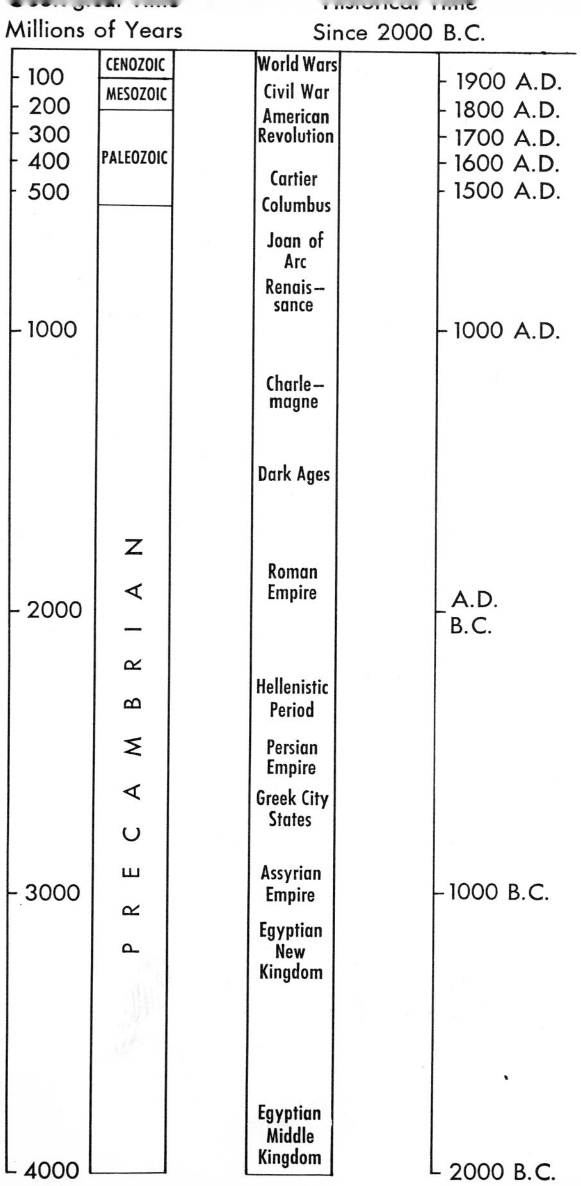

Fig. 3–7. Comparison of the length of geological time with the last 4000 years of the history of civilization.

Millions of Years — Dated Samples | Time Divisions Based on Mammalian Fossils | Approximate Correlation with Epochs

Time Divisions Based on Mammalian Fossils	Approximate Correlation with Epochs
	Pleistocene
Blancan	
Hemphillian	Pliocene
Claredonian	
Barstovian	
Hemingfordian	Miocene
Arikareean	
Whitneyan	
Orellan	Oligocene
Chadronian	
Duchesnean	
Vintan	
Bridgerian	Eocene
Wasatchian	
Clarkforkian	
Tiffanian	
Torrejonian	Paleocene
Puercan / Dragonian	
Cretaceous	Cretaceous

Millions of Years
0
10
20
30
40
50
60

Fig. 3–6. Dating of the Cenozoic age division based on mammalian fossils by potassium-argon determinations on tuffs. The stratigraphic position of the dated samples is shown in the second column. (Modified from Evernden and others.)

Years' War between Britain and France and the heroic deeds of Joan of Arc would correspond roughly to the beginning of the Ordovician Period. The end of the Paleozoic would correspond to the mid-1700's, when the English of the American and Canadian colonies were struggling with the French for domination of the New World. The end of the Mesozoic would correspond to 1904, when Teddy Roosevelt was starting his second term as President and the Boer War was just over in South Africa. The Cenozoic Era would correspond to the 65 years since then. On our scaled-down calendar, man would have arrived on the scene just last year. In all the 4000 years representing geological time on the one-millionth scale, man's span occupies only a single year.

SUMMARY

The discovery that the earth has been in existence for over four billion years and that life has existed for perhaps half that time has had a profound effect on astronomy, biology, philosophy, and historical geology.

The history of the earth can be described in terms of a relative time scale without recourse to absolute dating methods. The relative time scale of periods and eras was built up by reference to successions of sedimentary rocks in Europe that were originally defined as systems, but which came to have time significance as geologists compared other sequences with them by means of fossils.

Time terms (era, period, epoch) refer to time and are intangible units; biostratigraphic terms (system, series, stage) refer to rocks laid down during an interval of time that is defined by the ranges of fossils; lithologic terms (group, formation, member) are defined independently of time, purely on differences in lithology.

The placing of sedimentary rocks in the relative time scale involves detailed zonation by fossils of the type sections and comparison of local faunas with these standard zone fossil assemblages.

The lead method of determining absolute ages is based on the disintegration of two isotopes of uranium and thorium to isotopes of lead. Radon loss and leaching of lead may lead to discordance among the three ages that can be calculated from a single uranium-bearing sample.

The potassium–argon method for dating rocks is based on the disintegration of potassium 40 to argon 40 and calcium 40. It may be applied to a wide range of rocks and minerals because potassium is widely distributed in the earth's crust.

Rubidium substitutes for potassium in many minerals. Because its radioactive isotope, rubidium 87, disintegrates very slowly to strontium 87, it can be used to date the same samples.

Several isotopes, notably carbon 14, are created by the cosmic ray bombardment of the atmosphere. Their short half lives limit their use to the dating of relatively recent events.

Only by the isotopic dating of accurately stratigraphically placed samples can the dates of the periods and epochs be determined. The use of the potassium–argon method on lavas, tuffs, glauconite, and intrusions that are accurately dated in the relative time scale has been most valuable in this work.

QUESTIONS

1. If the study of stratigraphy had started in North America or Africa, instead of in northern Europe, would we be using the same time-stratigraphic units (with different names of course) as now?

2. Lyell based his division of the Cenozoic epochs partly on the percentage of living species in the faunas of the rocks. In the light of the nature of the fossil record (Chapter 2), discuss why such a system could not be extended to the whole of the time scale and why it was not satisfactory even in the Cenozoic.

3. Design an investigation, using methods of age dating, to test the hypothesis that the rate of sedimentation has not been constant throughout geological time.

4. Taking into account the shortcomings of the various methods described in this chapter, list the properties of a radioactivity series that would make it ideal for dating.

5. Why can determinations by both the potassium–argon and the rubidium–strontium methods be made on the same sample? What are the peculiar advantages of each method and how might discrepancies between them be explained?

6. Invent and describe the geology of an ideal quarry in which as many as possible of the methods described in this chapter could be used to make a correlation between the relative and absolute time scales.

REFERENCES AND SUGGESTED READINGS

Committee on Nuclear Science. "Geochronology of North America," *National Academy of Sciences—National Research Council, Nuclear Science Series Report 41*, Publication 1276, 1965. This volume is largely a compilation of isotopic age determinations from North American rocks up to 1964. It also contains a paper on the status of geochronological methods and a map showing the distribution of the determinations.

Geological Society of London. "The Phanerozoic Time Scale," *Quarterly Journal of the Geological Society*, 120s: 1–453, 1964. In this symposium volume, many authors summarize accumulated knowledge of the correlation of the relative and absolute time scales.

HOLMES, A. "A Revised Geological Time Scale," *Transactions of the Edinburgh Geological Society*, 17(3): 183–216, 1959. A summary of critical dates in the geological time scale written by one of the pioneer students of isotopic dating.

KULP, J. L. "Geologic Time Scale," *Science*, 133: 1105–14, 1961. Important dates in the correlation of the absolute and relative time scales are summarized that necessitate a considerable change in the formerly accepted time scales.

KULP, J. L. (Ed.). "Geochronology of Rock Systems," *Annals of the New York Academy of Science*, 91: 159–594, 1961. A collection of papers on the methods of isotopic dating, the geological time scale, and the age of the basement rocks of the world.

OSBORNE, F. F. (Ed.). "Geochronology in Canada," *Royal Society of Canada Special Publication 8*, 1964. A collection of nine papers which deal with the dating of various parts of the geological time scale or the interpretation of the geological history of various parts of Canada on the basis of isotopic dates.

4

Matter, Stars, Galaxies, and Planets

The historical geologist can read the record of the rocks only since the beginning of geological time, yet conditions at that time can be understood only in terms of what has gone before, in pregeological time when the earth was born. Speculation about the infant earth can be carried on against a background of theories concerning the way in which the earth and the rest of the planets of the solar system were formed and the relationship of all of them to the sun. The sun is a typical star and, to understand the relationship of the planets to it, we must study the origin of stars and the nature of the galactic systems (Fig. 4–1) in which they are found. We find that the composition of the earth and some other planets does not harmonize with that of the rest of the universe. Soon our investigation, which started out as historical geology, is deep in the sciences of cosmogony, astronomy, and nuclear physics. Obviously we can only scratch the surface of these disciplines to see what they contribute to our understanding of the early stages of the history of the earth.

THE EARTH'S PLACE IN THE UNIVERSE

Our Galaxy

The earth is one of a family of nine planets which circle the sun. The planets have a common direction and zone of movement around the sun, and all spin on their axes in the same direction. All the planets except the farthest and the two nearest to the sun have satellites (or moons), most of which circle their primaries in the same sense that the planets circle the sun. The planets can be divided into an inner set (Mercury, Venus, Earth, and Mars) with high specific gravities of about 4 or 5, and an outer set (Jupiter, Saturn, Uranus, and Neptune) with much lower specific gravities of 0.7 to 1.3. Pluto, the outermost planet, does not fit into several of these generalizations and may be an escaped moon of Neptune rather than one of the original planets. The sun is an average star with a diameter of 864,000 miles, a specific gravity of 1.42, an exterior temperature of about 6000 degrees absolute, and a central temperature of about 10 million degrees ab-

Fig. 4–1. Spiral nebula in Pisces, a system of stars like our own galaxy, the Milky Way. Taken with the 200-inch telescope. (Photograph from the Mount Wilson and Palomar Observatories.)

solute. We know of no other planetary systems in space, but even if planets existed around the nearest star they would be invisible to our most powerful telescopes. The stars are so greatly separated in space that light traveling at 186,000 miles per second from the nearest one takes more than 4 years to reach us. One of the units which astronomers use to express distance is the **light year,** the distance traveled by light in a year, or about 6,000,000,000,000 miles.

The sun and all the stars visible to the naked eye belong to our galaxy, the Milky Way, and most of them are within 1000 light years of the earth. This system is a vast disc of stars and dust, bulging at the center and thinning outward toward the edges. The galaxy is about 100,000 light years in diameter and rotates slowly. Not all the matter in the galaxy consists of stars and planets; about 2 per cent is diffused between the stars as dust and a gas made up of hydrogen, helium, neon, etc., which are uncondensed even at space temperatures near absolute zero. The way in which the interstellar matter scatters and blocks light shows that part of it is solid.

Fig. 4–2. Dark, obscuring clouds of interstellar matter block out the light from behind in the "Horsehead" nebula in Orion. Taken in red light by the 200-inch telescope. (Photograph from the Mount Wilson and Palomar Observatories.)

This dust is not mineral matter but appears to be elongate particles, about 1/50,000 of an inch across, of frozen compounds of hydrogen, such as methane and ammonia.

The dust in places builds up into great masses that obscure the stars behind them (Fig. 4–2). The gas, which contains perhaps a hundred times more atoms than the dust in a given space, may fluoresce under the ultraviolet radiation of neighboring stars (Fig. 4–3). Some of the hydrogen atoms in the gas attain an excited state through collisions with other atoms and, in reverting to a ground state, give off radiowaves with a wavelength of 21 cm. Radiotelescopes can determine the density of the hydrogen by the intensity of this 21-cm radiation.

The discoidal shape of our galaxy can be verified by the observer who examines the sky on a clear night and notes how the stars pile up into dense masses along the Milky Way and how sparsely scattered they are at right angles to this starry girdle at the galactic poles. The stars appear more densely

Fig. 4–3. Luminous interstellar matter distributed thinly in the filamentary nebula in Cygnus. (Photograph from the Mount Wilson and Palomar Observatories.)

spaced in the Milky Way because the observer must look through 25 to 75 light years of stars along the length of the disc. In other directions his line of sight passes through a shorter distance and fewer stars before encountering the starless space outside the galaxy. Our galaxy is difficult to map from our position inside it, but great advances have been made in recent years using radiotelescopes. By mapping the zones in which hydrogen is dense, radioastronomers have defined five concentric bands which constitute the "spiral arms" of our galaxy (Fig. 4–4). The sun is near the inner edge of the Orion arm, about 27,000 light years from the dense, mysterious core of the galaxy, which obscures the spiral arms on the side opposite the sun. By measuring the spectral shift (see p. 69) in the hydrogen clouds of various parts of the galaxy, astronomers can study the motions of the spiral arms. The sun is moving at a speed of 150–200 miles per second in the direction of the constellation Cygnus, and will make a complete revolution of the galaxy in roughly 200 million years.

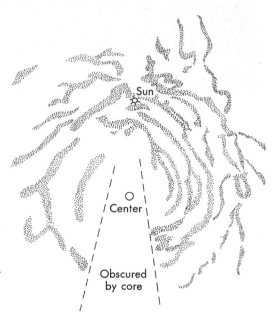

Fig. 4–4. Structure of the spiral arms of our galaxy as revealed by radioastronomy. The shaded areas mark bands in which hydrogen is concentrated. The dense matter in the core of the galaxy obscures the structure of the side away from our sun. (Courtesy of Oort, Kerr, and Westerhout.)

Fig. 4–5.   Spiral nebula in Andromeda, a galaxy of the local group believed to be much like our own galaxy.   (Photograph from the Mount Wilson and Palomar Observatories.)

Far beyond the boundaries of our own galaxy we see in other galaxies stars, disc-like shapes, and spiral arms similar to those we are mapping from inside our own.

Extragalactic Star Systems

Stretching as far as the penetrating eyes of our most powerful telescopes can see are thousands of galactic systems. Because they appear fuzzy in low-power telescopes, early astronomers called them nebulae (clouds). The only one of these that can be seen easily by the naked eye, the great spiral nebula in Andromeda (Fig. 4–5), is similar in shape to our galaxy but considerably larger. The average galaxy is separated by about 1 million light years from its nearest neighbor. If the galaxies were the size of pennies, on this scale they would be separated by about 3 yards and stretch away for about 10 miles to the limit of our telescopic observation. However, the galaxies are not evenly distributed but are clustered into groups. The local group, of which our galaxy is a member, is about 2 million light years in diameter and includes the nebula in Andromeda. We can detect vast amounts of dust and gas in these galaxies just as in our own.

When the light received by telescopes from these distant star systems is passed through a prism, it is broken up into a spectrum which reveals something about the composition of the light sources. Edwin Hubble found that the spectra originating in these galaxies are displaced toward the red end relative to corresponding spectra originating on earth, and that the amount of this displacement is proportional to the distance of the systems from us. The farther these exterior galaxies are from our galaxy, the greater is the amount of this red shift. There have been several attempts to explain this phenomenon, but the only one consistent with the known properties of light suggests that the shift in wavelength is due to the recession of the exterior galaxies from our own and is known as the "Doppler effect." The farther the star systems are from us, the faster they appear to recede, and the farthest detected optically so far is traveling at a rate of 86,000 miles per second, almost half the velocity of light. This galaxy is at present about 6 billion light years away.

The galaxies extend in space to the outer limits of observation with our largest telescope, the 200-inch Hale reflector at Mount Palomar. We are not sure what we would see with a telescope double the range of this instrument, one that could penetrate to where the galaxies are receding at a rate close to the speed of light. The universe cannot extend beyond the point at which receding matter reaches the speed of light, and its radius, the Hubble radius, has been calculated to be about 13 billion light years.

From the recession of the galaxies some scientists have concluded that, initially, all matter was in a condensed state from which it is still expanding. The rate at which the galaxies are receding indicates that the galactic explosion took place about 10–13 billion years ago.

The Abundance of the Elements

By means of the spectrograph, astronomers can determine the chemical composition of stars and other luminous celestial bodies. In

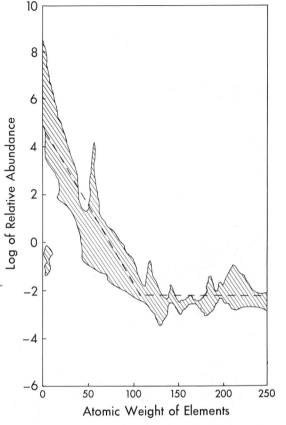

Fig. 4–6. Abundance of the elements in the universe. The ruled area encloses the points which formed the original plot of the abundance of the element against its atomic weight. The dashed line emphasizes the two parts of the curve: the rapidly decreasing abundance of elements of atomic weights 0–100, and the relatively similar abundances of elements of atomic weights greater than 100.

Fig. 4–6, the relative cosmic abundances of the elements are plotted against their atomic weights. These chemical data are determined largely from observations in our own galaxy, but astronomers believe that they are representative of the universe as a whole. Note that the scale of abundances is a logarithmic one. The graph shows that elements of low atomic weight are much more abundant than heavier elements and that hydrogen and helium are far more abundant than all of the other elements combined.

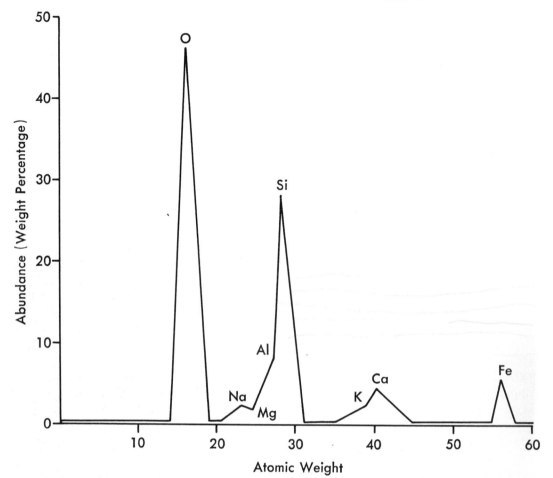

Fig. 4–7. Abundance of the elements in the earth's crust plotted according to their atomic weights. Note the great contrast to Fig. 4–6. (Plotted from data in Ahrens, *The Distribution of the Elements in Our Planet.*)

About 92 per cent of all the atoms in the universe (55 per cent by weight) are hydrogen and 7 per cent (44 per cent by weight) are helium. The general trend of the graph can be resolved into two straight lines, one line sloping down to the right for elements with atomic weights up to 100, and the other a horizontal line for elements with atomic weights above 100.

Where is all the hydrogen and helium? Certainly not on the earth. A comparison of Figs. 4–6 and 4–7 demonstrates that the earth is a very atypical member of the universe, in that heavy elements are far more abundant than light ones. Some of the hydrogen in the universe is a diffuse interstellar gas, but by far the greatest part is contained in the stars and is the "fuel" they burn to shine. The sun and nearly all luminous stars give off great amounts of energy through thermonuclear reactions. This intense radiation is the result of nuclear changes between hydrogen, carbon, nitrogen, and helium, which take place at temperatures of several millions of degrees absolute. One of these changes involves the conversion of hydrogen —through several intermediate steps—to helium, but during the conversion there is a loss of mass of about 0.7 per cent. This lost mass is converted into energy in the relationship that should be familiar to those living in the atomic age, $E = mc^2$. This equation, proposed by Albert Einstein, expresses the relationship between the energy released (E) by conversion of a mass of material (m) and the speed of light (c). This source of energy can be tapped only at the expense of hydrogen and at temperatures that have been reached on the earth's surface only in thermonuclear explosions of the hydrogen bomb.

At present about half of the sun's mass is hydrogen and it is being converted to helium at a rate of 800 million tons per second (only 4×10^{-19} of its mass per second).

STELLAR EVOLUTION

Scattered among the dust clouds in the galaxy are dark, globular masses that can be seen against the luminous background (Fig. 4–8). The masses of these globules are approximately that of a star and astronomers

Fig. 4–8. Dark clots of dust against a luminous background in Sagittarius. The masses of dust may be embryonic stars. (Courtesy of the Lick Observatory.)

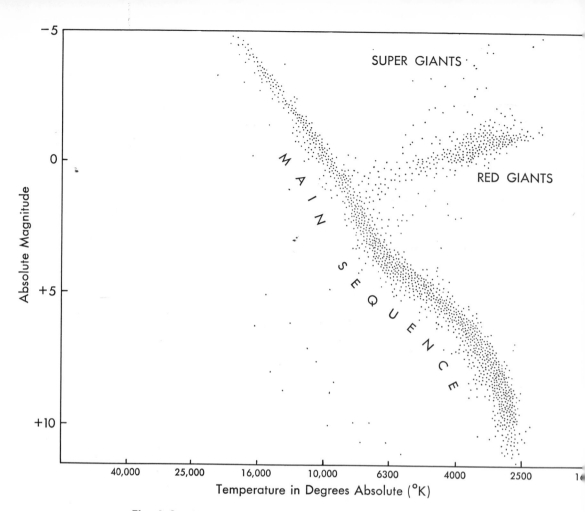

Fig. 4–9. Hertzsprung–Russell diagram showing the classification of stars according to magnitude and temperature. (After G. Abell, *Exploration of the Universe.* New York: Holt, Rinehart and Winston, Inc., 1964.)

believe that they may be stars in the process of formation. The processes by which the diffuse dust particles are collected into dark globules and then into stars are not well understood, but light pressure is believed to be one of the forces. Although this force is too weak to overcome the resistance of the earth's atmosphere, in space the radiation from surrounding stars propels dust particles in the directions of their shadows and tends to herd them together into the spaces between the stars. As they move closer, the gravitational attraction between them will speed up the collecting process and the globules will attract more dust particles. Gravitation becomes more effective as the particles approach, and eventually the mass will contract rapidly. During the contractive phase, a self-luminous star is formed.

Figure 4–9 shows a graph in which the luminosity or so-called magnitude of stars is plotted against their surface temperatures. The surface temperatures are measured from the color or spectral class of a star; those of relatively low temperature are red; those of high temperature, blue. Such a graph is called a Hertzsprung–Russell diagram in honor of the two astronomers who discovered this relationship. The diagram shows three regions which are important in the evolution of stars: a band running from low-luminosity red stars to high-luminosity blue stars called the "main sequence"; an area to the right on which stars called red giants are plotted; and an area to the left on which white dwarf stars are plotted.

Contracting dust clouds of different sizes will produce stars of different masses and luminosities. As they contract by gravitation, the dust globules get hotter and approach the main sequence on the Hertzsprung–Russell diagram from the right, at a height proportional to their mass (as indicated in Fig. 4–10). When the heat generated by their contraction reaches the critical temperature, thermonuclear reactions begin: hydrogen is converted into helium, great quantities of energy are given off, and stars are born. At this stage the star has reached the main sequence in its evolution and will remain in this position on the Hertzsprung–Russell diagram until its hydrogen fuel has reached a critical value.

A star of mass comparable to our sun can be expected to stay in the main sequence for more than 10 billion years before it becomes unstable. At this stage in its evolution the exterior zones swell, become diffuse, cool, and redden, and the star passes into the field of the "red giants" on the Hertzsprung–Russell diagram. The star begins to use its hydrogen much faster and to brighten. Astronomers believe that in later stages the star moves to the left in the diagram; much of its mass streams out into space and its instability is reflected in cyclical explosions as the inner zones collapse. These stellar explosions are called novae or supernovae. When the nuclear fuel has been expended in these last explosive phases, only a feebly glowing, dense, contracting mass called a white dwarf is left.

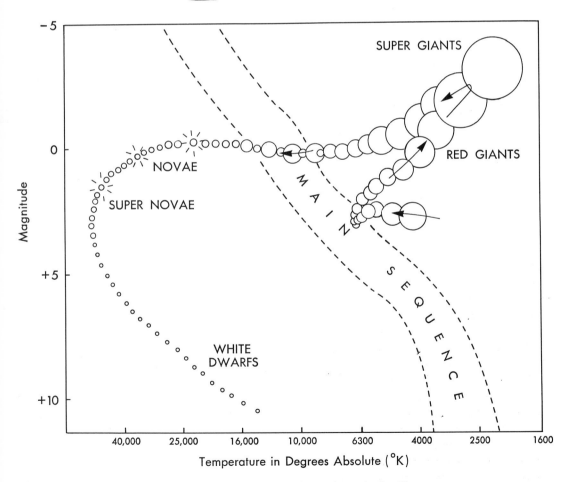

Fig. 4–10. Evolution of a typical star through the Hertzsprung–Russell diagram. (After G. Abell, *Exploration of the Universe*. New York: Holt, Rinehart and Winston, Inc., 1964.)

COSMOGONY

Cosmogony is the science of the origin of the universe or cosmos. Among other things, the cosmogonist must explain the nature of the solar system, the evolution of stars, the formation and recession of galaxies, and the relative abundance of the elements. Two theories of the origin of the universe are currently held by astronomers, but data are as yet insufficient to negate either one.

The Evolutionary Universe

George Gamow and his coworkers believe that the recession of the galaxies indicates that about 13 billion years ago the universe was in a highly condensed state compared with its present attenuated condition. The matter which now is spread thinly through the universe was at that time condensed into energy. From this state an expansion occurred which continues to the present day. During the first seconds of the expansion elemental particles such as neutrons, protons, and electrons appeared. During the first few hours the chemical elements were formed, from the lightest to the heaviest, largely by a process of neutron capture.

Gamow postulates that the nuclei of all the elements were formed by the addition of

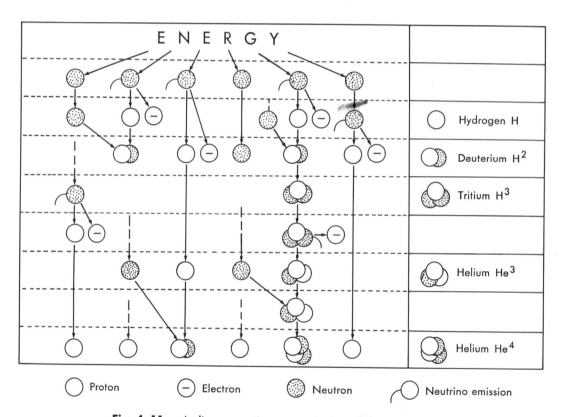

Fig. 4–11. A diagrammatic representation of the neutron-capture theory for the origin of the lighter elements from a mass of neutrons which have been derived from energy. In the first stage, hydrogen is produced by the decay of a neutron into a proton and an electron. Further changes are brought about by neutron capture and decay. Below the first line, the introduction of neutrons from the original neutron pool is shown by dashed lines.

neutrons to lighter nuclei, starting with that of hydrogen, which consists of a single proton (Fig. 4–11). Each neutron added produced a new isotope (by changing the atomic weight); the disintegration of some neutrons into a proton and an electron produced new elements (by changing the atomic number).

The initial expansive phase of the formation of the universe was followed by a condensation of the atoms formed by the expansion into galaxies and stars. Before this could happen the temperature of the expanding matter must have dropped to a point at which the atoms could unite to produce solids within the gas of the lighter elements (at this stage about 1 milligram of dust and several micrograms of gas are supposed to have been dispersed per million cubic kilometers of space). During the condensation stage, which continues today, the uneven distribution of atoms in space was accentuated by their clustering under the force of gravity into masses now represented by galactic groups, galaxies, stars, and eventually planets. Gamow calls this series a "hierarchy of condensations."

The Steady-State Universe

The astronomers Bondi, Gold, and Hoyle have expanded a suggestion made much earlier by James Jeans to explain the expansion of the universe in terms of the continuous creation of hydrogen in interstellar space. They postulate that the continuous loss of matter over the boundary of the velocity of light at the edge of the observable universe is counterbalanced by the appearance of atoms of hydrogen throughout the universe. The matter in the universe is in a steady state, continually expanding and drifting into nothing at its margins, continually being created and condensing into galaxies and stars. They believe that the ability to form hydrogen spontaneously is a property of all space and needs no further explanation.

In the steady-state universe, hydrogen is abundant because it is continuously created. By the processes described above, hydrogen is believed to condense into stars. In the

stellar interiors thermonuclear reactions form the heavier elements at extremely high temperatures. At temperatures of about 20 million degrees, which exist in red giant stars, combinations of nuclear particles form elements such as carbon and oxygen, but temperatures of billions of degrees, which are believed to exist in novae and supernovae, may be necessary to produce an environment in which the heaviest elements can be formed. Once formed, these heavier elements may be ejected again into space in stellar explosions to take part once more in the condensation process.

Like the evolutionary theory, the steady-state theory has its weaknesses. Critics have pointed out that its prediction of the distribution of the galaxies in space does not correspond to the pattern presently being discovered in radioastronomy. However, the distribution and origin of the elements can be explained satisfactorily by the hypothesis that they were transmuted in the interiors of evolving stars.

THE ORIGIN OF THE SOLAR SYSTEM

Satellites rotating around their planets, planets swinging around the sun, and stars revolving about a galactic center make strikingly similar patterns. The generally accepted theory of the origin of these patterns is that they were derived from the condensation of rotating dust clouds of various sizes. The solar system is believed to have originated as a large cloud of dust and gas, with a central dense zone that was to become the sun. Because this large dust mass was embedded in a rotating galaxy, different parts had different velocities and the contraction of such a mass gave it a rotational motion. Continuing contraction probably increased the speed of rotation and pulled the mass into a disclike form with a central, globular core. Carl von Weizsäcker was the first to analyze mathematically the turbulence pattern to be expected in the dust-cloud plate and to plot the paths of eddies and swirls in a cloud whose mass approximated our solar system. Gerald

Kuiper modified this theory into what is now known as the **protoplanet hypothesis.** He calculated that, as the solar dust cloud contracted and increased in angular velocity, about one-tenth of its mass was distributed in the rotating disc of dust and gas and nine-tenths in the central globule. The gravitational attraction between the dust particles began to pull them together into larger masses. As collisions and coalescence increased the size of the masses and gravitation gathered them together, swarms of particles took shape within the dust-cloud plate, each rotating about its center and revolving around the main center. These swarms of particles, or **protoplanets,** were much larger than the present planets but occupied the positions in the disc that were to become the planetary orbits. The protoplanets consisted of the interstellar dust, that is, hydrogen and helium, simple compounds of hydrogen in solid form, and a relatively small amount of the heavier elements. When the central mass of the solar dust cloud had been heated by contraction to the critical temperature, it began to shine as the sun does today. The great release of radiation in the center of the condensing dust cloud heated the protoplanets near the sun, swept their gaseous content out into space, and vaporized the solid compounds such as methane and ammonia. The protoplanets in the outer part of the disc were not heated to the temperatures of those between Mars and the sun and therefore retained most of their original light gases and solid compounds. The outer planets have much lower specific gravities than the inner ones and are believed still to consist largely of these lighter gases. When the sun was born, the earth's protoplanet may have lost as much as 500 times its present mass in lighter matter, so that only the heavier elements were left as a concentrate.

Each of the protoplanets circling the sun differentiated into satellites in the same way that the solar disc differentiated into protoplanets. The number of moons separating from the protoplanet swirls seems to have depended on their distance from the disturb-

ing gravitational attraction of the sun. Eventually, the particles of the protoplanets were drawn together by gravitational attraction into the solid masses of the planets.

The moon, however, is much more massive in relation to its planet than any of the other satellites of the solar system and its origin demands another explanation. The same side of the moon is always presented to the earth because its period of rotation is the same as the period of its orbit around the earth. Two explanations have been put forward to account for the size of the moon and its peculiar relationship to the earth. One theory, first proposed by George Darwin, is that the moon separated from the earth at an early time in the latter's history and since that time has been steadily receding. Darwin believed that the Pacific Ocean was the scar left by the separation, and recently this theory has been reintroduced in modern form. The other explanation is that the moon was a large particle in the solar dust cloud that was captured by the earth's gravitational field during the early phases of the condensation into protoplanets. Neither of these theories, however, is a completely satisfactory explanation of the relationship of earth and moon.

The features of the protoplanet theory of particular significance to the historical geologist are that (1) the earth originated by the collection of solid particles from a cloud of interstellar matter; (2) this aggregate originally included hydrogen, helium, methane, and ammonia; and (3) these gases and "ices" were driven off the protoplanet by solar radiation.

The time at which these events occurred has been deduced from a study of **meteorites.** These objects, which strike the earth from outer space, are believed to have been formed during the early phases of the differentiation of the planets, when one of the larger masses in the dust cloud disintegrated. Nearly all the age determinations on meteorites give an age of 4.5 billion years and this has generally been accepted as the approximate time of the origin of the solar system.

Fig. 4–12. Aerial photograph of the New Quebec crater near the northern tip of Quebec. This symmetrical lake is believed to mark the impact of a large meteorite on the surface of the Canadian Shield. It is about 2 miles across. (Courtesy of the Geological Survey of Canada.)

THE PREGEOLOGICAL ERAS

The protoplanet theory suggests that the earth was formed by the consolidation of a swarm of small particles. The resulting planet would be expected to be of generally uniform composition, for there is no reason why the infalling particles should arrange themselves before taking their places in the compacting earth. From studies of earthquake waves, however, geophysicists have discovered that the earth is not of uniform composition throughout but has a **core** 3400 km in diameter of iron and perhaps some nickel, a **mantle** of heavier silicates, and a thin **crust** of light silicates. This differentiation of the earth into layers of various densities could only have occurred during a hot stage when the iron throughout the primitive earth melted and was drawn by gravity toward the core. Gravitational compaction may have helped to heat the earth to the 2000 degrees Centigrade required to mobilize the iron. The heat was most probably derived from the disintegration of many short-lived radioactive isotopes that were present at the time but which have now disappeared, and others that were present in quantity but have since become rare as they progressively were converted into their daughter products. Whatever the cause, soon after the planet was formed a major change occured in the balance of the earth and the gravity differentiation took place.

During this early stage in the earth's history, the infall of large and small particles— the remnants of the solar dust cloud and protoplanet—was much greater than at present. The largest of these particles would have made impact craters on the earth similar to the famous Meteor Crater in Arizona. Perhaps the earth at this stage looked much like the surface of the moon—pock-marked with circular depressions. These marks have persisted on the moon because no erosion can take place without an atmosphere, but on the earth they were soon obscured by erosion. Such craters, believed to have been made by meteor impact hundreds of millions of years ago, can still be detected in the rock of the Canadian Shield, as seen in an aerial photograph (Fig. 4–12).

Astronomers estimate that the moon is receding from the earth at a rate of 2–4 inches per year. Space does not allow a consideration of the reasoning and measurements from which this figure is derived, but the historical geologist should be aware that early in the history of the earth the moon was much closer. The moon affects the earth largely through the tides it raises in the seas, and these in turn influence sedimentary processes. Tides in the early oceans must have been considerably higher than those at present because of the nearness of the moon, but their influence has not been detected as yet in the sedimentary record.

During these pregeological eras, the major surface features of the earth's crust were beginning to form. Geophysical measurements have demonstrated that the continents are plates of light granitic rock overlying a layer of denser basaltic rock which also floors the ocean basins. The difference in elevation of the continental and oceanic blocks is a reflection of this difference in density. Geologists are not agreed on how the continental plates were originally formed or whether they were formed in place or have moved laterally to their present position (see Chapter 6). Some geologists believe that during the hot stage of the earth there was a gravitational separation or differentiation of the outer material into two phases and that the granitic phase collected on the surface of the heavier basaltic phase. Others believe that the continents accumulated as a sort of scum on the surface of the mantle. Many believe that the mantle of the earth is affected by convection currents, caused by the uneven heating of the base of a layer; the rising of the lighter, hotter material; and the falling of the heavier, colder material. A boiling pot in which jam is being made is a good example of this mechanism. The continents correspond to the scum which accumulates along the edges of the pot as the convection current rises in the middle of the pot and falls at the sides.

Other geologists postulate that the continents have been built up through erosion, sedimentation, and metamorphism. During the process of erosion and sedimentation elements such as sodium, potassium, aluminum, and silicon, which are characteristic of the more "acidic" minerals of igneous rocks, are preserved; elements such as magnesium, iron, and calcium, which are characteristic of the more "basic" constituents, are carried away as solutions of their salts. These geologists reason that initially high basaltic areas would be eroded and would supply more "acidic" products to the sediment around them. Metamorphism of these "acidic" sediments could result only in granitic rocks. Thus the initial high spots would be built up into continents by erosion, sedimentation, and metamorphism. Another theory suggests that the continents represent granitic meteorites the size of the asteroids, which were plastered onto the earth in the last stages of its accretion. When more information on the structure of the continents accumulates, through the work of geophysicists, a choice between these alternative theories may be possible.

The Oldest Rocks

The problem of determining the condition of the earth in pregeological time can be approached by examining the oldest rocks to discover the environment in which they were deposited. Some of the oldest rocks in the world come from South Africa. The granite cutting the highly metamorphosed Sebakian sedimentary rocks has been dated by the potassium–argon method to be 3.4 billion years old. In Swaziland, granites cutting metamorphosed sediments give minimum ages of about 3.4 billion years. Similar ages have also been obtained from the Kola peninsula in northeastern Russia. In North America, the oldest rocks extend in a belt from the southern part of the Canadian Shield in eastern Manitoba southwest through Minnesota to the Rockies. Zircon from Minnesota has been dated at about 3.3 billion years. In the Beartooth Mountains of Montana, zircons up to 3.1 billion years old have been analyzed. All of these age determinations have been made on intrusive rocks that have penetrated a thick sedimentary sequence. As explained further in Chapter 5, granitic intrusives represent the end of a cycle of sedimentation and metamorphism which may have taken many hundreds of millions of years. The oldest sedimentary rocks in the intruded sequences are therefore at least 3.5 billion years old and may be as old as 4 billion years. The sedimentary nature of these first rocks shows that running water was present on the earth's crust as early as 3.5–4 billion years ago and, therefore, that the average surface temperature was neither above the boiling point nor below the freezing point of water. The luminosity of the sun during that period could not have been much greater or less than it has been throughout geological time.

The Atmosphere and Hydrosphere

Speculation about the nature of the early atmosphere of the earth and its evolution to the present atmosphere is common, but as yet no consensus on what changes took place or when they took place has been reached. The earth's protoplanet must originally have been surrounded by gases that were lost by the inner planets but retained by the outer planets. If the composition of the outer planets now is representative of this protoplanet atmosphere, then it probably consisted of a mixture of methane, ammonia, and water vapor with some hydrogen and helium. If this atmosphere has since escaped into space, where did we get the present one?

Some of the gas of the protoplanet must have been trapped between the particles during the accretion of the earth and, as the earth compacted, probably escaped through fissures and vents in the crust. This degassing process has continued throughout geological time, for even today volcanic vents give off immense quantities of water vapor, carbon dioxide, nitrogen, sulfur, and other gases. According to one theory of this evolution, the atmosphere was originally composed of water vapor, hydrogen, methane, and ammonia, which had escaped by the early degassing of the earth. In this atmosphere many photochemical reactions could take place using the energy supplied by the ultraviolet rays of the sun (Fig. 4–13). Primitive plant life may have developed before any free oxygen was present in the atmosphere, for experiments have shown that low forms of life can live in an atmosphere of ammonia and methane. However, not until free oxygen appeared from the photochemical dissociation of water could animal life as we now know it come into existence, and not until the oxygen produced by this dissociation had combined with all the methane in the atmosphere to produce carbon dioxide, and with all the ammonia to produce nitrogen, would free oxygen be permanently available. Once plants appeared, they began to convert carbon dioxide into oxygen and may have been responsible for building the oxygen content of the atmosphere to its present level.

The original atmosphere under which the first sediments were eroded and deposited was probably not oxidizing as today but reducing. Geologists are not agreed as to the time in the earth's history when free oxygen first appeared in the atmosphere. Some have suggested that it was not present in quantity until as late as the start of the Cambrian Period, when animal life suddenly increased in abundance and complexity. Others have tried to find the oldest red sediments, whose oxidized iron would indicate that they were the product of weathering in an oxygen-rich atmosphere. In British Guiana there are sandstones colored with hematite at least 2.5 billion years old. If our reasoning is correct, the transition to an oxygen-rich atmosphere must have taken place prior to this time.

As the atmosphere is believed to have emanated from the earth throughout geological time, so also the water of the oceans is believed to have been supplied continuously from vents in the earth. If the present rate of volcanism is taken as typical of the geological past, volcanic emanations were quantitatively capable of supplying all the water in the oceans and atmosphere in the

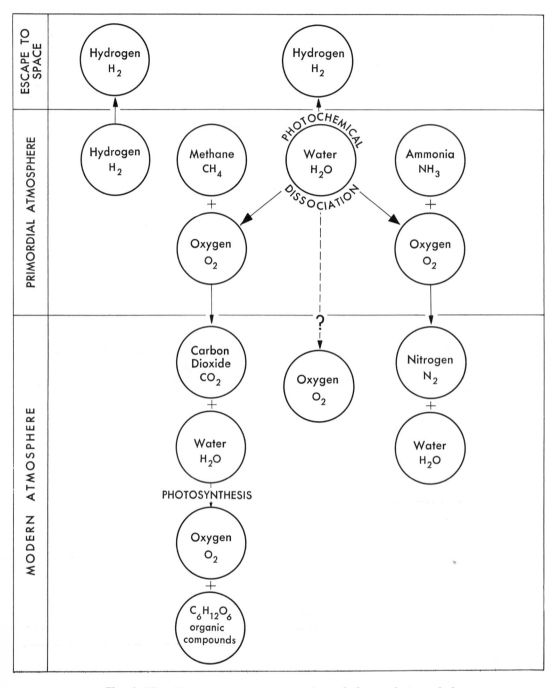

Fig. 4–13. Diagrammatic representation of the evolution of the early atmosphere of the earth. The reactions were probably much more complex than shown here.

billions of years since the earth was formed. If the volume of water at the surface of the earth has been increasing throughout geological time, then the capacity of the ocean basins must also have been increasing. Ancient marine sedimentary rocks lying on the continental platforms show that the water of the oceans has overflowed the basins, spilling onto the continents at least since the beginning of the Paleozoic Era. If the basins had had their present capacity in the early stages of the accumulation of the oceans, the limited amount of water would have been confined to their depths and could not have spilled over onto the continents. Therefore, the early basins must have been very shallow and their capacity must have steadily increased by subsidence, as the volume of water also increased.

Much of this chapter has recounted speculation, and on many of the matters discussed we are still far from an answer. Through the work of astronomers, nuclear physicists, geophysicists, and geologists, we are coming to understand more and more about the evolution of our earth from the hydrogen of interstellar space to the heat of the contracting globules, through the thermonuclear reactions of supernovae to the dust cloud surrounding our sun, and through the protoplanet to the planet.

SUMMARY

The planet earth is one of a family of nine planets revolving around an average star, our sun. Myriads of other stars like our sun, together with interstellar gas and dust, make up our galaxy.

Other galaxies are receding from ours and from their neighbors at a rate proportional to their distance from us.

Hydrogen and helium, by far the most abundant elements in the universe, form most of the stars and interstellar material.

The gravitational contraction of masses of gas and dust heats them to 8 million degrees absolute, when the nuclear transmutation of hydrogen to helium takes place and they become self-luminous stars.

Stars evolve from the hydrogen "burning" stage (like our sun), to red giants, to variable stars, and finally to novae and supernovae (if their mass is appropriately large), before becoming white dwarfs.

The evolutionary theory of cosmogony states that the universe expanded suddenly from a state of condensation about 10 billion years ago and that during this expansion the elements were formed largely by neutron capture.

The steady-state theory of cosmogony states that the continued expansion of the universe results from the creation of hydrogen between the stars. Its proponents believe that the elements heavier than hydrogen have been "cooked" by nuclear reactions within stars.

The protoplanet theory of the origin of the solar system states that the earth was formed by the cold accretion of particles out of a disc-shaped, rotating cloud of dust and gas surrounding the sun.

The density stratification of the earth was formed when, heated by radioactive elements now extinct or less abundant, the heavier constituents were drawn by gravity to the center and the lighter constituents rose toward the surface.

Oxygen was not a constituent of the earliest atmosphere but must have appeared early in Precambrian time, perhaps through the agency of plants.

The oldest rocks indicate that temperatures on the earth 3.5 billion years ago were not greatly different from today.

QUESTIONS

1. Draw a series of diagrams in progressively larger scales showing the relationship between: (*a*) the earth and the sun, (*b*) the sun and our galaxy, and (*c*) our galaxy and the Andromeda galaxy, which is located at the edge of the local group of galaxies 1.6 million light years away. What would be the diameter of the dot representing the earth in diagram (*c*)?

2. By consulting a modern text on astronomy, draw up a table contrasting the properties of white dwarf and red giant stars.

3. How would the distribution of galaxies differ according to the steady-state and evolutionary hypotheses of cosmogony?

4. Describe the origin of the planet Jupiter according to the protoplanet hypothesis and explain why it has 12 moons, a minute core of iron and rocks, a small shell of frozen water, methane, and ammonia, and an immense envelope of hydrogen and helium.

5. With binoculars and a star map, locate on a clear November night some of the major stars, the Milky Way, the luminous nebulosity in Orion, the spiral nebula of Andromeda, Algol (the variable star in the constellation Perseus), the dark cloud of the Coal Sack against the Milky Way in Cygnus, and the great cluster of stars in Perseus.

REFERENCES AND SUGGESTED READINGS

ABELL, G. *Exploration of the Universe*. New York: Holt, Reinhart and Winston, Inc., 1964. 646 pp. A fine general textbook on astronomy in which a more extensive discussion on the structure and evolution of stars can be found.

BROMS, A. *Our Emerging Universe*. New York: Doubleday and Co., Inc., 1961. 260 pp. This book presents modern theories of the universe in a highly popularized form. It is also available as a paperback (Dell Books, 1964).

COLEMAN, J. A. *Modern Theories of the Universe*. New York: Signet Books, 1963. 211 pp. A popular account in paperback form of such subjects as the expanding universe, relativity, and the age of the universe and the steady-state and evolutionary theories of its origin.

DONN, W. L., DONN, B. D., and VALENTINE, W. G. "On the Early History of the Earth," *Geological Society of America Bulletin*, 76: 287–306, 1965. The oldest rocks indicate that running water must have been present on earth 4 billion years ago and that the luminosity of the sun has therefore changed little since then. The sialic continents must also have been present very early in geological history.

5

The Geosynclinal Theory

The **geosynclinal theory** is one of the great unifying principles in geology. In many ways its role in geology is similar to that of the theory of evolution, which serves to integrate the many branches of the biological sciences. The geosynclinal theory is of fundamental importance to sedimentation, petrology, geomorphology, ore deposits, structural geology, geophysics, and in fact all branches of geological science. It is a generalization concerning the genetic relationship between troughlike basinal areas of the earth's crust which accumulate great thicknesses of sediment and are called **geosynclines,** and major mountain ranges. Just as the doctrine of evolution is universally accepted among biologists, so also the geosynclinal origin of the major mountain systems is an established principle in geology.

The geologist examining rocks in western and central New York finds a sequence of flat-lying shales and limestones a few hundred feet thick. If he follows these beds eastward across the state and looks for beds of the same age in New Hampshire, he will find that in the northern Appalachian Mountains they are thousands of feet thick. The relationship between this abnormal thickness of sedimentary strata and the structure and elevation of mountains is the foundation of the geosynclinal theory.

The principles of the origin of species through natural selection and the origin of mountains from geosynclines were proposed at about the same time, a little over 100 years ago. In 1857, James Hall, a paleontologist from the state of New York, expounded before the American Association for the Advancement of Science a theory for the origin of mountains. Hall had noted that the folded strata in the Appalachian Mountains were much thicker than those in the plains to the west, where the rocks are not folded. He deduced that the site of the Appalachian ranges was originally a troughlike depression which became filled with sediments, and that the folding of the rocks was due to the collapse of the sediments into the center of the trough (Fig. 5–1). He offered no explanation for the elevation of the mountains but believed that the amount of uplift was dependent on the thickness of the sediment. As James Dana later caustically remarked, Hall had ". . . promoted a theory for the origin of mountains with the origin of mountains left out." However, Dana accepted the theory in large part and developed it in classic papers published later in the nineteenth century. Dana proposed the name "geosynclinal" for the trough, but this was soon modified to "geosyncline." He believed that the formation and subsequent folding of the geosyncline were caused by compressive forces acting horizontally rather than by the collapse of the sediments toward the center of the geosyncline. Dana postulated that the depression of the geosyncline would displace material below the crust and cause an adjacent block of the crust to rise. This rising block, he believed, would be eroded to supply sediment to the sinking geosyncline. Dana also suggested that, after a geosyncline

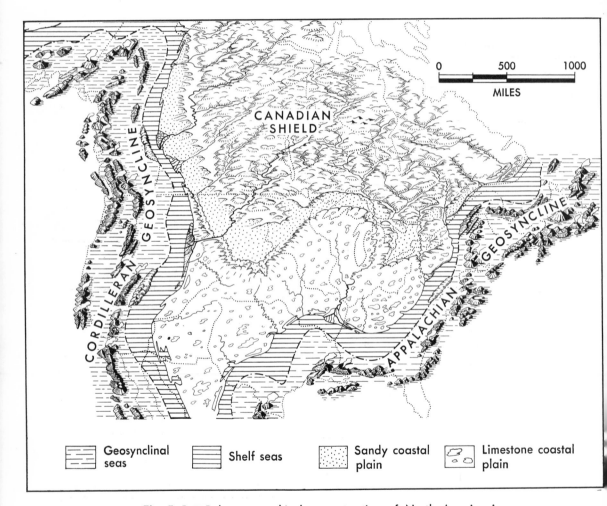

Fig. 5–1. Paleogeographical reconstruction of North America in Middle Ordovician time. The Canadian Shield is bordered by a broad coastal plain of Upper Cambrian sandstone and Lower Ordovician limestone dipping gently seaward. The Cordilleran and Appalachian geosynclines, dotted with volcanic islands, occupy the western and eastern coastal areas. (Modified from Marshall Kay.)

had been folded on the flanks of a continent, another would develop parallel to it on the oceanward side. At the turn of the century, Emile Haug extended the geosynclinal theory to include troughs that lay between two continental masses rather than at the margin of a continent. He also recognized the similarity between the oceanic troughs of the eastern Pacific, which he called **foredeeps**, and geosynclines. In 1923, Charles Schuchert proposed a classification of geosynclines, naming the classes by adding prefixes to obtain such names as monogeosyncline, polygeosyncline, etc. None of Schuchert's terms is in common use today but a similar, widely used set was introduced by Hans Stille in 1940. Stille noted that most geosynclines have an oceanward side containing volcanics interbedded with the sedimentary rocks, and a continentward side without volcanics. These parts he named the **eugeosyncline** (true geosyncline) and **miogeosyncline** (lesser, or less of a geosyncline), respectively. Stille included as well basinal areas within the continents which are not folded into mountains. These he called **parageosynclines.** This concept was further developed by Marshall Kay, who proposed several different names for such basins.

The recognition and classification of ancient geosynclines stimulated investigation of the deep oceanic troughs which several geologists have suggested are modern geosynclines. Geophysicists have determined that the troughs and their adjacent arcs of islands are associated with gravity and isostatic anomalies. Harry Hess suggested that the geophysical anomalies associated with these troughs are best explained by a deep, closed downfold of the light part of the earth's crust into the heavier substratum. He called this downfold a **tectogene.** The lower gravity values measured in these belts can be explained as owing to the thickening of the lighter part of the crust by folding. Whether or not these oceanic troughs of the eastern Pacific and West Indies are typical of ancient geosynclines will probably be answered after further research into both structures.

SEDIMENTARY TECTONICS

Not only are sedimentary rocks thicker in mountainous areas than in the plains but their lithology is also different. The rocks of the plains are clay shales, quartz sandstones, limestones, and dolomites; those of the mountains are metamorphosed mudstones, arkoses, graywackes, cherts, and tuffs interbedded with volcanic flows. To understand sedimentation in geosynclines, the geologist must study the relationships between the lithology of sedimentary rocks, their thickness, and the structural behavior of both the source area and site of deposition. The term **tectonics** refers to the structural behavior of an area as a whole, whether stable, subsiding, rising gently, or being thrust into mountain ranges.

The nature of the sediment deposited in a basin depends on many factors, among the most important of which are: the type of rock eroded to produce the sedimentary particles, the climate under which the processes of weathering and transportation take place, the tectonics of the source area, the nature of the transporting process, and the environment and, particularly, the tectonics of the basin of deposition. If a source area is high and of rugged topography, the particles supplied by weathering to the streams for delivery to the basin of deposition will be coarser than if the topography of the same source area in the same climate were low and subdued. Climate has an important influence on the size of particles supplied by weathering and erosion. For example, high ranges, if located in a hot, humid climate, will be weathered largely by chemical decomposition and will supply only the finest detrital particles; low hills, if located in an arid region where mechanical weathering is dominant and rainfall is infrequent but violent, will supply boulder- and cobble-sized particles. The historical geologist must therefore recognize that a change in the sedimentary record from coarse to fine sedimentary particles can be interpreted in various ways—as a change in topography of the source area, for example, or as a change in climate.

Wave Base

Most of the sediments that a geologist studies are deposited in the sea or in large lakes. Large bodies of water may be divided into a turbulent zone, or zone disturbed by the action of waves, and a still-water zone that lies below their influence. No simple, permanent surface separates these two environments; the boundary changes from moment to moment with the character of the waves. Although the boundary between the two environments is gradational and impermanent, the differences in sediments deposited in the two zones are important to the stratigrapher. By far the greatest energy for erosion and modification of sedimentary particles is available near the shoreline, where surf is active. The indefinite plane down to which wave action extends is called wave base; the plane to which surf action is effective is much shallower.

Sedimentary rocks deposited in the zone of wave motion (sometimes referred to as a high-energy environment) are much different from those deposited in deeper, quieter water (low-energy environment). Mechanically or chemically stable mineral grains deposited in the zone of wave motion are well rounded and sorted according to size by the constant grinding and shifting action of the waves. If mechanically or chemically unstable mineral grains are brought into such an environment, they are shifted about by the waves on the sea floor until the mechanically unstable minerals, such as feldspar and mica, are broken into fragments of clay size, and the chemically unstable minerals, such as augite and hornblende, have decomposed to clay minerals and soluble compounds. Only the most stable constituents, such as quartz and clay minerals, are left. The sorting action of the waves then distributes the particles into areas of differing wave competency where they are deposited. The clay is deposited in the quietest water; the sand, in the more agitated water. As a result, sediments in the high-energy, wave-moved zone, in addition to being composed of rounded grains of only the most stable minerals, are separated into quartzose sandstone and shales composed of clay minerals.

Sedimentary particles introduced into a basin whose surface of deposition is below wave base are incorporated in the accumulating sedimentary rock with little modification. If coarse, unsorted particles of unstable minerals are delivered to the basin, they will be deposited without being sorted, abraded, or decomposed. The mud, sand, and silt of such sediments are mixed together to form "dirty" or "impure" sandstones, such as graywacke and arkose, rather than sorted into quartz sandstone and clay shale (Fig. 5–2). **Graywacke** is a greenish-gray, poorly sorted, impure sandstone containing a high proportion of rock fragments, feldspar, mica, and other chemically and mechanically unstable grains. **Arkose** is a generally brown sandstone containing at least 25 per cent feldspar. Geologists differ on the precise definitions of these two rocks. Such sediments are often referred to as "poured in" sediments.

In areas that are subsiding rapidly, the surface of the sediment will continuously be carried below the zone of the waves as even more detritus is brought into the basin, and the strata deposited will be of the "poured in" type. In areas of slow subsidence, the surface of deposition will stay in the zone of the waves for a long time and the motion of the waves will grind and sort the sedimentary grains. If the supply of sedimentary detritus is small, the slowly subsiding area will remain a shallow-water environment, but, if the supply is too great for the waves and currents to shift away, the surface of deposition will rise above sea level and a subaerial delta will form. Such deltaic sediments, because they are not wave washed, tend to be similar to those deposited in rapidly subsiding basins. The tectonic behavior of the depositional site therefore determines to a great extent the character of the sediment deposited, and, conversely, the degree of tectonism of the site can be interpreted from the sediment.

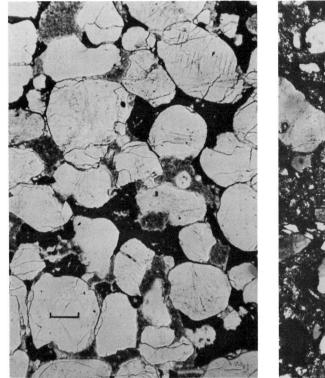

Fig. 5–2. Photomicrographs of two Lower Cambrian sandstones to show the contrasting textures of the wave-worked and "poured-in" types of sandstones. *Left:* A quartz sandstone composed of rounded, well-sorted grains of quartz cemented by iron oxide. The black line is ¹⁄₁₀ mm long. *Right:* Angular, poorly sorted grains in a clayey matrix, characterizing the texture of graywackes.

The thickness to which sediments can accumulate, as well as their character, is also determined by the subsidence of the basin of deposition. The limit to which sediments can accumulate in a large basin of deposition is the upper surface of a delta built into the basin. Additional sediment brought to the top of a delta which is not subsiding does not add to the thickness of the accumulating sediments but is carried onward by the distributary streams and dumped over the edge of the delta to extend it seaward. A deltaic deposit can grow in thickness only by the subsidence of the floor on which it is being built. If a large quantity of sediment is en-

tering a basin, so that it is silted up near the distributary streams, the thickness of the accumulating sediments will be dependent on the subsidence; if a small quantity is entering a basin in which subsidence is rapid, the thickness will be dependent on the supply, for the sedimentary surface will never approach wave base.

Sediments deposited in small lakes, intermontane basins, and river flood plains are subject to no such controls. These deposits are temporary compared with those in the sea, and slight changes in the regimen of erosion will remove them from the sedimentary record. The older systems are represented by very few continental deposits compared with the younger systems, for erosion has had a greater time to destroy them. The farther above sea level continental sediments are deposited, the less likely they are to become part of the permanent stratigraphic record.

DEFINITION OF TECTONIC ELEMENTS

Some terms that will be used in the following discussion of the evolution of geosynclines to mountain ranges are listed below:

geosyncline—a belt in the earth's crust that subsides for long periods so that it acts as a trap or collecting basin for sediments eroded from adjacent uplifted areas of the crust and for lavas and ash erupted from fissures and volcanoes. When the geosyncline becomes unstable, its sedimentary filling is deformed, metamorphosed, granitized, intruded, and eventually uplifted into mountains.

craton—the central stable area of a continent, around which the more mobile, marginal geosynclines are grouped. In North America the craton includes not only the large area where Precambrian rocks of the Canadian Shield are exposed, but also the broad, surrounding platform of essentially flat-lying, post-Precambrian rocks.

cratonic basins—an area within, or on the edge of, the craton which subsides more rapidly than the surrounding area and collects a greater thickness of sediments.

shelf—an area on the craton between the cratonic basins which subsides slowly and as a unit, receiving a thin veneer of shallow-water sediments analogous to the continental shelves of the present day.

Although the term "miogeosyncline" is widely used, the authors find the concept difficult to justify and believe that it does not contribute to the understanding of geosynclinal sedimentation. Neither miogeosynclines nor eugeosynclines are referred to in subsequent discussions. The geosyncline referred to in this book is essentially the eugeosyncline of Stille and Kay. The miogeosyncline is considered to be a kind of cratonic basin at the depressed margin of the craton. The sedimentary filling of the miogeosyncline does not differ from that of a cratonic basin until the geosyncline is uplifted in orogeny, when it is the principal vessel for the reception of the flood of clastics eroded from the rising ranges. The main reason for considering the cratonic edge to be a geosyncline is that it is folded along with the geosyncline in mountain making. The authors consider this deformation to be a secondary result of the primary forces deforming the geosyncline itself.

THE GEOSYNCLINAL CYCLE

Development of the Trough

The geosynclinal cycle must begin with a shallow downfold in the earth's crust which continues to deepen and to receive sediments. Unfortunately, the first sediments deposited in geosynclines undergo subsequent episodes of deformation which obscure the record of this earliest period in most mountain ranges. Geologists are not agreed, after nearly a century of investigation, on what mechanism starts or maintains the subsidence of the trough. James Hall thought that the depression of the earth's crust to form a geosyncline was a response to the weight of accumulating sediments. Although the weight of a load of sediments will depress the crust, its effect is strictly limited and could not account for the tens of thousands of feet of shallow-water sediments that were deposited in geosynclines. James Dana thought that the subsidence was due to compressive forces which buckled down the crust, and his theory has been perhaps the most popular among geologists. Recently, phase changes at the base of the crust below the geosyncline have been suggested to explain the subsidence. Under pressure applied by accumulating sediments, the gabbro or amphibolite at the base of the crust is believed to change into a denser form, eclogite, with a decrease in volume of about 15 per cent. Little evidence has been found to support this theory, and the extrusion of lavas on the floor of the geosyncline in the early stages of its evolution suggests that tension and expansion, rather than pressure and compression, characterize the base of the geosyncline. Others have suggested that geosynclinal subsidence is due to tensional forces induced by drifting continents or by the world-wide expansion of the crust. Another theory postulates that large-scale convection currents exist within the mantle, rising under the oceans and falling along the continental margins. The downward drag of the descending current might also account for the depression of the crust into a geosyncline.

Geosynclines form either between two continental blocks or between a continental block and an ocean basin. None of the first type has been discovered in North America, but they have played a dominant role in the development of Europe and Asia. The greatest of these **intercontinental geosynclines** stretched from Spain to the East Indies. It was deformed in Cretaceous and Cenozoic times to produce such ranges as the Pyrenees, Alps, Atlas, Apennines, and Himalayas. The trough was formed at the southern boundary of the Eurasian continent and was compressed by the approach of the Eurasian, African, and Indian crustal blocks. The Urals are another example of mountains formed from an intercontinental geosyncline.

The junction between continental segments and oceanic basins is apparently a zone of weakness, for many of the geosynclines in the Western Hemisphere are located here. The greatest group of such **marginal geosynclines** forms a ring around the Pacific Ocean. Other geosynclines have bordered the Atlantic Ocean and the Caribbean Sea. The behavior of marginal and intercontinental geosynclines is different both before and during mountain building. Because this book is concerned primarily with the evolution of the North American continent, the behavior of geosynclines marginal to continents is stressed in the following discussion.

Before we discuss the evolution of a typical geosyncline, a word of caution is necessary about the word *typical*. Geosynclines are remarkably diverse, but geologists usually consider the geosyncline with which they are most familiar to be typical of them all. As a result, the European concept of a geosyncline is related to the Alpine geosyncline and its ancestral sea, Tethys, but the North American geologist is more likely to consider the Appalachian geosyncline to be normal because it is familiar and the one on which the geosynclinal concept was first based. Most geologists would agree that a geosyncline is a trough that receives a great thickness of sediments usually associated with volcanics and is eventually folded into a mountain range, but they would differ according to their backgrounds over the nature of the geosynclinal filling and the sequence of changes in the geosynclinal cycle. The events described below are typical of North American geosynclines and may not be universally applicable. They are illustrated at greater length in later chapters.

Supply of Sediments

Into geosynclines are poured sediments that accumulate to thicknesses of tens of thousands of feet. Some of these beds have sedimentary structures, such as cross-bedding and ripple marks, suggestive of deposition above wave base, but many beds show structures indicative of deposition below wave base. A gradation in the size of sedimentary particles from coarse at the bottom to fine at the top is common (Fig. 5–3). Such **graded beds** have been interpreted as the deposits of turbidity currents spreading out at depth on the geosynclinal floor. A **turbidity current** is a flow of water which contains sediment suspended by the turbulent motion within a body of clearer water. The turbidity flow may be triggered by the slumping of sediments on a relatively high slope, and once set in motion it is capable of maintaining its integrity and flow for distances of tens of miles on very low slopes. When the slope along which the current is traveling decreases, and its velocity and competence fall, the particles in suspension are deposited at the base of the flow in order of size to pro-

Fig. 5–3. Graded bedding in the sandstones of the Appalachian geosyncline. Ordovician rocks of the Kamouraska area, Quebec. (Courtesy of E. W. Mountjoy.)

duce a graded bed. Scour markings on the base of the graded bed reflect the direction from which the turbidity current flowed. Another structure common in **turbidites, as the deposits of turbidity currents are called, is convolute bedding.** Bedding is said to be convolute when the layers are complexly contorted and disrupted. This disturbance of bedding is caused by the slumping of unconsolidated sedimentary layers on the flanks of the sedimentary basin. The alternation of graded sandstone beds with beds of shale that have been deposited between turbidity flows is typical of geosynclinal sequences.

The total volume of the geosynclinal filling is enormous. Where does this supply of sediments come from? The direction of origin of sedimentary rocks can be determined from their provenance; their mineral composition, which is a reflection of their source rock; directional sedimentary structures within them (such as cross-bedding, scour marks, and grain orientation) that indicate the direction of transporting currents; and regional relationships such as thickening and facies changes. Study of these properties shows that, initially, the geosyncline was supplied with sediment from the interior of the continent and was open to the ocean on the other side. The sediments in North American geosynclines indicate, by coarsening and thickening, that subsequently the source shifted to uplifts both within the geosyncline and between it and the ocean basin. The character of the typical geosynclinal assemblage of sediments gives evidence of the nature of their source as follows:

1. Rock fragments in the graywackes are composed of metamorphic, sedimentary, and volcanic rocks, indicating a source area of complex geology that had already taken part in a cycle of sedimentation, mountain building, metamorphism, and volcanism.
2. The continuing coarseness of the clastics over long intervals of time indicates either that the source was continually renewed in height as it was eroded or that it was replaced by other similar uplifted areas.
3. Lava flows, tuffs, and abundant siliceous sediments imply that volcanoes were near.

This evidence has led geologists to conclude that the source areas were volcanic islands of complex geology fringing the continents (Fig. 5–1). Groups of islands that appear to correspond today to the sediment suppliers of ancient geosynclines are arranged along the west side of the Pacific Ocean in a series of festoons or arcs. The Japanese island arc is representative, for it includes a complex of sedimentary, metamorphic, volcanic, and intrusive rocks.

Another view, widely held a few years ago, was that the source areas of the sediments were crustal blocks of continental dimensions (called "borderlands") that have since subsided into the ocean. As geophysical investigations revealed the structure of the ocean floor and failed to find a large mass of lighter continental rocks that had subsided into the ocean, this theory became untenable.

Tectonic Activity of a Geosyncline

During the history of a geosyncline, the trough subsides as the sediments accumulate. No completely satisfactory explanation of this long-continued subsidence has been formulated, but many of the events of the geosynclinal cycle can be explained if the trough is considered to undergo horizontal compression. The compressive force applied to the trough seems to increase during the cycle, and it yields slowly. The tightening vise bends and crumples the geosyncline, thrusting up islands of high relief. Conduits to deep-seated reservoirs are opened in the weakened crust, and lava pours out on the ocean floor. The islands thrust up as arcs in the geosynclinal sea act as suppliers of sediment as soon as they are raised above sea level into the zone of erosion. They are composed for the most part of folded and slightly metamorphosed sediments and lavas that were deposited previously in the geosyncline, but they also include rocks that floored the original trough and that have since been elevated by upthrusting. The geosynclinal sediments may, in this way, be recycled several times. As the geosyncline might appear to be devouring itself, this type of sediment supply has been called "cannibalistic."

Thrusting, folding, and erosion in the geosyncline are slow processes. The shorter-lived ridges and islands have an existence of only a few million years, whereas others are present throughout the lifetime of the geosyncline. Suppose it were possible to get a record of these events by setting a motion picture camera a great distance above the geosyncline to take a single frame every million years. If such a record were projected at normal speed, we would see the processes immensely accelerated and the crustal blocks might look like ice cakes breaking up and jamming together in the spring thaw of some northern river. Blocks would be tipped up and shoved over their neighbors, only to crumple in some further movement of the water below. The analogy cannot be carried very far, but it is suggestive of the violent tectonic activity of the geosyncline.

Orogeny, as geologists call mountain making, and volcanism are practically continuous in the geosyncline, but the intensity of the processes varies from time to time and place to place. In periods of intense activity (perhaps when compression is greatest), deformation may spread from the geosyncline to the cratonic margin (Fig. 5–4). Usually several such periods of deformation throughout the trough and cratonic margin occur before final consolidation. These preliminary phases may be so intense as to stabilize parts of the geosyncline and exclude them from further tectonic activity.

Geosynclinal Consolidation

The mobility which is said to characterize geosynclines is exhibited in subsidence, uplift, deformation, volcanism, and intrusion. When this mobility is lost, the geosyncline is consolidated and is converted into a mountain range. Although this process of consolidation is progressive, in that each stage of orogeny throughout the history of the geosynclinal cycle results in local loss of mobility, it also reaches a climax when the processes of deformation, volcanism, and intrusion rise to a crescendo. The events leading to this mountain-building climax are spread over millions of years, but in the vast perspective of geological time they seem to be rapidly completed.

As the mass of sediments in the geosyncline grows in thickness, its deepest parts penetrate zones of higher and higher temperature in the earth's crust. Eventually a limit of stability seems to be reached, and the sedimentary and volcanic filling of the whole geosyncline is deformed and metamorphosed.

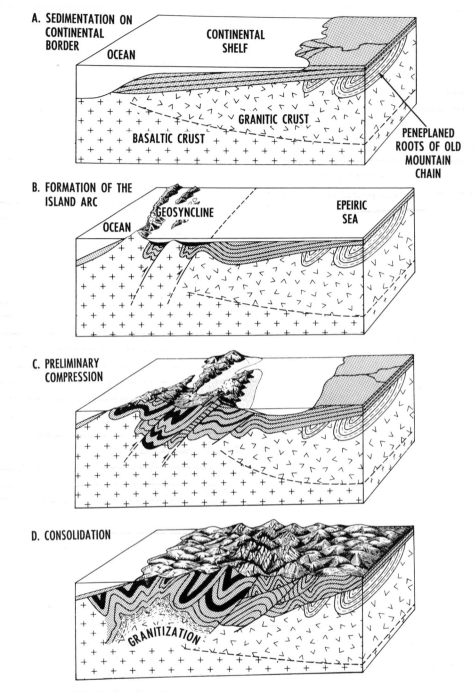

Fig. 5–4. The geosynclinal cycle. *A.* Sedimentation begins to build a thick wedge of sediments at the continental margin after the erosion of the old mountain chain. *B.* Instability of the margin results in the formation of an island arc, with volcanoes that supply lava and gray-wackes to the geosynclinal sea. *C.* Preliminary compression results in the growth of the island arc, the metamorphism of early sediments and lavas, and the introduction of deltaic sediments into the shelf seas. *D.* In the early stages of the climactic orogeny, the whole mass of sediments and lavas is thrust toward the continent, and granitization of the roots of the geosyncline begins.

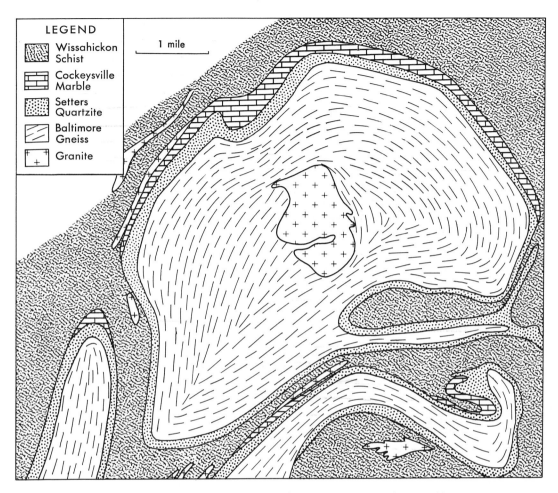

LEGEND

- Wissahickon Schist
- Cockeysville Marble
- Setters Quartzite
- Baltimore Gneiss
- Granite

1 mile

Fig. 5–5. Geological map of the Woodstock gneiss dome in Maryland. Note how the sediments that mantle the Precambrian Baltimore gneiss and granite dip away from the dome, suggesting that vertical forces existed in the axis of the geosyncline. (After E. Cloos, courtesy of the Geological Society of London.)

The structure of the deformed geosynclinal filling indicates that the forces involved in the climactic orogeny are both vertical and horizontal. Geologists are not agreed on which of these two forces is the primary one. In the axis of geosynclines, where the deformation is most intense, bedding and alignment of metamorphic minerals are generally vertical. The domal structures of gneisses and granites also suggest that the dominant force was vertical uplift (Fig. 5–5). On the flanks of geosynclines the deformation seems to be largely due to horizontal compression, for the structure is characterized by overturned folds and thrust faults. This pattern of deformation suggests that the primary deforming force is a vertical uplift and that the compressional structures of the flanks are the result of the sliding of large masses along the slopes of the uplifted region. Whether gravity is sufficient to transport blocks of sedimentary rock hundreds of square miles in area tens of miles down a slope of a few degrees is a question that will be answered only by further research into the physical properties of large masses of crustal materials. Compression alone, however, could cause the vertical structure of the axes of geosynclinal ranges, for in the zone of most intense deformation the limbs of anticlines and synclines would close on each other, becoming vertical and subparallel.

Although the ultimate cause of geosynclinal deformation is unknown, its effects have been thoroughly investigated. The sediments of the geosyncline are deformed into shear folds, flexure folds, and recumbent folds. They are cut by reverse faults that commonly dip to the oceanward side of marginal geosynclines. Regional metamorphism, with zones of decreasing intensity away from the axis, develops. The sediments deposited at the edge of the craton are affected by the outward thrust from the geosyncline. They are deformed into open folds, broken by low-angle thrust faults, and piled like overlapping roof tiles over the craton.

Each orogeny is composed of periods of intense deformation known as pulses or phases, separated by periods of relative tectonic quiet. The Late Paleozoic Variscan orogeny in Europe has been divided into nine pulses, ranging in age from Late Devonian to Late Permian. In some regions of the Rocky Mountains eight pulses can be recognized in the Cordilleran orogeny. In other geosynclinal belts the record is not so well preserved, and we can only guess at the number of pulses making up the orogeny.

Batholithic Intrusion

The growing orogenic forces may shove the base of the geosynclinal trough down into the hotter regions of the earth's crust. The descent of the geosynclinal keel is slow enough so that the rocks take on the temperature of the deeper zones as they are forced downward. At higher temperatures and pressures deep in the center of the geosyncline, chemical reactions, metamorphic processes, and replacements which are impossible in the surface environment may take place. Sedimentary rocks are changed to

schists and gneisses by shearing stress, increased temperature, increased pressure, and replacement solutions. Though they remain solid, sedimentary rocks affected by hot replacement solutions, recrystallization, and recombination of their mineral constituents may pass through metamorphic stages to become granitic rocks. This process, called granitization, is a normal part of the final stages of the geosynclinal cycle. Such batholiths are characterized by gneissic texture and general concordance with the bedding of surrounding rocks.

Application of greater heat results in selective melting of some mineral constituents, and thin sheets of molten magma form between the remaining solid beds. Such rocks consist of thinly alternating bands of igneous and metamorphic rock. When they solidify, they have a strikingly banded appearance and are called migmatites (mixed rocks). At higher temperatures wholesale melting may take place, and great lenses of magma several miles across may form in the depths of the geosynclinal prism. This liquid may work its way upward by breaking from its roof and engulfing and replacing country rock, until it solidifies in the cooler parts of the crust as an igneous granite batholith. Such batholiths are characterized by roof pendants, cupolas, contact aureoles, xenoliths, dikes, and sills. Several episodes in which both replacement and magmatic granites are formed may accompany the deformation of a geosyncline.

During the formation of granites in the depths of geosynclines, solutions are generated in which compounds of metals are dissolved. These solutions escape into the country rock and deposit their dissolved salts as veins or as replacements. Many of the great ore deposits of the world are associated with batholiths formed during or immediately after orogeny.

Erosion and Disruption

Theories of the origin of mountains should explain both their structure—faults, folds, batholiths, etc.—and their elevation. Little evidence can be found to show that the de-

Burney Mehl Ed. 636 ?

formation of geosynclinal rocks is either directly caused or immediately followed by their elevation into a mountain range. We shall see in later discussions that the elevation of mountains may sometimes be delayed after their structure has been formed; yet, in other orogenic episodes, elevation seems to accompany the structural deformation. If the hypothesis of the uplift of the core of a geosyncline in orogeny and the sliding of sedimentary plates by gravity away from this central elevation is correct, then the geosynclinal range should have considerable height early in its history. If lateral compression is the main force causing deformation, the piling up of thrust slices at the surface and the rise of anticlinal crests should cause a moderate immediate elevation. As the detailed relationships between the structures formed during orogenic episodes and the sedimentary deposits associated with them are investigated in geosynclinal ranges, the interdependence of structure and uplift will be clarified.

The elevation of the geosynclinal tract after deformation seems to be a response to the disturbance of isostasy caused by subsidence and orogeny. A widely accepted theory explaining the elevation of geosynclinal mountains postulates that the crust is thickened at the site of the geosyncline by the accumulation of a great wedge of sediments. During its evolution, the geosynclinal filling is pushed down into the denser and weaker layers of the earth to form a "root" for the new mountain chain. The introduction of this wedge of lighter rock into the denser layer at the base of the crust will produce a disturbance in isostasy which will last as long as the lighter rocks are held down. Such disturbances in the isostasy of the crust are now found in areas of island arcs, like those in the East and West Indies. These disturbances have been interpreted as indications of the downfolding of lighter rocks from the top of the crust (sial) into the denser rocks at its base (sima) and of the beginning of a new geosyncline. When the unknown force that causes the subsidence of the geo-

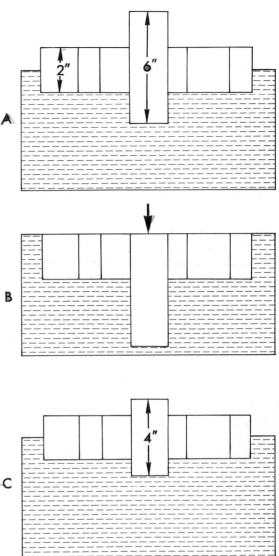

Fig. 5–6. Blocks of wood floating in water illustrate the principle of isostatic equilibrium and uplift after erosion.

syncline relaxes after the deformation, the root will raise the geosynclinal tract into isostatic equilibrium to eliminate the anomaly. The subsequent evolution of a mountain chain can be easily understood by an analogy to blocks of wood floating in water (Fig. 5–6A). Suppose that in a tub of water representing the weak but heavy substratum of the crust we float several blocks of wood 2 inches thick and one block 6 inches thick. These blocks represent the lighter layers of the crust floating in isostatic equilibrium. If the blocks float with half of their thickness under water, the 6-inch block, representing the part of the earth's crust that is thickened by mountain building, will float 2 inches above its neighbors. The lack of isostasy of the geosyncline before orogeny can be simulated by depressing the 6-inch block until its top is level with its neighbors (Fig. 5–6B). When the depressing force on the 6-inch block is released, isostasy is re-established, and the block floats higher because it is thicker. Similarly, a mountain range stands higher than the surrounding plain because the crust beneath it has been thickened. The effect of erosion on the range may be simulated by planing 2 inches off the 6-inch block and again placing it in the water (Fig. 5–6C). Although the removed portion equals the thickness by which the block stood above its neighbors, the block still floats 1 inch above them. Not until it has been reduced to 2 inches will the blocks stand even. Throughout the erosional episode, this tendency to maintain isostasy keeps the mountains rising, so that continual uplift occurs less and less markedly until the crust is reduced to normal thickness.

Recent geophysical interpretations of the paths of seismic waves from chemical and atomic explosions suggest that the crust beneath the North American Cordillera is not thickened into a root and that therefore the cause of the uplift of mountain chains must be sought in the upper part of the earth's mantle. Further work on this subject and on the nature of the mantle–crust boundary is necessary before it will be possible to determine the mechanism of regional crustal uplift.

The crust of the earth is much stronger than the analogy to wooden blocks suggests —it is strong enough so that the isostatic rebound does not immediately compensate for erosion. During this lag, erosive agents such as rivers, wind, and glacial ice may reduce local areas or the whole mountain system to a surface of low relief. Such erosion surfaces will be uplifted and dissected when isostasy is re-established. The crust of the earth is not homogeneous enough, however, to adjust to this uplift from below without breaking into segments. At some point in the history of nearly every geosynclinal mountain range studied so far, the erosion surfaces were disrupted by deep faults cutting the region into blocks.

Some of these faults are normal faults and seem to have been caused by tensional forces; others are strike-slip or wrench faults caused by a horizontal couple. Displacement along some of the latter type of faults is measurable in tens of miles and causes a whole system of lesser, branching faults. Tensional and shearing forces within the crust jostle the segments so that they resemble a box of toy blocks that has been accidentally kicked. Some blocks stand with a point upward, but most have an edge in the air and a few show no sign of disturbance. In the confusion of joggled rock segments there is usually no outlet for the streams and rivers which form in the valleys, and they are forced to drop their sediment and to evaporate in closed depressions. Downfaulting of some segments of the new mountain region may create basins deep enough to admit the sea and to accumulate tens of thousands of feet of marine sediments.

The normal and strike-slip faults penetrate to the basaltic part of the crust and allow molten basalt to rise and to issue, in part as volcanoes, but mostly as fissure eruptions. The sediments of the faulted basins are cut by sills and dikes. Fissure eruptions build thick plateaus of flows of basalt so highly liquid that they are known to cover a quarter of a million square miles.

In the final act of the geosynclinal cycle, erosion and isostatic adjustment along faults play the major role until the anomalous thickness of the crust has been eliminated and the last uplifted segment eroded to a terminal peneplain.

THE STRUCTURAL FRAMEWORK OF NORTH AMERICA

The North American continent may be considered to be composed of three distinct tectonic elements (Fig. 5–7):

1. The craton, or nucleus of the continent.
2. The geosynclinal mountain systems.
3. The coastal plains and modern marginal geosynclines now developing on the continental shelves.

The Craton

The stable, central area of the continent may be divided into two parts whose tectonic behavior is similar but whose surface geology is different. These parts are the **Canadian Shield,** underlain by Precambrian rocks, and the crescent-shaped **platform** surrounding it on three sides and underlain by essentially flat-lying sedimentary rocks of post-Precambrian age. The Precambrian rocks of the Shield extend out under the whole of the craton and project through younger rocks as isolated outcrops along its edge in Texas, Arizona, Wyoming, South Dakota, etc. Deep wells in the plains of the United States and Canada penetrate Precambrian rocks beneath the flat-lying, younger sedimentary rocks. The boundary between these two parts is marked by the erosional edge of the younger sedimentary rocks and is constantly moving outward as erosion strips the covering from the Shield. Compared to the thickness of the continental crust (20 miles), the unfolded sediments of the plains are a mere veneer on the Precambrian basement rocks, but they reach a thickness of several tens of thousands of feet in Colorado and Alberta.

The rocks of the Canadian Shield consist of schists, gneisses, granites, and sedimentary and volcanic rocks—all so deformed and interwelded that this large area of the crust has lost its mobility and now acts as a single, more or less rigid block. In Chapter 16 we shall see that the Shield encompasses many geosynclines that passed through several episodes of orogeny before becoming immobilized. Since late Precambrian time the whole area has been subjected only to broad movements of uplift and subsidence. Because the rocks of the Canadian Shield are highly deformed, their orogenic history can be interpreted only after a study of the more recent mountain belts; the description of the Shield, therefore, is reserved for Chapter 16.

The tectonic behavior of the platform has been similar to that of the Shield, but since the beginning of the Paleozoic Era it has had longer periods of subsidence, particularly around its edges. As a result, the sediments of the shallow seas that flooded the craton remain at its margins, whereas they have been eroded from, or perhaps never covered, the Canadian Shield. The lesser stability of the platform, or outer part of the craton, is reflected in its division into basins which subsided more rapidly than the area in general and arches which were gently uplifted or subsided less rapidly (Fig. 5–8). Along the margin of the craton subsidence was more rapid and frequent, and sedimentary rocks tens of thousands of feet thick were deposited adjacent to the geosynclines (in areas called "miogeosynclines" by Kay and Stille). The cratonic margin has been deformed as a result of the thrust of the geosynclines toward the continents and is now uplifted into such ranges as the Valley and Ridge Province of the Appalachians and the Rocky Mountains of the western states and Canada. The sedimentary rocks and tectonic behavior of the craton are more fully treated in Part II of this book.

The Marginal Mountain Systems

Marginal geosynclines were located around the craton during Paleozoic time (Fig. 5–7). As successive orogenies deformed these geosynclines, the craton became enclosed in a ring of highlands. Between the craton and the Atlantic Ocean on the southeast lay the Appalachian geosyncline. Although treated here as a marginal geosyncline, the Appalachian trough might actually have been an

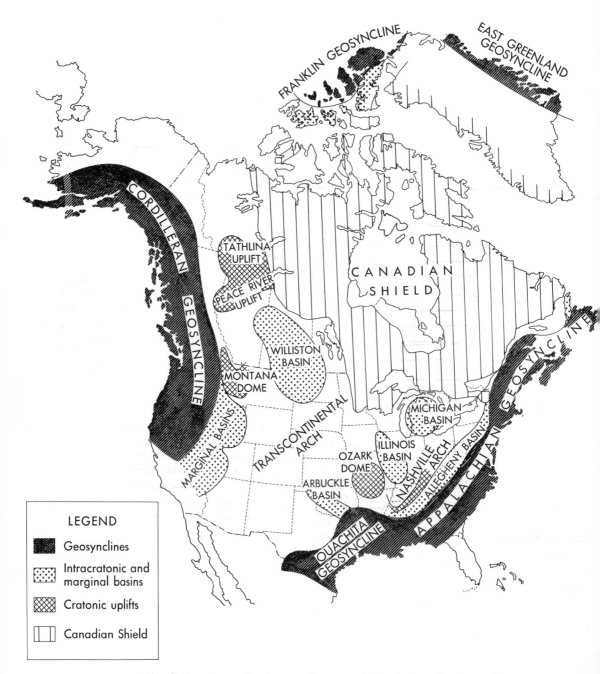

Fig. 5–7. Generalized tectonic map of North America in early Paleozoic (Ordovician) time. Although the Transcontinental arch is a prominent modern structure along which no lower Paleozoic rocks are found, there is little evidence that it was uplifted in early Paleozoic time.

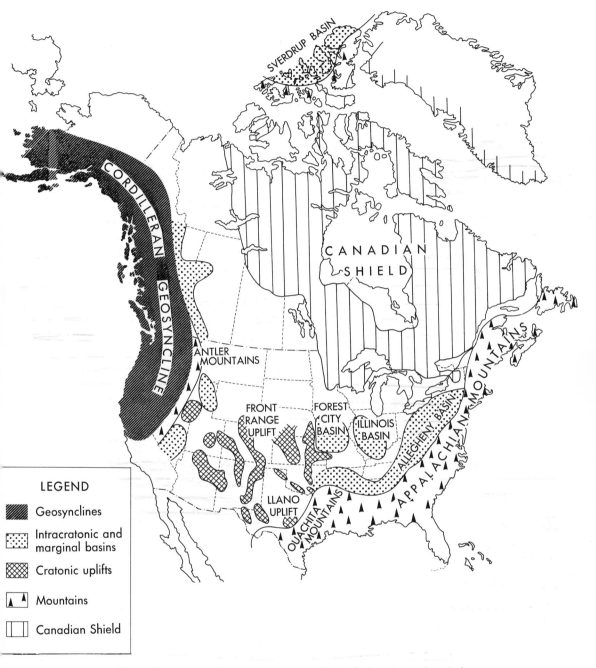

Fig. 5—8. Generalized tectonic map of North America in late Paleozoic (Pennsylvanian) time. The arches of the southwestern United
States are shown in more detail in Fig. 8—23. The small basins between
these arches are omitted from this map for simplicity.

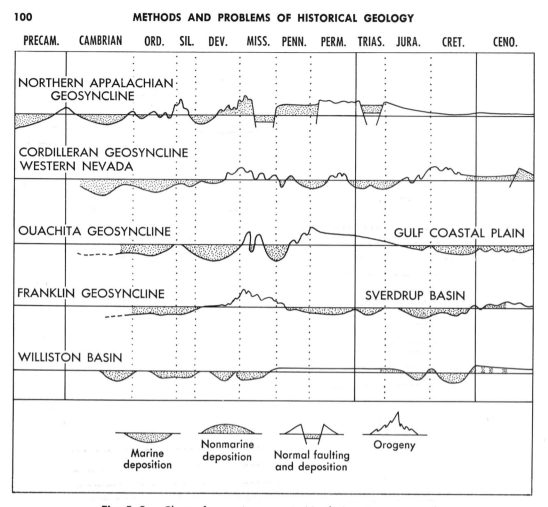

| PRECAM. | CAMBRIAN | ORD. | SIL. | DEV. | MISS. | PENN. | PERM. | TRIAS. | JURA. | CRET. | CENO. |

NORTHERN APPALACHIAN GEOSYNCLINE

CORDILLERAN GEOSYNCLINE WESTERN NEVADA

OUACHITA GEOSYNCLINE   GULF COASTAL PLAIN

FRANKLIN GEOSYNCLINE   SVERDRUP BASIN

WILLISTON BASIN

Marine deposition   Nonmarine deposition   Normal faulting and deposition   Orogeny

Fig. 5–9. Chart of tectonic events in North American geosynclines and basins. The width of the subdivisions of the chart is proportional to their time span.

intercontinental geosyncline—if Europe and North America were adjacent in the Paleozoic. Deposition in this trough began in late Precambrian time and continued until the end of the Paleozoic Era. Its history was punctuated by periods of intense orogeny in late Ordovician, late Devonian, and Permian times (Fig. 5–9). During the Permian the geosyncline was consolidated. The subsequent history of the Appalachian Mountains was one of block faulting, uplift, and erosion.

The southern margin of the craton was bordered by the Ouachita geosyncline. The similarity of its history to that of the Appalachian geosyncline suggests that it was a west-

ward extension of the southern end of that trough. The relationship between these two geosynclines and their histories are discussed in more detail in Chapters 12 and 13.

Western North America was bordered from Precambrian to Cenozoic times by the Cordilleran geosyncline, named after the backbone ranges of North America that were elevated from this trough in the Mesozoic and Cenozoic. The early Paleozoic history of this geosyncline is obscure, but typical geosynclinal sedimentary rocks and volcanics dating from the Precambrian have been found. The geosyncline was deformed at least twice during the Paleozoic, in the

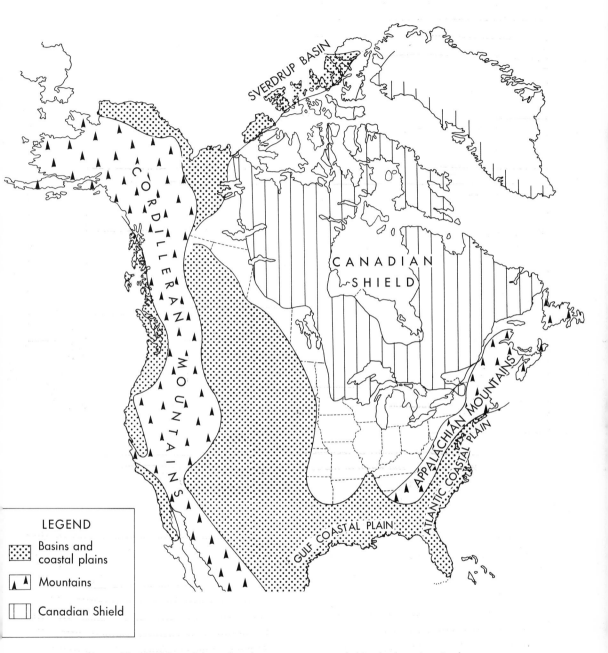

Fig. 5–10. Generalized tectonic map of North America in late Mesozoic (Late Cretaceous) time.   The large basin mapped beneath the plains was at times divided into smaller basins.

middle and at the end of the era. It was consolidated during Late Jurassic and Early Cretaceous times, but the deformation of the cratonic margin continued until mid-Cenozoic time. The Cordilleran Mountains are now in the stage of uplift, erosion, and fragmentation.

The ring of North American geosynclinal ranges is closed by the Innuitian mountain system, which crosses the Arctic Islands and northern Greenland. The Franklin geosyncline, from which these mountains arose, received a thick sequence of early Paleozoic sediments and was deformed in the late Paleozoic. In Mesozoic time a major basin, the Sverdrup basin (Fig. 5–10), subsided on the site of the Franklin geosyncline and accumulated a great thickness of sedimentary rocks before being gently deformed in the Cenozoic Era. The eastern coast of Greenland was the site of a branch of this geosynclinal system which was deformed in early Paleozoic time.

The Coastal Plains

Along the Atlantic and Gulf coasts a thick wedge of clastic sedimentary rocks accumulated in late Mesozoic and Cenozoic times. The shales and sandstones of this wedge underlie a low coastal plain and the broad continental shelf extending to the edge of the ocean abyss. No such mass of sediments has been deposited on the flank of the younger Cordilleran mountain system, but, along the coast of the Arctic Ocean in Alaska and the Arctic Islands, a narrow strip of rocks similar in lithology and structure to the Gulf Coastal Plain has accumulated. Beneath the Atlantic continental shelf and slope, geophysicists have detected two troughs parallel to the coastline which continue to accumulate a thick sequence of clastic sediments and shales. The wedge of sediment that has accumulated during Mesozoic and Cenozoic times in the northern part of the Gulf of Mexico is widely known as the Gulf Coast geosyncline. Many geologists believe that these sediments are being deposited in a new generation of marginal geosynclines now forming on the oceanward side of their folded predecessors. This problem is more fully discussed in Chapter 14. The east side of the North American continent seems to be a grand example of Dana's principle of the growth of continental nuclei by the accretion of marginal geosynclines.

SUMMARY

The nature of sediments deposited in a basin depends on the lithology of the source, the climate of the source area, the agents of erosion and transportation, and the tectonics of the source area and depositional basin.

Sediments deposited in the zone of wave motion consist of rounded and well-sorted grains of stable minerals. Sediments deposited below wave base consist of poorly sorted grains of both stable and unstable minerals.

The thickness to which sediments can accumulate in an area is dependent on the subsidence of the basin of deposition, provided that the source supplies enough sediment to keep the basin filled.

In the initial stages of the geosynclinal cycle, the earth's crust is depressed by unknown forces and receives sediments, first from the continent and then from arcs of islands elevated by orogeny.

A geosyncline is eventually consolidated by batholithic intrusion, metamorphism, and deformation which spreads to the cratonic margin.

The final stage in the geosynclinal cycle involves (1) the uplift of the consolidated geosyncline by the re-establishment of isostasy and (2) the fragmentation of the mountain system by normal and strike-slip faults, erosion, deposition in the fault basins, and volcanism.

North America consists of a central, stable craton, marginal mountain systems that have resulted from deformed geosynclines, and coastal plains beneath which new geosynclines may be developing.

QUESTIONS

1. What can a geologist learn about the nature of the source area from the structure and petrology of sedimentary rocks?

2. What characteristics of sedimentary rocks are dependent on the climates of the source area and area of deposition?

3. Make a chart to compare and contrast the processes and products of shelf deposition above wave base and of geosynclinal deposition below wave base.

4. List the types of mountains that are not geosynclinal in origin.

REFERENCES AND SUGGESTED READINGS

AUBOUIN, J. *Geosynclines.* New York: Elsevier Publishing Co., 1965. This book provides a good summary of European ideas on the geosynclinal theory and traces the application of these ideas to the geology of the Greek segment of the Alpine mountain chain.

HOLMES, A. *Principles of Geology,* 2d ed. New York: The Ronald Press Co., 1965. Chapter 30 of this excellent elementary textbook is an interesting discussion of mountain building and its relationship to geosynclines.

KAY, G. M. "North American Geosynclines," *Geological Society of America Memoir 48,* 1951. A summary of the geosynclines of the continent and the nature of sedimentation in them. Several types of structures regarded as basins in this chapter are described as geosynclines in this monograph.

KRUMBEIN, W. C., and SLOSS, L. L. *Stratigraphy and Sedimentation,* 2d ed. San Francisco: W. H. Freeman and Co., 1963. Chapter 11 of this book, on sedimentary tectonics, amplifies many of the ideas only briefly touched upon in this chapter.

SLOSS, L. L. "Tectonic Cycles of the North American Craton," *Geological Survey of Kansas Bulletin,* 169: 451–60, 1964. The concept of marginal basins rather than miogeosynclines is concisely justified and cratonic sequences are discussed at length in the latter part of this paper.

WELLER, J. M. *Stratigraphic Principles and Practice.* New York: Harper & Row, 1960. Chapter 8 of this book on tectonics deals with many of the subjects included in this chapter.

6

Polar Wandering and Continental Drift

Even Greek philosophers recognized that the marine sedimentary rocks on dry land proved that the oceans had at times overflowed their basins. As early as the beginning of the nineteenth century geologists recognized the shallow-water origin of these rocks and concluded that they were not evidence that the continents had ever been ocean basins. The absence of deep sea sediments on continental areas reinforced this conclusion. The principle of the **permanence of continents and oceans** states that the main masses of the continental plates have always been continents and the ocean basins have never been uplifted to form continents. This principle has had ample backing from modern geophysical studies, which show that the two elements owe their difference in elevation to fundamentally different crustal structures which would not allow an exchange of behavior.

Most geologists subscribe to the principle of the permanence of continents and oceans but hold a wide range of views on whether the continents have always been located as at present with respect to each other and to the axis of rotation of the earth. The idea that the continents have moved can be traced back to the writings of Francis Bacon in the seventeenth century. In the middle of the nineteenth century Antonio Snider revived the idea and drew maps showing that the Americas had drifted westward away from Africa and Europe since the Late Paleozoic. The early writers were impressed by the way the shorelines of Africa and South America seem to fit together when these continents are drawn next to one another, and this fit remains one of the most convincing items of evidence for movement of the continents. In the second decade of this century the theory was given impetus by the publication of one version of it by Frank Taylor and another by Alfred Wegener. During the twenties and thirties the pros and cons for the movement of the continents were widely discussed, and geologists tended to be divided into two camps—those who had worked in the Southern Hemisphere, especially in South Africa, and were in favor of

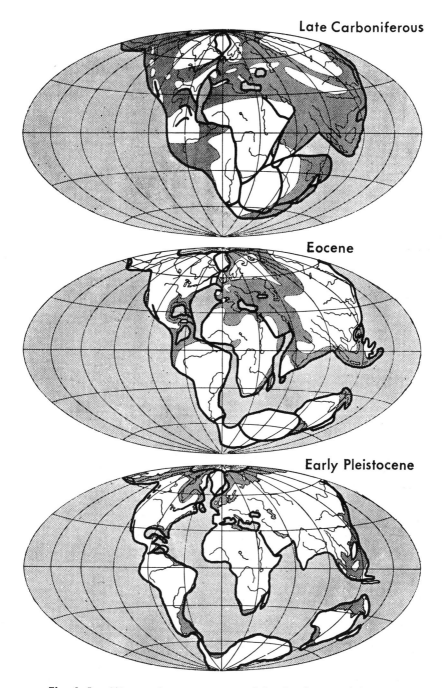

Fig. 6–1. Wegener's reconstruction of the distribution of the continents during Carboniferous, Eocene, and Pleistocene times. The darker areas on the continents represent shallow seas. (After A. Wegener, 1915, from Arthur Holmes, *Principles of Physical Geology*, Second Edition. New York: The Ronald Press Co., 1965.)

the theory, and those who had not and found no reason to consider it seriously. This impasse has been broken within the last twenty years by the discovery throughout the world of new facts that are difficult to explain without recourse to the hypothesis of continental drift.

Alfred Wegener believed that until the late Paleozoic the continents of the world were united in a single continental mass. His assembly of the continents is illustrated in Fig. 6–1. According to his hypothesis, toward the end of the Paleozoic Era rifting began on the site that was to be the Atlantic Ocean, and South America started to drift westward away from Africa. This rift slowly spread northward, but the major separation of North America from Europe was thought by Wegener to have been postponed until the Cenozoic Era. During the Mesozoic, as the Americas drifted westward, India separated from southeast Africa and drifted northward

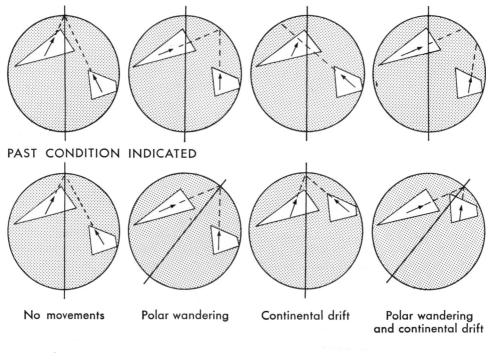

Fig. 6–2. Combinations of polar wandering and continental drift. The irregular white polygons are diagrammatic continents. The circles represent the earth and the lines through them, their axes of rotation. The short arrows are indicators of the direction of the pole—such as the orientation of magnetic minerals for some period in the past. A. No indication of change in the past position of poles and continents is found. B. The ancient polar indicators point to a position that is not the modern pole; this anomaly may be accounted for by the postulation of polar movement. C. The indicators do not point to the modern pole but the discrepancy can be explained by an assumption of continental drift. D. Movement of both poles and continents may be postulated to explain anomalous ancient polar positions.

to impinge on the Asiatic continent; and Australia, at first attached to Antarctica, drifted eastward. Where the leading edges of these continental rafts encountered opposition from the oceanic floor, they were compressed into folded mountain ranges such as the Cordillera of the Americas. The conspicuous island loops between the Americas and between South America and Antarctica represent threads of continental crust left behind as the main plate moved westward.

The theory of polar wandering has been associated commonly with that of continental drift, but the two must be clearly separated. Four types of hypotheses regarding the positions of the continents and the axis of rotation of the earth have been proposed (Fig. 6–2):

1. No change in the relative position of the continents has taken place with respect either to each other or to the poles.
2. The continents have maintained the same position relative to each other but the whole of the outer layer of the earth has slipped across the axis of rotation over the interior so that the position of the poles with respect to the continents has changed.
3. The continents have changed position relative to each other but the position of the poles relative to one of them has not changed.
4. The positions of both poles and continents have changed relative to each other.

GEOLOGICAL EVIDENCE OF CONTINENTAL DRIFT

The Jigsaw Puzzle

The theory of continental drift has been successful in accounting for relationships between the continents of the Southern Hemisphere and has also been helpful in drawing attention to the interrelationships between the geology of Europe and North America. Although many geologists have worked geography like a jigsaw puzzle in an effort to reconstruct the original positions of the continents in a variety of ways, almost all agree

that South America must have fitted against Africa, that Europe must have been at one time much closer to North America, and that India and Australia must have been located east of South Africa.

In examining a globe no one can fail to be impressed by the similarity in coastline of the Atlantic shores of Africa and South America (Fig. 6–3). If the two continents are moved together and rotated slightly, promontories fit neatly into bays and bays into promontories. S. Warren Carey has suggested that the fit is better at a depth of 650 feet below sea level at the edge of the continental shelf than at the coast, and a computer, in comparing the fit at 600, 3000, 6000, and 12,000 feet below sea level, has shown that the best correspondence of the two continental masses is at a depth of 3000–6000 feet. The coastlines are followed by the trend of the Mid-Atlantic Ridge, which according to some geologists marks the position of the rift, and according to others marks the place where new oceanic crust is welling up to fill the space where the crust has parted.

The correspondence between the two southern continents is not only topographic but geological. The Paleozoic stratigraphy of the southern continents is strikingly similar, and parallels between the sequence of formations in South America and Africa are easily drawn (Fig. 6–4). The Cape system of Paleozoic folded mountains which crosses the southern tip of Africa is believed to be continued in the Paleozoic folds of the Sierra de la Ventana of Argentina. On both sides of the South Atlantic a late Precambrian to Cambrian zone of deformation paralleled the coastlines and may have determined the fractures along which the continents later parted. The most convincing stratigraphic evidence for the connection between the southern continents is the similarity of their upper Paleozoic stratigraphy. Although nearly all the formations can be matched from one side of the ocean to the other, the most striking similarities are concerned with the glacial formations at the base of the sequence. In South Africa the Dwyka tillite

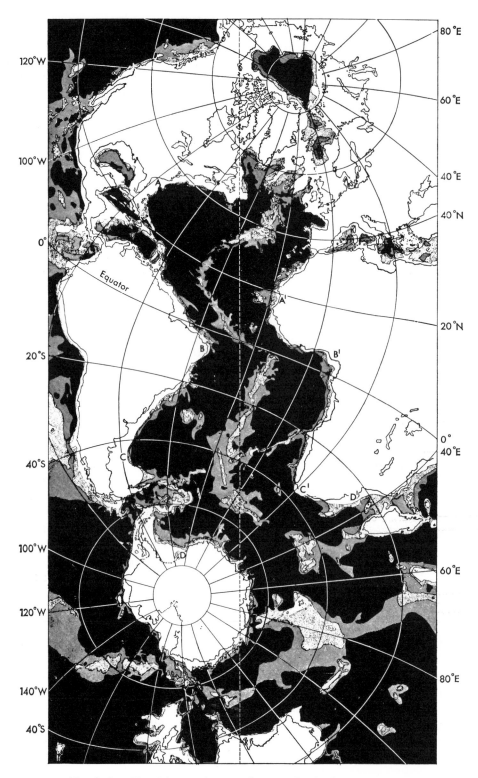

Fig. 6–3. The Atlantic Ocean, showing the bathymetric contours and the Mid-Atlantic Ridge. (Courtesy of S. Warren Carey, from Arthur Holmes, *Principles of Physical Geology,* Second Edition. New York: The Ronald Press Co., 1965.)

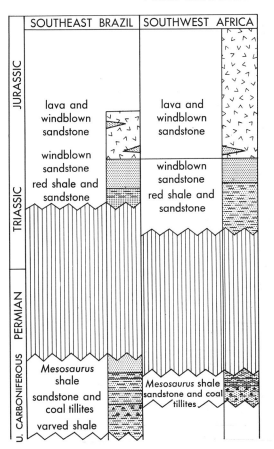

	SOUTHEAST BRAZIL	SOUTHWEST AFRICA
JURASSIC	lava and windblown sandstone	lava and windblown sandstone
TRIASSIC	windblown sandstone red shale and sandstone	windblown sandstone red shale and sandstone
PERMIAN		
U. CARBONIFEROUS	Mesosaurus shale sandstone and coal tillites varved shale	Mesosaurus shale sandstone and coal tillites

Fig. 6–4. Comparison of stratigraphic sequences across the South Atlantic Ocean. (From information of H. Martin, courtesy of the *Journal of the Geological Society of South Africa*.)

around South Africa and the pole was situated closer to Africa. This is not the place to review the many other geological similarities between the continents that have been assembled by African geologists, notably Alexandre du Toit, but suffice it to say that they convinced geologists in that part of the world—but not those elsewhere—that drift had occurred.

Why were North American geologists skeptical of continental drift when their southern colleagues were enthusiastic? Perhaps because Europe and North America do not fit together as well as Africa and South America. Although many have compared the geology and paleontology of the two continents, these comparisons have not been as convincing of drift as those of the Southern Hemisphere. In uniting the two continents, we must join the mountain ranges that end at either side of the Atlantic shoreline. In northern Europe the late Paleozoic Hercynian folds strike westward through Brittany, Cornwall, and southern Ireland, and the late Silurian Caledonian folds strike southwestward through Scotland. On the west side of the ocean the late Paleozoic Appalachian folds strike east across southern New England and the late Devonian and late Ordovician Acadian and Taconic mountain folds strike northeast through Newfoundland and Nova Scotia. In addition a late Silurian belt of deformation strikes south from east Greenland into the North Atlantic (Fig. 6–6). The joining of these skeins has been attempted by several geologists but no completely acceptable solution has as yet been proposed to account for the differences in times of deformation (neither the Late Ordovician nor the Late Devonian is a time of intense orogeny in Europe) or the crossing of the belts of deformation. The stratigraphy on either side of the North Atlantic has also been compared, but the similarities are much less striking than those in the Southern Hemisphere.

The joining of the open ends of geosynclines and their resultant mountain chains is open to several interpretations. In western

covers wide areas and overlies a polished and striated pavement of basement rocks. From these striations and other indicators the direction from which the ice moved can be determined. Similar beds occur at this position in India, South America, and Australia. The striations in central Africa indicate that the ice crossed the present equator and in India that it came from the direction of the present equator (Fig. 6–5). In southeastern Africa the ice came from the east, the direction of the present Indian Ocean. The distribution of glacial deposits and the directions of ice movement make sense only if the continents of the Southern Hemisphere were united

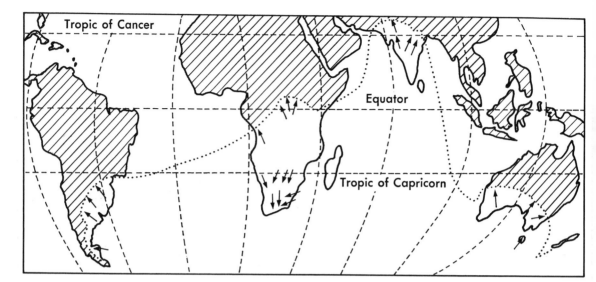

Fig. 6–5. Extent and direction of late Paleozoic glaciation with continents arranged as at present. (Modified from Arthur Holmes, *Principles of Physical Geology*, Second Edition. New York: The Ronald Press Co., 1965.)

North America the Cordilleran geosyncline is part of a continuous ring around the Pacific, and the Franklin and Ouachita geosynclines seem to branch from it. The lack of open ends around the Pacific has suggested to some geologists that all geosynclines were at one time interconnected to form world-encircling belts of mountain making, and that open-ended geosynclines on the Atlantic coasts have been broken off by the movement of the continents. So far we are not able to trace the structure of mountain systems from the land beneath the thick sedimentary wedge of the continental shelves to the abyssal ocean floors. Much work remains to be done in the geophysical investigation of the ocean floor before we discard the possibility that the orogenic belt of the Appalachian geosyncline extended between Europe and America across the Atlantic floor. Perhaps mountains were never elevated from this part of the geosyncline because, like the oceanic trenches of the western Pacific, it was too far from land to receive a sedimentary filling.

In our study of the geology of North America we must keep in mind the possibility that the Atlantic Ocean and the Gulf of Mexico did not exist until the end of the Paleozoic Era and that the Appalachian Mountains are only half of a mountain system whose other side may be in Spain and along the northwest coast of Africa. Although the Appalachian geosyncline is treated here as a marginal geosyncline, it may have developed as an intercontinental geosyncline between Europe and North America.

Distribution of Organisms

The open ocean is as much a barrier to the spread of shallow-water marine organisms as is a strip of land. Most marine invertebrates spread during a short swimming stage when they are larvae. Even though they may be capable of swimming for part of their life, organisms adapted to coastal environments will not encounter the proper food along the route across the ocean. When the short

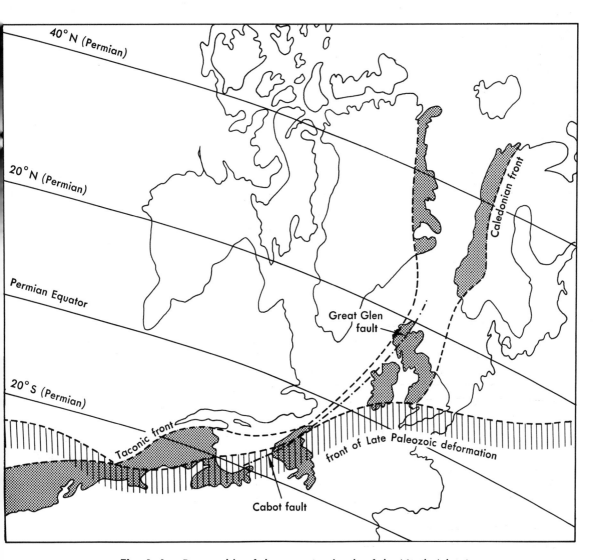

Fig. 6–6. Reassembly of the opposing lands of the North Atlantic. The shaded area was affected by early Paleozoic deformation. The position of the lines of magnetic latitude (isoclines) is shown and the continents are moved so that they are continuous from Europe to North America. (Modified from Arthur Holmes, *Principles of Physical Geology*, Second Edition. New York: The Ronald Press Co., 1965.)

larval stage during which they can swim is over, they must settle down in a shallow-water environment in order to live. Nevertheless, during the Paleozoic Era many shallow-water invertebrates were common to both sides of the Atlantic Ocean. To account for transoceanic faunal similarities paleontologists have invented land bridges, strips of land crossing the oceans, to provide shallow-water migration routes for such faunas. Geophysicists are skeptical that such thin strips of continental crust crossing the ocean basins could have existed. The Cambrian trilobites of the Canadian Maritime Provinces are good examples of faunal similarity in the Northern Hemisphere because they more closely resemble the trilobites of northern Europe than the trilobites of the rest of North America. The best example from the Southern Hemisphere is the little fresh-water reptile *Mesosaurus*, which is found in a similar stratigraphic position in both South America and Africa (Fig. 6–4) but would have been incapable of crossing the ocean. The distribution of the *Gangamopteris–Glossopteris* flora in the Southern Hemisphere is also difficult to explain if the continents have always occupied their present positions.

Such distributions have been used as proof that at one time the continents were closer together. Their significance is, however, a matter of opinion, and explanations other than land bridges and continental drift are possible for most distributions.

Paleoclimatology

The geological record is full of evidence that the climate of a given place on the earth's crust has changed in geological time. Coral reefs, now confined to the tropics, have been found in Paleozoic rocks in the Arctic; coal formed of plants from warm climates is common in areas that are now Arctic tundra; desert sandstone underlies tropical rainforests. The properties of sedimentary rocks that give information about the climate of the past are many, and only a few can be

mentioned here. The excess of the growth of vegetation over its decay required for the accumulation of coal exists in the equatorial zone and in two zones in the high latitudes. The dryness required for the accumulation of evaporites is common at present in two zones about 20 degrees on either side of the equator. Modern red sediments have been derived from the erosion of lateritic soils and are confined to tropical areas. Coral and other types of reefs are at present confined to tropical waters where the water temperature does not drop below an average of 72 degrees Fahrenheit for the coldest month and probably their distribution was similarly controlled in the past. Maps of these and other indicators suggest that the ancient equator was not in the position it now occupies with respect to the continents.

Wegener and several other geologists after him have used this information in order to show that the poles have wandered with respect to the continents and the continents have moved relative to one another. The distribution of Carboniferous glacial deposits in the Southern Hemisphere has been mentioned as evidence of continental drift and concurrent polar wandering. Paleoclimatic evidence is open to interpretation, and different geologists have drawn different conclusions from it.

Although the interpretation of the climates of the past is difficult without recourse to polar wandering and continental drift, some paleontologists have used similar data to show that neither of these phenomena existed. Anomalies of ancient climate such as coal deposits in the Arctic may be explained as due to the less precise differentiation of the earth's climatic belts in the geological past than at present and a greater uniformity of climate. Other anomalies can be explained as results of warm or cold ocean currents or winds modifying the influence of latitude on climate. Although, in general, the climate of an area is dependent on its latitude, many complicating factors make the distribution of the present world's climate highly irregular.

The modifying influence of the warm Gulf Stream on the climate of northern Europe is a well-known example. These considerations have made many geologists hesitate before accepting the evidence of paleoclimatology for continental drift and polar wandering.

PALEOMAGNETISM

Remnant magnetism is the magnetically induced field that remains in a substance susceptible to magnetism after the field that induced it has changed or disappeared. Paul Mercanton recognized in 1926 that the remnant magnetism in rocks could be used to test hypotheses of polar wandering and continental drift, but only in the last twenty years has the impact of this method been felt on these theories. Where the geological evidence failed, the recent results of research in paleomagnetism have convinced many geologists of the reality of both these movements.

Sensitive instruments have determined that many sedimentary and igneous rocks retain a record of the magnetic field in which they were deposited or crystallized. For the common magnetic minerals the critical temperature above which magnetic properties are lost is about 600 degrees Centigrade. Mineral grains crystallizing below this temperature take on the magnetic field in which they are located. All minerals originating in or on the earth are subject to the earth's magnetic field; those with magnetic susceptibility retain a record of that field. Magnetic mineral grains settling through water or air will tend to be aligned and to record the earth's field.

The Earth's Magnetic Field

The major component of the present field of the earth can be represented as a bar magnet whose axis is inclined at 11.5 degrees to the axis of rotation. In addition, there are areas of rapid change a few thousand miles across, which drift westward at a speed of about 0.2 degrees of longitude per year. Although these temporary foci produce some departure from the typical magnetic field of the earth, the axis is not changed more than 2 degrees.

The geomagnetic poles, which represent the emergence of the axis of the magnetic field at the earth's surface, have wandered 5 degrees in longitude and a fraction of a degree in latitude in historic times. Measurements of the remnant magnetism of rocks of recent and late Pleistocene age show that within the last one or two hundred thousand years the axis of the field, averaged over a few thousand years, has corresponded closely to the rotational axis of the earth.

For paleomagnetic measurement the samples collected are cylinders of rock accurately oriented with respect to the earth's present field. The direction (an azimuth with respect to the modern geomagnetic poles) of the remnant magnetic field in the rock shows the direction of the ancient poles. The inclination of the remnant field with respect to the horizontal shows the magnetic latitude of the specimen or its distance from the ancient poles. The inclination, like that of a dip needle, is horizontal at the geomagnetic equator, vertical at the geomagnetic poles, and of intermediate value between.

Igneous rocks rich in iron compounds, such as basalts, and sedimentary rocks with iron-rich cements, such as red sandstones, are satisfactory for determinations of remnant magnetism. The direction of magnetism of the country rock baked by a dike or sill can be measured and is related to that of the metamorphosing intrusion. As the magnetic field of the earth has short-term variations that are not significant for the location of poles, determinations from a number of samples representing several thousand years of geological time are averaged so that these minor variations will be canceled out.

Reversal of Fields

One of the most interesting results of magnetism studies has been the discovery that the direction of magnetization of rocks of certain ages is reversed with respect to the

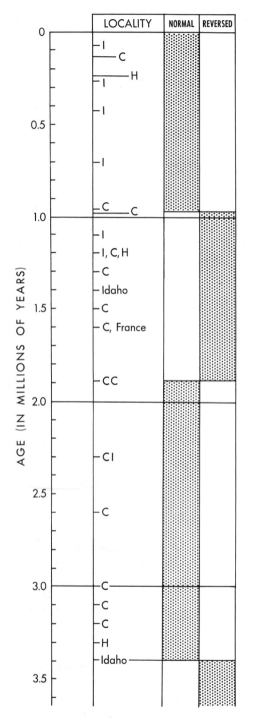

present field of the earth. The reversal of remnant magnetism in rocks seems to be caused by (1) a 180-degree change in the field of the earth, and (2) self-reversal mechanisms in the rock itself. Such data as those presented in Fig. 6–7 leave little doubt that during certain intervals in the past the polarity of the earth's field differed by 180 degrees from the present polarity. Insufficient determinations have been made to allow the times of reversal during the earth's history to be plotted except in the Cenozoic Era, but results to date indicate that this reversal of polarity has been a common phenomenon throughout geological time.

The mechanism of reversal has not been satisfactorily explained, but the phenomenon may have an important influence on the interpretation of the history of the earth. The magnetic field of the earth deflects charged particles from the sun into paths along the magnetic lines of force to produce the Van Allen radiation belts. If the magnetic field were removed, the higher dose of radiation from the sun (the so-called solar wind) would have a major effect on life. Some groups of animals might not survive such radiation. Geneticists have shown that radiation in less than lethal doses produces new variants and causes monstrosities by its effects on the reproductive systems of organisms. A burst of radiation sufficient to result in the speeding up of evolutionary processes or the extinction of large groups would occur when the earth's field reached the zero point in the reversal process. As new results show that polar reversal occurred many times in the past, explanations of catastrophic changes in life by this mechanism lose their force. The periodic increase in radiation that would follow collapse of the Van Allen belts may have influenced the rate of evolution of life, but the record does not show a catastrophe every two or three million years.

Fig. 6–7. Evidence of recent reversals of the earth's field. The location of the samples which were dated by potassium–argon methods and whose direction of magnetization was determined is indicated by letters as follows: *I*, Italy; *C*, California; *H*, Hawaii. Two episodes of normal polarity and two of reversed polarity are defined within the last 3½ million years. (From information by Evernden and others.)

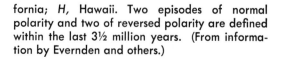

Polar Wandering, Continental Drift, and Paleomagnetism

When the positions of the north pole are plotted from the remnant magnetism of North American rocks, the pole is determined to have been in the central Pacific Ocean during much of the early Paleozoic. From there it moved toward Japan in late Paleozoic time and during the Mesozoic it moved in an arc through western Siberia toward its present position. Another way of illustrating the change in the earth's field through the ages is to plot the geomagnetic equator and **isoclines** (lines of equal magnetic inclination) on either side of it (Fig. 6–8). Such maps show the equator crossing from southwest to northeast through the central part of the continent during much of the early Paleozoic Era and forming an arc from northern California to Newfoundland as late as the Permian Period. Although these results are startling, they provide answers to many paleoclimatological problems, such as the distribution of Paleozoic reefs, evaporites, and coal deposits, which will be discussed in detail later.

As long as our paleomagnetic investigation is confined to North America, a single, unequivocal polar wandering curve can be plotted. If the investigation is extended to Europe, the polar wandering curve for that continent is found to be distinctly different. As Fig. 6–9 shows, it is displaced to the east of the curve for North America by about 30 degrees longitude in the Permian and follows a parallel course to it until Triassic time when the two curves begin to converge toward their present meeting at the north magnetic pole. Because the remnant magnetism of rocks from the two continents must have been oriented to the same geomagnetic pole throughout geological time, the present divergence can be explained only as the result of the relative movement of the continents. The direction of this movement can be determined from the relationship of the two curves. This initial parallelism of the two polar curves shows that the continents were welded together and acted as one up to early Mesozoic time, but the distance between the curves is a reflection of the counterclockwise rotation of North America necessary to close the North Atlantic gap. As the continents drifted apart toward their present positions the curves approached each other and eventually merged (Fig. 6–9).

The pattern of the magnetic equator and isoclinal lines for North America cannot be reconciled with that for Europe for some periods in the past unless the continents have moved (Fig. 6–6). The movement deduced from paleomagnetism is a bringing together of the two continents in much the same way as was suggested by the proponents of continental drift who relied solely on geological evidence.

Not as much work has been done on the patterns of paleomagnetism in the Southern Hemisphere, but the pole determinations for these continents are not consistent with those in the Northern Hemisphere. They can be reconciled with the Northern Hemisphere poles, however, by a relocation of the continents around South Africa.

If, as most "drifters" suggest, the two movements of continental drifting and polar wandering were concurrent, their effects are difficult to separate. Polar wandering implies the shifting of the whole outer crust over the inner part of the earth, and although no mechanism to accomplish this has as yet been suggested, the possibility that it has occurred cannot be rejected. As our paleomagnetic information becomes more accurate, the separation of the polar wandering from the drifting component may become possible in the future.

THE SEARCH FOR A MECHANISM

Many geologists rejected the early hypotheses of continental drift because the proponents could suggest no adequate force for moving the continents. This objection does not invalidate the theory as a whole, for many phenomena in earth science which have

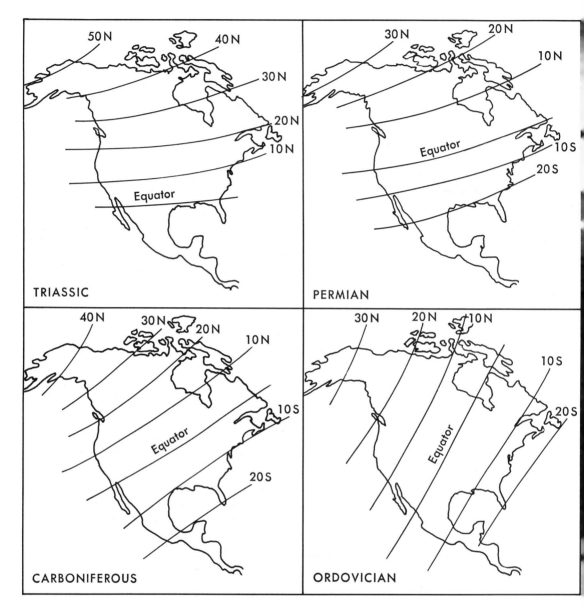

Fig. 6–8. Position of the ancient magnetic equator and magnetic latitude lines (isoclines) for North America during four periods in the past. (Modified from E. Irving, *Paleomagnetism and Its Application to Geological and Geophysical Problems.* New York: John Wiley & Sons, Inc., 1964.)

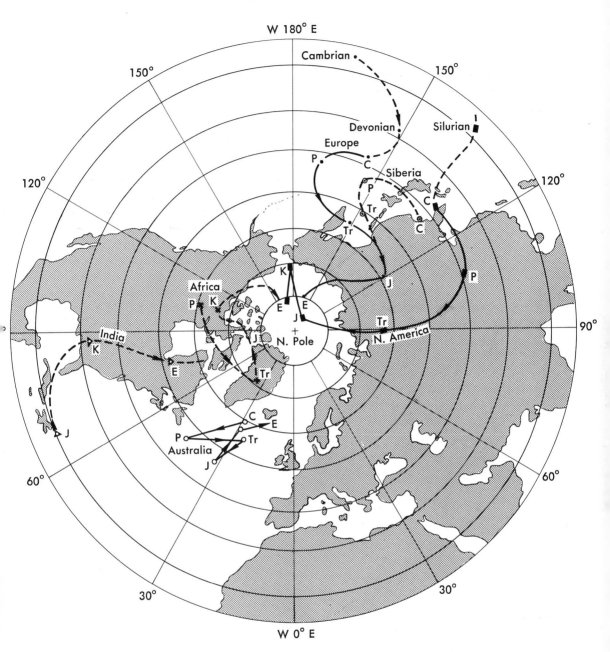

Fig. 6–9. North polar projection of most of the Northern Hemisphere showing the position of the magnetic poles of various continents for various times in the past. The difference in the polar wandering curves for the different continents is strong evidence that they have moved in geological time relative to one another. Note the parallel yet separate curves for North America and Europe, which indicate that they were a unit in the Paleozoic and separated in the Mesozoic Era. (Modified from Arthur Holmes, *Principles of Physical Geology*, Second Edition. New York: The Ronald Press Co., 1965.)

certainly occurred cannot as yet be satisfactorily explained. Taylor suggested that the movement of the continents was due to the capture of the moon by the earth in Cretaceous time. The tidal force resulting from the capture pulled the continents toward the equator and pushed up mountain ranges where they collided. Two main objections to Taylor's mechanism are that (1) it fails to account for mountain building before the Cretaceous, and (2) the tidal force necessary to move the continents would slow the earth's rotation to a halt. Wegener ascribed the drift of the continents toward the equator to the gravitational attraction of the earth's equatorial bulge, but this force is far too small to be effective. He thought the westward drift of the continents could be explained as a consequence of the greater gravitational attraction of the sun and the moon for the higher and therefore nearer continental plates than for the ocean basins. The differential attraction would "brake" the continents more effectively than the rest of the earth, and cause them to lag behind as the globe rotates. This force also is far too weak to be effective.

Convection Currents

Modern advocates of the drift theory favor explanations involving either convection currents or an expanding earth. As mentioned in Chapter 4, the continents may have been formed by the accumulation of a sialic scum where convection currents in the mantle turned downward. Supporters of the convection current hypothesis believe that the currents bear the continents along like rafts on a river. Figure 6–10 illustrates a suggested pattern in which the current rises under the ocean center from which the continents drifted apart and descends under the continents. As rifting takes place under the mid-oceanic ridges, new crust is supposed to be forming by the upwelling of subcrustal material. That the floor of the oceans may be younger near the central ridges than at the edges is suggested by the fact that the isotopic ages of volcanic flows on oceanic islands increase toward the edges of the oceans. The second discovery which supports this theory is that the ocean floor can be divided into irregular bands underlain by rocks whose remnant magnetism differs by 180 degrees in adjacent bands. Each band is believed to represent the material added to the ocean floor during a single polarity epoch; each boundary between the bands represents a reversal of the geomagnetic field. The reversal of the magnetic field is believed to act as a pendulum of irregular period marking off the increments to the oceans into episodes of oceanic spreading. Whether the mantle

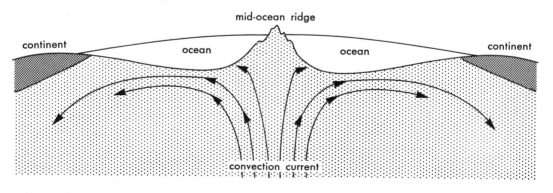

Fig. 6–10. Hypothetical pattern of convection currents causing rifting beneath an ocean basin. (Modified from E. Bullard, courtesy of the Geological Society of London.)

has physical properties that will allow convective movement is a matter of debate among geophysicists, and even among those who favor this mechanism there is little agreement on the pattern of the convective cells required.

The Expanding Earth

The theory that the earth as a whole is contracting and that the collapse of the outer shell on the inner layers causes mountain building is a very old one. Only within the last 30 years has the suggestion that the earth may be expanding been seriously examined. The application of the expanding earth hypothesis to continental drift has been made by S. Warren Carey. This mechanism can be pictured by thinking of the continents as pieces of cardboard pasted in a single interlocking mass on a balloon that is half inflated. As the balloon is fully inflated the pieces of cardboard separate and drift apart. Several lines of evidence indicate that the radius of the earth has been increasing at a rate of about 0.6 mm per year. If the oceans are considered to be the result of the fragmentation of a continental crust that completely covered the earth when it was formed 4.5 billion years ago, then the rate of expansion of the earth's radius to form the oceans must have been 0.58 mm per year. Accurate astronomical observations show that the length of the day has been increasing at a rate of about 2 seconds per 100,000 years. These changes in the earth's rate of rotation are not fully understood and appear to have been sudden rather than progressive, but if they are due to the expansion of the globe alone then the necessary rate of expansion would be about 0.6 mm per year. Another approach to this problem has been made through investigation of growth lines on corals. Recent corals show minute daily lines of growth because the rate of secretion of calcium carbonate by the organism is greatest during daylight hours. On Paleozoic corals about 400 similar growth lines can be counted within the longer annual growth cycles. These corals suggest that the day has been increasing in length so that there are now fewer days in a year, or expressed another way, the earth's rotation has been slowing down for the past 300 million years. If this change in the length of the day is due to the expansion of the earth, its radius must have increased by about 0.6 mm per year. The consequences of acceptance of the expanding earth hypothesis upon historical geology have not been worked out in detail but, like those related to the hypotheses of continental drift and polar wandering, they will be profound.

Continuing Problems

The hypotheses discussed in this chapter offer hope of solving many problems of earth history, such as the distribution of climatic belts, the open ends of geosynclines, the glaciation of the Southern Hemisphere, migration routes and distribution of fossil fauna, directions of remnant magnetism, and the distribution of mountain chains. The hypotheses of continental drift, polar wandering, and the expanding earth still face formidable obstacles before they can be accepted. Opponents of the drift theory point out that the geophysical characteristics which distinguish the continents from the ocean basins extend deeper than the crust. If the sialic continents have overridden the simatic oceanic crust, then the deeper part of the crust beneath the continents should be like that of the oceans, but this is not the case. The topography of the ocean floors suggests rifting along the mid-oceanic ridges to some geologists, but to others the ridges of the Indian Ocean indicate that India could not have moved northward relatively recently, as suggested by the "drifters." The mechanisms suggested for drifting, like those suggested for orogeny, are not acceptable to many geologists. Interpretation of paleomagnetic data in a manner that is not favorable to the drift hypothesis has also been suggested. For instance, some geophysicists doubt that the present magnetic field of the earth has been in existence throughout geological time, and some claim it was stabilized as late as the Mesozoic. Others have cast doubt on the correspondence of the magnetic and rotational poles throughout geological time.

The hypotheses of continental drift, polar wandering, and the expanding earth have stimulated much geological research by those trying to prove or disprove them. None of them in its present form is likely to be the last word in our understanding of the complex earth.

SUMMARY

Wegener's hypothesis of a single, large continent which broke up in late Paleozoic time and whose pieces drifted westward and toward the equator was the first attempt to work out the consequences of the theory of continental drift in detail.

The topographic and geological similarities on either side of the South Atlantic are difficult to explain unless Africa and South America were united in Paleozoic time; the similarities on either side of the North Atlantic are demonstrable but not as striking.

Continental drift has been used to explain the similarities on either side of the Atlantic of organisms incapable of crossing the open ocean.

Maps of the climatic zones of past epochs based on climatic indicators in sedimentary rocks suggest that the poles have not been in their present positions throughout geological time, and that the equator crossed North America from southwest to northeast during much of the Paleozoic Era.

Remnant magnetism in sedimentary and igneous rocks records past positions of the magnetic field of the earth. Reversals of the earth's field seem to have occurred at intervals of the earth's history. Such reversals probably had an effect on the evolution of life.

North pole positions plotted from North American rocks indicate polar movement westward across the Pacific in Paleozoic time, and northward in Mesozoic time. The polar wandering curve for Europe was in the Paleozoic parallel to that for North America but converged on it during the Mesozoic. The polar wandering curves can be explained as being due to the separation and rotation of the continents in the Mesozoic.

Convection in the mantle and the expansion of the whole earth are mechanisms which have been suggested to explain the drift of the continents.

QUESTIONS

1. From the speculation recorded in the last three chapters, summarize the various theories of the development of the ocean basins and of the water in them.

2. Earthquakes, volcanoes, and geosynclines were or are arranged at the margins of the Pacific Ocean. How does the theory of continental drift account for the very different pattern of these three features around the Atlantic?

3. If the earth is expanding at the rate postulated in this chapter, what would be the value of gravity in the early Paleozoic? What evidence of a different value of gravity would you expect to find in the rocks and fossils of that time?

REFERENCES AND SUGGESTED READINGS

BULLARD, E. C. "Continental Drift," *Quarterly Journal of the Geological Society of London*, 120: 1–33, 1964. A recent review of continental drift largely from the point of view of the geophysicist. The paleomagnetic evidence is considered in some detail.

HOLMES, A. *Principles of Physical Geology*, 2d ed. New York: The Ronald Press Co., 1965. The late Arthur Holmes was a proponent of the continental drift hypothesis for many years when it was not as popular as today. In pages 1193–1252 he summarizes modern thought on this hypothesis for the elementary student.

IRVING, E. *Paleomagnetism and Its Application to Geological and Geophysical Problems.* New York: John Wiley & Sons, Inc., 1964. A summary of this rapidly expanding field, with chapters on magnetic properties of rocks, the geomagnetic field, reliability of paleomagnetic determinations, reversals, and paleolatitudes.

Recent Symposia on Continental Drift

BLACKETT, P. M. S., BULLARD, E. C., and RUNCORN, S. K. "A Symposium on Continental Drift," *Transactions of the Royal Society of London,* 253A: 1–323, 1965.

MUNYAN, A. C. (Ed.). "Polar Wandering and Continental Drift," *Society of Economic Paleontologists and Mineralogists Special Publication 10,* 1963.

RUNCORN, S. K. (Ed.). *Continental Drift.* New York: Academic Press, 1962.

More Technical Papers

COX, A., and DOELL, R. R. "Review of Paleomagnetism," *Geological Society of America Bulletin,* 71: 645–768, 1960.

UFFEN, R. J. "Influence of the Earth's Core on the Origin and Evolution of Life," *Nature,* 198: 143–44, 1963.

VAN HILTON, D. "Presentation of Paleomagnetic Data, Polar Wandering and Continental Drift," *American Journal of Science,* 260: 401–26, 1962.

why polar wandering.

II

THE
NORTH AMERICAN
CRATON

7

Epeiric Seas of the
Early Paleozoic Era

Most extensive transgression Lt. Ord + Mid Sil.

Topographically, North America has a low interior region of plains encircled by mountains which border the ocean basins. This topography reflects a tectonic pattern of geosynclines now folded into mountains surrounding a stable interior, or craton. The word craton is derived from the Greek word *kratos* (power or strength) and refers to the stability of the central part of the continent in contrast to the mobility of the geosynclines. If, as some geologists believe, the continents grow by the acquisition of geosynclinal belts, then the craton expands through the addition of geosynclines that have undergone orogeny, been stabilized by mountain building, and reduced by erosion to low relief. The dimensions of the early Paleozoic craton and its neighboring geosynclines are illustrated in Fig. 5–7.

At present the craton can be divided into a region of Precambrian rocks and a region of flat-lying sedimentary rocks called the platform, which covers the Precambrian basement to a thickness of a few thousand feet. As explained in Chapter 5, the map boundary between these regions is not stationary; it advances on the Canadian Shield as seas depositing sedimentary rocks cover it and retreats as erosion strips away the veneer so deposited. These movements of the sea from the ocean basins over the continents are called **transgressions.** The area of the exposed Precambrian granites, gneisses, and schists changed from period to period, and, after some extensive transgressions of the sea, the whole Shield may have been covered. Isolated outliers on the Shield of Late Ordovician and Middle Silurian limestones—erosional remnants of once-continuous sheets—indicate that these epochs were the times of most extensive transgression.

The shallow seas which spread across the interior of the continent are called **epeiric** (from the Greek word *epeiros,* a continent or mainland) or **epicontinental** (from the Greek prefix *epi,* upon). They were present for a shorter time than the seas that occupied the geosynclines, and between transgressions the land stood in low hills and coastal plains just above sea level.

The tectonic behavior of the craton contrasted markedly with that of the bordering geosynclines. Whereas subsidence and sedimentation were rapid and nearly continuous in the geosynclines, they were slow and frequently interrupted in the craton. This tectonic behavior is reflected in the thinness of the sediments that cover the craton; their composition of clean sandstones, limestones, and evaporites; and the prevalence of unconformities interrupting the sedimentary record.

TECTONIC DIVISIONS OF THE CRATON

The Canadian Shield

During the Paleozoic Era the Canadian Shield rose and fell; parts of it were tilted and received the sea, but generally the Shield acted as a unit. A saucer-shaped mass of Ordovician, Silurian, and Devonian rocks occupies the Hudson Bay basin in the middle of the Shield. Recent geophysical surveys have suggested that these Paleozoic or older sediments are as thick as 10,000 feet in the center of this basin. Although the Shield was not a mountainous area, facies maps show that it supplied limited sediments to the epeiric seas at various times and was an important source of sediments in the late Paleozoic.

Arches and Basins

In the part of the craton covered with sedimentary rocks, the strata are not strictly horizontal but undulate into broad synclines, anticlines, basins, arches, and domes. In deformed areas the dips on the limbs of folds are measurable in degrees, but on the craton they are so low that they must be expressed in feet per mile. The Michigan basin is a good example of a basin in the Paleozoic rocks near the edge of the Shield. The geological map (Fig. 7–1) shows that the strata dip toward the center of the basin from all sides and resemble a set of stacked measuring spoons of progressively smaller sizes.

The Cincinnati arch serves as an illustration of the cratonic anticlinal structures. Its axis can be followed southward from Ohio to Tennessee, where it is generally known as the Nashville arch or dome. Ordovician rocks are exposed in the breached crest of this anticline and Pennsylvanian rocks occupy the basinal areas on either side.

The present structure of the Michigan basin and Cincinnati arch is clear, but the history of these and other cratonic structures has been a subject of disagreement. Such basins and arches may be either depositional or erosional, or both. If an arch is purely depositional, it will subside more slowly than the surrounding shelf and basins during deposition. Because the thickness of the sediments that accumulate is proportional to the amount of subsidence of an area (see Chapter 5), each layer of sediment will be thinner over the arch (Fig. 7–2A). If an arch is purely erosional, the sedimentary layers that are eventually arched upward will be deposited in a shelf environment of uniform subsidence and will be of uniform thickness. The structure is later gently folded into an anticline and eroded to a flat surface (Fig. 7–2B). The arch may also be formed by intermittent uplift and truncation of the beds, producing a series of unconformities (Fig. 7–2C). The problem of whether these cratonic structures were active during the deposition of their sediments is one that requires careful study.

The geologist has many tools to determine whether a cratonic structure is entirely erosional or partly depositional. One of the most effective is the isopach map (see p. 15). Figure 7–3 illustrates two such maps for formations of the Upper Cambrian Series of the Cincinnati arch area. The maps show that the sedimentary layers grow thin over an archlike structure passing through Ohio about 60 miles east of the axis of the Cincinnati arch. This early Paleozoic structure, which has no surface expression, has been called the Waverly arch and seems to be unrelated to the Cincinnati arch. The thinning of the formation indicates that the arch was an area of slower subsidence than that of the surrounding basins during the interval in the Upper Cambrian represented by the maps.

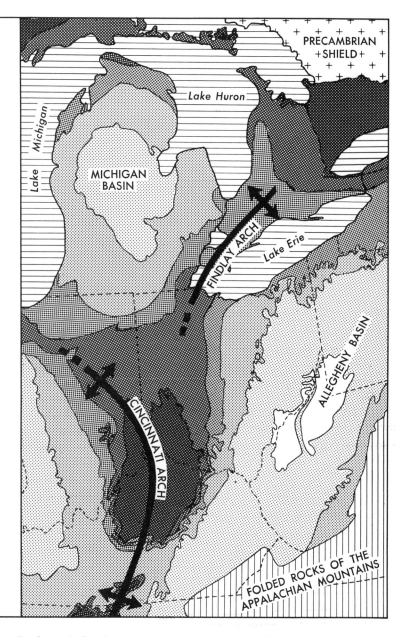

Fig. 7–1. Geological sketch map of the region of the Cincinnati arch showing the pattern of outcropping sedimentary strata around cratonic arches and basins. (Simplified from the Geological Map of North America.)

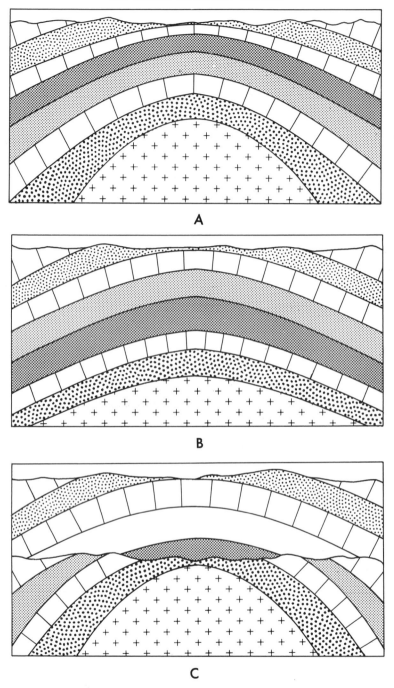

Fig. 7–2. Cross-sections of three types of cratonic arches. A. The strata thicken away from the crest of the arch and the dip of the limbs therefore increases downward, indicating that the area of the arch subsided less than the surrounding basins during deposition of the sediments. B. The thickness of the strata does not change over the arch, indicating that the structure was formed after sedimentation had stopped. C. A complex arch that was active during sedimentation, arched, eroded, and arched again after the deposition of a sequence of sediments.

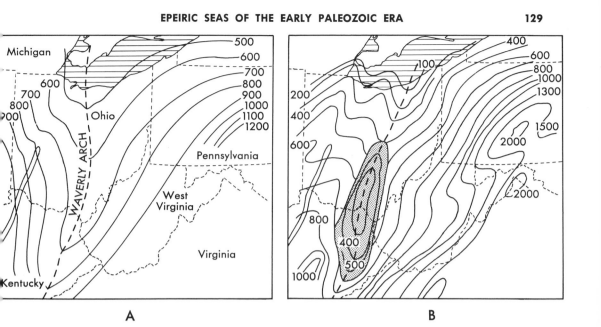

A   B

Fig. 7–3. Isopach maps of two formations in the Upper Cambrian Series of the eastern United States showing the effect of the Waverly arch. The position of the structural axis of the Cincinnati arch is shown by the hollow line on the left of each map. A. Lower part of the Upper Cambrian Series. B. Middle and upper parts of the Upper Cambrian Series. The shaded area has been thinned by post-Early Ordovician erosion (see also Fig. 7–4). (After H. P. Woodward, courtesy of the *American Association of Petroleum Geologists Bulletin.*)

This thinning cannot be a result of erosion because no evidence of postdepositional erosion was found, and the formation is overlain conformably throughout by a younger formation. Part of the thinning of some formations along the Waverly arch is due to erosion, as shown in Fig. 7–3, but the thinning is superposed on changes in thickness caused by differential subsidence during deposition (Fig. 7–4). The isopach maps show no thinning under the site of the broad anticline whose axis passes through Cincinnati. Studies of the thickness of Paleozoic sediments on the west flank of the Cincinnati arch have been made in Indiana. The dip of the strata to the west is essentially constant at 25 to 35 feet per mile throughout the geological column from Cambrian to Pennsylvanian strata. Had the arch risen during deposition, the dips on its flanks would increase progressively downward. Such evidence suggests that the Cincinnati arch was a broad anticline formed at the end of the Paleozoic, when deposition ended, and had no influence on the course of deposition. Despite this evidence, the presence of mud cracks and erosion surfaces, signs of emergence of late Ordovician sediments, leaves the issue of the early Paleozoic uplift of the arch in doubt.

The problem of the past activity of domes and basins may be approached from another direction. Figure 7–5 shows a map and cross-section of the southern continuation of the Cincinnati arch in eastern Tennessee. The Middle Ordovician stratigraphy of this area shows that the region of the arch localized various kinds of limestone believed to be characteristic of water shallower than that indicated by limestones on the flanks of the arch. The distribution of limestone facies is interpreted as indicating that the arch was

E. Indiana   E. West Virginia

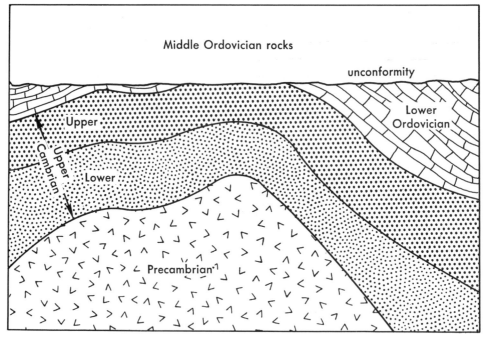

Fig. 7–4. Cross-section of the Waverly arch from eastern Indiana to eastern West Virginia showing the strata represented in the isopach maps of Fig. 7–3. Note that the uppermost Cambrian beds and the Lower Ordovician beds have been eroded beneath the post-Early Ordovician unconformity. Vertical scale is exaggerated. (After H. P. Woodward, courtesy of the *American Association of Petroleum Geologists Bulletin.*)

active during much of Ordovician time. These facies variations, and others, which will be described in detail later, leave little doubt that such structures as the Michigan basin are largely depositional and only in part erosional. The evidence for the tectonic behavior of the northern end, the Cincinnati arch, is still unclear but the Early Paleozoic uplift of the Nashville sector influenced Ordovician sedimentation.

In summary, the past behavior of cratonic structural elements may be determined by isopach studies, which distinguish periods of slow uplift and subsidence; by cross-sections, which show periods of intermittent uplift resulting in unconformities; and by facies studies, which show whether the relief of the ocean floor or the rate of subsidence was sufficient to affect the character of sedimentary rocks.

Early Paleozoic Basins and Arches

Early in the Paleozoic Era, the basins and arches that became prominent later in the Paleozoic were not sharply differentiated from the surrounding shelf. Adjacent to the Shield was a group of basins separated by radial arches. South of the Shield the Michigan basin formed, along with what was later to separate as the Illinois basin, a spoon-shaped depression opening southwestward across these and neighboring states (see Fig. 5–7). The largest of the radial arches is marked by the southwestward projection of

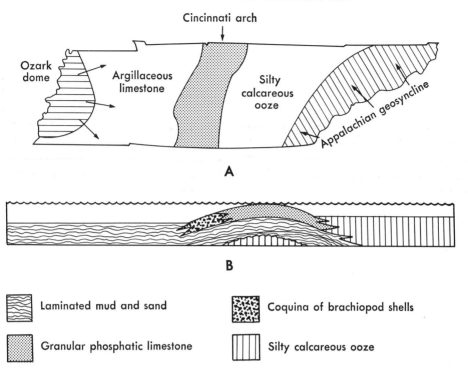

Fig. 7–5. A. Map of Tennessee showing the main facies belts associated with the Nashville section of the Cincinnati arch in Middle Ordovician time. B. Cross-section of central Tennessee showing facies changes in the Middle Ordovician Hermitage Formation. (Modified from C. W. Wilson, courtesy of the *Geological Society of America Bulletin*.)

the edge of the Shield into Minnesota. In South Dakota, in line with this salient, a hill of Precambrian rocks projects through the Mesozoic and Paleozoic beds to form the Sioux uplift. The salient in the outline of the Shield and the Sioux uplift mark the northern end of a broad arch that crosses the craton from Ontario to Arizona, known as the Transcontinental arch. The exposures of Precambrian rocks in the mountains of Colorado and southern Arizona may be an expression of this uplift, but along most of its length the structure lies deeply buried beneath Mesozoic and upper Paleozoic sedimentary rocks. Although no lower Paleozoic rocks extend across the crest of the northern sector of the arch, the continuity of facies patterns from

one side of the arch to the other, and the absence of thinning (other than by erosion) in formations as they approach its crest, is evidence that early Paleozoic seas crossed the arch and that their sediments were later removed by erosion. In Colorado some early Paleozoic strata still extend across the arch at a structurally low part called the Colorado Sag.

During the later Paleozoic, a more complex pattern of basins and arches emerged as the cratonic margins showed a tendency for increased mobility. The behavior of tectonic elements changes with time, and basins and arches may exchange roles. For example, the Peace River arch, which was persistently high during the early Paleozoic, became the site of a basin in late Paleozoic and Meso-zoic time. On the other hand, some areas such as the Front Range of Colorado seem to have been uplifted intermittently through hundreds of millions of years. The cause of their movement remains a puzzle for the stratigrapher and the geophysicist alike.

STRATIGRAPHIC DIVISIONS OF CRATONIC ROCKS

The cratonic rocks of North America have for years been divided into the systems and series of the standard relative time scale. This division, as discussed in Chapter 3, reflected the main stratigraphic divisions of northern Europe. Geologists in North America soon realized that the boundaries of the systems, determined by paleontological correlation with Europe, have little stratigraphic significance and that most of the major breaks in deposition in North America do not correspond to the period boundaries. This does not mean that the standard time scale cannot be applied to North American rocks or that it is difficult to apply here, but merely that it is a scale independent of the major physical events of cratonic sedimentation. A stratigraphic division of the cratonic rocks can be made, however, on the basis of transgressions and regressions (retreats of the sea from the craton) and can be thought of as the relative time scale that might have been adopted if stratigraphic geology had originated in North America.

The stratigraphic record of the central part of the continent is full of unconformities. They are marked by missing fossil zones, surfaces of relief, basal conglomerates, ancient soils, zones of leaching, etc. Until the cratonic basins were explored by drilling, geologists could not trace these unconformities laterally to determine which were regionally persistent, and which died out into regions of continuous deposition. They found that a few of the unconformities, ones not easily recognizable at a given locality, extended across basins and arches, and that about six

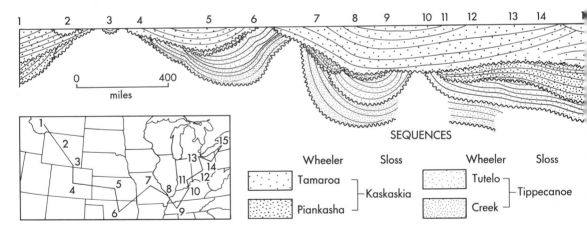

Fig. 7–6. Cross-section of the North American platform along the line indicated in the index map, showing the regional unconformities used in defining sequences in middle Paleozoic rocks. Wheeler's and Sloss's divisions of the rocks into sequences are illustrated. Sloss does not believe that the Tamaroa–Piankasha and Tutelo–Creek unconformities are of sufficient extent to justify using them to define sequences. (Modified from H. E. Wheeler, courtesy of the *American Association of Petroleum Geologists Bulletin.*)

extended across the entire continent. Figure 7–6 is a cross-section of the craton drawn to a highly exaggerated vertical scale to show the division of part of the sedimentary record by such regional unconformities. The stratigraphic units which are bounded by these regional unconformities are called sequences. Lawrence Sloss recognizes three unconformities as useful for defining four sequences in the Paleozoic, and Harry Wheeler has suggested that five unconformities define six sequences. The sequences proposed by Sloss are used in the subsequent discussion.

Each Paleozoic sequence was deposited as the sea transgressed an erosion surface, reached full flood level, and then retreated from the craton. The transgressive part is represented by a thick succession of strata; but sedimentary rocks deposited during the regression are rarely preserved, for the with-drawal of the sea is usually a response to either the uplift of the continent or a drop in sea level, both of which bring regressive deposits into the zone of erosion. Only when regression is caused by the building out of the land, as in a delta where rivers are delivering more sediments than the basins can accommodate below wave base, are regressive deposits retained in the stratigraphic record. Neither upper nor lower boundaries of the sequences are of the same age throughout the craton. The transgressing sea is present for a longer time at the margins than in the center of the continent (Fig. 7–7) because it starts at the edges, spreads inward to the center only at its greatest flood, and retreats again to the margins. For this reason the time span represented in a sequence will differ from place to place. For example, the Sauk sequence, the lowest of the Paleozoic

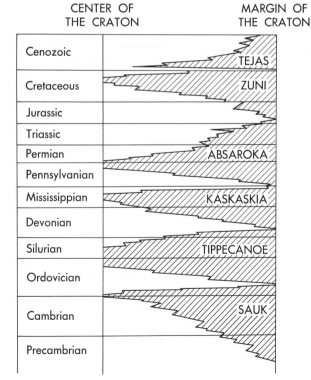

Fig. 7–7. Time relationships of the cratonic sequences recognized by Sloss. The vertical scale is geological time. The cross-hatched areas are the times represented by the sedimentary rock record. Note that the sequences are separated by time gaps that lengthen toward the center of the craton. (After L. L. Sloss, courtesy of the *Geological Society of America Bulletin*.)

sequences, is represented in Wisconsin only by Late Cambrian sedimentary rocks, but in eastern Tennessee it includes rocks ranging in age from Precambrian to Early Ordovician.

According to Sloss, the unconformities which divide the cratonic Paleozoic rocks into sequences record three periods of withdrawal of the sea from the craton: at the end of Early Ordovician time, at the end of Early Devonian time, and at the close of the Mississippian Period. These unconformities separate the Sauk, Tippecanoe, Kaskaskia, and Absaroka sequences. Younger rocks are divided into the Zuni and Tejas sequences by unconformities that record withdrawals in Early Jurassic time and at the end of the Cretaceous Period. Wheeler believes that the unconformities at the top of the Ordovician and Devonian systems are comparable to the other three in extent, and divide the Tippecanoe sequence into the Tutelo and Creek sequences and the Kaskaskia sequence into the Piankaska and Tamaroa sequences (Fig. 7–6). The major transgressions and regressions typical of cratonic sedimentation are classified by the division of rocks into sequences, but these structural divisions should not be confused with the biostratigraphic division of the rocks by fossils into stages, series, and systems.

THE SAUK SEQUENCE

Base of the Cambrian

Along the southwestern edge of the craton, crystalline Precambrian rocks have been uplifted in Wyoming, Montana, and the Grand Canyon of Arizona. These metamorphic rocks are overlain by successions of late Precambrian sedimentary rocks tens of thousands of feet thick. Along the western margin of the craton, the oldest Cambrian rocks overlie the late Precambrian strata with apparent conformity, showing that the transgression of the Sauk sea from the geosynclines to the craton began in Precambrian time.

By convention, the boundary between the Paleozoic and Precambrian eras—the beginning of the Cambrian Period—is drawn at the first appearance of fossils of complex life, usually either brachiopods or trilobites. This horizon occurs on both the eastern and western edges of the craton, within a thick succession of sandstones which shows no physical stratigraphic change at the boundary (Fig. 7–8). Fossils of marine algae are common in Precambrian rocks, but fossils of complex forms of life are absent or exceedingly rare. In the basal sandstones of the Sauk sequence of the northern Rocky Mountains, fossils occur only in thin, interbedded shale lenses. Either the fossils of animals that lived during the time of deposition of the sandstone have been destroyed or the sandy sea bottom was not a suitable place for animals to live. If complex organisms bearing preservable hard parts appeared at the same instant all over the continent, their appearance would be recorded immediately by fossils in areas where shale was accumulating, but would be delayed to a later time and higher stratigraphic level in an area that was not receiving mud to form shale. Earliest complex fossils are unlikely to occur at the same time in different sections. Because this method of dating the beginning of the Cambrian is unlikely to mark a time plane, as required for the base of a geological system, some geologists suggest that the first break in sedimentation, or unconformity, below the appearance of complex fossils be taken as the base. This horizon is not likely to be a time plane either, but it is much easier to locate. The problem of defining the base of the Cambrian will not be resolved until an easy and reliable method of dating all kinds of sedimentary rocks by radioactivity is available.

Basal Sauk Sandstones

In the thick sandstone groups that bridge the Precambrian–Paleozoic boundary in the Rockies, cross-bedding shows the direction from which the sand grains were transported.

Fig. 7–8. Late Precambrian and Early Cambrian quartzites at Postern Peak in the Canadian Rockies. A thickness of almost 4000 feet of these sedimentary rocks at the base of the Sauk sequence is exposed in this cliff. (Courtesy of Canadian National Railways.)

To determine the source of supply, the geologist measures the direction of dip of as many cross-beds as possible in an outcrop. If necessary, he corrects these directions for the deformation of the beds in mountain building. These measurements are treated statistically to produce an average direction for each outcrop or group of outcrops, and these directions are placed on a map (Fig. 7–9). Such maps show that the sand was derived from the east, that is, from the Canadian Shield.

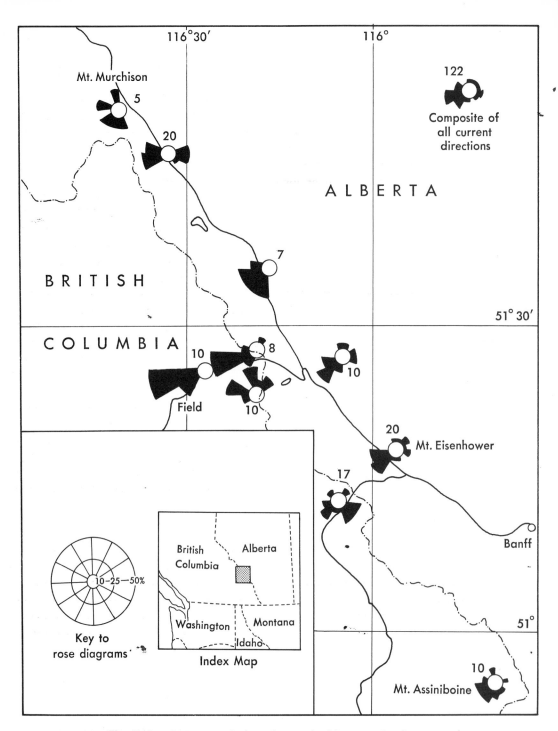

Fig. 7–9. Direction of dip of cross-bedding in Cambrian sandstones (upper 200 feet of the Gog Group) in the southern Canadian Rocky Mountains. The number of determinations recorded is shown for each locality. The directions of the cross-beds are grouped into classes of 30 degrees, and the length of the pie-shaped segment is proportional to the percentage of determinations in each class according to the scale in the lower left corner. Most of the cross-beds dip westward, as shown by the rose diagram at each locality and by the composite diagram of all localities in the upper right corner. (After E. W. Mountjoy, courtesy of the Alberta Society of Petroleum Geologists.)

At the beginning of the Paleozoic Era, Precambrian rocks were exposed over the entire craton. They had been open to the agents of weathering for an unknown time at the beginning of the Cambrian and continued to be exposed for at least 50 million years, until the end of the Middle Cambrian Epoch. Extensive weathering of this region of low relief must have formed the thick sandy regolith covering Precambrian gneisses, schists, granites, and sedimentary rocks.

The sea of the Sauk sequence spread from the margin of the craton in Early Cambrian time across the western shelf in Middle Cambrian time; by the beginning of the Late Cambrian it covered the southern half of the craton, stretching from Montana to New York in a great epeiric sea. As the sea spread inward, it deposited first a group of cross-bedded sandstones over the unconformity developed on the Precambrian rocks. Rivers from the Shield swept quantities of sand to the advancing sea. The sand was sifted and reworked by the waves to form a clean, arenaceous sea floor for tens of miles behind the advancing coastline. The surface of the Precambrian Shield exposes 80 per cent granite (including granite gneiss) at present, and was probably similar in composition in Cambrian time. When this bedrock was weathered, clay was formed from the decomposition of the feldspar and the dark minerals (hornblende, pyroxene, biotite, etc.) of the granite, but the chemically stable quartz grains were left unchanged. The great quantity of sand and the comparative absence of shale in Cambrian deposits of the craton have suggested to some geologists that the wind played a part in Cambrian sedimentation. The average igneous rock after weathering produces 79 per cent shale, 13 per cent sandstone, and 8 per cent soluble material eventually deposited as limestone and evaporites. The weathering of a quantity of Precambrian rock sufficient to produce the sand in the Cambrian succession must have produced a great deal more clay. The clay may have been sifted from the sand by waves in the epeiric sea and transported to the deeper water of the geosynclines and ocean basins, but Paul D. Krynine has suggested that it was winnowed from the sand by the wind and blown into the oceans before the transgressive sea inundated the sand dunes left behind.

The Sauk Transgression

As the continent was depressed or the sea level rose (we are uncertain which), the sandstone facies spread inward until it covered the southern part of the craton. In the epeiric sea that covered an increasing proportion of the continent as Cambrian time went on, sediments accumulated in three concentric facies belts. The inner, near-shore belt consisted of light-colored sands, silts, and muds with thin limestone beds. The intermediate belt, which lay seaward of the first, was the site of accumulation of pure limestones and dolomites of many types. The outer belt, near the marginal geosynclines, was characterized by dark-colored silts, muds and sands, impure limestones, and chert deposited in deeper water. During Cambrian time these facies belts shifted back and forth across the craton so that the various lithologies now interfinger.

The pattern of sedimentary facies in a transgressing sea is beautifully illustrated along the walls of the Grand Canyon, as shown in Fig. 7–10 (see also Fig. 9–6). While the Lower Cambrian Tapeats Sandstone was being deposited in the shore zone, the Bright Angel Shale was accumulating in deeper water offshore. In the walls of the canyon the beds of the Tapeats Sandstone can be traced laterally into the Bright Angel Shale, which in turn grades into the Muav Limestone. The Bright Angel Shale is a good example of a formation that represents different intervals of deposition at different places. As the shoreline slowly moved eastward, the site of shale deposition moved eastward with it so that the formation, which is partly of Early Cambrian age in the western part of the Canyon, is wholly of Middle Cambrian age in the eastern part. Formations with different ages in different places are products

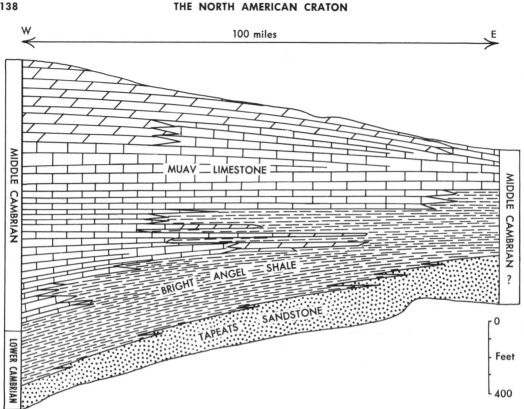

Fig. 7-10. Facies changes in the Middle and Upper Cambrian rocks of the Grand Canyon. (After E. D. McKee, redrawn from C. O. Dunbar and J. Rodgers, *Principles of Stratigraphy*. New York: John Wiley & Sons, Inc., 1957.)

of every transgressing sea and are therefore commonplace in stratigraphy, but their relationships are more obvious in the deposits of the craton, where the transgressions were so slow.

In the east the transgressing relationship of the basal sandstone is illustrated by the Potsdam Sandstone of Ontario, Quebec, and eastern New York. Careful study of its fossils has shown that in eastern New York it is entirely Late Cambrian in age, but along the border of the Shield it is Early Ordovician (Fig. 7-11).

The Greatest Extent of the Sauk Sea

The sediments deposited in the Sauk sea at its greatest extent in Late Cambrian time are shown in Fig. 7-12. The sandstone facies

extended as a collar about the edge of the Canadian Shield, from Montreal to Alberta. Beneath the upper Mississippi drainage basin, the sandstone that is exposed along the border of the Shield in Wisconsin and Minnesota grades into limestone and dolomite that is exposed in the Ozark, Llano, and southern Oklahoma uplifts. Well records show that only under the western plains does a shale facies intervene between the sandstone and limestone. This lateral facies change from sandstones directly to limestones, with shale omitted, is common in sediments of the shelf environment. In the limestone sea on the southern part of the craton, the water was warm and clear and a precipitate of calcium carbonate accumulated undiluted by detrital sediments from the distant land. (The term

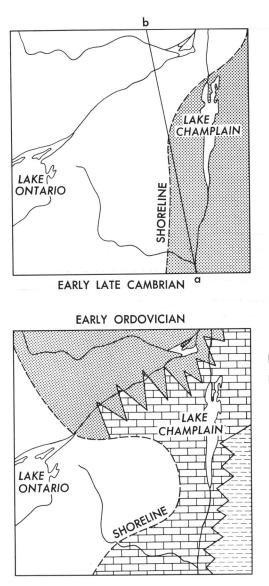

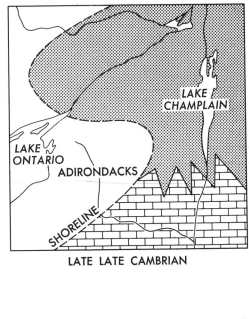

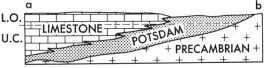

Fig. 7–11. Sediments deposited in the Late Cambrian and Early Ordovician transgression of the sea across New York, Ontario, and Quebec. As a result of the slow shift of both the shoreline and the boundary between limestone and sandstone facies, the Potsdam Sandstone is entirely Late Cambrian in the south and partly Early Ordovician in the north.

detrital refers to sedimentary particles that have been eroded from other rocks.) Animals that extract calcium carbonate from the sea water for their shells had not evolved in sufficient numbers at that time to form organic limestones. For this reason the limestones are believed to be either inorganic precipitates from saturated sea water or precipitates formed by marine algae. Common textures in these Cambrian limestones are: oolitic (composed of spheres of concentric structure the size of fish eggs), pisolitic (spheres the size of peas), and pelletoidal (formed of ellipsoidal, structureless pellets made by animals that pass the sediment through their bodies for nourishment).

The pattern of Late Cambrian sedimentation persisted into Early Ordovician time with little change. On the edges of the Shield sand was laid down, and limestone continued to accumulate over most of the southern and marginal parts of the continent in Early Ordovician time. No physical break marks the boundary of the periods in the

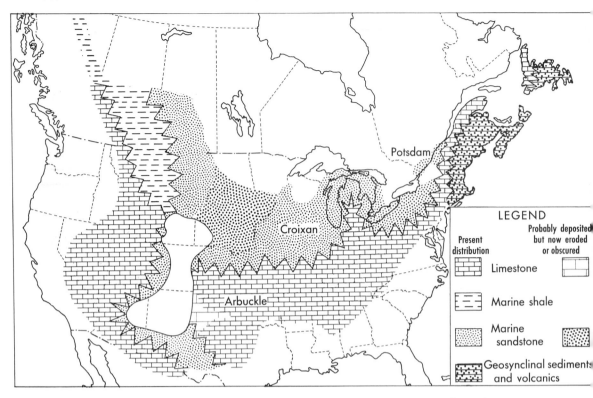

Fig. 7–12.   Facies of the Upper Cambrian Series in central North America.

sandstone or limestone units, but the Early Ordovician parts can be distinguished from Late Cambrian parts on the basis of fossils.

Fossils of marine algae are common in the limestone. Figure 7–13 shows a large mass of algal limestone embedded in Late Cambrian sedimentary rocks along the Llano River of Texas. In Early Ordovician limestones, cabbage-like algal structures called *Cryptozoon* are common (Fig. 7–14). Similar structures consisting of concentric layers of calcium carbonate built one upon another are found in limestones that range in age from Precambrian to Recent. By analogy to structures now forming in such areas as the Bahama Islands and northern Australia, each layer is believed to be a fine precipitate of calcite or aragonite that was trapped periodically on the gelatinous surface of blue-green algae. These structures in Late Precambrian rocks have been called *Collenia* (see Fig. 9–5).

BASAL BEDS OF THE TIPPECANOE SEQUENCE

Multicycle Sandstone

The initial beds of most sequences are sandstone, which blankets the unconformity over which the sea transgressed. At the beginning of the Middle Ordovician Epoch, the Tippecanoe sea transgressed the unconformity created by the total regression of the Sauk sea at the close of Early Ordovician time. No deposits in the rocks under the unconformity mark the regression of the Sauk sea, but the great difference in the fossils found above and below the boundary suggests that the time represented by the unconformity was long enough for the evolution of a new fauna; no one knows, however, how long this might have been. In the basal beds of the Tippecanoe sequence, corals, stromatoporoids, bryozoans, pelecypods, and ostracods are abundant for the first time.

Fig. 7–13. Reef of algal limestone embedded in Upper Cambrian shale, Llano River, Texas. (Courtesy of P .E. Cloud, Jr., from P. E. Cloud, Jr., and V. E. Barnes, *University of Texas Publication 4621.*)

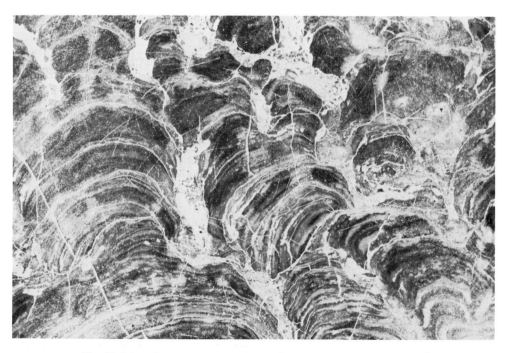

Fig. 7–14. *Cryptozoon,* a stromatolitic structure in Lower Ordovician carbonates. A polished slab about 6 inches across. (C. W. Stearn.)

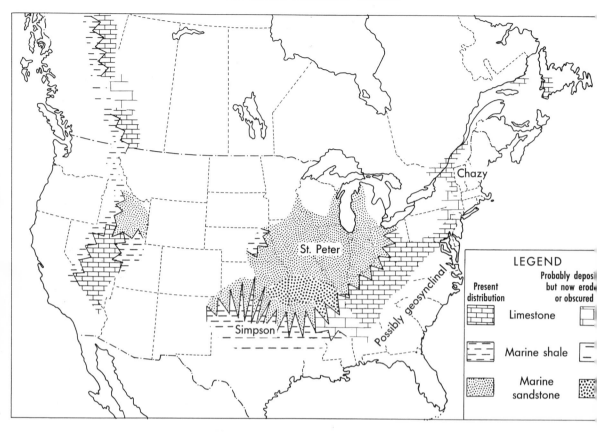

Fig. 7–15. Facies of the lower part of the Middle Ordovician Series in central North America. Stratigraphic units plotted on this map are referred to as the Whiterock, Marmor, and Ashby stages. The Harding Sandstone, although in the same position as the St. Peter Sandstone at the base of the Tippecanoe sequence, is slightly younger than the rocks on this map and therefore not plotted.

At the margins of the Shield in the Upper Mississippi Valley, the transgressing Tippecanoe sea worked on the semiconsolidated Late Cambrian and Early Ordovician sandstones that had been laid down only a few million years before, regrinding the grains in the mill of its unceasing waves. Rivers from the north contributed additional sand that had been eroded from the crystalline rocks of the Shield. As the grains became smaller and more nearly round, they drifted outward from the shore on the shallow sea floor and spread over a large area that is now the west side of the Mississippi Valley (Fig. 7–15). We deduce these conditions of deposition from the St. Peter Sandstone. The formation is composed of extremely well-rounded and well-sorted grains of quartz which, though possibly the result of wind action, could equally be due to long-continued marine work. The quartz content of the sand is about 99 per cent, so high that it is extensively used in glass making. Such purity cannot be attained in a single cycle of weathering, transportation, and deposition. Sandstones which are the products of the weathering of an older sandstone are said to be **second cycle;** those which are derived from second-cycle sandstones are called **multicycle.**

Sandstones can be classified according to the "maturity" impressed on them by the agents of weathering, erosion, and deposition. Those which have a high proportion of poorly sorted, angular grains of mechanically and chemically unstable minerals are said to be **immature.** Those sandstones which are aggregates of rounded and sorted grains of chemically and mechanically stable minerals are said to be **mature,** for they have been subjected longer to the agents which decompose, break, sort, and round the sedimentary particles. In this classification the St. Peter Sandstone might be called **supermature,** for nearly all the minerals except well-rounded and well-sorted quartz grains have been eliminated.

Sedimentary formations like the St. Peter Sandstone are called **blanket deposits** because they are large in two dimensions and small in thickness. The St. Peter Sandstone is generally about 100 feet thick (although it reaches 400 feet in certain areas) and covers an area of approximately 3000 square miles.

The basal sandstones of the Tippecanoe sequence are slightly younger west of the Transcontinental arch. One of these formations, the Harding Sandstone of the Front Ranges of Colorado and Wyoming, is important for its content of fossils of primitive fish (see p. 431).

Chazy Limestone and the First Coral Reefs

While sandstones were accumulating in the central and western part of the craton, limestone and interbedded shale, which constitute the Chazy Group, were being deposited at the base of the Tippecanoe sequence along its eastern margin from Alabama to Quebec. The fauna and the lithology of these limestones are interesting contrasts to the fauna and lithology of the limestones of the Sauk sequence. Much of the Chazy limestones can be variously described as **calcarenites, fossil-fragment** limestones, **skeletal** limestones, or **bioclastic** limestones. These terms all imply that the rock is composed of wave-broken fragments of the hard parts of lime-secreting animals. Plates of cystoids and crinoids and the shells of brachiopods, notably genera called *Rostricellula* and *Mimella,* are the important constituents of the Chazy limestones. The particles were moved by waves in the shallow water of the epeiric sea until they were broken or ground to sand size. Pre-Tippecanoe limestones, as mentioned above, are only rarely of this nature, but post-Sauk limestones are commonly composed of fossil fragments.

The Chazy rocks of the Lake Champlain and southern Quebec regions form low domes in the flat countryside. In these domes the limestone is poorly bedded, compared with the equivalent beds between the domes, and contains many fossils of stromatoporoids, corals, bryozoans, and algae (Fig. 7–16). The first three of this group are colonial animals that were just beginning to become abundant in the Middle Ordovician. Corals and algae are the principal reef builders of modern times.

The fossil fauna of these limestone domes is comparable to that of modern reefs and suggests that the domes are ancient reefs. In the nautical definition, a reef is a projection of the sea floor so close to sea level that it is an obstruction to navigation. Geologists, however, are most interested in reefs built by organisms and, strictly speaking, should refer to them as "organic reefs"—but commonly the word "organic" is understood rather than expressed. An **organic reef** is a mound constructed on the sea floor by organisms which rises to the zone agitated by the waves. The importance of this rise close to sea level is that mounds on the sea floor which do not penetrate wave base have little effect on the sediments accumulating in the vicinity. When the reef penetrates the zone of the waves, it reaches an environment of abundant food, light, and nutrients; but it is also subject to the erosion of the waves. A true organic reef should have a fan around its base of particles from the mound that were broken by the waves. The reef mound will also incorporate a large quantity of this

Fig. 7–16. Stromatoporoid colony in the Chazy limestones, Isle Lamotte, Vermont. From a laminar base the colony has grown upward into a domelike structure. Note the second stromatoporoid at the upper right. (Courtesy of E. W. Mountjoy.)

debris between the skeletons of the reef-building animals. The reefs in the Chazy Group are small, rarely more than a few hundred yards across, but the great amount of carbonate fragments incorporated in the core that formed carbonate clastic beds around the mounds shows that they were true organic reefs, in that they penetrated the zone of wave action. They were the first reefs in the stratigraphic record to be built of corals, stromatoporoids, and bryozoans, a combination that was to become extraordinarily successful in Silurian and Devonian times.

MEDIAL TIPPECANOE EPEIRIC SEAS

Late Ordovician Limestones

West of the Transcontinental arch the basal Tippecanoe sandstones are overlain by a thin group of limestones of distinctive fauna and wide extent. Segments of this limestone blanket are given different names, such as Bighorn (Wyoming), Montoya (New Mexico), Beaverfoot (Alberta), and Red River (Manitoba); but over much of the west side of the continent (Fig. 7–17) the limestone is lithologically almost the same and contains a dis-

Mid Ordivician. 1st Reefs.

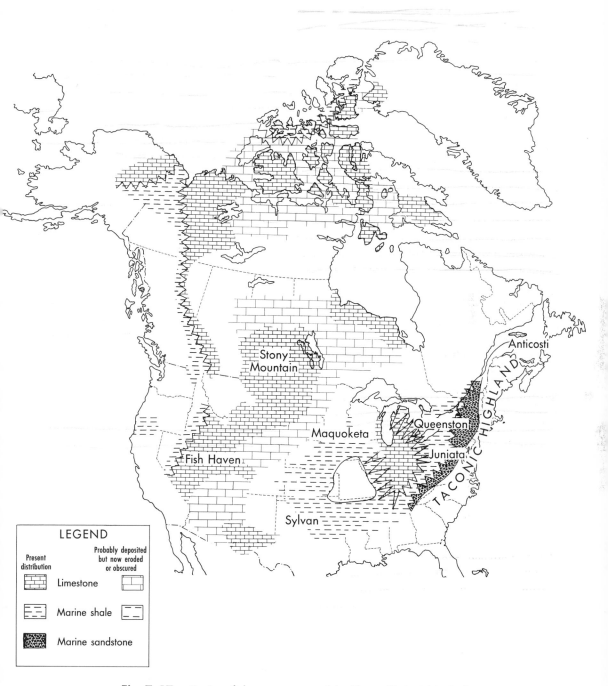

Fig. 7–17. Facies of the upper part of the Upper Ordovician Series in North America. Rocks of the Richmond Stage have been plotted where precise correlations are available; in other places, all Upper Ordovician rocks have been plotted.

tinctive fauna of large corals, cephalopods, and brachiopods, referred to as the Arctic Ordovician fauna. Not only does this limestone form a continuous sheet over much of the western part of the craton, but it has been found in many outliers scattered throughout the Canadian Shield. The limestones were laid down in the most extensive of the North American epeiric seas at the height of the Tippecanoe transgression.

The medial Tippecanoe sea was typical of later epeiric seas and serves as an example of conditions in general in such bodies of water. The rocks, sedimentary structures, and fossils in the area all indicate that the sea was shallow and that its floor was continually within range of wave and current motion. In such an inland sea minor warpings of the crust or small changes in sea level could shift the shoreline hundreds of miles, and either lay bare hundreds of square miles of sea floor or inundate the land. Mud cracks and edgewise breccia in the limestone record the emergence of the sea floors. The position of the shoreline cannot be mapped accurately, for it was constantly changing. Microscopic plant life thrives in shallow, turbulent, sunlit waters and provides plenty of food for larger animals. When the animals died, their shells and skeletons were either ground up or broken by scavengers, borers, and wave motion to form lime sand or lime mud; more rarely, they were buried intact in the calcareous debris of other shells. Because subsidence over the craton was slow, calcareous debris was reworked by the waves so that most of the myriad fossil shells were reduced to fragments before final burial took place. In the shelf areas of the craton the limestone layer is a few hundred feet thick, but it thickens to as much as 2000 feet at the edge of the craton in Texas and Idaho.

Much of the limestone in the northern part of the continent is dolomitized along irregular channels that pass in a branching pattern through the rock. Along these channels the fine-grained, gray limestone is stained brown and contains coarse crystals of dolomite.

The pattern of the channels suggests that the dolomitizing process may have been localized by branching algae (seaweeds) which grew on the Ordovician sea floor and have since decayed. At present, dolomitization in the Persian Gulf, the Bahamas, and Florida is taking place in association with algal mats. The partial dolomitization gives the stone an attractive pattern, and it has been extensively used for trimming public buildings in all parts of Canada.

Paleoclimatology

The lithology and fauna of the beds west of the Transcontinental arch are essentially uniform from Death Valley, California, to the shores of eastern Greenland. The uniformity and wide distribution of these limestones pose several problems for the paleogeographer who is also interested in climates. Similar fossil faunas are found in regions whose mean July temperature now ranges from 90 degrees (Nevada) to 40 degrees (Greenland). Regions so greatly different in climate have no faunal similarity today and probably did not have in the past. Such faunal distributions have led many geologists to consider polar wandering as an explanation (Chapter 6), but the following alternatives should also be kept in mind:

1. Climatic zones which roughly follow lines of latitude may not have been as well differentiated in Ordovician time as they are at present, so that the temperature of the epeiric sea would have been approximately the same at latitude 35°N. as at 70°N. This is difficult to reconcile with what we know of the present condition of the ocean.

2. A strong, warm current, such as the present Gulf Stream, might have kept the marine environment of the epeiric sea uniformly warm even in the north. This hypothesis cannot be tested, however, for we know of no comparable modern epeiric seas in which such currents might be found.

One plausible explanation of the distribution of the limestone and its fauna is that the climatic zones of Ordovician time did not cross the North American continent as they do at present, but were so arranged that the area of deposition fell within the tropical zone of Ordovician time. The abundant fauna of large invertebrates suggests a warm water environment near the equator, and this is remarkably confirmed by the paleomagnetic evidence (Fig. 6–8) which locates the Ordovician equator across North America from Hudson Bay to the Gulf of California.

Correlation

Sedimentation on the eastern side of the craton during the Middle and Late Ordovician epochs was greatly influenced by the uplift of the Appalachian geosyncline in the Taconic orogeny. (The events of the orogeny and the deposits from its mountains will be discussed in detail in Chapter 12.) Fine-grained detritus eroded from the rising Taconic mountains made the upper part of the Ordovician System east of the Transcontinental arch more argillaceous than its western counterpart, and this difference in facies was accompanied (and probably caused) by a corresponding difference in fauna. The argillaceous Middle Ordovician limestones from Virginia to Quebec, and the Upper Ordovician limestones of the Cincinnati arch area, contain many beautifully preserved fossils which often weather free of their matrix (Fig. 7–18). The fossils of these shaly limestones have attracted many to the science of paleontology, and several great American paleontologists had their interest kindled by the fossils of such cities as Cincinnati, where the Upper Ordovician limestones are well exposed. The difference between the fossils found in the Ordovician limestones of the west and the east has led to controversy concerning their correlation. The crest of the Transcontinental arch interrupts the continuity of these two facies, so that they cannot be traced into one another. The time-stratigraphic division of the

Fig. 7–18. Weathered bedding surface on Late Ordovician limestone from Cincinnati, Ohio, showing the abundance and fine preservation of the fossils.

Ordovician used for correlation has been based on sections in New York and Ohio, where the following stages are now recognized:

	Stages
Upper Ordovician Series	Richmond
	Maysville
	Eden
Middle Ordovician Series	Barnveldt
	Wilderness
	Porterfield
	Ashby
	Marmor
	Whiterock

The Eden Stage is based on rock sections composed of highly argillaceous limestone or shale and contains a fauna characteristic of

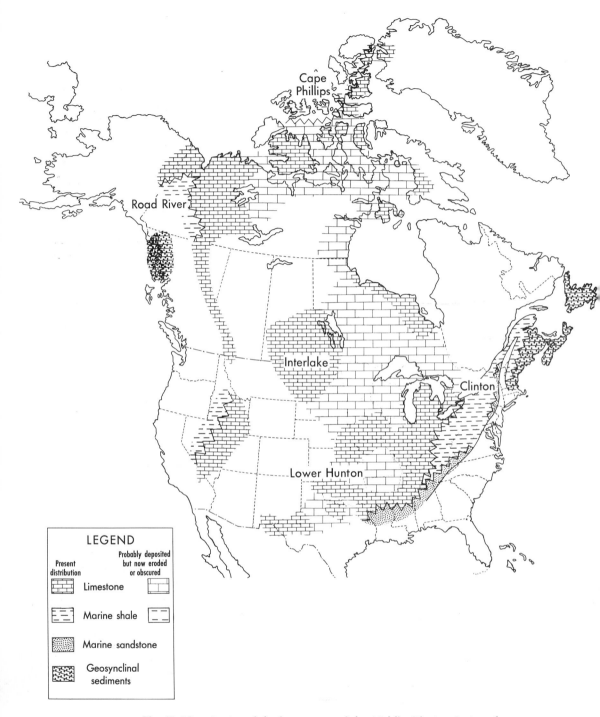

Fig. 7–19. Facies of the lower part of the Middle Silurian Series of North America (Clinton Stage). Some geosynclinal rocks of this age are probably represented in the metamorphic terranes of the Cordilleran and Appalachian mountains.

such rocks. The fauna of the Arctic Ordovician limestones was for many years compared with the fauna of the limestones on either side of the Eden interval, that is, with the Richmond–Maysville and Barnveldt faunas; paleontologists could not agree, however, as to which it resembled more closely. Fossils that are not controlled by facies—enigmatic, jawlike fossils called conodonts—have recently shown that the Arctic Ordovician limestones correlate with the Eden Stage. The correlation of the western Ordovician limestones illustrates the difficulties that may arise from matching fossils of different facies and the necessity of using fossils that are independent of facies control for correlation.

Three Zones of Sedimentation

Over large areas west of the Transcontinental arch, Upper Ordovician limestone is overlain by Silurian dolomites. These younger dolomites were deposited in an epiric sea that rivaled the Ordovician sea in extent; like the Ordovician limestone, the Silurian dolomites appear as outliers scattered on the Canadian Shield. The extent of this unit is illustrated in Fig. 7–19. In the Williston basin some of the dolomites in the Interlake Group are extremely fine-grained, like porcelain. This texture suggests that they have been precipitated directly from highly saline sea water, for the process of replacement of calcium carbonate mud by magnesium-rich solutions, which is believed to occur in the formation of most dolomite, involves recrystallization and enlargement of the grains. The Silurian dolomite has local intraformational breccias, shows domed bedding characteristic of algal growth, and contains hopper-shaped molds of salt crystals which formed in the mud of some exposed shore as the sea water evaporated. Small coral–stromatoporoid reefs are common at certain levels. All these features of the Silurian sediments point to a shallow-water environment and deposition on a stable shelf. This environment of deposition is duplicated

today on the flat shores of the southern part of the Persian Gulf.

Alan Shaw believes that the slope of the epeiric sea floor was as low as 2–10 feet per mile. M. L. Irwin has suggested that it may have been as low as a fifth of a foot per mile. Irwin describes the sedimentation in such seas in terms of three zones (Fig. 7–20). In the middle zone, which is tens of miles wide, the sea bottom is agitated by the waves and tides, and the characteristic sediments are oolitic and fossil-fragment limestones. In the near-shore zone the water is extremely shallow for hundreds of miles and is disturbed only during extraordinary storms, for tidal and wave motion is dissipated by friction in the middle zone. In this zone evaporation is high, causing evaporites and "primary dolomites" to precipitate from the sea water. In the offshore zone the bottom is below the influence of the waves, and only fine carbonate mud that has passed seaward in suspension from the middle zone is deposited as fine-grained limestone. Most of the Silurian rocks of the Williston basin seem to have been deposited in the near-shore zone, but some are characteristic of the turbulent zone and others of the reefs that grew into the zone of waves from the offshore zone.

Paraconformities

Subsurface correlation of the Interlake Group across the Williston basin is facilitated by the presence of the shaly and sandy thin beds which are widely distributed in the dolomites. Because of their thinness, they are not easy to locate from the cuttings brought up in wells, but they appear as characteristic "kicks" on electric and radioactivity logs and can be traced across the basin in this manner. These key beds represent minor influxes of silt, sand, and clays into an otherwise carbonate basin of deposition. Their parallelism over great distances is an indication of the stability of conditions in this basin during Silurian time.

The Silurian stratigraphy of the region east of the Transcontinental arch is represented

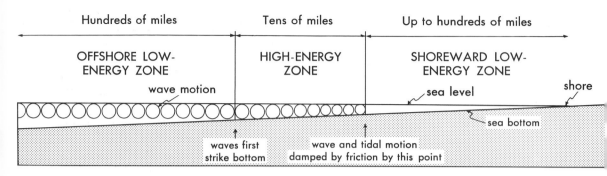

Fig. 7–20. Three zones of sedimentation in epeiric seas. (After M. L. Irwin, courtesy of the *American Association of Petroleum Geologists Bulletin.*)

by the beds exposed along the Niagara escarpment, described in Chapter 1. Fossils in the basal beds of the Interlake Group suggest a correlation with the basal beds of the Clinton Group in New York and Ontario. Beds equivalent to the Cataract Group of New York appear to be missing from the Williston basin, yet there is little evidence of a period of erosion between the uppermost Ordovician strata and the Silurian dolomites. Such a break in the succession of strata that is hidden by both the parallelism of adjacent layers and the lack of evident erosion is called a paraconformity. Some geologists believe that paleontological evidence is insufficient to demonstrate this break in sedimentation and that the apparent lack of an irregular erosion surface, the absence of truncation of the beds below the surface, and the remarkable parallelism of the key beds in the Ordovician and Silurian rocks make it highly unlikely that the basin was open to erosion throughout the millions of years of early Silurian time during which the Cataract beds were deposited in the east.

Other paraconformities have also been subjects of disagreement. In southern Oklahoma the Late Silurian Henryhouse argillaceous limestone seems to be overlain conformably by the Early Devonian Harragan Formation of almost identical lithology (Fig. 7–21). Although no sign of an erosion

Fig. 7–21. Controversial paraconformity between the Henryhouse and Harragan formations in the Arbuckle Mountains of southern Oklahoma. The tape marks the highest occurrence of Henryhouse fossils of early Late Silurian age; the hammer, the lowest occurrence of Harragan fossils of Early Devonian age. Latest Silurian beds are missing between these two markers. (From T. W. Amsden, courtesy of the Oklahoma Geological Survey.)

surface exists between these two formations, paleontologists have determined by painstaking work that the upper stages of the Silurian System are missing and that the two formations must be separated by a paraconformity. Geologists working with evidence from bore holes in the basin of central Oklahoma have found in the regional relationships no evidence of such a period of erosion between the Harragan and Henryhouse formations.

Although stratigraphers and paleontologists disagree about these two paraconformities, no one doubts that paraconformities do exist and that they are very difficult to detect except by fossils. The best known paraconformity in North America is exposed in the region of Louisville, Kentucky, where Middle Silurian limestone is overlain without break by Middle Devonian limestone. Fossils, which are common on both sides of the paraconformity, accurately date the limestones and leave no doubt that Late Silurian and Early Devonian rocks are missing from the succession; yet no sign of erosion or irregularity of bedding betrays the hidden boundary. The significance of paraconformities is another stratigraphic problem that will be solved when all types of sedimentary rocks can be dated accurately in years.

Silurian Organic Reefs of the Michigan Basin

While the Interlake Group was being deposited in the Williston basin, a group of organic reefs became established around the edges of the Michigan basin. The sea water was apparently warm, for coral reefs grew in the Great Lakes area to an extent unrivaled in any other period (Fig. 7–22). Although coral reefs as old as Middle Ordovician have been found, not until Middle Silurian time were conditions of fauna and climate favorable for their extensive growth. Ancient reefs are composed of limestone or, more commonly, dolomite, which can be distinguished from the limestone that nor-

mally surrounds the reef by its lack of bedding, its high porosity (in the form of holes or vugs), and its association with limestone breccias and conglomerates composed of fragments of reef rock. The reef is composed of two elements: framebuilders, which form a rigid, interlocking, wave-resistant framework of organisms in position of growth, and which may be spatially only a minor part of the reef although structurally the most important part; and loose organic debris which fills the spaces between the framebuilders. The framebuilders include the corals, certain calcareous algae, some sponges, the stromatoporoids, and a few other groups of largely local importance. The spaces between the framebuilders are partially filled by fragments—torn loose and ground up by the surf —of the shells of animals that live in the reef but are not builders, such as brachiopods, gastropods, pelecypods, and crinoids. In most reefs, this granular debris does not entirely fill the framework and the reef core is left highly porous. Boring organisms weaken, undermine, and break up the reef. The breaking waves tear off blocks which accumulate around the mound as an underwater talus deposit. This reef talus may be greater in volume than the reef core itself.

Although the covering and surrounding muds lose their moisture and are compacted to less than half their original thickness under the weight of the accumulating sedimentary layers, the reef core does not change in thickness and the beds above are flexed or "draped" over the reef. The steep dips of the beds that flank organic reefs are due not only to the original slope around the reef but also to this compaction.

The shape of reefs is controlled largely by subsidence and the efforts of the reef organisms to keep themselves at or as close as possible to sea level. At sea level the waves aerate the water, supplying an abundance of oxygen, which the reef animals need. Microscopic plant life, which thrives in the sunny water near the surface, makes up the food of many reef-building organisms, and the reef

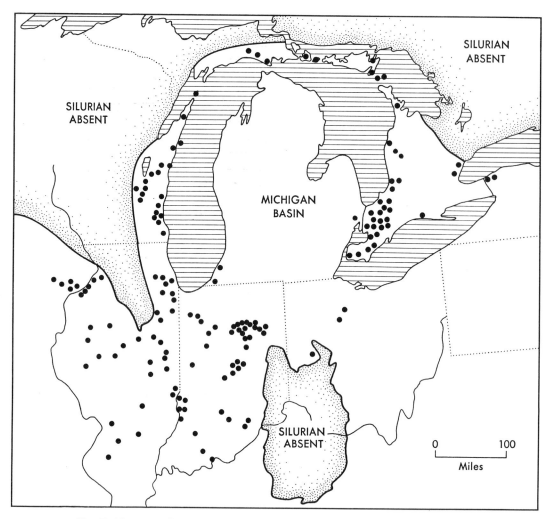

Fig. 7–22.   Distribution of Middle Silurian patch reefs in the Great Lakes area.   (Compiled from Lowenstam, Shouldice, and Corden.)

algae require the light of surface waters to carry on photosynthesis.

If the floor on which the organic reef is being built sinks relative to sea level, the organisms tend to grow upward and consequently build the reef vertically to keep its top near sea level, the zone of optimum light, food, and oxygen. In this continued compensation for subsidence, they may construct a column of reef rock hundreds of feet high. This column later appears to have penetrated the surrounding limestone beds, although the beds actually accumulated progressively around the reef. The Silurian reefs of the Michigan basin grew in a zone around the basin where subsidence conditions were optimum. The reefs on the inner side of the reef tract were built into thin, spindly columns, for the energy of the growing animals was concentrated on keeping the growing face of the reef near sea level. However, the reefs on the outer side of the tract near the shelf are stubby and spreading, for in the zone of slower subsidence the energy of the organisms could be expended in lateral rather than vertical growth.

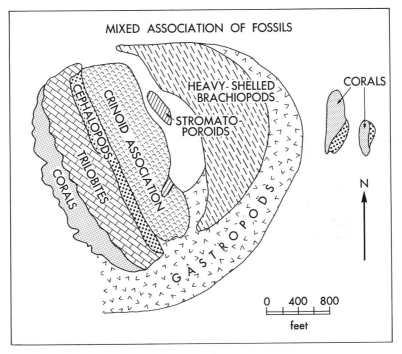

A

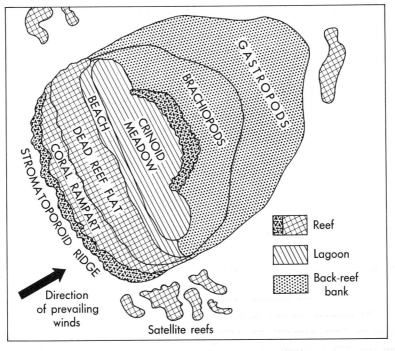

B

Fig. 7–23. Thornton Reef complex (Middle Silurian, Illinois). A. Distribution of fossil communities in the reef complex. B. Interpretation of the distribution of fossils and lithologies in terms of the reef environment of Silurian time, showing the inferred direction of the prevailing winds. (After J. C. Ingels, courtesy of the *American Association of Petroleum Geologists Bulletin*.)

With respect to shape, Paleozoic reefs may be divided into two types: the long-ridged barrier reefs that enclose a lagoon behind them (like the present-day Great Barrier Reef of Australia), and the approximately columnar patch reefs that are surrounded by debris broken from the core by waves. Most mid-Silurian reefs were of this latter type, but those of the Upper Devonian and Permian, which are discussed in Chapter 8, were of the barrier type.

Like modern reefs, many ancient reefs show a distinct zonation of the animals that lived on them. Different types of animals had different ecological requirements: some liked the surf zone on the windward side of the reef; others preferred the quiet waters of the lagoon, sheltered by the reef from the waves; and others preferred deeper water. Just as a map can be made of a modern reef showing the domains characterized by particular faunas, so maps can be made of the animals that grew in ancient reefs. From these maps such features of the former environment as the direction of winds and currents can be deduced. The fauna and lithology of the Thornton Reef complex, exposed in a quarry in northeastern Illinois, have been mapped in detail (Fig. 7–23). In this illustration the core of framebuilding animals is small compared with the large area occupied by detritus broken from this core and carried leeward to the lagoon and back reef bank. These asymmetrical reefs preserve a record of the winds and currents of the past; if sufficient analyses of such reefs around the Michigan basin were made, the geologist might be able to relate the ancient equator, which may have crossed North America nearby (Fig. 6–8), to the ancient trade wind systems which surrounded it.

Faunal zonation of Niagaran reefs can be detected in vertical section as well as in plan. The fauna of the reef changes as the reef grows upward from quieter, deep water into the zone of wave turbulence, and animals capable of withstanding the surf attack become more abundant (Fig. 7–24). Massive stromatoporoids and tabulate corals increase in numbers; strong box-crinoids replace their more delicate relatives; and trilobites and mollusks increase in numbers. Such paleoecological changes can help determine whether a mass of imbedded carbonate rock believed to be an organic reef did actually rise above wave base in ancient seas.

Because coarse organic fragments and framebuilders accumulate in a helter-skelter manner, reefs are commonly very porous and are therefore good reservoirs for the trapping of oil. The Middle Silurian reefs of Ontario and Illinois have produced small quantities of oil and gas. One of the most notable of these is the horseshoe-shaped Marine Pool Reef of southern Illinois (Fig. 7–25). In Illinois the reefs are surrounded, and their oil sealed in, by flanking argillaceous limestones; in southern Ontario, however, they protrude several hundred feet from the top of the Middle Silurian Guelph Dolomite and are surrounded by salt and gypsum deposits of the succeeding Salina Group.

Facies in an Evaporite Basin

As the Tippecanoe sea ebbed from the craton in Late Silurian and Early Devonian time, deposition of evaporites took place in Michigan and New York. The circulation of sea water by currents, tides, and waves, which normally keeps the water of the oceans at approximately the same concentration, became restricted in the Michigan basin and in another basin in western New York. The restriction may have been caused by the ring of patch reefs that grew around the edge of the basin at the end of Middle Silurian time, but, since these did not form a continuous barrier, it was more likely due to a lip or sill formed by the more rapid subsidence of the center of the basin compared with the periphery (Fig. 7–26). The Late Silurian climate must have been hot and dry, for the sea water in the basins evaporated and the concentration of the salts in it increased. As water was lost by evaporation more was drawn in over the lip, but little of the concentrated

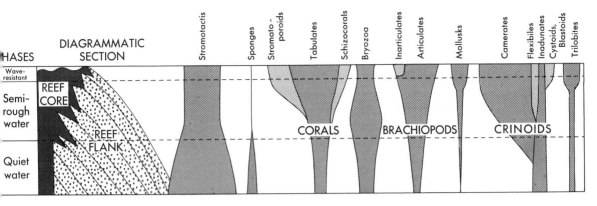

Fig. 7–24. Vertical changes in the fauna of the Middle Silurian reefs of Illinois. The changes in abundance of the organisms as the reefs grew from the quiet, to the semirough, to the wave-resistant stage are shown by the width of the areas on the right. (After H. A. Lowenstam, courtesy of the *Geological Society of America Bulletin*.)

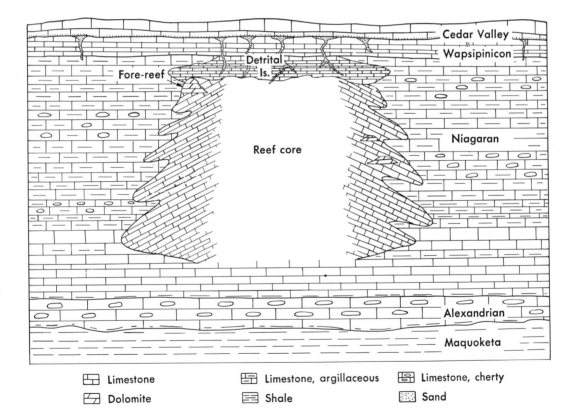

Limestone   Limestone, argillaceous   Limestone, cherty

Dolomite   Shale   Sand

Fig. 7–25. Cross-section of the Marine Pool Reef of southern Illinois, showing the detrital deposits of broken limestone around the reef core. These outward-dipping deposits interfinger with horizontally bedded Niagaran limestone. (From H. A. Lowenstam, courtesy of the Illinois Geological Survey.)

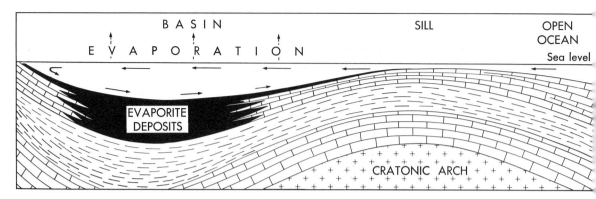

Fig. 7–26. Cross-section of a cratonic basin and arch illustrating a model for the deposition of evaporites. The shallow-water sill restricts the inflow of normal sea water to the basin, causing evaporation to increase its concentration. Note the thickening of the formation in the center of the basin.

brine escaped to the open sea. In this way, the concentration of the brine in the basin increased until the salts could no longer be held in solution and crystallized out as small particles held up by the surface tension of the water. When the crystals grew too large to be held up by this force, they fell through the brine and collected on the sea floor, building up a layer of evaporites. When sea water evaporates, the order in which the salts crystallize out of solution depends on their solubility and abundance. The first salt to precipitate is calcium carbonate because of its low solubility, but very little is dissolved in sea water. When the original liquid has been reduced to about 25 per cent of its initial volume, gypsum and anhydrite (hydrous calcium sulfate) begin to precipitate; when about 90 per cent has evaporated, halite (rock salt) comes out of solution. Not until 99 per cent has evaporated do potassium salts precipitate. In an ideal basin, the evaporite deposits will be geographically zoned as the incoming water, moving away from the inlet, increases in concentration through progressive evaporation. The most soluble salts will be farthest from the inlet, and the least soluble near the inlet. As the

amount of water allowed into the basin by the movement of the sill changes, the evaporite facies in the basin shift laterally and the different evaporite suites are superposed and interfinger. Commonly, a cyclical repetition of evaporites is found in stratigraphic sections, reflecting either the cyclical tectonic behavior of the basin or cyclical climatic changes. Figure 7–27 is a lithofacies map of the Michigan basin showing an increase in the proportion of halite toward the center of the basin and a zone of anhydrite deposition separating the halite zone from carbonates accumulating on the surrounding shelves. The areas in which tongues of carbonate rocks have intruded the evaporites of the basin are interpreted as the channels where normal sea water entered, diluting the more saline brines. From such a map the pattern of circulation of water and the paleogeographic conditions can be reconstructed in some detail. The association of evaporites with cratonic basins and reefs is almost universal in North American stratigraphy, and variations in the pattern shown by Late Silurian evaporites will be described from the Devonian of western Canada and the Permian of west Texas in Chapter 8.

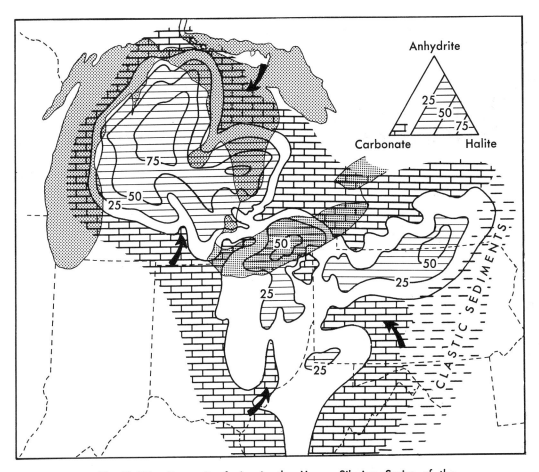

Fig. 7–27. Evaporite facies in the Upper Silurian Series of the Great Lakes area. The contour lines show the percentage of halite in the evaporite sequence. Note that the evaporite basins are surrounded by areas of carbonate deposition. Tongues of the carbonate rocks (emphasized by arrows) projecting into the basin are interpreted as marking the entry of normal sea water. (After L. A. Briggs and H. L. Alling, courtesy of the *American Association of Petroleum Geologists Bulletin.*)

SUMMARY

The North American craton consists of the Canadian Shield area, where Precambrian rocks are exposed, and a platform area, where they are buried by a veneer of post-Precambrian sedimentary rocks.

The tectonic history of cratonic arches and basins can be determined by plotting isopach maps for each sedimentary formation that crosses the structure, studying the facies changes in it, and determining whether its boundaries are unconformities.

The cratonic deposits of North America can be divided into seven sequences on the basis of regional unconformities. Each sequence represents the transgression and regression of an epeiric sea, but the regressive deposits have usually been eroded.

The base of the Cambrian System has been defined on the basis of either the first appearance of complex fossils or the first break in sedimentation below this appearance, but neither of these criteria is likely to define the time line required for the boundary of a system.

The basal formations of sequences are clean quartz sandstones that, in transgressing time planes, become younger toward the centers of cratons.

In the deposits of epeiric seas, facies changes from sandstone to limestone without the intervention of shale are common, especially where the sand is derived from the Shield.

The boundaries between systems are not marked by changes in the physical stratigraphy of cratonic sedimentary rocks.

Sandstones composed almost entirely of well-rounded and well-sorted grains of quartz have passed through several cycles of weathering, erosion, and deposition.

Algae contributed extensively to limestones of the Sauk sequence, but lime-secreting animals were not present in sufficient abundance to make the extensive contribution they made to younger limestones. Most Sauk limestones are inorganic precipitates.

Organic reefs are mounds on the sea floor constructed by organisms which grew into the zone agitated by waves.

Uniformity of lithology and fauna in a zone transverse to modern climatic belts may indicate polar wandering.

Successions that differ in lithology may be difficult to correlate because they contain fossils from different environments.

Because waves and tides lose their energy by friction with the gently shelving sea bottom, shallow epeiric seas may have a near-shore zone of quiet water in which evaporation is high.

Paraconformities are gaps in the stratigraphic record which have no physical expression but can be detected by a discontinuity in the succession of fossils.

Organic reefs are composed of a relatively small part of framebuilders and a large part of fragments that have been broken from the reef by the surf and deposited within and around the growing core.

The shape of reefs is related to subsidence, growth potential, marine currents, and wind direction.

Paleoecological zonation of reefs enables geologists to reconstruct conditions in the epeiric seas and to determine whether or not the reef broke wave base.

In a dry climate, if differential subsidence forms a sill restricting the inflow of sea water, evaporites will be deposited in cratonic basins. The entry points of ocean water can be determined from the distribution of facies.

QUESTIONS

1. Compare and contrast the terms *sequence*, *system*, *group*, and *period*.

2. Discuss the concept of maturity in sedimentary rocks and cite the examples of immature and mature sediments mentioned in this book. What is the difference in mineral content between mature and immature sediments composed of clay-sized particles?

3. How do we know that Paleozoic reefs composed of animals now extinct, such as stroma-toporoids and tabulate corals, did not grow in deep water?

4. Review the evidence from which a stratigrapher recognizes unconformities in sedimentary successions.

5. Draw a reconstruction of eastern North America similar to Fig. 13–25, showing the distribution of reefs, the evaporite basins, the outlets to the open ocean, and the clastics coming from the Appalachian region at the beginning of Late Silurian time. Use the information given in Figs. 7–19, 7–22, and 7–27.

REFERENCES AND SUGGESTED READINGS

ALLING, H. L., and BRIGGS, L. I. "Stratigraphy of the Upper Silurian Cayugan Evaporites," *American Association of Petroleum Geologists Bulletin,*" 45: 515–47, 1961. Lithofacies maps of the evaporites can be interpreted in terms of the salinities of the ancient basins, and these patterns indicate the intrusion of less saline water when the sea entered the basins.

INGELS, J. J. C. "Geometry, Paleontology, and Petrography of the Thornton Reef Complex, Silurian of Northeastern Illinois," *American Association of Petroleum Geologists Bulletin,* 47: 405–41, 1963. In this detailed study of a Silurian patch reef that has been extensively quarried, the distribution of fossils and lithologies is used to reconstruct the reef environment.

IRWIN, M. L. "General Theory of Epeiric, Clear Water Sedimentation," *American Association of Petroleum Geologists Bulletin,* 49: 445–60, 1965. A clear reconstruction of conditions in ancient epeiric seas, where the damping of wave motion in shallow water resulted in a broad near-shore zone in which evaporites and dolomites were deposited.

SHAW, A. B. *Time in Stratigraphy.* New York: McGraw-Hill Book Co., 1964. 365 pp. Although much of this book is concerned with biostratigraphy, the writer devotes considerable space to the reconstruction of conditions in epeiric seas.

SLOSS, L. L. "Sequences in the Cratonic Interior of North America," *Geological Society of America Bulletin,* 74: 93–111, 1963. The division of cratonic strata into the sequences used in this book is described, and simplified cross-sections of the unconformities that bound them are given.

WHEELER, H. E. "Post-Sauk and Pre-Absaroka Stratigraphic Patterns in North America," *American Association of Petroleum Geologists Bulletin,* 47: 14–97, 1963. This paper presents a different division into sequences of the middle Paleozoic rocks, based on the recognition of two additional regional unconformities.

8

The Kaskaskia and
Absaroka Sequences

INTRODUCTION

During the interval between the withdrawal of the Tippecanoe sea and the transgression of the Kaskaskia sea the rising arches of the craton were eroded and the tilted edges of the sedimentary layers were truncated on the margins of the basins. When the new seas converged on the center of the continent they laid down an initial stratum which, over wide areas, cuts across the bedding in the formations below (Fig. 7–6). The dip of these lower beds is so low that the truncation cannot be seen in any one outcrop or detected in a single well record but is revealed in regional relationships. In the mid-continent region of Oklahoma and Missouri the basal beds of the Kaskaskia sequence overlie beds ranging in age from Early Ordovician on the crest of the arches to Early Devonian in the centers of basins. The overlap is illustrated by a **paleogeological map,** which shows the geology of an area as if the beds above a particular unconformity were stripped away. A paleogeo-

logical map of the sub-Kaskaskia surface (Fig. 8–1) can be thought of as having been made by a geologist living in Early Devonian time.

The Kaskaskia transgression was interrupted at the end of the Devonian Period by a regression of the epeiric seas which Harry Wheeler has claimed is comparable to those which define the sequences. Yet the withdrawal of the sea was not complete, for along the margins of the craton and in the basins, deposition continued uninterrupted into the Mississippian Period. The Kaskaskia sea reached its greatest extent about the middle of the Mississippian Period, and Late Mississippian sedimentary rocks of the basins mark its recession. The sequence is named after the Kaskaskia River of south-central Illinois.

The Absaroka sequence is named after the Absaroka Range in northwestern Wyoming, where beds ranging in age from Early Pennsylvanian to Triassic form a representative exposure of the deposits of this transgression. During the deposition of the Absaroka se-

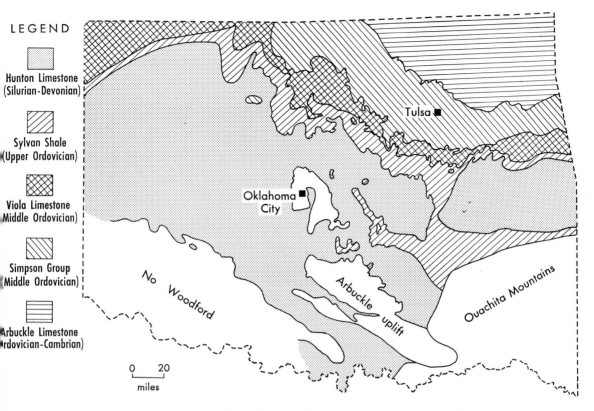

Fig. 8–1. Paleogeological map of Oklahoma at the base of the Woodford Shale (at the sub-Kaskaskia unconformity). The map represents the geological formations that would appear at the surface if the rocks younger than Devonian were removed. The sub-Kaskaskia surface crossed beds ranging in age from Ordovician to Devonian. (After R. S. Tarr, courtesy of the *American Association of Petroleum Geologists Bulletin.*)

quence conditions were different from those in Early and Middle Paleozoic times. On all sides of the continent mountains were rising in the geosynclines and the craton rose into arches and subsided into deep basins of an amplitude unknown in the Early Paleozoic. As a result the Absaroka rocks are largely detrital sediments derived from the rising Shield, uplifted segments of the platform, and neighboring geosynclinal highlands. The withdrawal of the Absaroka sea was long and oscillating, lasting through much of Permian and Triassic time and leaving the southwestern part of the platform covered with red beds and desert sandstones.

Worm's-Eye Maps and Heavy-Mineral Analysis

The oldest beds of the Kaskaskia sequence in North America are generally considered late Early Devonian in age. In the eastern part of the craton the basal beds are clean quartz sandstones similar to the basal Sauk and Tippecanoe sandstones but not as widely distributed. Figure 8–2 shows basal Middle Devonian rock types above the sub-Kaskaskia unconformity. Such maps have been called "worm's-eye" maps because they depict the lower surface of a stratigraphic unit as if viewed from below. The sandstone which

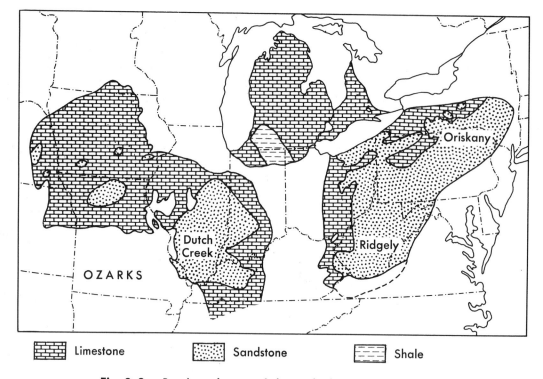

Fig. 8–2. Basal sandstones of the Kaskaskia sequence in eastern North America. On this "worm's-eye" map the lithology of the beds above the sub-Kaskaskia unconformity is plotted. (After C. F. Burk, in *Lithofacies Maps.* New York: John Wiley & Sons, Inc., 1960.)

covers the eastern side of the map is called the Oriskany Sandstone in New York and Pennsylvania, and the Ridgely Sandstone farther south. Like the St. Peter, the Oriskany and its correlatives are blanket sands; the Oriskany is used in glass making because it is highly siliceous. The sand has been derived from several source areas but its purity suggests that these source areas exposed older sandstones whose grains were recycled in Devonian seas.

The source area of a sediment may be determined by its content of diagnostic mineral grains. Quartz is not much help in such studies for, although some geologists have claimed they could identify the sources of various kinds of quartz, most quartz grains are undistinguished and could come from the erosion of sedimentary, igneous, or metamorphic rocks. The rarer and more interesting grains are usually heavier and can be separated from the quartz by the use of bromoform or other heavy liquids. In such liquids the quartz will float and the heavier minerals will sink. Identification of these heavier minerals may then give a clue to the source area for the sandstone, for some, such as sillimanite and cyanite, are peculiar to metamorphic sources, whereas others, such as rutile and apatite, characterize igneous rock sources. Heavy-mineral studies suggest that the sands shown in Fig. 8–2 were derived from several sources, including sedimentary rocks raised up in the Appalachian geosyncline, the main body of the Canadian Shield, and its extension, the Adirondack dome. The grains of the Dutch Creek Sandstone of Illinois were eroded from the St. Peter Sandstone exposed in the Ozark dome to the southwest.

THE DEVONIAN EAST OF THE ARCH

The Michigan Basin and the Solution of Evaporites

In Middle Devonian time much of the craton east of the Transcontinental arch was under shallow, warm, clear seas in which limestone was deposited. In these waters corals thrived and built small scattered reefs. Conditions of subsidence that had led to the deposition of salt and anhydrite in the Michigan basin in Late Silurian time returned in Middle Devonian time, and more salt beds were laid down. The restriction of water circulation was apparently due to a sill formed by differential subsidence, for no barrier of reefs surrounded the basin. Silurian salt has been extensively leached on the edges of the basin, causing the Devonian strata laid down above it to collapse into caverns and forming a spectacular breccia (Fig. 8–3). Some blocks in the Mackinac Breccia, at the Straits of Mackinac between Lakes Michigan and Huron, are hundreds of feet across.

Not until the oilman's drill had probed the centers of cratonic basins did stratigraphers realize the prevalence of evaporites, particularly salt, in the stratigraphic record. Salt beds never come to the surface in a humid climate—they are dissolved by rain and groundwater faster than mechanical erosion wears down the adjacent beds. The overlying strata settle or collapse into the space leached out and the gap in the section is hidden. Middle Devonian evaporites on the east flank of the Williston basin in Manitoba are obscured like the Silurian and Devonian salt in Michigan. The zone where the salt beds might come to the surface is marked by saline springs and collapse structures much like the Mackinac Breccia, but salt, gypsum, or anhydrite cannot be found at this horizon except by drilling in the basin away from the exposed edge. Even in the depths of sedimentary basins, dissolution of evaporites causes collapse along vertical faults in the overlying strata.

THE DEVONIAN OF THE WILLISTON BASIN

Under the plains of western Canada, North Dakota, and Montana, Devonian rocks record the complex interplay between basin subsidence, the growth of reefs, and the accumulation of evaporites. Because the Devonian reefs localize Canada's major oil fields and contain much of her petroleum reserves, they have been extensively drilled from Montana to the Arctic Circle. Most of the information on the Devonian history of the Williston basin comes from drilling records, but the rocks of this period are exposed in the Front Ranges of the Rockies (Fig. 8–4) and can also be examined along the margin of the Canadian Shield.

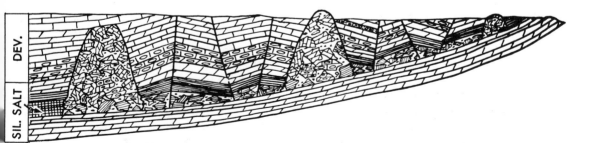

Fig. 8–3. Diagrammatic cross-section of the Mackinac Breccia showing how solution of Silurian salt (cross-hatched area) has resulted in the collapse of the higher Silurian and Devonian rocks. (From K. K. Landes, courtesy of the Michigan Department of Conservation.)

Fig. 8–4. Devonian rocks exposed at Hummingbird Creek, Alberta. The dark strata on the left are the dolomites of the Cairn Formation; the light, massive beds in the center are the reefal dolomites of the Southesk Formation. In the foreground, in the valley of the creek, the light dolomite passes abruptly into shale at the margin of the ancient reef. The reefal dolomite is overlain by shale and more resistant beds of Palliser Limestone, which form the crest of the mountain.

Middle Devonian Reefs and Evaporites

The Kaskaskia sea entered the Williston basin from the northwest either at the beginning of Middle Devonian time or at the end of Early Devonian time, depending on the age assigned to the basal deposits (Fig. 8–5A). After an initial phase of restricted seas and highly saline water, the sea moved southeastward until it covered much of eastern Alberta, southern Saskatchewan, western North Dakota, and northeastern Montana (Fig. 8–5B). The transgressing sea freshened the water in the Williston basin and, for a period, evaporite deposition stopped, limestones and dolomites accumulated, and many patch reefs were formed. Toward the end of the Middle Devonian Epoch the patch reefs growing in the region of the Tathlina arch formed a barrier reef, a nearly continuous wall of growing organisms reaching almost to sea level (Fig. 8–5B). The effect was to restrict the supply of oceanic water to the Williston basin and convert it into a gigantic evaporating pan. The reef-building animals were soon killed as the water became more

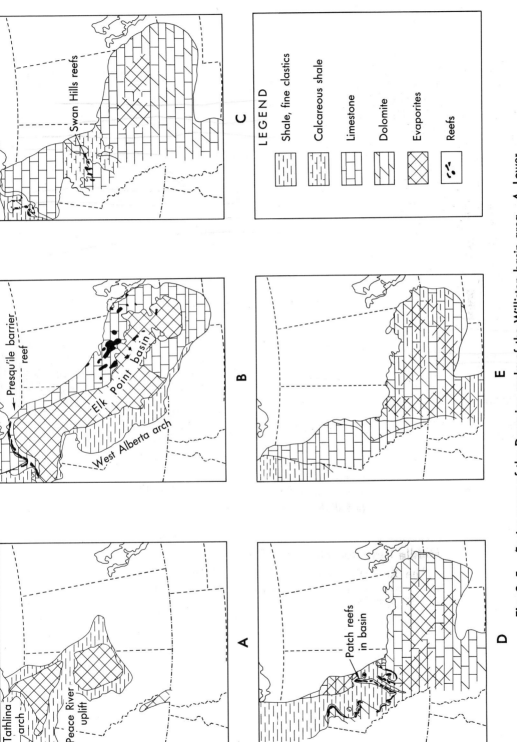

Fig. 8–5. Facies maps of the Devonian rocks of the Williston basin area. *A.* Lower Elk Point Group. *B.* Upper Elk Point Group. *C.* Beaverhill Lake Formation. *D.* Woodbend Group. *E.* Palliser Formation and equivalents. (From information in *Geological History of Western Canada,* courtesy of the Alberta Society of Petroleum Geologists.)

saline. The salt beds, called the Prairie Evaporite, underlie most of southern Saskatchewan and northeastern Alberta and reach a thickness of 1000 feet in the center of the Williston basin. Enough water passed southward over the restricting barrier reef to keep the basin from drying up, but eventually the concentration of the brine reached the point where potassium salts began to precipitate over a large area. The upper 100–200 feet of the Prairie Evaporite beneath Saskatchewan contain about half the world's potash reserves, or about 50 billion tons of potash salts.

Late Devonian Reef Patterns

The sea may have regressed from the Williston basin at the close of Middle Devonian time, but it spread as far south as South Dakota at the beginning of the Late Devonian Epoch (Fig. 8–5C). The facies patterns in this sea were not much different from those of Middle Devonian time, but the West Alberta ridge, which had joined the land areas of the Montana and Peace River domes separating the Williston basin from the Cordilleran geosyncline during mid-Devonian time, was covered by the sea. Along the Tathlina arch a group of patch and barrier reefs grew, separating the shale accumulating to the northwest from limestones and evaporites accumulating to the southeast. Recent drilling has discovered large gas reserves in these reefs. South of the Peace River dome another group of stromatoporoid patch reefs now surrounded by argillaceous limestones grew in muddy waters.

As the transgression of the Late Devonian sea progressed southward, the pattern of reef growth changed. The shale facies which had been confined to the northwest corner of the basin until middle Late Devonian time moved into central Alberta. The line of abrupt transition between the carbonate and shale facies (sometimes called the "carbonate front") then swung in a broad arc across southern Alberta (Fig. 8–5D). At this stage, reef-building organisms thrived in two environments: along the northern edge of a shelf which underlay much of southern Alberta; and along low ridges extending northeastward into the basin from the shelf (Fig. 8–6). Corals, stromatoporoids, and algae at the shelf edge built a discontinuous barrier reef, but those growing along the ridges within the shale basin produced patch reefs. On the shelf behind the barrier reefs a broad, shallow lagoon stretched for several hundred miles southward to a low shore in Wyoming. In this shallow sea, dolomite was laid down near the reefs; but farther south and east, away from the open ocean, anhydrite and other evaporites were deposited in the more saline water. Small, low patch reefs grew in the lagoon and stromatoporoids spread out like underwater carpets in the sunlit water.

Most of the reef rock is unbedded, coarsely crystalline, unfossiliferous dolomite (Fig. 8–7), but in some of the reefs that have escaped dolomitization original textures and fossils are preserved. The contact between the basinal shale facies and the reef facies is abrupt, with a minimum of interfingering, as if the organisms had built a rigid wall against the basin. The longest of the patch reef trends within the shale basin extends from near Calgary to near Edmonton and contains some of Canada's largest oil fields; the oil has been trapped in the porous reef and sealed there by the enclosing impermeable shale.

Reef growth in Alberta stopped before the close of the Devonian Period, perhaps because the sea withdrew from the basin for a short time in the middle of the Late Devonian Epoch. The youngest Devonian strata were laid down in an epeiric sea that covered most of the Williston basin, but they formed a blanket deposit without reefs now represented by the resistant and cliff-forming Palliser Limestone of the Front Ranges. This unit shows the facies changes typical of a gently shelving epeiric sea (Fig. 8–5E; compare Fig. 7–20). Shale in the quiet-water offshore zone gave way shoreward to limestone, which was laid down in the high-energy zone. The passage southeastward

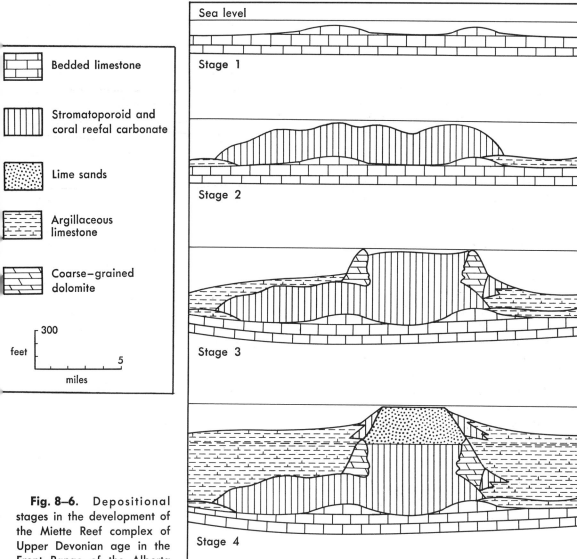

Bedded limestone

Stromatoporoid and coral reefal carbonate

Lime sands

Argillaceous limestone

Coarse-grained dolomite

300 feet

5 miles

Sea level

Stage 1

Stage 2

Stage 3

Stage 4

Stage 5

Southesk Formation

Mt. Hawk

Cairn Formation

Perdrix

Fig. 8–6. Depositional stages in the development of the Miette Reef complex of Upper Devonian age in the Front Range of the Alberta Rocky Mountains. From a platform of bedded limestone the stromatoporoids and corals built a mound fringed by frame-building organisms and filled by carbonate sand broken by the waves from the reef wall. In the final stage, when reef growth had stopped, the site of the reef was a low mound of carbonate sand. (After E. W. Mountjoy, courtesy of the Geological Survey of Canada.)

Fig. 8–7. Core of dolomite from an oil well in the Fenn oil field, Alberta, showing the vuggy porosity of the Devonian reservoirs.

from dolomite alone, to a mixture of dolomite, anhydrite, and halite, and finally to red shales is a record of increasing salinity in the near-shore zone of quiet water.

A study of Devonian sedimentation in the Williston basin suggests several generalizations concerning the development of facies changes in cratonic basins. We have seen that large areas of the craton can be cut off from the open ocean by relatively short barrier reefs across the outlet to the basin. Such reefs hold the conditions in the basin in a delicate balance; if they are highly restrictive, the salinity may rise to a point where potassium salts are precipitated; if they are moderately restrictive, halite or gypsum and anhydrite are laid down behind them; if they are breached, reef growth and carbonate deposition may spread into the basin. Both barrier and patch reefs tend to grow on elevated areas in an epeiric sea, as illustrated by the persistence of reefs about the Tathlina arch. Reefs like those of Alberta need not be associated with conspicuous talus deposits like those of west Texas, to be discussed below, but the carbonate may pass abruptly into basinal shales along their flanks. Finally, reefs are favorable areas to prospect for oil and gas, for these fluids seem to have migrated into the porous reef carbonates from the dark, organic shales which surround them.

MISSISSIPPIAN BLANKET DEPOSITS

The Chattanooga Shale

Some geologists believe that a total withdrawal of the epeiric sea from the craton at the end of the Devonian Period divides the Kaskaskia sequence; others recognize a recession but do not believe it was complete. Certainly, over the whole interior of the continent, a marked change in sedimentation took place, with the appearance of a remarkably persistent black shale called the Chattanooga Shale in the eastern states but known by a variety of local names in other areas. Although this black shale is generally less than 30 feet thick, it can be followed from Alabama to Michigan, from New York through the Midwest to Oklahoma, or across the Transcontinental arch (which it almost certainly covered) into the Williston basin (Fig. 8–8).

Lithologically the Chattanooga Shale and its correlatives are bituminous, organically rich (15–20 per cent), non-calcareous shales

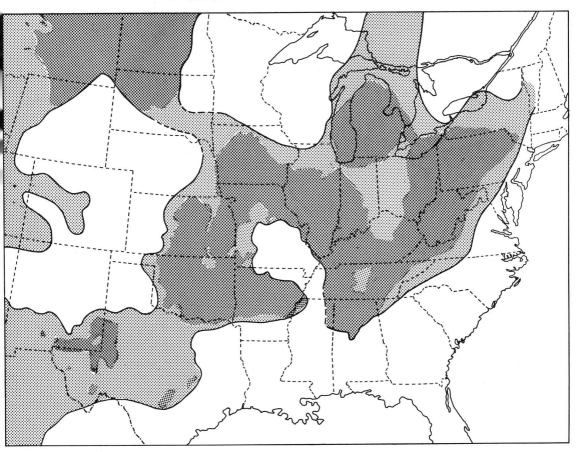

Fig. 8–8. The extent of the Chattanooga Shale and its equivalents in the United States. The present extent of the formations is indicated by the darker pattern, their probable former extent by the lighter stippling. (After L. C. Conant and V. E. Swanson, courtesy of the United States Geological Survey.)

with a relatively high content of uranium and low content of fossils. The fossils are represented by the enigmatic, chitinous, jawlike objects called conodonts; linguloid brachiopods; and a few plants. This meager evidence indicates that the lower part of the formation is Devonian in age and the upper part is Mississippian. The shale has been dated by the lead method as 350 million years old, a date which is a valuable correlation point for the relative and absolute time scales (see p. 60).

The conditions under which the Chattanooga Shale and its correlatives were de-posited remain a mystery. The brachiopods, scour channels, silt layers, and gradation upward into shallow-water sediments all indicate that the shale was deposited near sea level. Its high content of organic matter and restricted fauna of benthonic animals suggest that it accumulated slowly and that the water was stagnant during its deposition. How a shallow sea could be maintained in a stagnant condition over such an extensive area of the continental interior for any length of time is an unsolved problem. No other stratigraphic unit in North America is quite like this one.

Middle Mississippian
Fossil-Fragment Limestones

Mississippian rocks of North America are divided into four series based on subdivisions of the type section of the system along the upper Mississippi Valley of Illinois and Missouri. The most persistent formation of the basal series, called the Kinderhook (Fig. 8–9), is the Chattanooga Shale; the other formations are local in extent. The overlying Osage Series is characterized by cherty limestones, and the Meramec Series by limestones made of fragments of shells, microfossils, and oolites. Oolitic limestone has the texture of fish roe (Fig. 8–10) and is composed of myriads of tiny spheres of calcium carbonate. In marine localities where oolitic limestone is being formed today, such as the Bahama banks and the northern Red Sea, the water is clear, shallow, and moved by currents, and slightly more saline than normal. Calcium carbonate is precipitated chemically in concentric layers around nuclei to form minute spheres. Some of the limestones of the Meramec Series are made of these oolites, but many are composed of sand-sized grains of shells that have been broken, sorted, and rounded by the waves in shallow water. In some of the limestones the shells of the small, rounded foraminifer *Endothyra* are abundant. These "sandy" carbonate rocks make excellent building stone and they are extensively quarried in Indiana, particularly around Bedford. The many plants operating in Indiana produce about 10 million dollars' worth of shaped limestone blocks yearly, and make this state by far the largest producer of dimension stone in the United States. "Indiana Stone" is popular for exterior trim on buildings because of its pleasant light cream color, the ease with which it can be cut into complex patterns to form bas-reliefs, and its regular compact texture.

Among the main constituents of the limestones made of fossil fragments are the columnals and plates of crinoids. The crinoids reached their greatest abundance in the warm, shallow Mississippian seas of the Midwest and the Williston basin. We can

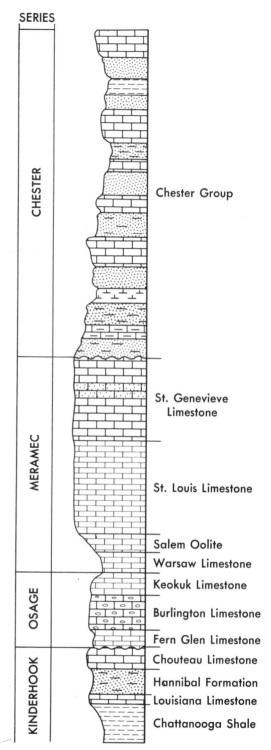

SERIES

CHESTER — Chester Group

St. Genevieve Limestone

MERAMEC

St. Louis Limestone

Salem Oolite
Warsaw Limestone
Keokuk Limestone

OSAGE

Burlington Limestone
Fern Glen Limestone
Chouteau Limestone

KINDERHOOK

Hannibal Formation
Louisiana Limestone
Chattanooga Shale

Fig. 8–9. Stratigraphic section of the Mississippian System in the type region. Total thickness about 2500 feet. (Modified from J. M. Weller and others.)

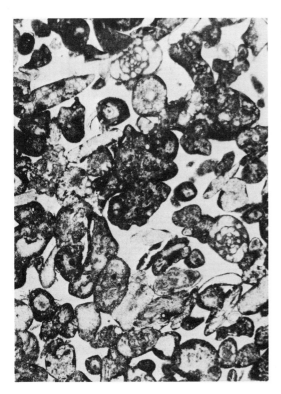

Fig. 8–10. Photomicrograph of the Salem Limestone showing its granular texture and microfossils (magnification × 15). (Courtesy of the Illinois Geological Survey.)

imagine that they grew in extensive submarine meadows, rippling in the waves on their long, thin, graceful columns like garden flowers in the wind. On rare occasions they were preserved whole, flattened to the bottom by a storm and quickly covered with lime mud. Where this type of preservation has taken place, for instance at Crawfordsville, Indiana, and Legrand, Iowa, collectors have quarried huge slabs containing hundreds of perfect crinoids. Unfortunately, the organic matter connecting the plates and columnals of the stem nearly always rotted in the water and the plates were scattered and sorted by the waves to form **crinoidal limestones.** Such limestones appear to be coarsely crystalline, for each plate and columnal is secreted as a single crystal of calcite and breaks along its rhombohedral cleavage, producing flat, glistening surfaces. Where the fragments were carried by cur-

rents these limestones may be either cross-bedded or ripple-marked. In the Williston basin and Rocky Mountains of Montana the Mission Canyon Limestone of Osage age contains a high proportion of crinoidal beds (Fig. 8–11). Correlative and lithologically similar formations form prominent cliffs in the eastern Cordillera from the Grand Canyon of Arizona to the Northwest Territories and are thousands of feet thick. The number of crinoids required to supply such a deposit staggers the imagination.

Granular limestones, such as those of the Osage and Meramec series, may have modest initial **intergranular porosity** (spaces between the grains). When such limestones are dolomitized, weathered, and leached, the pores are enlarged and the rock becomes a satisfactory petroleum reservoir. Such secondary changes in Middle Mississippian fossil-fragment limestones have produced reservoirs in which oil and gas are trapped in the Canadian Rocky Mountains, the western states, and the Williston basin.

Retreat of the Kaskaskia Sea

The Chester Series is the youngest of the Mississippian System. The restriction of the Chester Series to the middle of cratonic basins and the margins of the craton is partly a reflection of the withdrawal of the Kaskaskia sea at the end of Mississippian time, and partly due to the period of erosion that followed its deposition and removed part of the last layers deposited by the regressing sea. The regressive deposits of neither the Sauk nor the Tippecanoe sequences are preserved, but the slower regression of the Kaskaskia sea, the continuing subsidence of the basins, the uplift of the Shield, and perhaps the shorter period of erosion before the next transgression could have been the reasons for the preservation of the record of the late Mississippian regression.

The Chester Series of the Mississippi Valley consists of a persistent basal sandstone overlain by cyclically alternating sandstone and limestone formations which are laterally not persistent. Since these sands

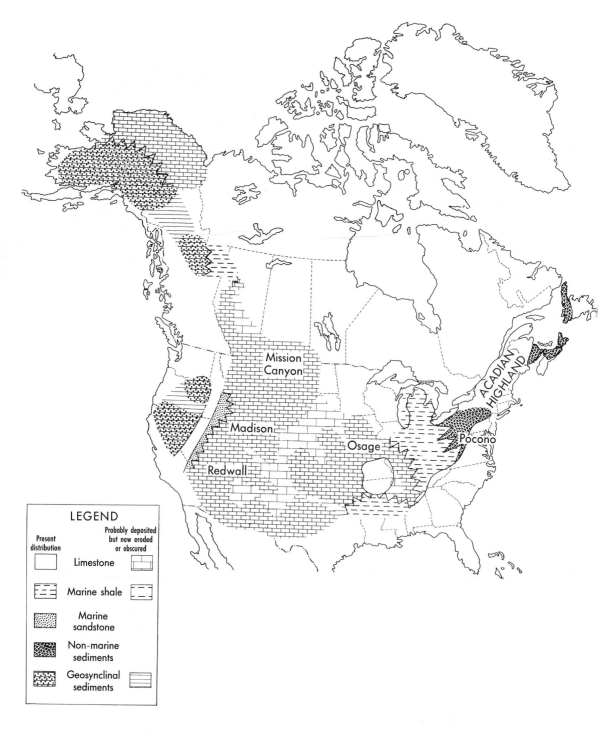

Fig. 8–11. Facies of the Osage Series (Middle Mississippian) in North America.)

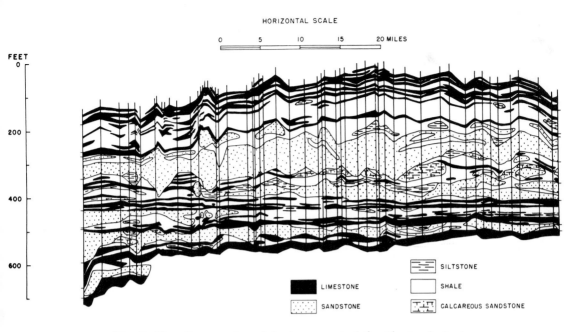

Fig. 8–12. Cross-section of the lower part of the Chester Series in southeastern Illinois showing the lack of lateral persistence of the limestone and sandstone units. The section runs from northwest to southeast. (From D. H. Swann and E. Atherton, *Journal of Geology*, courtesy of the University of Chicago Press.)

are reservoirs for petroleum in the center of the Illinois basin, they have been extensively drilled, and detailed cross-sections such as Fig. 8–12 can be drawn to show how the layers pinch and swell. Detailed maps of the thickness of these sandstones show that they are thickest along sinuous branching trends whose shapes suggest the filling of stream channels (Fig. 8–13). The direction of the dip of cross-bedding in these Chester sandstones is recorded in Fig. 8–14. Cross-beds are not all oriented in the same direction. In a river system or under shallow water the transporting currents rarely run directly down the regional slope but meander or are deflected by irregular topography. Yet if directions of dips of the cross-bedding are averaged over a sufficient area, these random deflections from the slope should cancel out and the mean direction of transport should be revealed. In southern Illinois and adjacent states the currents which deposited the cross-bedded sandstone throughout most of

Chester time flowed from the northeast to the southwest. In individual sandstone formations this direction is closely correlated with the geometry of the sand distribution. Similar studies of cross-bedding and channel shape of younger systems in the same region confirm that the river system arising between the Canadian Shield in Quebec and the highlands of the northern Appalachians persisted through Paleozoic time into the Cenozoic Era.

PRE-ABSAROKA UNCONFORMITY

In Europe the rocks of Pennsylvanian and Mississippian age are united into the Carboniferous System, but in North America a craton-wide unconformity and a distinct break in tectonic behavior and hence in pattern of sedimentation separate the two systems. Uplift and erosion of the strata below the unconformity are most conspicuous in Nebraska and Kansas. In Kansas, a

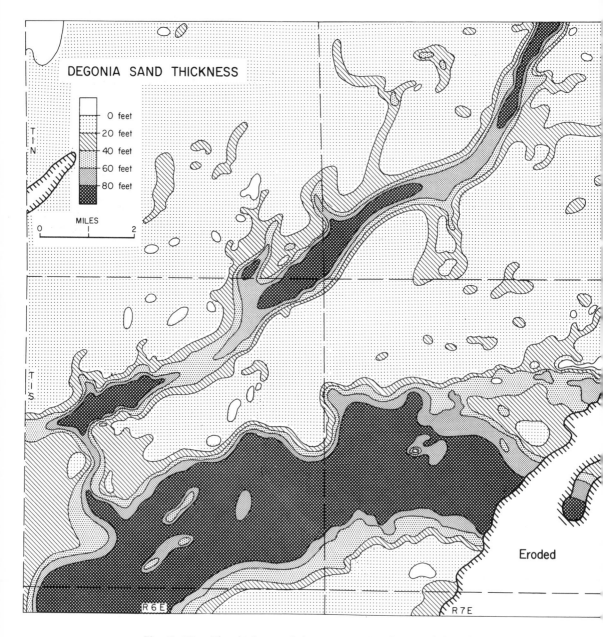

Fig. 8–13. The thickness of the Degonia Sandstone of the Chester Series of southern Illinois. This detailed isopach map shows that the sandstone is distributed like a channel filling in a dendritic pattern. The direction of the "tributaries" suggests that the sand was transported from the northeast and east. (From D. H. Swann, courtesy of the American Association of Petroleum Geologists Bulletin.)

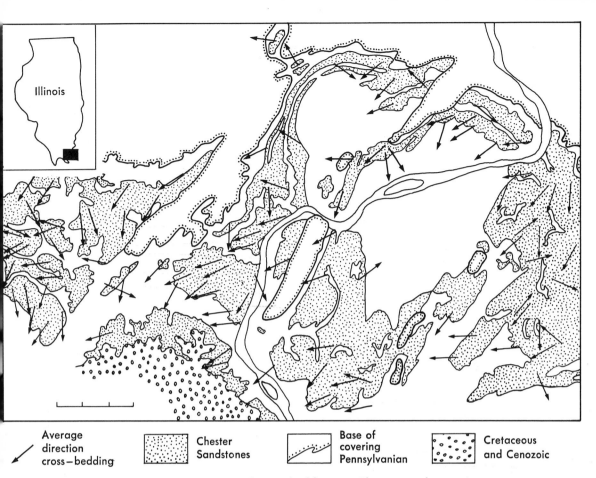

Fig. 8–14. Direction of cross-bedding in Chester sandstones in southern Illinois and Kentucky. (After P. E. Potter and others, courtesy of the *American Association of Petroleum Geologists Bulletin*.)

Legend:

Average direction cross–bedding

Chester Sandstones

Base of covering Pennsylvanian

Cretaceous and Cenozoic

---

low arch called the central Kansas uplift was elevated and stripped by erosion to the Arbuckle Limestone, which is Late Cambrian and Early Ordovician in age. The truncated edges of the Arbuckle beds were covered by the basal shales of the Absaroka sequence. Along this unconformity a group of oil fields has been localized where petroleum migrating up the dip of the porous limestone has been trapped in minor folds against the impermeable shale (Fig. 8–15). Another pre-

Fig. 8–15. Paleogeological map and cross-section of the Norton oil field, illustrating the manner of entrapment of oil on the central Kansas uplift by the truncation of porous reservoir beds and the sealing of the exposed edge by impervious shales. The area of the oil field is ruled. (After P. F. Merriam and E. D. Goebel, courtesy of the Kansas Geological Survey.)

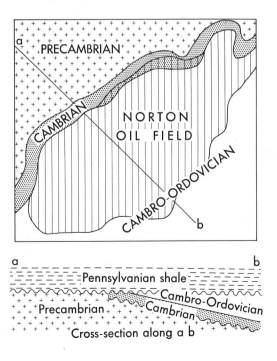

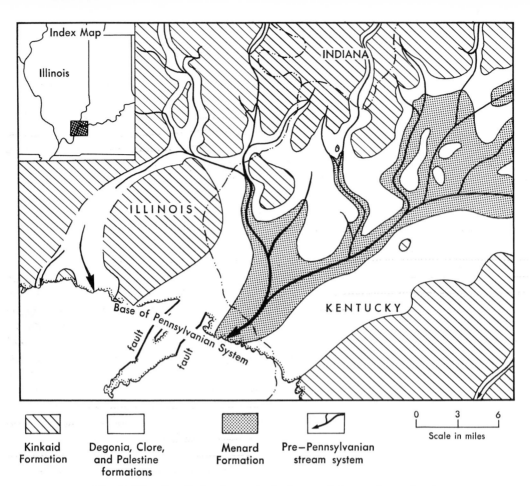

INDIANA

ILLINOIS

Base of Pennsylvanian System

fault

fault

KENTUCKY

| Kinkaid Formation | Degonia, Clore, and Palestine formations | Menard Formation | Pre—Pennsylvanian stream system | Scale in miles 0 3 6 |

Fig. 8–16. Detailed paleogeological map of the pre-Pennsylvanian surface at the boundaries between Illinois, Indiana, and Kentucky. The pattern of outcrops of the various formations of the Chester Series below the Mississippian–Pennsylvanian unconformity defines a stream system because the older formations are exposed where the valleys have been cut deepest and the pre-Pennsylvanian highlands are underlain by the younger Mississippian formations. (After P. E. Potter and F. J. Pettijohn, *Paleocurrents and Basin Analysis.* New York: Springer-Verlag, Inc.)

Absaroka uplift, the Nemaha ridge of eastern Nebraska and Kansas (discussed further below), was also important in trapping oil.

In the type region of the Mississippian System the Chester Series was deeply eroded during the pre-Absaroka interval. Channels up to 300 feet deep were cut into the flat-lying beds and subsequently filled with basal Pennsylvanian rocks. By plotting detailed paleogeological maps from well records the incision of these channels into the lower formations can be detected and the direction of the streams and their tributaries can be accurately plotted (Fig. 8–16).

CYCLOTHEMS

Although Pennsylvanian sedimentary rocks are now restricted to the mid-continent area and the Appalachian, Michigan, and Illinois basins, they once formed a continuous sheet stretching from the Appalachian geosyncline to Colorado and from North Dakota to Texas. Deposition over this vast area of the platform took place in cyclical repetitions of marine and non-marine strata. A **cyclothem** is a succession of different sedimentary rocks which occurs repeatedly in a larger stratigraphic unit. Since cyclothems were first described, geologists have been trying to re-construct the peculiar conditions under which they were deposited.

The Typical Illinois Cyclothem

Figure 8–17 represents the idealized succession of lithologies of a cyclothem in the Illinois basin. The cycle starts at the unconformity and contains ten members. The first member (1) consists of a massive, cross-bedded sandstone showing signs of having been deposited rapidly near the shore under deltaic conditions. It is commonly overlain by a sandy shale (2) and limestone (3) containing plants and fresh-water invertebrates, respectively. The fourth member (4) is a clay, called the underclay, that has been extensively leached so that only silica and clay minerals remain. It commonly contains tree roots and is overlain by the coal member (5). Coal is economically the most important member of the cyclothem, but many of the coal seams are only a few feet thick and are therefore uneconomical to mine. In Illinois 50 coal seams have been found in the

Pennsylvanian System, and in Pennsylvania more than 100. Some of the finest Pennsylvanian fossils have been found in the shale that overlies the coal (6). On Mazon Creek, near Morris, Illinois, iron-rich calcareous concretions weather from shales in this stratigraphic interval and accumulate like pebbles in the creek bed. Many species of fish, amphibians, plants, insects, other arthropods, and mollusks have been preserved in these nodules, some so faithfully that impressions of the soft parts can be seen.

Members 6–10 of the cyclothem are marine members and consist of alternating units of limestone and shale with a rich marine fauna of invertebrates. The cycle ends with an erosion surface whose channels may cut deeply into the sediments that were just deposited. The deposition of another deltaic sandstone above the erosion surface begins another cyclothem. Each cyclothem does not contain all ten members; usually several are missing in any given cycle.

The interpretation of the sequence of events which led to the succession of beds in

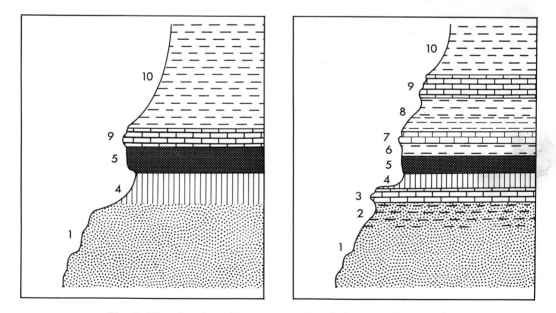

Fig. 8–17. Stratigraphic sections of cyclothems. *Left:* Cyclothem with all ten members well developed. *Right:* Cyclothem in which several members have not been deposited. (Modified from J. M. Weller, courtesy of the Geological Society of America.)

a midwestern cyclothem is relatively simple. Members 1–5 were deposited in non-marine environments and represent a period of peneplanation in which a deltaic swamp was built out at the edge of a regressing sea. Members 2 and 3 represent the deposits of lakes on the growing deltaic plain. The underclay of member 4 has been thought to be the soil on which the swamp developed, but not all coal geologists agree with this theory. (The conditions in these coal swamps are considered in detail below.) With the transgression of the sea during the deposition of member 6, the plants of the swamp were poisoned and drowned and the sea began the deposition of the upper marine members of the cycle (6–10). At the end of the cycle, a rapid retreat of the sea was followed by subaerial erosion, or the cutting of channels below shallow water, and the formation of the unconformity. Each cyclothem represents a retreat and an advance of the sea; this much is clear, but whether these advances and retreats were caused by structural behavior of the basin, eustatic movement of sea level, changes in climate, or compaction of the coal-bearing succession, or a combination of these factors, remains a problem.

Regional Variations

If observations on cyclothems are extended westward and eastward from Illinois, we find that the individual members of the cycles are remarkably persistent and some of the coal beds, although only a few feet thick, can be traced for hundreds of miles. The individual members seem to be of the same age over the whole area of deposition, but evidence that they cross or do not cross time markers is difficult to find because closely spaced, time-parallel horizons have not yet been defined in this succession. Regional variations take place in the lithology of the cyclothem, as shown in Fig. 8–18. In the lower part of the Brereton cyclothem in Illinois the beds are channel and deltaic sands deposited at the sea's edge, but in Kansas and Oklahoma they are marine limestone. Although the cyclicity of the sedimentary suc-

cession remains, in Kansas and Oklahoma the marine members are much thicker than the non-marine members and in Pennsylvania the opposite is true—the non-marine members predominate to the virtual exclusion of the thin marine members. In the mid-continent region the coal beds are very thin or absent in some cycles; in Pennsylvania and West Virginia they are thickest and most abundant. The regional variations in cyclothems are reflections of the presence of the sea during most of the Pennsylvanian Period in Kansas; its general absence in the Appalachian area; and its presence for about half the time in the area between.

In addition to those features already mentioned, any theory of the origin of cyclothems must account for the proximity of all the environments of deposition to sea level, the intercalation of cyclothems at the margins of the craton, and the occurrence of similar cycles in other continents. The faunas of the marine limestones of the cyclothems show that even these members were deposited in shallow water, and paleontologists have estimated that the sea on the craton never reached a depth greater than 200 feet during Pennsylvanian time. In the middle of the basins and at the edge of the craton, where the Pennsylvanian System thickens, coal seams and other members of the cyclothem may split and additional cyclothems may be introduced. In Pennsylvania, where the system is thick, many more cyclothems can be counted than in Illinois or Kansas. Finally, the cyclothemic repetition of beds found in North America is common in sedimentary sequences of late Paleozoic age on many continents of the world; therefore, a mechanism proposed to explain North American cyclothems must be applicable in Europe and elsewhere.

Theories of Origin

Many theories have been proposed to explain cyclothems, but only three will be considered here. One group of stratigraphers holds that the cyclic transgression and regression of the sea over the continental interior

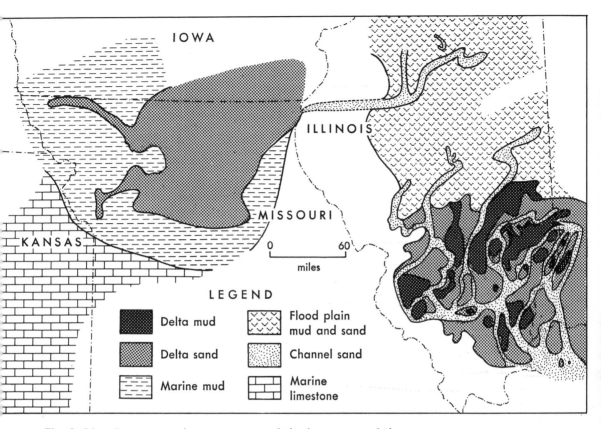

Fig. 8–18. Environmental reconstruction of the lower part of the Brereton cyclothem in the mid-continent region. The unpatterned areas were largely low-lying lands. A channel sand has been extended across the Mississippi Valley to supply the delta in northern Missouri, although Pennsylvanian deposits have been eroded from the valley. (Modified from H. R. Wanless and others, courtesy of the Geological Society of America.)

was caused by alternating episodes of depression and uplift of both the source area of the clastic sediments and the basin itself. During the numerous depressions, the alluvial plain was inundated by the sea; during each uplift, the emergence of the plain and its acquisition of newly eroded sands resulted in the movement of the shoreline hundreds of miles seaward. As the basin subsided and the highlands of the source were reduced by erosion, the sea slowly encroached on the delta, edging the shoreline landward until another uplift of basin and source forced it back. The pulsating behavior of the platform during the formation of the cyclothems is related by this theory to the general instability of the continent in late Paleozoic time and to orogenic episodes in the bordering geosynclines.

The cyclical transgressions and regressions have also been ascribed to variations in sea level in a steadily subsiding basin. Proponents of this hypothesis believe that sea level rose and fell throughout the world—perhaps more than a hundred times—in the rhythm of the cyclothems. The reason for the repeated lowering of sea level has been sought in the removal of water from the sea to form the ice that periodically covered much of the Southern Hemisphere in Permian and Pennsylvanian times (see Chapter 6). During the recent Ice Age, sea level was lowered 300–

400 feet. The water evaporated from the ocean was not returned through rainfall or by streams, but accumulated as ice on the continents. A similar effect must have accompanied the late Paleozoic glaciation. An equal number of glacial advances and cyclothems is called for by this theory, but so far the number of glaciations recorded in the Southern Hemisphere is far too low, and most of them seem to be of Permian age, younger than many of the cyclothems. The theory also fails to account for the cyclothems in parts of Pennsylvania which are composed entirely of continental beds and were therefore independent of sea level.

A third theory accounts for the cyclical variations in sedimentation by cyclical variations in climate. Climatic variations could affect the precipitation, vegetation, rate of weathering, and, most important, the discharge of the streams. Increase in the discharge would bring more sediment to the basin, building out the deltas on which the coal swamps became established. Channel cutting even below sea level could accompany an increased discharge and could produce local unconformities. As subsidence and compaction carried the surface of deposition downward, and as discharge decreased, the sea would transgress the delta and begin the marine part of the cycle.

The source areas for the clastic particles of the cyclothems may be located by studies of cross-bedding and of the shapes of channel sandstones. The sands of the Illinois basin were carried southwestward by the river that was active also in Mississippian time, and to a lesser extent by streams draining the Shield from the northwest (Fig. 8–19). The sands of the Allegheny basin were transported from the east, from highlands that were forming during the late Paleozoic in the Appalachian geosyncline. In the west, domes within the craton supplied some detritus to the Pennsylvanian basins, and in southern Oklahoma and Texas erosion of the mountains rising in the Ouachita geosyncline poured sands and muds northward onto the edge of

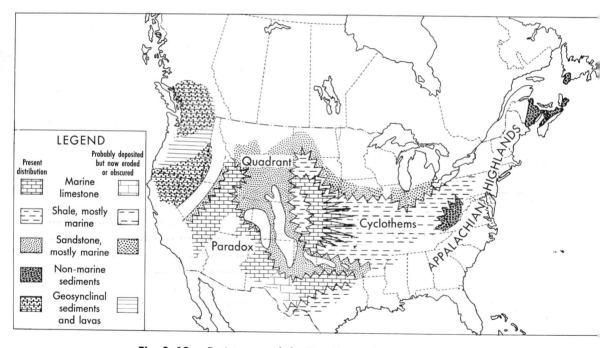

Fig. 8–19. Facies map of the Des Moines Series (Middle Pennsylvanian) of central North America. The complex interfingering of lithologies in the cyclothems of the center of the continent can only be suggested here.

the craton. (The history of these geosynclinal sources will be considered at greater
length in Chapter 13.) The interior basins
during the late Paleozoic seem to have been
almost surrounded by source areas. The
portal by which the sea entered the craton is
not obvious, but entry from the south seems
most likely.

COAL

The Nature of Coal

Coal is "stored sunlight" and is one of the
great energy sources of the world. The
search for additional coal resources depends
upon an understanding of the environment in
which coal is formed. The Pennsylvanian
Period was the time of accumulation of the
most important coal resources, not only of
North America but of the other continents of
the Northern Hemisphere. Coal itself, and
the sequence of sediments in which it occurs,
furnishes much evidence for the reconstruction of the environment of its deposition.

To the trained observer coal is obviously
the product of plant growth, for traces of
twigs and leaves are commonly found in the
lower ranks * of the coal or in the beds immediately adjacent to it. If a slice of bituminous coal is ground so thin that light will pass
through it, the microscope reveals that it is
composed of amorphous, brown organic matter in which are embedded plant spores and
shreds of plant matter still bearing the cellular structure of wood (Fig. 8–20). The micro-
structure of coal is most clearly revealed in
"coal balls," rounded nodules in which the
coal has been impregnated naturally by pyrite or dolomite.

Coal is highly condensed plant matter
partly decayed and compressed to a compact, dense bed from a porous tangle of
branches, roots, trunks, and leaves, and their
debris. Much of the evidence indicates that
coals accumulated in place and were not

* The rank of coal depends upon its degree of
compaction and is accurately determined by chemical analysis. The three major ranks of coal in order
of increasing compaction are lignite, bituminous, and
anthracite.

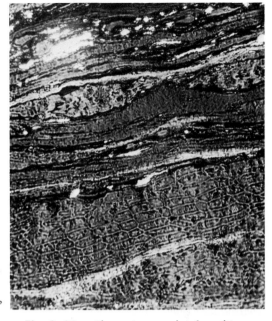

Fig. 8–20. Photomicrograph of a thin section of bituminous coal from Illinois showing the
cellular structure of the wood preserved in some
parts. (Courtesy of the U. S. Bureau of Mines.)

carried and distributed in the basin by
streams. The microscope reveals that the
plants of the coal measures grew under conditions differing little from those of the temperate or possibly the subtropical zones of
the earth today. The absence of rings in the
wood of tree trunks indicates that there was
little seasonal variation in temperature in the
coal forests. Their large leaves, their big
breathing pores, and their aerial roots indicate a moist, equable climate. The roots of
the coal-forest trees did not reach downward
into the soil in search of water but spread out
laterally just beneath the surface. This root
pattern suggests that water was plentiful.
The forest floor must have been a spongy
mass of half-decayed plant matter somewhat
like the muskeg bogs of the northland today. The climate is believed to have been
temperate to subtropical rather than tropical.
Although vegetation grows at a maximum
rate in the tropics today, bacterial decay of
the dead plants is rapid enough to disperse
the organic material before it accumulates.

Conditions in the
Pennsylvanian Coal Swamps

The coal swamps of eastern North America occupied a basin bordered on the south and east by highlands of the Appalachian orogenic belt and on the north by the low swell of the Canadian Shield. The deltaic plain sloped southward and southwestward for hundreds of miles to the sea with a very low gradient, perhaps as low as 1 or 2 feet per mile. At many times in the period this whole vast plain was green with living plants ranging in size from scale trees 100 feet high to ground-trailing ferns (see Fig. 20–2). The trees grew on a mush of organic material and upon death made their own contribution to this peaty layer. Bacterial decay was limited by lack of oxygen in the stagnant water of the organic mush, and branches and leaves could have been only partly decayed before being buried by more fallen vegetation. Summer and winter, rain-heavy clouds from the inland sea, swept eastward up the gentle slope, discharged their wet burden on the jungle below. Storms must have been rare, since the trees were not strong enough to stand against strong winds. Only when the sea encroached upon the swamps and the salt water poisoned the trees did coal deposition cease, and the organic mush was covered by layers of marine shale and limestone. As the swamp deposit sank deeper under the ever increasing weight of the accumulating strata, water was pressed from it, and the whole mass was consolidated until every 10 feet of wet, porous, peaty material was converted into about 1 foot of solid coal. (The types of trees and animals that inhabited these forests are described in Chapter 20.)

The Coal Fields

Erosion has attacked the sheet of Pennsylvanian sediments that once stretched continuously from the Appalachian Mountains to the Cordilleran geosyncline, breaking it into the segments of the Appalachian, Michigan, Illinois, and mid-continent fields (Fig. 8–21).

The eastern sector of the Pennsylvanian delta underlies one of the greatest coal fields in the world. In the plateau country of Pennsylvania, West Virginia, Kentucky, Ohio, and Alabama the sediments that yield coal are horizontal or very gently flexed. The coal is all of bituminous rank and is used almost entirely by industries such as steel mills, which are concentrated in this section of the United States. The most valuable seam in this basin is the Pittsburgh coal, which is about 14 feet thick near Pittsburgh and potentially productive over 6000 square miles. The coal wealth of the Appalachian basin can be appreciated by a review of some of the production figures. Mines in this basin produce a total of about 374 million tons annually. From Pennsylvania and West Virginia, the two most productive states of the field, more than 15.2 billion tons of coal have already been mined. Even with production proceeding at 72 million tons a year in Pennsylvania, the remaining reserves of the state are still estimated at 71 billion tons. It will be centuries before the reserves from this field are exhausted.

The Appalachian field is separated from the Illinois field by the band of older rocks uplifted along the Cincinnati arch. In Illinois and Indiana the coal beds are thinner and fewer of the seams are worth mining. In areas where thin coal seams are near the surface, the light covering of drift and sedimentary rocks is removed and the coal is dug with power shovels; this method is known as strip mining.

The Illinois field is separated from the mid-continent field by the valley of the Mississippi River, which cuts through the Pennsylvanian System down into older rocks. Mining conditions and stratigraphy are similar in both areas but the coals are thinner farther west and can be extracted profitably only by strip mining. Some idea of the relative importance of the fields may be gained by a comparison of the annual production of about 1 million tons from Kansas, 51 million tons from Illinois, and 130 million tons from West Virginia.

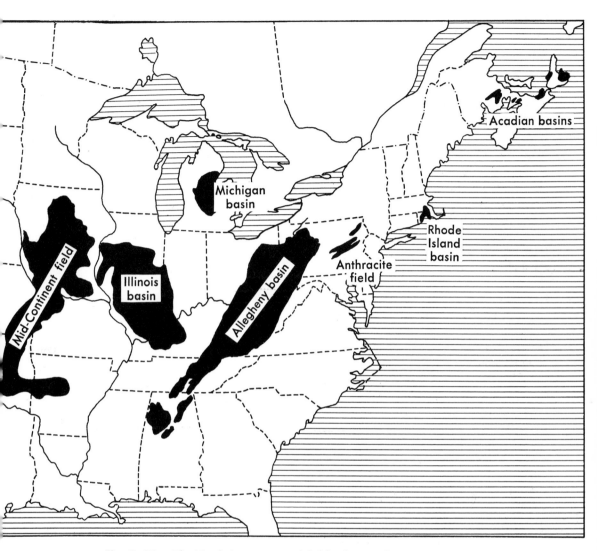

Fig. 8–21. The North American coal fields of Pennsylvanian age.

FRAGMENTATION OF THE SOUTHWESTERN CRATON

Yoked Basins

The cratonic domes and arches of the early part of the Paleozoic Era did not act as suppliers of clastic sediments and had little influence on the facies near them. In Pennsylvanian and Permian times, segments of the southwestern corner of the craton were strongly uplifted into arches and domes which were eroded, producing the coarse detritus of the basins nearby. This fragmentation has not been explained satisfactorily but may have been connected with the growing tectonic unrest in the Ouachita and Cordilleran geosynclines which embraced this corner of the craton.

A basin which received the sediments eroded from an uplift is called a **yoked basin** because its behavior seems to have been connected or yoked to that of the adjacent uplift. The elevation of one segment of the earth's crust seems to have resulted in the

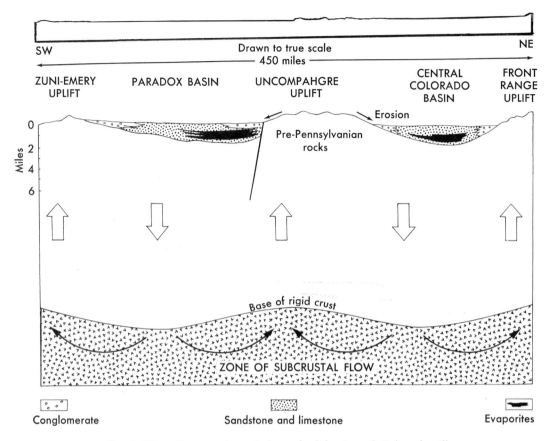

Fig. 8–22. Cross-section of the yoked basins of Colorado, illustrating the hypothetical relationship between the uplift of the highlands and the subsidence of the basins. In the lower part of the diagram the vertical scale has been greatly exaggerated, but in the upper part the true relationship between the thickness of the sediments in the basins and that of the crust is illustrated.

depression of another: the transfer of particles by erosion and sedimentation from the high to the low block must be compensated for below by a similar transfer of subcrustal plastic fluid material (Fig. 8–22). The boundary between the basin and its complimentary uplift was a simple flexure or a nearly vertical fault.

Figure 8–23 shows the principal basins and arches of Pennsylvanian time. The tectonic elements had diverse histories and not all were active at the same time. A group of uplifts in southern Oklahoma form what has been called the Oklahoma Mountains and others in Colorado are known as either the Ancestral Rockies or the Colorado Moun-

tains. The complex facies changes in late Paleozoic sediments and the structures and unconformities that resulted from the periodic uplift of the arches have all produced traps for oil and gas. The late Paleozoic rocks of Kansas, Oklahoma, and Texas yield a large portion of the total oil supply of the United States. The search for additional oil resources in these rocks is aided by an understanding of the history of the cratonic basins. Space is not available for a consideration of the history of all the basins and uplifts, but three areas are discussed: the Oklahoma Mountains and the Anadarko basin; the Paradox basin and its surrounding uplifts; and the Guadalupe basin of west Texas.

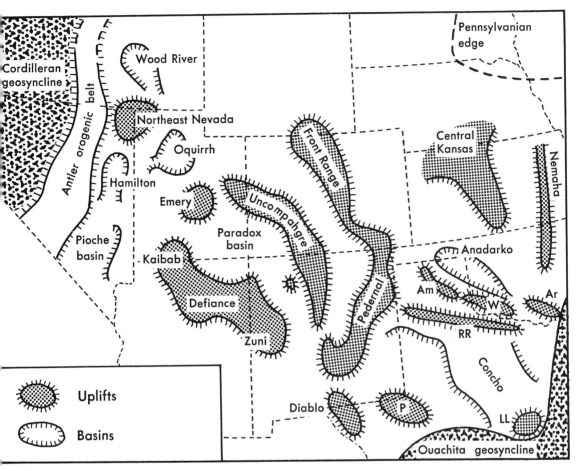

Fig. 8–23. Basins and uplifts of the southwestern states in the Pennsylvanian Period. *Am,* Amarillo ridge; *W,* Wichita uplift; *Ar,* Arbuckle uplift; *RR,* Red River uplift; *Ll,* Llano uplift; *P,* Pecos arch.

The Oklahoma Mountains and the Anadarko Basin

The history of the Ouachita segment of the Appalachian geosyncline will be considered in more detail in Chapter 13. During Pennsylvanian time the trough was folded, thrust northward and northwestward against the edge of the craton, and lifted into highlands that supplied detritus toward the north.

The Oklahoma Mountains consist of elongate domes of basement rock. A few of these domes form ridges and hills at the surface, but most are deeply buried beneath Permian, Mesozoic, and Cenozoic sedimentary rocks and have only been discovered in the search

for petroleum. Cross-sections of three of these structures are illustrated in Fig. 8–24.

The transgressing Absaroka sea first laid down the sandstones of the Springer Stage along the cratonic margin and in the center of the Anadarko basin. The marine rocks of the Pennsylvanian System in North America are generally divided into six stages as follows:

> Virgil
> Missouri
> Des Moines
> Atoka (or Derry)
> Morrow
> Springer

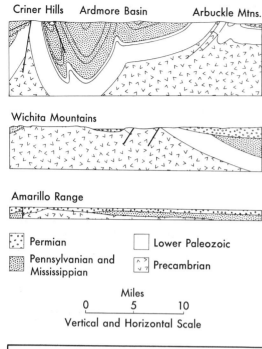

Criner Hills   Ardmore Basin   Arbuckle Mtns.

Wichita Mountains

Amarillo Range

Permian   Lower Paleozoic

Pennsylvanian and   Precambrian
Mississippian

Miles

0   5   10

Vertical and Horizontal Scale

The sea spread northward, reaching its great-est extent during the Missouri Age. The boundaries of the major facies changed with time, but the general pattern of Pennsyl-vanian sedimentation in Oklahoma and Kan-sas is illustrated in Fig. 8–25. Coarse clastic sediments were deposited near the Oklahoma and Colorado uplifts; mud from these uplifts and from the rising Ouachita geosyncline spread farther out into the sea; and limestone was deposited still farther from the source of clastic sediments over the shelf region of Kansas and eastern Colorado. The elevation

Fig. 8–24. North–south cross-sections of the ranges of the Oklahoma Mountains drawn to the same scale to show differences of complexity and relief of the structures. (Modified from A. J. Eardley.)

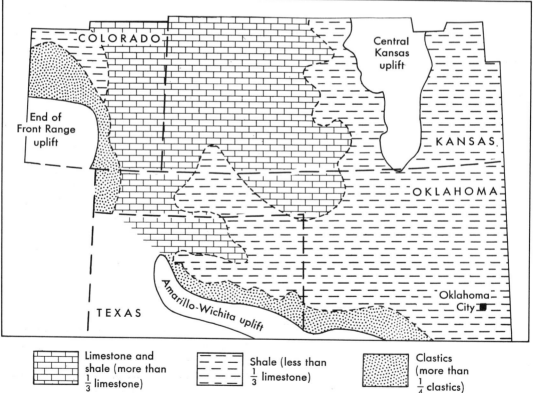

Limestone and shale (more than $\frac{1}{3}$ limestone)

Shale (less than $\frac{1}{3}$ limestone)

Clastics (more than $\frac{1}{4}$ clastics)

Fig. 8–25. Facies map of the Cherokee Group (Atoka Stage) in the Oklahoma–Kansas area. (After B. Rascoe, courtesy of the *American Association of Petroleum Geologists Bulletin*.)

of the Oklahoma Mountains began in Morrow time and continued to a climax at the end of the period. The first episodes of uplift, referred to as the Wichita orogeny, resulted in the stripping of up to 15,000 feet of pre-Pennsylvanian sedimentary rocks covering the granitic basement of the Arbuckle Mountains. The eroded material was carried to the Ardmore and Anadarko basins, which accumulated 17,000 feet of sedimentary rocks in this episode. The progressive stripping by erosion of the crests of the rising anticlines exposed older formations and is reflected in the type of sedimentary particles supplied to the basins. Although thin sandstone tongues spread from the mountains as far north as Kansas, most of the sediments were trapped in the rapidly subsiding basins. The sands from these uplifts, now folded by later movements, form reservoirs for many of the oil fields of southern Oklahoma.

In Kansas the rise of the central Kansas arch and the Nemaha granite ridge took place in early Pennsylvanian time. The Nemaha ridge is an acute uplift of early Paleozoic rocks, bounded on one side by a fault and stripped by erosion to its Precambrian core before it was covered by the basal shales of the transgressing Absaroka sea. Many of the most productive oil fields of the midcontinent region derive their oil from what are known as **bald-headed** structures on the Nemaha ridge. This type of trap results from the doming of strata containing a porous bed, their erosion to a more or less flat surface, and the sealing of the truncated edges of the reservoir bed by an impervious layer deposited over the unconformity. The sequence of events is illustrated graphically in Fig. 8–26. Two of the largest fields in cumulative production in the mid-continent area, the Eldorado and Oklahoma City fields, are located on bald-headed structures in which the major reservoir rock is the Upper Cambrian and Lower Ordovician Arbuckle Limestone.

The shale that seals the bald-headed structures in much of Kansas is the Cherokee

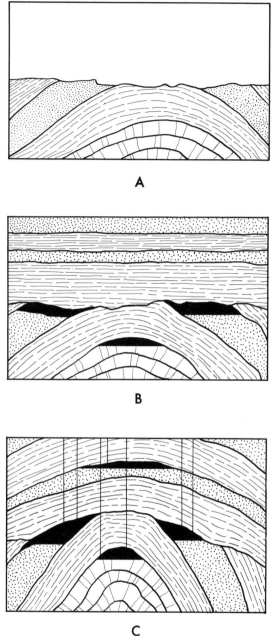

Fig. 8–26. Stages in the development of a "bald-headed" structure. A. Doming of the strata and their erosion to a surface that truncates the porous sandstone bed. B. Deposition of impermeable shale over the unconformity, sealing the porous bed and making a trap for oil (black) migrating up the dip. This is the "bald-headed" structure. C. Renewed uplift deforms the beds above the unconformity, forming additional traps.

Formation (of Atoka–Des Moines age). This shale contains long, thin lenses of sand, called "shoe-string" sands. Most of the Cherokee sands are believed to have been bars analogous to those now forming along the Atlantic Coast of the United States, but others appear to have been channel fillings. They form the reservoirs for several productive oil fields in Kansas.

The long regression of the Absaroka sea that continued with many interruptions through the Permian and Triassic periods began in Virgil time. Although marine sediments continued to be deposited in Kansas and Oklahoma as late as Middle Permian time, the great epeiric sea that had stretched from the northern Appalachians to Oklahoma was slowly restricted; more clastic sediments entered from bordering uplifts and before the end of the Paleozoic it was completely silted up.

Near the end of Pennsylvanian time (Virgil) and early in the Permian Period the Oklahoma mountain system was strongly uplifted in what has been called the Arbuckle orogeny. Up to this time the Oklahoma structures were simple and had been raised intermittently since Late Mississippian time, but in this vertical movement the rocks broke along a series of faults into horsts and graben. The complexity of the structure along the north front of the Arbuckle and Wichita mountains has been revealed by deep drilling in southern Oklahoma (Fig. 8–27). Along the front of the Arbuckle and Wichita uplifts the faults are nearly vertical and the deforming force seems to have been directed from below, not laterally. The Criner Hills uplift was raised and thrust northward toward the Arbuckle Mountains, pushing against the intervening sedimentary rocks of the Ardmore basin. Anticlines in the basin that were formed in the Early Pennsylvanian Wichita orogeny and then eroded were refolded and broken along high-angle faults. The complexity of stratigraphy and structure produced by this sequence of events is illustrated in the cross-section of the Velma field (Fig. 8–28). Petroleum has been trapped in many of these anticlines in beds that range in age from Ordovician to Permian, but mostly in Pennsylvanian sandstones. Some of the traps were formed in the crests of anticlines; others were formed where permeable beds have been brought against impermeable ones along faults; and still others were formed where sand tongues pinch out over the tops of buried hills.

In the western part of the Oklahoma Mountains, Late Pennsylvanian deformation was reflected in the Amarillo ridge largely as uplift; little folding or faulting took place. The regolith that had developed by the weathering of the granitic rocks was washed off into the surrounding basins by the rejuvenated streams. This **granite wash** is one of the most important reservoirs in the Panhandle oil and gas field of northern Texas. Along the flanks of the Oklahoma mountain system latest Pennsylvanian and early Permian sedimentary rocks are conglomeratic red beds derived from the erosion of the granitic cores of the ranges. As Permian red beds gradually built up, the ranges became progressively buried in their own debris and had little relief by the end of the period.

The Four Corners Area

That part of the Colorado Plateau where the states of Arizona, New Mexico, Utah, and Colorado come together has been called the "Four Corners." Investigation of the late Paleozoic stratigraphy of this area was stimulated by the discovery in the fifties of petroleum in the Paradox basin; since that time many oil wells and dry holes have revealed the history of the region. The late Paleozoic arches of Colorado, unlike those of Oklahoma, were rejuvenated in Cenozoic time and now form the highest peaks in the western states. The Front Range of Colorado is the successor to the largest of these uplifts, which extended from southern Wyoming to central New Mexico during its period of greatest elevation. The central Colorado basin separated the Front Range uplift from the subparallel Uncompahgre uplift to the west. The Paradox basin lay southwest of the Uncompahgre uplift and was partly enclosed on the west by several low domes that

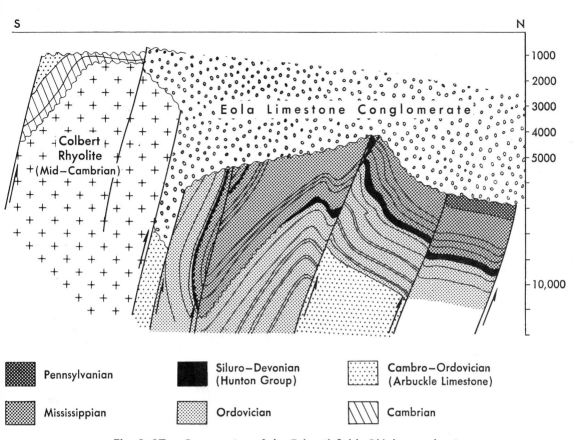

S   N

Eola Limestone Conglomerate

Colbert
Rhyolite
(Mid–Cambrian)

1000
2000
3000
4000
5000

10,000

Pennsylvanian

Siluro–Devonian
(Hunton Group)

Cambro–Ordovician
(Arbuckle Limestone)

Mississippian

Ordovician

Cambrian

Fig. 8–27. Cross-section of the Eola oil field, Oklahoma, showing the intensity of the deformation along almost vertical faults at the north side of the Arbuckle Mountains as revealed by drilling. Horizontal and vertical scales equal. (After B. H. Harlton, courtesy of the *American Association of Petroleum Geologists Bulletin*.)

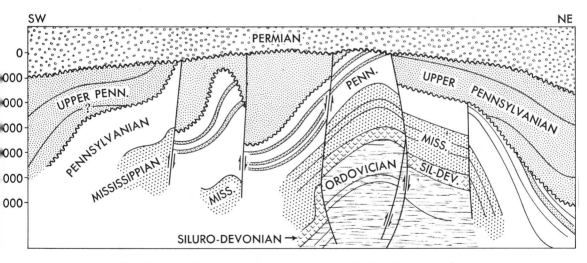

SW   NE

PERMIAN

0
000
000
000
000
000
000

UPPER PENN.
PENNSYLVANIAN
MISSISSIPPIAN
MISS.
PENN.
UPPER PENNSYLVANIAN
ORDOVICIAN
MISS.
SIL-DEV.

SILURO-DEVONIAN →

Fig. 8–28. Cross-section of the Velma oil field, Oklahoma, showing the type of deformation in the Ardmore basin. Note the high-angle faults indicative of vertical forces, and the unconformities in the succession indicative of periodic uplift of the basin and highlands. (After R. B. Rutledge, courtesy of the American Association of Petroleum Geologists.)

were sometimes connected into a broad land area in central Utah and northern Arizona, and sometimes separated by channels that allowed the sea to enter the basin. A group of basins separated by swells occupied eastern Nevada and southern Idaho. In northern Utah the Oquirrh basin, the most rapidly subsiding of the late Paleozoic basins, accumulated 25,000 feet of Pennsylvanian and Permian sandstones. Much of Wyoming was a shelf area where about 300 feet of calcareous sandstone, variously known as the Quadrant, Tensleep, or Webber Formation, were laid down. These Pennsylvanian and early Permian sandstones have large cross-beds that have been interpreted as dune structures. A study of the direction of dip of the cross-bedding (the bedding in dunes dips downwind) has shown that for much of late Paleozoic time the wind blew from the north obliquely toward the paleoequator (see Fig. 6–8), which crossed the United States from New York to California. The winds recorded

by the cross-bedding in the Carboniferous sandstones may have been the trade winds of 300 million years ago.

As soon as the cores of the Colorado uplifts were exposed by erosion of the covering sediments, they began to shed vast quantities of arkosic debris. **Arkose** is the feldspar-rich member of the sandstone group and is formed when granitic igneous rocks are eroded and the particles deposited rapidly in a nearby basin. From Pennsylvanian to mid-Permian time a thick succession of these red sandstones accumulated in basins adjacent to the Front Range and Uncompahgre uplifts. East of the Colorado Front Range these late Paleozoic sandstones are tilted vertically to form the fantastically weathered rocks of the "Garden of the Gods."

The Paradox Basin

Transgression of the Absaroka sea into the Four Corners area began in Early Pennsylvanian time (Morrow Age) over a surface of

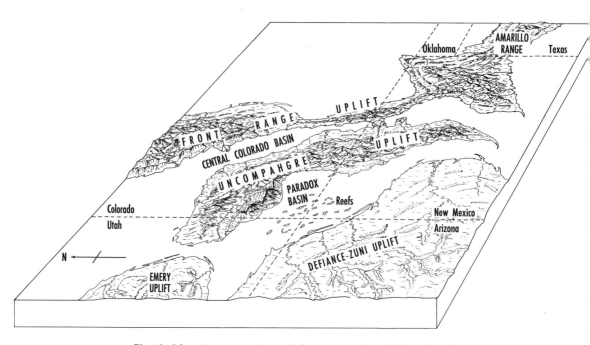

Fig. 8–29. Reconstruction of the geography of the Four Corners region in Middle Pennsylvanian time. The observer is looking from northern Arizona, across Colorado, to the inland sea. In the foreground evaporites accumulate in the Paradox basin, and reefs grow on the shelf on its southwest flank.

sediments of the Paradox basin into gentle folds, triggering the movement of the salt. The arkose, eroded from the uplift, accumulated to a greater depth in the synclinal troughs than in the anticlinal crests, squeezing the salt laterally toward the region of lesser hydrostatic pressure under the anticlines. Unconformities along the edges of the anticlines record the periodic uplift and erosion of the folds, as more Pennsylvanian and Permian sediments loaded the basin and their cores filled with salt from the neighboring synclines. Although most of the salt had been squeezed into the anticlines by the end of the Paleozoic Era, some growth of the structures seems to have persisted until Jurassic time.

The late Paleozoic geology of the Four Corners region illustrates several problems of historical geology. The behavior of yoked basins and the characteristic arkosic sediments derived from the erosion of their complementary dome can be investigated. The extraordinary persistence of some of these Colorado uplifts from the Pennsylvanian Period, through peneplanation in Cretaceous time, to rejuvenation in the Cenozoic Era is a phenomenon needing explanation. We see that salt can be deposited in basins surrounded by highlands as well as in the lowland basins of the early Paleozoic, and that this salt is capable of movement under pressure. Finally, studies of the cross-bedding in Pennsylvanian sandstones could put to good use the methods available for plotting ancient wind directions and relating them to movements of the equator.

Permian Basin of West Texas

The area immediately surrounding the Front Range and Uncompahgre arches continued to receive a halo of continental sediments from the highlands until the end of the Permian Period. Slowly, the sea that had occupied the mid-continent region for almost a period ebbed away toward the southwest, and by mid-Permian time, Kansas and Oklahoma were sites of continental deposition. In coastal lagoons evaporites were deposited in this regressive sea, forming salt deposits of economic importance in Kansas.

The Absaroka sea withdrew toward west Texas and southeastern New Mexico to a basin that was the site in Permian time of the most intensively studied barrier reef on the continent. During the early and middle Paleozoic Era, the southeast corner of New Mexico was the site of the slowly subsiding Tobosa basin, flanked on the east by the broad Conchos arch and on the south by the Ouachita geosyncline. During the Pennsylvanian Period the simple basin was divided by the Pecos arch and the Diablo platform (Fig. 8–23). In Late Pennsylvanian time the Ouachita geosyncline was being deformed, causing clastic sediments from the rising highlands to the east, and to a lesser extent to the south, to cover central Texas (Fig. 8–31A).

By Early Permian time the facies and topographic features that were to characterize the Permian history of the west Texas basin were established (Fig. 8–32). North of the highlands rising in the Ouachita geosyncline the Marfa, Delaware, and Midland basins developed (Fig. 8–32), separated by the Diablo platform and the Central basin platform (an extension of the Pecos arch). Early Permian sediments show a similar facies distribution of pale, granular shell limestone on the shelf north of the basins and the platforms between them, and black, bituminous limestones and shales in the basins where restriction of the circulation of the sea tended to cause stagnant water to form (Fig. 8–31B, C). Restriction of access of normal sea water to a shallow basin by a shallow sill in a dry climate will result in increased salinity and the deposition of anhydrite and salt; but if the basin is deep and the sill relatively deep, normal circulation may be maintained in the surface water while the water below the level of the sill stagnates and black, organically rich sediments are deposited. Without circulation of water the oxygen supply at the bottom of the basin is not renewed, but is used up by bacteria in the decay of organic matter falling from animals living

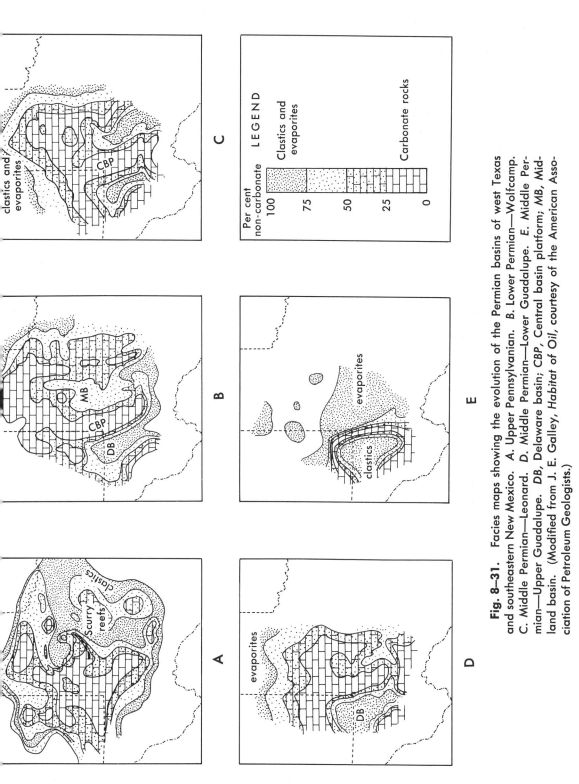

Fig. 8–31. Facies maps showing the evolution of the Permian basins of west Texas and southeastern New Mexico. *A.* Upper Pennsylvanian. *B.* Lower Permian—Wolfcamp. *C.* Middle Permian—Leonard. *D.* Middle Permian—Lower Guadalupe. *E.* Middle Permian—Upper Guadalupe. *DB,* Delaware basin; *CBP,* Central basin platform; *MB,* Midland basin. (Modified from J. E. Galley, *Habitat of Oil,* courtesy of the American Association of Petroleum Geologists.)

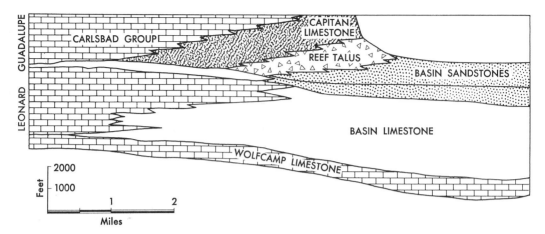

Fig. 8–34. Cross-section of the Middle Permian sediments of the Guadalupe Mountains showing the relationship of the reef to the other facies. (After N. D. Newell and P. B. King.)

posited in deeper water without leaving any trace of their passage in the sediments of the shelf. Organic matter buried in the bituminous black sandstones and limestones of the basin facies is thought to have been the source of the petroleum now found in the platform areas.

In the lagoonal environment behind the barrier reef the water was very shallow. Limestone and dolomite were deposited just behind the reef; but near the shore, farther from the open sea, gypsum and anhydrite were precipitated (Fig. 8–31D). In the lagoonal limestones of the Carlsbad Group, near Carlsbad, New Mexico, ground water has subsequently dissolved one of the largest cavern systems in the world. At the coastline in central New Mexico, the lagoonal evaporites pass into red silts and sands, with which the streams from the Oklahoma and Colorado uplifts had by this time covered most of northern Texas and New Mexico.

Although the principal framebuilders seem to have been algae and sponges, many other animals inhabited the Capitan reef and contributed their hard parts to the lagoonal, reefal, and basinal sediments. Figure 8–35 shows the distribution of these fossils across the reef as inferred by paleontologists. These relationships are inferred rather than directly observed because most of the fossils found

show evidence of having been transported and broken by the waves and may have been deposited far from their natural habitat. The pelecypods and gastropods preferred the lagoon just behind the reef barrier. The brachiopods and echinoderms lived in greatest abundance in the shallow, agitated water of the reef flat itself. Bryozoa favored the crest of the slope leading to the stagnant waters of the basin.

Late in Middle Permian time the Midland basin became highly saline and evaporites began to fill it (Fig. 8–31E). We deduce that either reef growth blocked the entrance of the sea to the west, or the entrance was raised to form a sill. At the end of Middle Permian time a similar fate overtook the Delaware basin and the reefs were killed by the rising salinity. The climate of the Late Permian time must have been exceedingly dry, for evaporation of sea water and precipitation of evaporites proceeded rapidly. As water was removed by evaporation, more was drawn in over the sill to maintain the level in the basin, and beds of thinly laminated anhydrite and salt were precipitated. Each pair of dark and light anhydrite laminae is taken to be the deposit of a single year. By a count of the number of these annual layers or, varves, the time taken to deposit the 4500 feet of evaporites in the Delaware basin can be

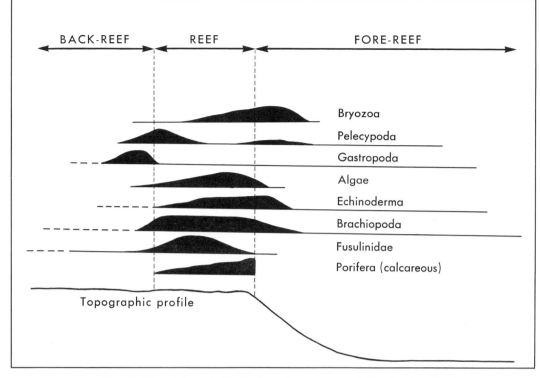

BACK-REEF   REEF   FORE-REEF

Bryozoa

Pelecypoda

Gastropoda

Algae

Echinoderma

Brachiopoda

Fusulinidae

Porifera (calcareous)

Topographic profile

Fig. 8–35. Inferred distribution of organisms of the Capitan Reef, west Texas. (From N. D. Newell and others, *The Permian Reef Complex.* San Francisco: W. H. Freeman and Co., 1953.)

calculated to be about one-third of a million years. This is one of the few deposits for which geologists believe they can determine accurately the rate of sedimentation. The salinity of the waters in the basins reached the stage at which potash salts precipitated; today, the annual value of production from these deposits in New Mexico approaches 100 million dollars.

The saline sea freshened for a short time at the end of the Permian Period and a thin dolomite formation was laid down above the thick evaporites. Thereafter the sea withdrew southward as the interior of the continent was uplifted and the Paleozoic Era drew to a close.

The distribution of facies in the west Texas basins demonstrates again that carbonates are shallow-water sediments of platform areas and may pass abruptly into detrital sediments accumulating in deeper water around them. The basins were deeper than those of the early Paleozoic, and stagnant conditions in

the bottom waters were more persistent. Such stagnant-water shales are also found in the Devonian basins of Alberta; the facies is thought to be the source of the oil in the Devonian reefs just as the basinal sediments of west Texas are thought to be the source of the Permian oil. The west Texas reefs have much more extensive talus deposits than those in Alberta. The contrast between the framebuilding organisms of the Capitan reef and those of earlier Paleozoic reefs reminds us that as some animals become extinct (for instance, the stromatoporoids, which were so important in the early and middle Paleozoic), others evolve to take their place in the environments available. The oil whose production has spurred the investigation of the Permian basins comes mainly from stratigraphic traps in Permian rocks associated with the reefs, but oil has also been found in structural and unconformity traps throughout the stratigraphic column down to the Cambrian System.

TRIASSIC RED BEDS AND DESERT SANDSTONES

The Era Boundary

The boundary between the Triassic and Permian systems is also the boundary between the Paleozoic and Mesozoic eras. Eras are defined on the basis of the total aspect of the life of the major intervals of geological time, and basic changes in the nature of marine invertebrate life mark the boundary (see Part V). Several of the largest divisions of the brachiopods, bryozoa, crinoids, and corals, along with the trilobites, became extinct at the end of the Paleozoic Era. North America is not a favorable area to study this faunal change: over large areas of the United States the beds at the boundary are continental, and the vertebrate fossils found in these beds do not show the faunal change so evident in invertebrate life. In Canada, although the basal Triassic rocks are marine, Late Permian beds are missing generally. The most famous section of the Permian–Triassic transition is the Salt Range of West Pakistan, where Lower Triassic limestones and sandstones succeed uppermost Permian shales. The beds throughout the succession are highly fossiliferous; yet of the 102 genera that have been identified in formations adjacent to the era boundary, only five are common to the two eras.

In west Texas the highest Permian beds are overlain unconformably by Upper Triassic red beds. In Colorado and Wyoming, however, evidence for any break in deposition is hard to find, and geologists disagree as to whether the relationship is disconformable or conformable.

Continental Beds of the Absaroka Regression

On the Colorado Plateau the Triassic System consists of three formations of nonmarine shales and sandstones with minor marine interbeds: the Moenkopi, Shinarump, and Chinle formations. The sedimentary structures and textures indicate that these formations were deposited largely by streams flowing from uplifts in southern Idaho and Arizona. As the facies maps (Figs. 8–36 and 8–37) show, the stream deposits grade westward into marine sediments in Nevada, but the scarcity of Late Triassic sediments in this area makes the shoreline difficult to place. Water percolating along buried stream channels in the Shinarump conglomerate has precipitated uranium salts. Successful prospecting for uranium on the Colorado Plateau depends in large part on the use of stratigraphic analysis and geophysics to locate promising channels.

Among the most interesting of the few fossils found in the Chinle Sandstone are the trunks of petrified conifers (Fig. 8–38). The wood of the trees that once grew on the Chinle landscape has been faithfully replaced by silica-bearing solutions, so that the microscopic structure of the wood is now preserved as brightly colored silica. The

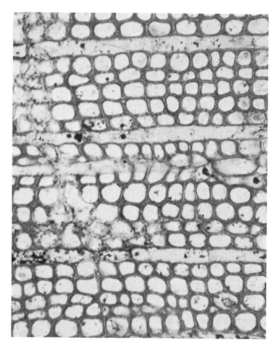

Fig. 8–38. Photomicrograph of a thin section of petrified wood from the Petrified Forest in the Chinle Formation, Arizona. Although this rock is all silica, note how the cellular wood structure has been preserved in the replacement process (magnification × 180).

Fig. 8–39. Dune cross-bedding in the Navajo Sandstone of Early Jurassic age, Zion–Mt. Carmel Highway, Utah. (Courtesy of the U. S. Geological Survey.)

larger trunks are more than 100 feet long and 10 feet in diameter at the base. Because of their resistance to erosion they lie about on the present surface as if they had recently fallen. From the evidence of its plants and sedimentary structures, the Chinle Formation is believed to have been deposited in a humid climate in broad alluvial basins.

The upper division of the Triassic System in the Colorado Plateau is characterized by clean sandstones, cross-bedded on a large scale, which are interpreted as dune deposits (Fig. 8–39). Thousands of feet of these cross-bedded sandstones of the Wingate and Navajo formations accumulated in the Colorado Plateau region in Late Triassic and Early Jurassic times. The systemic boundary is difficult to place in these unfossiliferous formations.

The desert sandstones of the Triassic–Jurassic boundary are the youngest deposits of the Absaroka sequence. The major cycle of sedimentation that had begun at the close of the Mississippian Period had taken more than three full periods to complete. The marine phase was over by mid-Permian time and the Triassic red beds can be considered to be the record of the final stages of the regression. They represent a type of cratonic deposit much different from the marine limestones and evaporites of the Paleozoic.

SUMMARY

The extent of deformation and erosion represented by the unconformity between two sequences is shown by a paleogeological map. Such a map may aid exploration for oil by suggesting drilling sites where porous beds are cut off by an impervious bed at the unconformity.

The sandstone layer basal to the Kaskaskia sequence is distributed irregularly. Study of its heavy minerals gives evidence of its source.

Evaporites, especially halite, once deposited, are subject to dissolution by groundwater, particularly on the flanks of sedimentary basins but also in the center, resulting in collapse and brecciation of overlying beds.

Middle Devonian reefs, bedded limestones, and evaporites in the Williston basin were

III

THE BACKBONE OF
NORTH AMERICA

Fig. 9–1. Mount McKinley (20,230 feet), the highest peak in North America. (Courtesy of Bradford Washburn.)

metamorphism; and the style of deformation in various parts of the crust much better than in any other North American mountain belt.

The geological and geographical divisions of the Cordillera can be studied by reference to a cross-section through the mountain system in the central United States from California to Colorado (Fig. 9–2). If we cross the Cordillera at 40°N. latitude we encounter first the highly folded Mesozoic graywackes and green schists, the volcanics, and the cherts of the Coast Ranges of California. Behind them lies the Great Valley of California, floored with relatively undisturbed Cenozoic sediments. The long western slope of the Sierra Nevada, eroded from a Mesozoic batholith and remnants of the metamorphosed rocks of its roof, borders the valley on the east. An active volcano, Lassen Peak, lies in the Sierra Nevada along our traverse. A zone represented by the Coast Range, Great Valley, and Sierra Nevada provinces and characterized by batholiths, volcanics, volcanoes, and intensely deformed geosynclinal sedimentary rocks can be followed northward through Oregon and Washington and the Coast Range of British

Columbia to the Alaska Range (Fig. 9–3).

The steep eastern face of the Sierra Nevada overlooks the Basin and Range Province of complexly folded and thrust-faulted Paleozoic rocks, which are cut by normal faults into blocks which stand up as mountain ranges in the desert plain. In the western ranges of this province the rocks are graywackes, volcanics, and slates, but in the eastern ranges they are limestones and clean sandstones. In central Utah, the Basin and Range structure changes abruptly at the margin of the Colorado Plateau, a broad desert upland of nearly flat-lying Paleozoic and Mesozoic sedimentary rocks. The Basin and Range and Colorado Plateau structures do not continue northward but are truncated by the flows of the Columbia lava plateau in Idaho, Oregon, and Washington. Still farther north, this central zone of the Cordillera is occupied by the interior ranges and plateaus of central British Columbia and the Yukon Plateau, both underlain by intensely deformed and metamorphosed sedimentary and volcanic rocks intruded by batholiths.

East of the Colorado Plateau the structure becomes more complex and the topography

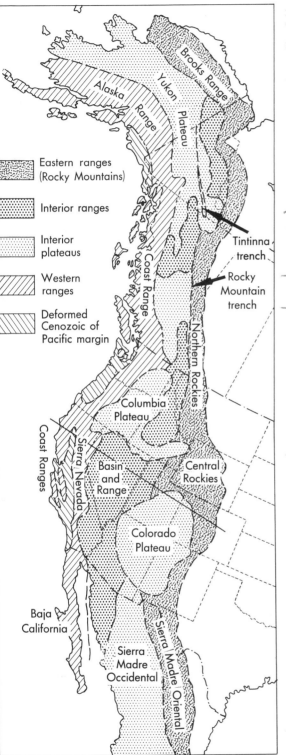

Fig. 9–2. Major physiographic divisions of the North American Cordillera. The line of cross-section discussed in the text is marked.

rises into the peaks of the Rocky Mountains. The Colorado segment of the Rockies was formed largely by mountains eroded from Precambrian granites and gneisses; but along strike in Wyoming, Montana, Canada, and the Brooks Range of northern Alaska, the Rockies are composed of faulted limestones, sandstones, and shales.

Some generalizations can be made from the diversity of mountain types within the Cordillera. The mountain system can be divided longitudinally into three zones: the western ranges, composed of intrusive and extrusive igneous rocks and highly deformed schists, slates, and graywackes; a zone of central plateaus underlain by batholiths, lava fields, and some highly deformed and metamorphosed sedimentary rocks; and an eastern Rocky Mountain zone, largely composed of folded and faulted limestones and sandstones without volcanics or large igneous intrusions. The present or past volcanoes are, with a few exceptions, located along the Pacific side of the Cordilleran system. Deformation and metamorphism are intense in the western mountains and seem to have affected the deeper layers of the crust; but in the eastern ranges the results of compression are superficial, characteristically thrust faults of low inclination and great displacement. Where the basement rocks have been affected by deformation in the eastern mountains, the movement was generally vertical. Batholithic intrusions are largely confined to the western and plateau ranges. The present differences between the eastern and western ranges are reflections of past differences in tectonic environment.

The western ranges and, at some latitudes, parts of the central ranges were formed from the Cordilleran geosyncline. The site of the geosyncline can be identified during geosynclinal evolution by the presence of volcanics, graywacke, shale, argillite, and chert in the sedimentary record, and—after geosynclinal revolution by metamorphism—granitization, intrusion, and intense structural deformation. The eastern zone and parts of the central zone of the Cordillera were founded on the edge of the craton.

Fig. 9–5. *Collenia undosa,* a stromatolite from the Belt Group of Montana. (Courtesy of the U. S. Geological Survey.)

Granite Gorge (Fig. 9–6). In southeast British Columbia, rocks of the Purcell Group, up to 45,000 feet thick, can be correlated with the Belt Group on the basis of the succession of lava flows in each unit. Isotopic age determinations on the rocks of the Belt and Purcell groups are not consistent but suggest that the rocks are about 1 billion years old.

Transition to the Paleozoic

Broad folding and normal faulting of this great thickness of sedimentary rock formed a highland along the margin of the late Precambrian continent from which streams carried sediment to a new basin on the west, where it accumulated to form the Windermere Group of northern Washington and southern British Columbia. The great thickness of lava flows present in this group, and in other late Precambrian groups believed to be correlative, indicates the presence of many volcanoes in the Windermere sea and the

Fig. 9–6. Grand Canyon of the Colorado River showing the two unconformities within the Precambrian part of the record and the Paleozoic rocks that form the steplike cliffs above the Granite Gorge in the foreground. (Courtesy of the U. S. Geological Survey.)

beginning of intense volcanism that was to characterize much of the later history of the Cordilleran geosyncline.

The Windermere sea moved slowly eastward, and during its advance, Precambrian time came to a close and the Paleozoic Era began. Three formations at the top of the Windermere Group were originally considered to be Precambrian in age, but because they have now been shown to grade laterally into beds containing Lower Cambrian faunas, they have been moved to the Cambrian System. No unconformity exists in eastern British Columbia between rocks classified as Precambrian and Paleozoic. The problems of defining the base of the Cambrian System have already been discussed (Chapter 7).

From the Precambrian record we can deduce that about a billion years ago the western margin of the continent was depressed along a line that crossed the structures of the older Precambrian rocks. Along the cratonic margin, a great thickness of sedimentary and volcanic rocks accumulated before the end of Precambrian time, perhaps as a coastal plain. The evidence suggests that the sedimentary rocks were all derived ultimately from the Shield to the east, and little evidence of an island arc to the west or of the paleogeography west of the site of deposition can be found. Our knowledge of conditions west of the thick Precambrian sequences is limited by the absence of either Precambrian or early Paleozoic sedimentary rocks in the western Cordillera.

CAMBRIAN ROCKS OF THE GEOSYNCLINAL MARGIN

Although the Early Cambrian sea spread farther eastward out of the geosyncline than the late Precambrian sea, the pattern of facies deposited in it did not change markedly. Sandstones whose cross-bedding indicates that they were transported from the east (see Fig. 7–9) continued to accumulate until a thickness of 10,000 feet was attained in southern California and 4000 feet had been deposited just north of the Continental Divide in Canada.

Middle Cambrian Rocks

As the shoreline moved eastward away from the geosyncline, the sand supplied from the Shield did not reach the Cordilleran area, and dolomite, limestone, and shale became the characteristic sedimentary rocks. Limestone, always a shallow-water sediment, was deposited along the rise on the edge of the craton that has been called the West Alberta ridge in Devonian paleogeography, while shale was laid down in deeper water on either side.

Middle Cambrian rocks are commonly referred to as the Albertan Series because they are grandly exposed in Alberta and British Columbia north of the Continental Divide, where they form a rugged terrane with towering cliffs and a relief of over 5000 feet (Fig. 9–7). The Cambrian geology of this mountain fastness was described systematically by the American paleontologist Charles D. Walcott. Since his work, the succession of Middle Cambrian beds has been revised as summarized in Fig. 9–8.

The Burgess Shale

Walcott's chief contributions to the geology of this region were paleontological. In 1910, he made one of the most significant discoveries of all time on the trail through the Burgess Pass. This trail starts from the town of Field and zigzags up the steep side of Kicking Horse Valley to a height of 7000 feet. From Burgess Pass it swings eastward toward Emerald Lake along the flank of a knife-edged ridge joining the twin peaks of Mt. Wapta and Mt. Field. On the trail below this ridge, one of the pack horses in Walcott's train overturned a slab of argillite, revealing fossils pressed like lustrous films on the bedding planes. This slab from the scree was easily traced back up the slope to the bedrock on "Fossil Ridge" from which it

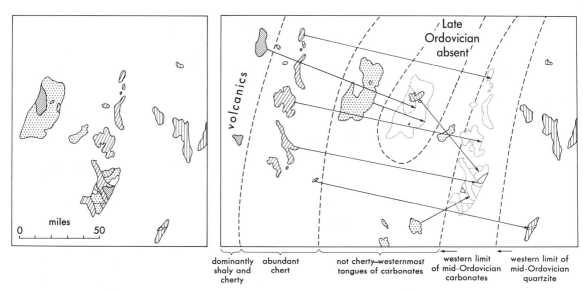

Fig. 9–9. Palinspastic restoration of the Ordovician rocks of central Nevada. *A.* The present position of the fault-bounded blocks with the different facies shown by different patterns. *B.* The present position of the blocks (dotted outlines) with the blocks moved westward to positions suggested by their facies to form a reasonable reconstruction of the succession of facies belts. Arrows indicate the direction along which some of the blocks were thrust eastward to their present position. (Modified from Marshall Kay and J. P. Crawford, courtesy of the Geological Society of America.)

produced when lava is extruded below water; others are altered pyroclastic sediments whose particles were blown out of a volcano. The "pillows" are believed to be formed by the repeated extrusion of ellipsoidal masses of viscous lava which cools rapidly in the water. The chert is in thin beds commonly interlayered with thin shale beds. The fine lamination and local complex contortion of the bedding suggest that these rocks were laid down on a low slope in deep water, below the zone agitated by the waves, and slumped and slid into folds while still unconsolidated. The sandstone beds, which are not common in these successions, were probably emplaced by turbidity currents bringing wave-washed particles from shallow water to the deeper basin of deposition. The geosynclinal facies contains only a few fossils of floating animals that lived near sea level, for the ocean floor was poorly oxygenated and inhospitable to life. In Ordovician and Silurian geosynclinal rocks these fossils are almost entirely graptolites.

Lava flows and pyroclastic sediments suggest that a volcanic island arc was located near the site of deposition. Limestone lenses containing archaeocyathids (see p. 411) may represent small reefs that fringed these volcanic islands in Cambrian time. Finely divided volcanic glass is ejected explosively from volcanoes and devitrifies on the sea floor, releasing silica into the sea water. If animals or plants which use silica, such as radiolaria, diatoms, or sponges, abound, they will extract the hydrous silica to form opaline shells and leave them behind as a siliceous ooze on the ocean floor when they die (Fig. 9–10). If no such organisms are present in the sea, the silica may form on the ocean floor a gel which in time will consolidate to chert. Chert in geosynclinal assemblages occurs as a bedded deposit or as nodules within limestone or other sedimentary rocks; outside the geosynclines, bedded cherts are rare, but nodular chert may be common. Some bedded and nodular cherts contain traces of radiolarians. Those that are unfossiliferous

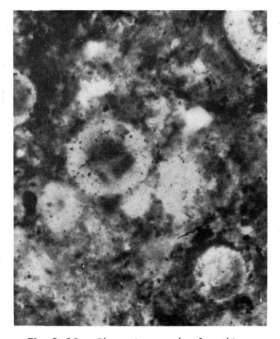

Fig. 9–10. Photomicrograph of a thin section of black chert from the Schoonover Formation of Carboniferous age, Independence Range, Nevada. Note the small tests of radiolaria (magnification × 150). (From J. J. Fagan, courtesy of the Geological Society of America.)

may have been formed inorganically or had their delicate fossils destroyed by dissolution before they were consolidated. Although the geosynclinal environment of deposition can be reconstructed in a general way, neither the facies changes within the geosyncline nor the position of the island arcs within the trough can be accurately outlined, because of the fragmentation of the record by three orogenies and its destruction by many periods of erosion.

At scattered places in the western Cordillera a record of the thick early Paleozoic geosynclinal facies has been preserved. Along the border of Idaho and Washington, argillaceous rocks of Ordovician and Silurian ages are tens of thousands of feet thick. Lenses of crystalline limestone interbedded with slates in southwestern Oregon have been known for many years to contain Devonian fossils, but recently Silurian fossils have also

been identified in rocks of this assemblage. Devonian lavas have been reported from extreme northwestern Washington. One of the best records of the Paleozoic rocks of the Cordilleran geosyncline is preserved in the panhandle region of southern Alaska, where graywacke, cherty slate, limestone, and conglomerate, interbedded with andesitic lavas and tuff, form a succession 21,000 feet thick representing Ordovician to Early Devonian time. Similar rocks underlie much of central Alaska.

This evidence establishes that a geosyncline with volcanic source areas, probably island arcs, occupied the western coast of North America from California to Alaska in early Paleozoic time. Local angular unconformities show that the Cordilleran trough was deformed in one place or another almost continuously, but evidence for a general quickening of the orogenic processes in the middle of the Paleozoic Era is much more widespread.

Early Orogeny in the Geosyncline

During Late Devonian and Mississippian times, the early Paleozoic sediments of western and central Nevada were folded and carried eastward along a major, almost horizontal, thrust surface, the Roberts Mountain thrust (Fig. 9–11). Above this thrust, the geosynclinal facies moved eastward, overriding the cratonic rocks and forming a highland that shed detritus as it rose. Because the structural and stratigraphic evidence is displayed in the Antler Peak area of Nevada, this orogeny has been called the Antler orogeny, and the belt passing across central Nevada from north to south where its effects are recorded is called the Antler orogenic belt. Clastic sediments from the Antler highland spread eastward over the edge of the craton and formed thick sedimentary units interfingering on their eastern margin with limestone that accumulated in western Nevada and eastern Utah during Mississippian and Pennsylvanian times. The Upper Mississippian Tonka Conglomerate (2000–3000 feet) and Diamond Peak Sandstone

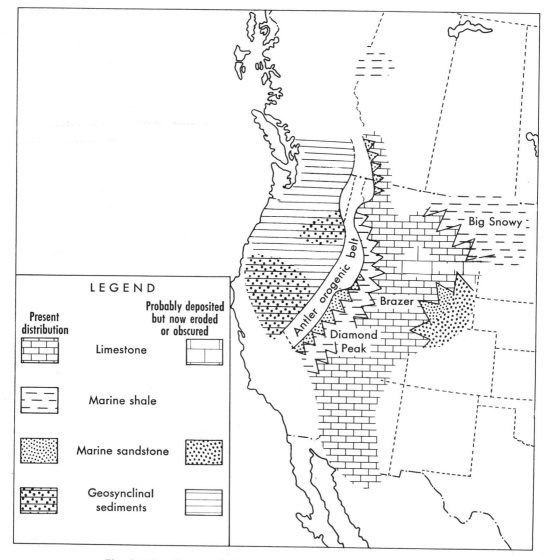

Fig. 9–12. Facies of the Upper Mississippian Chester Series in western North America, showing the clastics derived from the Antler orogenic belt and the shrinking of the sea in the Williston basin.

(3000 feet) are parts of the Antler clastics (Fig. 9–12).

A large area of southern British Columbia is underlain by metamorphic rocks of doubtful age which constitute the Shuswap Group. They are overlain unconformably by Permian beds, but the age of their metamorphism and deformation cannot be accurately placed. It could have occurred any time between late Precambrian (the best guess as to their age) and Permian time. Farther north in

British Columbia, in the Cariboo district, the evidence for mid-Paleozoic orogeny is better, for the beds below the pre-Permian unconformity are Lower Cambrian sandstones. This vaguely dated period of mid-Paleozoic orogeny has been called the Cariboo orogeny. If it was synchronous with the Devonian Antler orogeny of Nevada, it may be reflected in the Late Devonian sandstones that accumulated above the reefal limestones of the cratonic margin a short distance to the east.

Farther north, in the Yukon and Northwest Territories and the Brooks Range of Alaska, the upper part of the Devonian System, known as the Imperial Formation, consists of 6000 feet of coarse, deltaic clastic sediments (see Fig. 13–3). In the Richardson Mountains of this area the Devonian rocks have been faulted and tilted before being overlain by Mississippian carbonates, which formed an angular unconformity. In the nearby Barn Mountains a granitic intrusion dated as 353 million years old may have been associated with this Late Devonian episode of orogeny.

Although the evidence is scattered, it is consistent in pointing to a widespread orogeny in the Cordillera in Devonian time. Clastic sediments derived from the mid-Paleozoic highlands spread as wedge-shaped bodies out to the margin of the craton at the north and south ends of the geosyncline, but did not form in the middle section.

LATE PALEOZOIC ROCKS AND OROGENY

The Geosynclinal Filling

The sediments and volcanic rocks that entered the Cordilleran geosyncline in late Paleozoic time are similar to those deposited earlier in the era, but the pace of volcanism seems to have increased toward a climax of extrusive activity at the end of the era. After the Antler orogeny in Nevada, coarse conglomerate, limestone, and shale of Pennsylvanian and Permian ages covered the disrupted rocks, while to the west, in the geosyncline, the Havallah succession of coarse clastic rocks, shale, sandstone, chert, and volcanics was laid down to a thickness of over 8000 feet (Fig. 9–11). In the Antler Peak area structural disturbances continued into the late Paleozoic and flows and pyroclastic sediments more than 10,000 feet thick accumulated in Permian and early Triassic time. Late Paleozoic sedimentary formations rich in volcanics and of similar great thickness occur in the Sierra Nevada, in the Klamath Mountains of southwest Oregon and northern California, in the Blue Mountains of central Oregon, and in eastern Oregon. Farther north, the record of late Paleozoic volcanism is preserved in the Cache Creek Group of British Columbia. Chert in thin-bedded units of great thickness, as nodules in limestone, in breccias, and disseminated through other sedimentary rocks is the most conspicuous rock type in this group, but volcanics and limestone are also common. These rocks reach thicknesses of 25,000 feet in the central part of the province. The trace of the Permian volcanic trough recorded in sedimentary rocks of great thickness and in flows and tuffs can be followed through northern British Columbia and the southern Yukon into southern Alaska (Fig. 9–13).

Influence of Volcanism on Cratonic Sedimentation

The particles from explosive volcanoes active along the west coast during late Paleozoic time caused the deposition of chert in the geosyncline but were also carried eastward by winds and deposited at the margin of the craton. Because of structural disturbances subsequent to deposition, the bedded chert of the geosynclinal facies cannot be traced directly into the shelf facies to the east, but the chert content of the shelf sediment (Fig. 9–14) decreases systematically away from the Cordilleran and Ouachita geosynclines. Apparently, near the volcanoes the amount of silica derived from the submarine weathering of volcanic ash was sufficient to form bedded cherts; farther from the source, where the supply was less, the silica took the form of nodular replacements of other sediments.

In Middle Permian time, the peculiar Phosphoria Formation was deposited at the edge of the continent in the shallow sea over Wyoming and eastern Idaho. Although contemporaneous with the reefs and evaporites of west Texas, the Phosphoria sea appears to have been separated from them by a low land mass formed by the Colorado uplifts and their halo of detritus. The Phosphoria Formation consists of limestone, cherty lime-

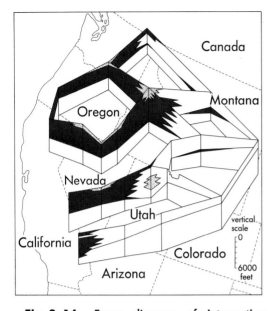

Fig. 9–14. Fence diagram of intersecting stratigraphic sections of the Mississippian rocks of the western United States, showing the decrease in siliceous sediments (shaded areas) in the system from the geosynclinal to the shelf facies. The stippled pattern represents sandstone; the unpatterned areas are other sediments. (Courtesy of H. J. Bissell, Society of Economic Mineralogists and Paleontologists.)

Late Paleozoic Orogeny

We have evidence that local orogeny occurred episodically throughout the Paleozoic in the Cordillera, but evidence of a major period of mountain building between Late Permian and Late Triassic time is found throughout the length of the mountain system.

The evidence has been brought together by Robert H. Dott, Jr., who groups it into five classes:

1. The widespread volcanics in both the Permian and Triassic systems, whose occurrence has already been reviewed, reflect increasing structural disturbance and igneous activity in the geosyncline.

2. Lower and Middle Triassic rocks are missing from the geosyncline from Oregon to Alaska, and in Nevada and California are mostly volcanics. The lack of sedimentary rocks suggests that at the beginning of the Mesozoic Era the Cordilleran area was lifted out of the zone of deposition.

3. Angular unconformities between Permian sedimentary and volcanic rocks and the overlapping Upper Triassic marine sediments are found at widely scattered localities in the geosyncline. In northwestern British Columbia this unconformable relationship is general. In the Okanagan Valley of Washington, Late Triassic limestone unconformably overlies the deformed greenstones of the Late Paleozoic Anarchist Group.

4. The conglomerates which overlie these unconformities contain fragments of the Paleozoic rocks that were uplifted and eroded at the end of the era. For instance, in southeastern Alaska the Late Triassic beds contain fragments of Permian sedimentary rocks and greenstones, as well as granites which are believed to have been intruded in the Devonian Period.

5. These conglomerates locally contain fragments of **ultrabasic** rocks which are common intrusions in the Permian rocks of the Cordillera. Ultrabasic rocks are igneous rocks composed almost entirely of dark minerals rich in iron and magnesium, such as pyroxene and olivine.

The ultrabasic intrusions in geosynclinal rocks are believed by Harry Hess to be characteristic of the certain stage in the geosynclinal cycle when the trough—or tectogene, in his terminology (see p. 85)—is first bent sharply down into the subcrustal layers. He has suggested that these small intrusive bodies occur in two bands on either side of the axis of the trough. In the Cordillera the two bands are not well defined geographically, nor are the times of their intrusion dated accurately. Some of the ultrabasic bodies must have been emplaced later in Mesozoic time, for they cut Jurassic rocks, but a great many of these bodies are confined to Permian rocks. Whether they were intruded before the end of Permian time is in many places unknown, since they are not seen in contact with the overlying Triassic rocks. The presence in some Triassic conglomerates of ultrabasic fragments proves that at least a few of the ultrabasic intrusions were associated with the Permian orogeny. The universal association of greenstone, chert, and ultrabasic intrusions with geosynclinal facies was first pointed out by G. Steinmann and has come to be known as "Steinmann's trinity." No name has been widely accepted for this orogeny, but William H. White has suggested the term Cassiar for the deformation in British Columbia, and the term Somona has been used for the mid-Permian movements of western Nevada.

Because the structures produced by late Paleozoic orogeny have been obscured by later periods of deformation, the height and extent of the late Paleozoic mountains can only be estimated from the clastic sediments derived from their erosion. Coarse conglomerates in the Permian and Triassic rocks of Washington, California, and Nevada suggest high relief locally in the geosyncline. However, on the cratonic margin to the east, where major uplifts of the geosyncline subsequently caused a flood of deltaic sediments, Permian and Triassic rocks are conspicuously fine-grained and thin. Early Triassic marine rocks are extensively distributed along the cratonic margin (in contrast to the geosyncline) and consist of limestones in the United States and calcareous siltstones in Canada (see Fig. 8–36). The oldest Permian rocks in this belt are the cherty and phosphatic limestones of the Phosphoria Formation and its equivalents. We can only conclude that although local areas of high relief existed in the Cordilleran geosyncline at the end of the Paleozoic Era, the geosyncline as a whole was not subjected to mountain-building forces comparable to those that deformed and uplifted it in late Mesozoic time.

SUMMARY

The North American Cordillera can be divided longitudinally into western ranges composed of intrusive and extrusive igneous rocks, schists, slates, and graywackes; a central zone of plateaus underlain by diverse geology; and an eastern, or Rocky Mountain, zone of thrust- or block-faulted and folded limestone and sandstone.

A great thickness of late Precambrian sedimentary rocks now exposed in the eastern Cordillera indicates that subsidence of the continental margin along a line which crossed older structures began in late Precambrian time.

The Burgess Shale accumulated in an isolated area in the Middle Cambrian sea where the bottom was stagnant and without scavengers. It contains a remarkable fauna of soft-bodied fossils, including the internal organs of some of the animals.

The geosynclinal facies of slate, graywacke, volcanics, and chert is well illustrated by the lower Paleozoic rocks of central Nevada, but the relationships of these rocks are obscured by their structural dislocation along faults. Palinspastic maps can be constructed to show the position of the facies before deformation.

Deformation in the Cordilleran geosyncline was probably frequent but was most intense in the middle Paleozoic Antler orogeny and the late Paleozoic Somona–Cassiar orogeny.

Volcanism may be reflected in bedded cherts in the geosyncline and in nodular cherty deposits in the adjacent shelf areas resulting from the release of silica during "submarine weathering" of pyroclastic sediments on the sea floor.

Evidence for a period of orogeny in a geosyncline may include: volcanics, missing parts of the sedimentary record, angular unconformities, and conglomerates containing igneous intrusives.

Ultrabasic intrusives characterize geosynclinal belts, but in the Cordillera they are not systematically distributed in space or time.

Despite the structural evidence of late Paleozoic orogeny, sediments on the edge of the craton show little evidence of highlands along the West Coast.

QUESTIONS

1. Describe the way in which a historical geologist would construct a palinspastic map of a deformed area.

2. Explain why the division of the cratonic rocks into sequences cannot be extended into the Paleozoic succession of the Cordilleran geosyncline.

3. Describe the way in which each of the following typical geosynclinal rocks is deposited: pillow lava, bedded chert, greenstone, tuff, turbidite, graywacke with graded bedding.

4. On the basis of what features of structure and lithology would you recognize an ancient geosyncline? A geosyncline now in the stage of subsidence?

REFERENCES AND SUGGESTED READINGS

DOTT, R. H., JR. "Permo-Triassic Diastrophism in the Western Cordilleran Region," *American Journal of Science,* 259: 561–82, 1961. A summary of the evidence for an orogeny at the end of the Paleozoic Era in the Cordillera.

EARDLEY, A. J. *Structural Geology of North America,* 2d ed. New York: Harper & Row, 1962. Chapter 6 is a summary of the structure and events in the Cordilleran geosyncline during the Paleozoic. The book contains many other chapters on the geology of the North American Cordillera.

FAGAN, J. J. "Carboniferous Cherts, Turbidites, and Volcanic Rocks in the Northern Independence Range, Nevada," *Geological Society of America Bulletin,* 73: 595–612, 1962. A description of a typical late Paleozoic geosynclinal facies.

GILLULY, J. "Volcanism, Tectonism, and Plutonism in the Western United States," *Geological Society of America Special Paper 80,* 1965. This review of the tectonic behavior of the Cordillera in the United States illustrates that volcanism is not necessarily connected with intrusion.

HESS, H. H. "Serpentines, Orogeny, and Epeirogeny," *Geological Society of America Special Paper 62,* pp. 391–407, 1955. A double belt of serpentinized peridotites occurs along the axis of most mountain chains. These intrusive bodies were emplaced on either side of the keel of the tectogene when it was downwarped into the mantle.

ROBERTS, R. J. "Stratigraphy and Structure of the Antler Peak Quadrangle, Humboldt and Lander Counties, Nevada," *U. S. Geological Survey Professional Paper 459–A,* 1964. A description of the area in central Nevada where the effects of the Antler orogeny are clearly displayed.

SILBERLING, N. J., and ROBERTS, R. J. "Pre-Tertiary Stratigraphy and Structure in Northwestern Nevada," *Geological Society of America Special Paper 72,* 1962. A summary of the stratigraphy (largely Paleozoic) of the geosynclinal rocks and the earth movements in which they were overthrust from the west.

WHITE, W. H. "Cordilleran Tectonics in British Columbia," *American Association of Petroleum Geologists Bulletin,* 43: 60–101, 1959. In this summary of the many periods of orogeny that affected the British Columbia sector of the Cordilleran geosyncline, periods of deformation in late Precambrian, mid-Paleozoic, and Permian times are recognized by the writer.

10

The Cordilleran Orogeny

The cycle of sedimentation and volcanism that had started in Precambrian time was brought to a close in a major orogeny that began in the middle of the Mesozoic Era and continued into the early part of the Cenozoic Era. The mountain-building movements of Paleozoic time had been confined to the geosyncline, but the deformation of late Mesozoic and early Cenozoic time spread beyond the confines of the geosynclines, moving, shearing, and crumpling the rocks on the edge of the craton to form the Rocky Mountains (Fig. 10–1).

From the scarcity of Lower Triassic rocks in the western Cordillera and other evidence reviewed in Chapter 9, we deduced that most of the geosyncline was above sea level in Early Triassic time as a result of late Paleozoic orogeny. By Late Triassic time volcanism and sedimentation were resumed throughout the length of the geosyncline, but some island highlands remained to shed coarse sediments and volcanics into the trough. In both Canada and the United States limestone is a significant constituent of the geosynclinal filling. Limestone is not typical of geosynclinal suites of sediments and is rarely present in quantity. Some of the limestones in geosynclines can be explained as the remnants of reefs around volcanic islands, but others may have been deposited in deeper water.

THE CLIMAX OF GEOSYNCLINAL SEDIMENTATION

Just before and during the deformation of the geosyncline in the Jurassic Period, some segments of the trough sank and received enormous thicknesses of graywacke, siltstone, conglomerate, tuffs, and flows. The rate and nature of this climactic sedimentation may be best illustrated by a review of a few typical areas. In southern British Columbia, the Jurassic System is nearly 25,000 feet thick and consists of shales, mudstones, tuffs, and conglomerate. In some places in the province, 18,000 feet of volcanics have been found in rocks of this age.

In California, Jurassic rocks are found as roof pendants in the Sierra Nevada batholith and in the Coast Ranges. In the Sierras the Middle and Upper Jurassic rocks are more than 20,000 feet thick and are composed of volcanics, sandstones, cherts, and conglomerates overlain by black slate and by

Fig. 10–1. Intense folding of lower Paleozoic rocks in the Stamford Range, British Columbia, the result of the Cordilleran orogeny. (Courtesy of the British Columbia Department of Mines and Petroleum Resources.)

graywacke with lavas. As orogeny and intrusion proceeded in the Sierra block, the site of sedimentation shifted westward to the region of the Coast Ranges of California in Late Jurassic time. From the mountains formed in the orogeny, great quantities of sand and mud poured westward into a trough where they were deposited to a thickness of 25,000 feet. These rocks, known as the Franciscan Group (after San Francisco), were deposited in deep water largely by turbidity flows during Late Jurassic and Early Cretaceous time. By Late Jurassic time geosynclinal volcanism was waning in British Columbia, and the sedimentary record passes upward from marine to non-marine, as parts of the geosyncline were thrust upward into mountains and deposition was confined to inter-

montane basins. In central British Columbia, just east of the Alaska panhandle, these Late Jurassic and Early Cretaceous non-marine sediments derived from the rising Cordilleran chain reach a thickness of 20,000 feet.

DEFORMATION OF THE GEOSYNCLINE

The Cordilleran Orogeny

Early in the investigation of the Cordillera, geologists recognized two main series of mountain-building movements: one at the end of the Jurassic Period, during which the Sierra Nevada batholith was intruded, called the Nevadan; and one at the end of the Cretaceous Period, when the Rocky Mountains were formed, called the Laramide. Evidence for many more pulses of mountain building than were originally recognized, spread over most of the Mesozoic Era, has progressively filled in the gap between the main Nevadan and Laramide movements. The climactic movements that resulted in the consolidation of the geosyncline can be conveniently grouped under the term "Cordilleran orogeny." The term was first suggested by Andrew C. Lawson and later revived by Robert H. Dott, and is adopted here to refer to the mountain-building movements that began early in the Jurassic Period and ended in the middle of the Cenozoic Era.

The Belt of Deformation

Folds and faults produced in the orogeny strike northwestward in the Coast Ranges and Sierra Nevada of California, and in the ranges of western Nevada (Fig. 10–2). The Klamath Mountains of northern California and southwestern Oregon continue the structural trend of the Coast Ranges but form an arc, convex westward, in which the strike of the structures turns toward the northeast. These northeast-striking structures cannot be followed far, for they are covered by the volcanic flows which blanket much of Oregon. In windows eroded through this lava blanket in eastern Oregon, the late Mesozoic structures strike northeastward; but in western Idaho they turn back to a northwestward strike and continue this trend through British Columbia until they swing westward in Alaska. The belt of deformation is roughly parallel to the western coastline of the continent, except where it makes this giant Z-shaped turn around the state of Washington. Donald Wise has suggested that this curve is the result of a giant couple that acted on the west side of the continent, as illustrated in Fig. 10–3. Some structures of the western side of the United States other than the trend of the geosynclinal folds are explained by the hypothesis of this couple, but some structures are not in accord with the stress field postulated.

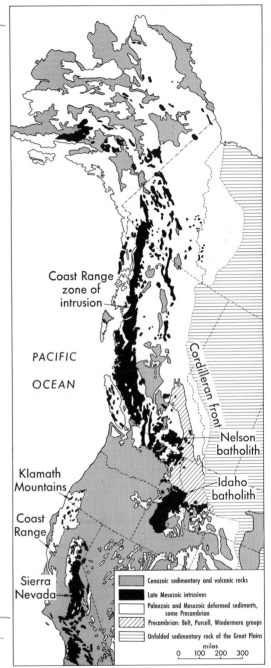

Fig. 10–2. Map of western North America showing the rocks deformed in the Cordilleran orogeny and the intrusives that accompanied the orogeny in the geosyncline. Note the great extent to which Cenozoic rocks obscure the deformed Paleozoic and Mesozoic rocks in the United States.

The Structure of the Deformed Geosyncline

In central Oregon the structure of the schists and argillites metamorphosed in the mid-Mesozoic orogeny is too complex and poorly exposed to be resolved. Over much of British Columbia the detailed structure in Paleozoic and early Mesozoic schists has not been determined in detail. Figure 10–4 is a cross-section of an area in the south-central part of the province showing the intense folding of a succession of quartzites, graywackes, and chlorite and mica schists revealed when distinctive beds can be traced in detail.

In the Sierra Nevada the beds of Paleozoic and Mesozoic geosynclinal rocks are complexly folded and dips are nearly vertical (Fig. 10–5). The rocks have been metamorphosed by the deforming forces and by intruding bodies of igneous rock to schists and greenstones.

The detailed structure of the geosynclinal rocks has yet to be worked out in many parts of the western Cordillera, or has been so obscured by covering beds and cross-cutting

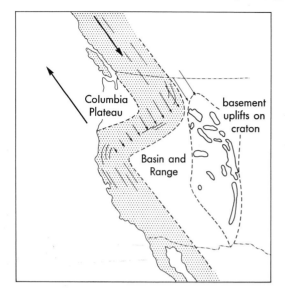

Fig. 10–3. Hypothetical stress distribution in the Cordilleran region of the western United States. The Z-shaped pattern of the deformed geosynclinal rocks is attributed to a couple acting as indicated by the large arrows. The amount of movement in various places along the belt is indicated by the smaller arrows, and the structural strike in the deformed belt is shown by the fine parallel lines. (Modified from D. U. Wise, courtesy of the Geological Society of America.)

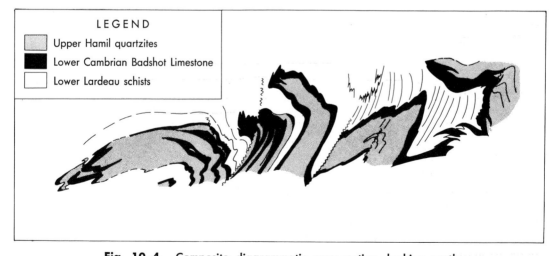

LEGEND
- Upper Hamil quartzites
- Lower Cambrian Badshot Limestone
- Lower Lardeau schists

Fig. 10–4. Composite diagrammatic cross-section, looking north, showing the structure at the northern end of Kootenay Lake, British Columbia. The width of the section is about 10 miles. Vertical and horizontal scales are equal. (From J. T. Fyles, courtesy of the British Columbia Department of Mines and Petroleum Resources.)

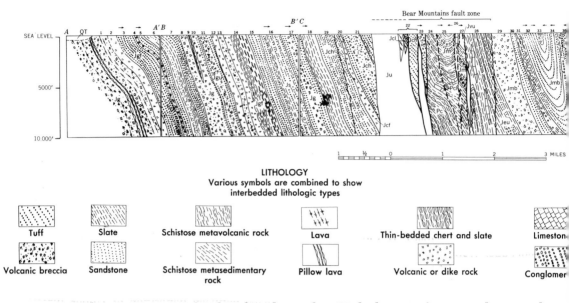

LITHOLOGY
Various symbols are combined to show
interbedded lithologic types

| Tuff | Slate | Schistose metavolcanic rock | Lava | Thin-bedded chert and slate | Limestone |

| Volcanic breccia | Sandstone | Schistose metasedimentary rock | Pillow lava | Volcanic or dike rock | Conglomerate |

intrusions that it may never be deciphered. The rocks were metamorphosed to slates, phyllites, and schists during the deformation, and on this regional dynamic metamorphism is superimposed local thermal metamorphism near the abundant igneous intrusions.

Batholithic Intrusion and the Dating of the Orogeny

During the consolidation of the Cordilleran geosyncline the filling was extensively granitized as batholiths were emplaced along the west coast from Baja California to Alaska. During this mid-Mesozoic episode of igneous activity, a greater area of plutonic rocks was formed in North America than at any time since the Precambrian. The bigger granitic intrusions include the Southern California, Sierra Nevada, Klamath, Idaho, and Nelson batholiths and the Coast Range zone of intrusion which occupies most of western British Columbia (Fig. 10–2). None of these intrusions is homogeneous. Although the commonest rocks are diorites, rocks of composition ranging from granite to ultrabasics form a multitude of interpenetrating igneous bodies. Detailed mapping has revealed that in any local area, a batholith is composed of many individual bodies intruded over an extended period of time in cycles progressing from dark-colored basic rocks to granitic

rocks. With the use of isotopic dating techniques the time relationships of these bodies can be studied in detail. Dating of intrusions in the central part of the Sierra Nevada suggests that igneous rocks were emplaced in three main episodes: in Early Jurassic time (150–180 million years), Late Jurassic time (125–136 million years), and Middle Cretaceous time (80–90 million years). The determination of the earliest ages is complicated by the metamorphic effects of later intrusions, which may have released argon from the feldspars of older igneous rocks, thus changing their radioactive "clocks." The ages of nine intrusions in the Yosemite Valley of the Sierra Nevada range from 77–95 million years. The age determinations confirm the order established by the cross-cutting relationships mapped in the field. Field relationships also suggest that each intrusion completely crystallized before its neighbor was intruded. If nine intrusions were emplaced in 18 million years, then, on an average, each took less than 2 million years to cool. The length of time taken by any one of the intrusions may have been considerably longer or shorter, but the calculation yields an order of magnitude for the rate of batholithic crystallization.

In the Klamath Mountains small intrusions and metamorphic rocks have been dated as

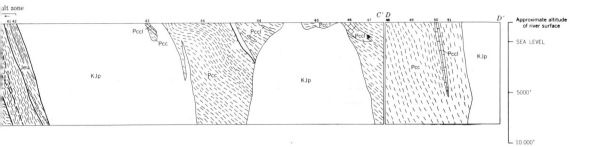

Fig. 10–5. Composite cross-section of the rocks deformed in the Cordilleran orogeny in the northern Sierra Nevada along the Moke-lumne River. *Pc,* Permian Calaveras Formation of phyllite, volcanics, and schist; *J,* largely volcanic rocks of late Jurassic age; *K,* Cretaceous igneous intrusions. (From L. D. Clark, *U. S. Geological Survey Professional Paper 410.*)

between 135 and 145 million years, suggesting that the major deformation there was within Late Jurassic time.

Potassium–argon dating of batholiths in British Columbia has shown that some of them are complex intrusions. In the area of the Nelson and Cassiar batholiths, the determinations suggest that igneous rocks as old as Permian and as young as Late Cretaceous are present. In the Cassiar igneous belt of northeastern British Columbia, periods of intrusion and metamorphism have been established at the beginning of the Triassic, the beginning of the Jurassic, the beginning and middle of the Cretaceous, and in early Cenozoic time. Obviously, no single age determination can now be considered adequate to date the time of intrusion of a batholith.

The relationship in time between the deformation of the geosynclinal filling and the emplacement of the batholiths is not clear. In the Sierra Nevada the igneous rocks seem to have forced their way into the sediments and volcanics and to have pushed them aside. Although the time of intrusion can now be determined in years, the time of deformation of the bedded rocks can only rarely be precisely dated, because of the lack of stratigraphic evidence. In the Sierra Nevada, such evidence indicates only that orogeny took place between deposition of Upper Jurassic and Upper Cretaceous strata. In the Coast Ranges west of the Sierra Nevada, clastic sediments of the Franciscan (Late Jurassic to early Late Cretaceous deep-water facies, partly turbidites), Knoxville (late Late Jurassic near-shore facies), Paskenta, and Horsetown (Early Cretaceous) formations derived from the rising mountains indicate that the uplift of the Sierra continued between Late Jurassic and Late Cretaceous time. Stratigraphic evidence concerning the relative ages of batholiths is provided by the time of the first appearance of the pebbles of their igneous rocks in neighboring sedimentary rocks. In central British Columbia, this sort of evidence confirms that some batholithic intrusion took place in Early Jurassic time, for by Middle Jurassic time the batholiths had been unroofed by erosion and were contributing detritus to adjacent basins. On Vancouver Island, deformation seems to have been largely in the Middle Jurassic Epoch, and by Early Cretaceous time the igneous intrusions of this episode of deformation had been unroofed and eroded.

In summary, the evidence reviewed demonstrates that the consolidation of the Cordilleran geosyncline was a protracted process consisting of episodes of deformation and intrusion through much of Mesozoic time.

Ore Deposits Associated with Cordilleran Batholiths

The batholithic intrusions were accompanied by fluids that deposited minerals in the surrounding country rocks and within the margins of the intrusive bodies. Most of the ore deposits of the Pacific states and of British Columbia were emplaced at this time, and a few examples may be mentioned to indicate the vastness of the mineral wealth we owe to the Cordilleran batholiths. With the Sierra Nevada batholith in California came a 120-mile-long system of gold-bearing quartz veins known as the Mother Lode belt. The great California gold rush of 1849 was set off by the discovery of placer gold concentrated in gravels from the erosion of the Mother Lode veins, from which over 1⅓ billion dollars' worth of gold has been recovered. Most of the mineral deposits of British Columbia, such as the mercury of Pinchi Lake, the gold of the Cariboo and Atlin districts, and the copper of the Britannia area north of Vancouver, are related to Cordilleran batholiths.

THE DEFORMATION OF THE CRATONIC MARGIN

The term "Laramide" (or, rarely, "Laramian") has been used for those pulses of Cordilleran orogeny that formed the structure of the Rocky Mountains in the interval from mid-Cretaceous to mid-Cenozoic time. The name is derived from the Laramie Mountains, which form the eastern range of the Cordilleran chain in Wyoming.

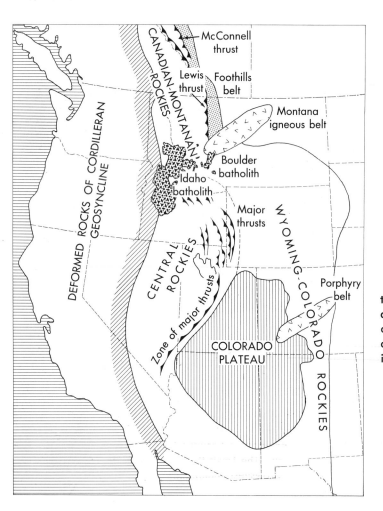

Fig. 10–6. Major divisions of the rocks of the cratonic margin deformed in the Cordilleran orogeny. Only the major areas of thrust faulting in this belt are indicated.

The rocks affected by these late Cordilleran movements had accumulated for hundreds of millions of years to a thickness as great as 50,000 feet locally on the depressed edge of the craton. The zone of deformation is about 200 miles wide in Canada but widens in Colorado and divides around the Colorado Plateau (Fig. 10–6). The branches join again in Arizona, south of the plateau, and continue across Mexico into Central America.

The Structure of the Northern Rockies

The diverse structures produced along 4000 miles of the cratonic margin by the Cordilleran orogeny had certain common features which can be illustrated by a brief review of the structures of selected segments of the Rocky Mountains.

In the Rocky Mountains of southern Canada and Montana, the ranges are composed of resistant limestones and quartzites of Precambrian, Cambrian, Devonian, and Mississippian ages. Each range is a fault block bounded on the east by a steeply westward-dipping thrust fault along which it has been pushed eastward (Fig. 10–7). The structurally weaker and more easily eroded Mesozoic sandstones and shales which underlie the valleys between the Paleozoic and Precambrian ranges have been closely folded, while the folds in the limestones and quartzites of the ranges tend to be broad and open. The steeply dipping thrust faults are believed to flatten as they pass downward and to approach parallelism with the bedding. On the Lewis fault, Precambrian rocks of the Belt Group have been thrust as much as 20 miles eastward over contorted Cretaceous shales to

Fig. 10–7. Aerial photograph of the Canadian Rockies at Crowsnest Pass, looking north. The ranges are composed largely of Mississippian limestone dipping westward and thrust eastward on thrust faults. The isolated peak at the upper right is Crowsnest Mountain, a klippe or outlier of an overthrust block. The Lewis thrust underlies the range in the right foreground and Crowsnest Mountain. (Royal Canadian Air Force Photograph.)

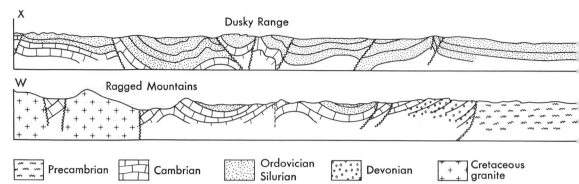

X — Dusky Range

W — Ragged Mountains

| Precambrian | Cambrian | Ordovician Silurian | Devonian | Cretaceous granite |

Fig. 10–8. Cross-section of the eastern Cordilleran mountain system at about latitude 63° N., showing the zones of intense deformation separated by relatively undeformed plateaus. (After Gabrielse and others, Douglas, and Norris, courtesy of the Geological Survey of Canada.)

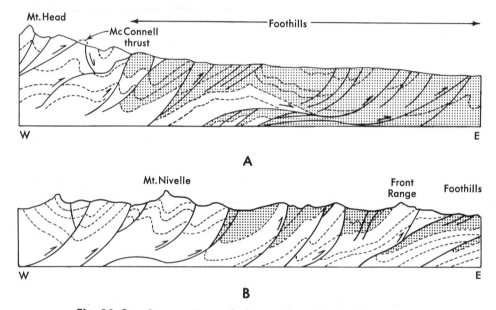

Mt. Head — McConnell thrust — Foothills

W   E

A

Mt. Nivelle — Front Range — Foothills

W   E

B

Fig. 10–9. Cross-sections of the northern Rocky Mountains. *A.* Foothills and Front Range in western Alberta. *B.* Front Ranges of the Canadian Rockies. (After F. K. North and G. G. L. Henderson.)

form the towering wall of the Lewis Range in Glacier National Park and Waterton Lakes National Park.

The regular surface of the Precambrian basement rocks can be traced by geophysical methods 50 miles westward beneath the deformed rocks of the Rockies in Alberta, suggesting that the sedimentary layers have been sheared off the essentially undisturbed basement.

Figure 10–8 is a cross-section of a part of the eastern Cordillera in the latitude of Great Slave Lake. In this area narrow belts of folding and faulting alternate with wide belts of plateau topography and flat-lying or gently warped sedimentary rocks. Most of the sedimentary rocks are of Paleozoic age, but large areas are underlain by late Precambrian sediments believed to be equivalent to the Belt Group. In the Ragged Mountains

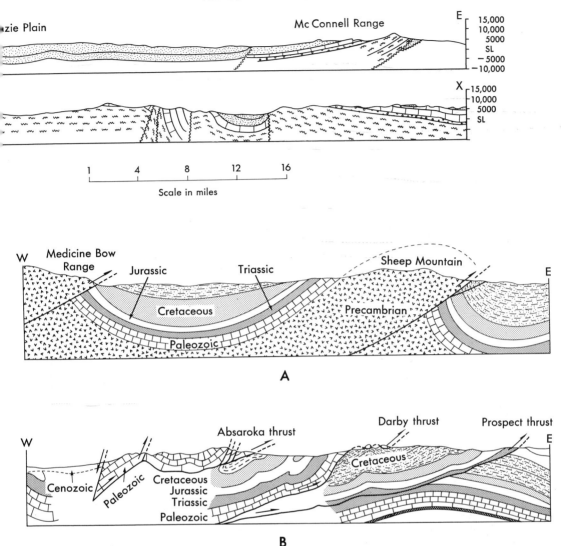

Fig. 10–10. Cross-sections of the Rockies of Wyoming. A. The asymmetrical broken anticlines with Precambrian cores of the Medicine Bow Range and Sheep Mountain in southeastern Wyoming. B. Low-angle thrust faults of great horizontal displacement that characterize the structure of western Wyoming. (After A. J. Eardley.)

Cretaceous batholiths penetrate the section in the zone of geosynclinal deformation.

Before the majestic limestone ranges of the Canadian Rockies lies the foothills belt, underlain by Mesozoic and lower Cenozoic shales and sandstones sliced into thin segments by many faults that branch from major zones of fracture at depth (Fig. 10–9). Anticlines in the buried Mississippian limestone have trapped large volumes of natural gas.

The Structure of the Central Rockies

In the Idaho–Wyoming thrust belt (Fig. 10–10) the main structural element is a series of almost horizontal thrust faults along which the upper blocks have moved eastward distances of tens of miles. Some of these fault planes were folded and cut by high-angle faults in later phases of the orogenic episode. This belt of low-angle thrusting is overlain on the north by Cenozoic lavas of the Snake River Plain, but it can be followed southward through Utah into eastern Nevada. In the southernmost part of Nevada the two main, almost horizontal thrusts have displacements of 5 and 15 miles. One of the advancing thrust sheets must have had considerable relief, for blocks eroded from its front are incorporated in contemporaneous sediments.

The nearly horizontal thrust faults of the central Rockies are typical of a style of deformation which has been called **decollement.** The term comes from the French word meaning "unsticking" and implies a sliding of upper parts of a sedimentary succession, on underlying beds or the basement, along surfaces lubricated by shales and evaporites. Thrust faults such as these are difficult to explain as being caused by a force applied from behind pushing the upper plate over the lower. Calculations of the friction to be expected along the thrust plane and the strength of the upper plate of strata demonstrate that a laterally directed force applied to the back of the plate would break it into many segments rather than transport it as a whole across the beds below. Geologists have therefore sought a force, such as gravity, that would have acted on every particle throughout the upper plate and not just on the western end. If gravity was the force required, the thrusts must have formed when the geosynclinal area was uplifted in orogeny, producing a gentle slope down which slabs of the crust several miles in each dimension slid for tens of miles. Some structural geologists consider that slopes of as little as 2 degrees would have been steep enough. Many geologists do not subscribe to this mechanism for emplacing these puzzling crustal masses, however, and much experimental and field work remains to be done before their emplacement can be satisfactorily explained.

The Wyoming and Colorado Rockies

The structure of the Rocky Mountains of central Wyoming and Colorado is much different from that of the thrust belts farther west (Fig. 10–11). The ranges are separated by broad basins floored by essentially unde-

Fig. 10–11. Aerial view southeast across the Granite Mountains of Precambrian rocks in the middleground to the Ferris Mountains in the background, showing the topography of ranges and broad dry basins typical of central and eastern Wyoming. (Courtesy of Page T. Jenkins.)

formed early Cenozoic sedimentary rocks. The ranges themselves have central cores of Precambrian rocks surrounded by Paleozoic and Mesozoic sedimentary rocks that dip away on all sides defining oval-shaped domes. The margins of these uplifts are of various kinds. In some areas the contact between the crystalline and surrounding sedimentary rocks is an unconformity; in others it is marked by a high-angle thrust fault; in still others it is a normal fault. Although the thrust faults along the flanks of some of the ranges suggest that horizontal compression was important in the formation of the structures, evidence from drilling and geophysics shows that these faults become vertical when traced downward, and that vertical uplift of the basement was the principal force responsible for the ranges.

The Rockies of Colorado were preceded by the Ancestral Rockies system and their structure was in part inherited from the Front Range and Uncompahgre uplifts of late Paleozoic time. During early Mesozoic time the Ancestral Rockies were progressively buried beneath their own debris. They were rejuvenated in Late Cretaceous and early Cenozoic time and eventually elevated to heights of more than 14,000 feet to form the highest peaks in the Rocky Mountains. The Front Range uplift, which had been a simple arch in late Paleozoic time, was uplifted into two parallel ranges with a valley comprising North, Middle, and South Parks between them (Fig. 10–12). On the eastern side of the Front Range anticline, Paleozoic and Mesozoic strata are tilted into a vertical position and eroded to form the weird scenery of the "Garden of the Gods." On the western

side of the Front Range and the Sangre de Cristo Range south of it, the structure is more complex, and eastward-dipping thrust faults cut the Precambrian and Paleozoic rocks.

To the west, the ranges of central Wyoming adjoin the intensely deformed central Rockies, but the Colorado Rockies are separated from this thrust zone by the subcircular Colorado Plateau. The plateau is underlain by gently warped and faulted Paleozoic and Mesozoic rocks which seem to have acted as a rigid block during the Cordilleran orogeny. Long, monoclinal flexures (Fig. 10–13) and normal faults are typical of this plateau area.

The Rocky Mountains continue from the United States into eastern Mexico as the Sierra Madre Oriental. These ranges consist of Mesozoic limestones and shales broadly folded and cut by low-angle thrust faults. The western side of the Cordillera at this latitude is covered by thick Cenozoic lava flows that make up the Sierra Madre Occidental.

The Deformation of the Cratonic Margin

The rocks of the cratonic margin and the geosynclinal filling were deformed in different ways by the forces of the Cordilleran orogeny. In the western Cordillera, tight folding, faulting, dynamic metamorphism of phyllites and schists, intrusion, and thermal metamorphism characterized the deformation. In the eastern Cordillera, thin sheets of sedimentary rock were detached along bedding planes and slid for many tens of miles. Folding was open and dynamic metamorphism rare. In most areas of the eastern Cordillera, basement rocks do not participate in compressional structures, and where base-

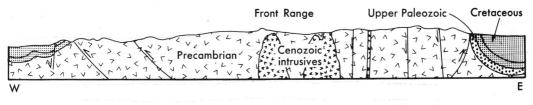

Fig. 10–12. Cross-section of the Front Range of Colorado. (After A. J. Eardley.)

Fig. 10–13. Monoclinal flexures of the Colorado Plateau at Independence Monument, Colorado. The cliff-forming strata of the Wingate Sandstone (Triassic), capped by the Kayenta Formation (Jurassic), bend down and pass below the Morrison Formation (Upper Jurassic) that floors the plains in the background. (Courtesy of S. W. Lohman, U. S. Geological Survey.)

ment rocks are involved in the deformation they seem to have been pushed up by vertical forces.

The differences in the types of deformation of the geosynclinal and the cratonic segments of the Cordilleran mountain system were the result of differences in initial structure and later history. During a long period of tectonic mobility, a very thick section of argillaceous and arenaceous sedimentary rocks, cherts, and volcanics accumulated in the geosyncline. The basins at the edge of the craton accumulated almost as thick a section of sediments near the geosyncline, but the sedimentary prism thinned rapidly eastward.

In deformation, the geosyncline was subjected to strong forces—apparently directed horizontally—which caused intense folding and dynamic metamorphism. The forces, either vertical or horizontal, that were deforming the geosyncline were transmitted to the edge of the craton, crumpling its veneer of limestones and sandstones into open folds and breaking it along low-angle thrust planes. The sediments of the craton may have been deformed by a horizontal force pushing toward the continent from the geosyncline or by slipping down the flanks of the uplifted geosyncline. Locally, vertical forces complicated this highly simplified pattern. The different types of deformation may be related ultimately to differences in the foundations of the two basins of deposition. The geosyncline was probably formed in the mobile oceanic crust of basaltic composition; the marginal cratonic basins were formed in the granitic continental crust that had been stabilized in former geosynclinal cycles and from then on successfully resisted further deformation. However, the predominantly intermediate (andesitic) composition of the volcanics in the Cordilleran geosynclinal filling has suggested to some geologists that the geosyncline could not have been formed in the basaltic rocks of the ocean basins, but must have been part of the continental plates.

Igneous Intrusions in the Eastern Cordillera

The Idaho batholith is the easternmost of the large batholiths in the Cordillera. It was intruded, according to the evidence of isotopic age determinations, about the middle of the Cretaceous Period. Many satellitic igneous bodies, such as the Boulder, Tobacco Root, Philipsburg, and Marysville batholiths, surround the Idaho batholith. These smaller masses must be younger than the deformation of the sedimentary rocks into which they were intruded, since they cut the structures in these rocks. They are also younger than the Idaho batholith and were probably emplaced near the end of the Cretaceous Period or at the beginning of the Cenozoic Era. The magma of the smaller batholiths was accompanied by ore-forming fluids that deposited the rich ores mined in the Butte and Coeur d'Alene districts. Butte, Montana, has, with reason, been called the "richest hill on earth." From its depths in a recent sample year there were taken ores which produced 80,000 tons of copper, 3200 tons of lead, and 24,000 tons of zinc, and many other metals as by-products of ore refining. Butte was the largest zinc producer, the third largest copper producer, and the fifth largest lead producer in the United States in that year.

In Montana a belt of intrusion extends across the folded and faulted structures into the plains (Fig. 10–6). It includes a great variety of igneous rocks intruded as dikes, sills, stocks, and laccoliths. Laccoliths in this belt, especially the Shonkin Sag laccolith, have been extensively studied by petrologists because the minerals in the intrusive magma appear to have separated according to their specific gravities to form bands of different compositions within the intrusion. Another belt of igneous intrusions trends southwest from Denver, Colorado, toward the Four Corners region. This zone is commonly called the porphyry belt because most of its dikes, sills, and stocks consist of porphyries of a variety of compositions. The intrusions, which range in age from Late Cretaceous to the end of the Paleocene, are of major importance because many of them contain low-grade copper ores of great value known as porphyry copper deposits.

Sedimentation and the Pulsating Nature of Orogeny

The pulsating or episodic nature of orogeny is revealed by several kinds of evidence in the sedimentary record. Sediments derived from the mountains raised in an early pulse may be folded in a later movement. Unconformities formed during one pulse may be folded or faulted by later movements of the earth. Thrust faults formed as plane surfaces may be folded or intersected by later faults. All these conditions serve as clues by means of which geologists decipher the sequence of the earth movements that formed mountain chains (Fig. 10–14).

In the multitude of pulses by which the structure of the central Rocky Mountains was formed, three times of major deformation can be recognized: the middle of the Late Cretaceous, the end of the Cretaceous, and the end of the Eocene. One of the finest records of the pulsating nature of orogeny is preserved in the Wasatch Range of eastern Utah. The geological record indicates uplift and possibly folding in Early Cretaceous time; two periods of thrust faulting and one of folding in middle Late Cretaceous time; renewed thrusting at the end of the Cretaceous Period; folding in mid-Paleocene time; and folding again at the beginning of the

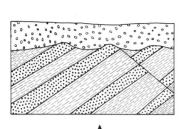
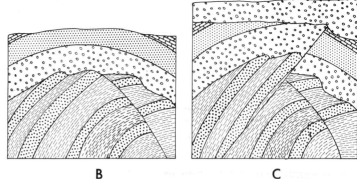

Fig. 10–14. Evidence for multiple phases of orogeny. *A.* A single episode of faulting has taken place. *B.* An episode of faulting was followed by sedimentation and folding. *C.* The sequence of events continued with thrust faulting. These episodes may be accurately dated if the coarse sediments derived from the uplifts contain fossils.

Eocene Epoch. An episode of crustal warping in Oligocene time might also be included as a pulse of Cordilleran orogeny. The structural effects of most of these pulses were confined to a relatively small area. The deformation was most intense in the central Wasatch Range in the middle of the Late Cretaceous Epoch, in the northern Wasatch Range at the end of the Cretaceous Period, and in the Bighorn basin of Wyoming at the end of the Paleocene or in the Eocene Epoch. In the foothills of the Canadian Rockies, the youngest beds deformed are the upper Paleocene Paskapoo Sandstone. In an intermontane valley near the international border where a small area of Eocene sediments has been preserved from erosion, two periods of deformation within the Eocene Epoch have been distinguished. From these facts and from the coarseness of Oligocene gravels on the plains east of the mountains, we deduce that the major orogeny was of Eocene age in Alberta. The record of individual pulses of this orogeny in Alberta is not as good as it is in Utah because early Cenozoic sedimentary rocks that record the various earth movements are not preserved in basins within the mountains.

In Wyoming the Late Eocene was a time of crustal instability, expressed in some mountain ranges as compression and in others as vertical uplift. The Heart Mountain thrust, along which a thin plate of sedimentary rocks slid 30 miles eastward, was formed at this time. In the Front Range of Colorado thrusting continued from Cretaceous into Late Paleocene and locally into Early Oligocene time. The arch of the Uinta Mountains, whose summit rises 6000 feet above the Green River basin, was elevated largely in Eocene time, although minor movements had occurred earlier.

Limitations of space do not allow extensive treatment of the many pulses that made up the Cordilleran orogeny in various sectors of the mountain system. Each sector yielded in its own manner to the forces that deformed the earth's crust, and the time of deformation varied from sector to sector within an interval encompassing a large part of the Mesozoic Era and the first half of the Cenozoic Era. Within this complex Cordilleran orogeny geologists have tried to distinguish as subdivisions times when the deforming forces were more intense, but such divisions have generally been shown, as more knowledge accumulates, to be of only local validity or usefulness.

REFLECTIONS OF OROGENY IN SEDIMENTATION

The deformation of a mountain belt is revealed in the structures of the ranges. The elevation of mountains may be recorded in the sediments deposited during and after orogeny in intermontane basins, but this record is commonly interrupted by unconformities, obscured by faulting and folding, and quickly attacked by erosion. The best record is the sedimentary strata that accumulate along the flanks of the mountain chain. From the rising mountains, sand and mud are carried by rivers and dropped where their gradient lessens, to form a vast alluvial coastal apron. The total prism of conglomerates, sands, and shales may be several miles thick near the mountains, but it thins to a feather edge away from them and is therefore appropriately called a **clastic wedge.** In interpreting these clastic wedges we must resist the temptation to attribute each spread of the coarser clastic facies into the limestone or shale facies solely to a pulse of uplift in the geosyncline, for, as emphasized in Chapter 5, the size and quantity of clastic particles supplied to a basin of deposition are controlled as much by climate as by the relief of the source area.

During most of the Paleozoic Era the basins marginal to the west side of the craton received little clastic sediment and accumulated carbonates and evaporites. The small amount of shale and sandstone which reached the basins was chiefly eroded from the crystalline rocks of the Shield, from sedimentary rocks exposed along the edges of the Shield, and from cratonic uplifts of basement rocks such as the Ancestral Rockies. Only rarely, for instance in Devonian and Pennsylvanian time, did the geosyncline supply any clastic sediments to the marginal cratonic basins and their adjacent shelves. In Middle Jurassic time a complete reversal of this pattern of sediment supply was brought about by the Cordilleran orogeny.

Triassic seas of the western edge of the craton were eastward extensions of those in the Cordilleran geosyncline (see Chapter 8). In Alberta the Triassic System is composed of fine-grained clastic rocks whose facies relationships suggest that they were derived from the craton to the northeast. In the Colorado Plateau, where much of the Triassic is non-marine (Chinle and Moenkopi groups), the debris seems to have been derived from the uplifts of the Ancestral Rockies and from the cratonic margins of the basin of deposition. The source areas were essentially unchanged in Early Jurassic time, when the desert sandstones of the Wingate and Navajo formations accumulated. In Canada also, the facies pattern established in early Mesozoic time continued until late in the Jurassic Period.

Jurassic Seaways

The Jurassic System of the Canadian Rockies consists largely of dark shales which form the Fernie Group. Until Late Jurassic time the only sand entering this muddy sea came from the northeast, as in the Triassic Period. The Jurassic System is divided into time-stratigraphic zones on the basis of ammonites that occur plentifully in the type sections of northern Europe. In the Fernie Group many of the ammonites of the type section are found, but others that characterize certain zones and stages are missing. Their absence is interpreted by paleontologists as proof that the Fernie Group does not record the whole of Jurassic time and that the sea withdrew at least three times from the margin of the craton.

In Middle Jurassic time the sea spread southward over the desert sandstones that were laid down early in the period in the southern Rocky Mountain states, and eastward into the Williston basin. The marine deposits of this sea were interrupted near the end of Middle Jurassic time by the uplift of an arch in northern Montana and southern Alberta; by the restriction of access of marine water to the Williston basin, so that evaporites were deposited; and by the distribution of a thin layer of non-marine sediments along most of the western margin of the craton. At the beginning of the Late Jurassic Epoch the sea returned, covering much of the Rocky Mountains and western plains in the most extensive of the Jurassic transgressions. By this time the direction of sediment supply had changed: the Cordillera was being elevated and sands entering the predominantly muddy sea were coming largely from the west, no longer from the Shield (Fig. 10–15). These sands are the first representatives of a

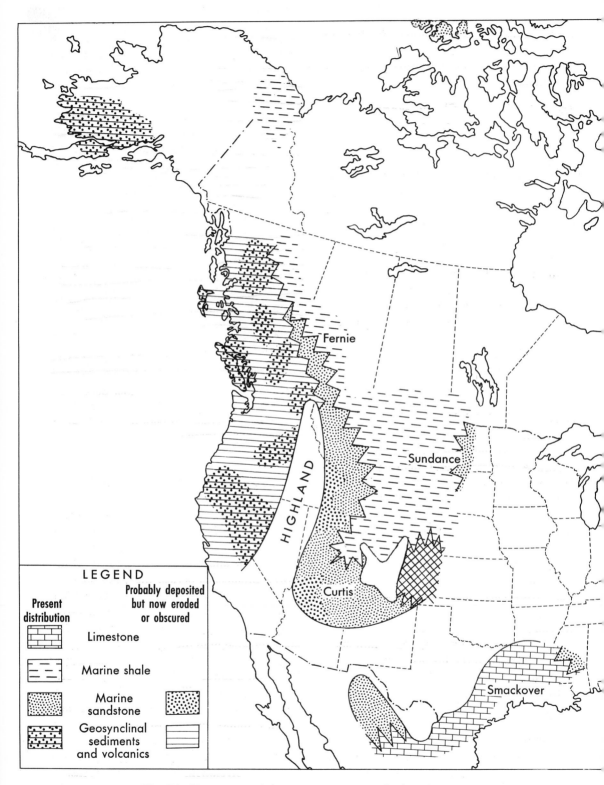

Fig. 10–15. Facies of the Upper Jurassic Oxfordian Stage in western North America. Note the beginning of the late Mesozoic clastic wedge supplied by the rising Cordilleran Mountains.

clastic wedge of great complexity that was formed on the edge of the craton by sands and mud derived from the rising geosynclinal mountains.

The Late Mesozoic Clastic Wedge

Gradually the supply of sediments to the seas on the western edge of the continent reached and surpassed the rate of subsidence of the marginal basins, and the basins were silted up by streams forming an extensive alluvial apron along the growing and advancing Cordilleran mountain front. These sediments are entirely different from the pure quartz sandstones and clay shales derived from the Shield. The sandstones are rich in clay, mica, and unstable minerals, and may be either graywackes or arkoses depending on whether they were supplied by the erosion of a metamorphic–volcanic terrane or by the erosion of a terrane in which granite batholiths have been unroofed. As the ocean waters retreated, the basin behind was filled with layers of clay, silt, and sand that now constitute the brightly colored Late Jurassic Morrison Formation. It contains a rich fauna that included the largest dinosaurs, the first primitive mammals, and many plants and fresh-water invertebrates (Fig. 10–16). The bones of giant dinosaurs of this formation, such as *Stegosaurus*, *Antrodemus*, *Brontosaurus*, and *Diplodocus*, are displayed in several American museums. Nearly all these skeletons were collected toward the end of the nineteenth century by O. C. Marsh, of Yale University, and E. D. Cope, of the Philadelphia Academy of Sciences. The bitter competition that grew between these men in the collection and description of new specimens embellished the history of geology with many anecdotes and enriched the museums with many specimens that would otherwise still be in the ground.

The greatest volume of clastic sediments eroded from the rising Cordilleran mountains is contained in the Cretaceous System (Fig. 10–17). The system in western North America can be divided into stages and zones by means of fossils, or into formations and facies by means of lithology. Rocks of this age in

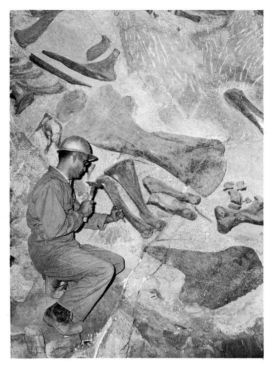

Fig. 10–16. Collecting dinosaur bones from the Morrison Sandstone at the Dinosaur National Monument, Colorado. (Courtesy of the U. S. National Park Service.)

Europe are divided into zones on the basis of ammonites; these zones are grouped into stages, nine of which are commonly recognized as useful for world-wide correlation. Three of these stages—the Neocomian (oldest), Aptian, and Albian—are divisions of the Lower Cretaceous Series; the other six—the Cenomanian, Turonian, Coniacian, Santonian, Campanian, and Maestrichtian (youngest)—comprise the Upper Cretaceous Series. Because the system in the type section along the English Channel is divided into an upper chalk and a lower sandstone facies, the Cretaceous System, unlike most other systems, has no middle series. Comparison of ammonites found in the western states and provinces with those of Europe allows the paleontologist to make precise age determinations and correlations in Cretaceous rocks.

The Cretaceous sedimentary rocks of the Rockies and plains can also be described in terms of facies. A sedimentary succession as

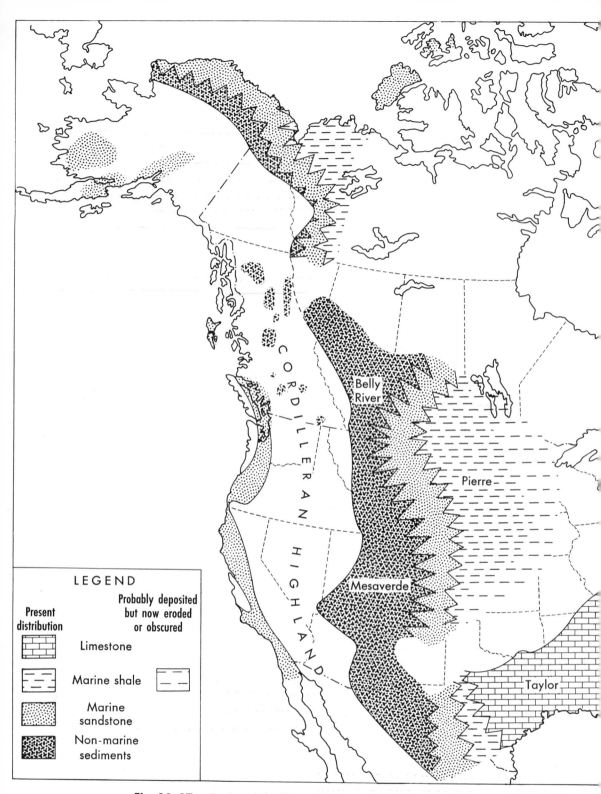

Fig. 10–17. Facies of the Upper Cretaceous Montana Group and its equivalents in western North America. Most of the western and central Cordillera had been uplifted by this time, and deposition was confined there to small intermontane basins. Downfaulting and warping of basins along the Pacific coast allowed the sea to enter and deposit marine sandstones.

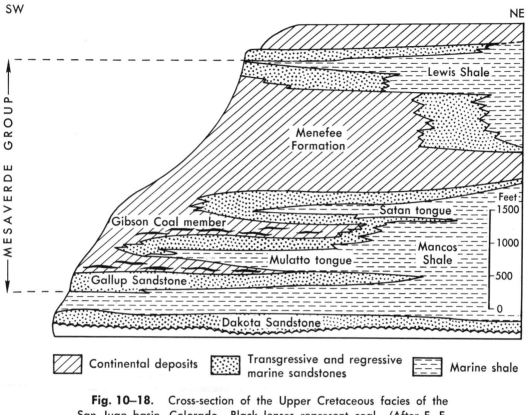

Fig. 10–18. Cross-section of the Upper Cretaceous facies of the San Juan basin, Colorado. Black lenses represent coal. (After F. F. Sabins, Jr., courtesy of the *American Association of Petroleum Geologists Bulletin*.)

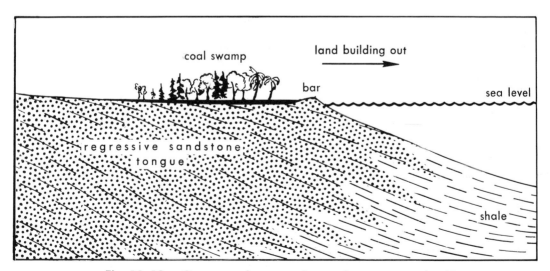

Fig. 10–19. Geometry of a regressive sandstone tongue showing the irregular, gradational lower border and the position of the coal deposition.

extensive and thick as this one contains a multitude of lithologies, but Robert J. Weimer has suggested that they can be grouped into four basic facies: light-colored limestone (deposited in relatively deep marine water); gray-to-black shale (deposited in shallow marine water); light-colored sandstone (deposited near the shore); and gray shale with lenticular sandstone and coal interbeds (deposited on land or in coastal swamps). As the shoreline moved back and forth across the edge of the craton, these facies belts followed, producing a complexly interfingering set of marine and non-marine formations.

The limestone facies was deposited at times when little detritus from the mountains reached the epeiric sea. Two limestone formations divide the shales of the Cretaceous System—the Niobrara Chalk above and the Greenhorn Limestone below. The Niobrara Chalk is noted for the large, beautifully preserved vertebrate fossils that have been found in it. These include ichthyosaurs, flying reptiles, birds, turtles, and fish. The unbroken and articulated state in which the specimens have been preserved indicates that the waters of the Niobrara sea were untroubled by waves and currents. The chalk covers a large area of South Dakota, Nebraska, Kansas, western Oklahoma, and Texas. Northward into Canada the Niobrara and Greenhorn limestones lens out, but their positions are indicated in the thick shales by two zones of tiny white calcareous spheres known in subsurface correlation as the "first and second white specks."

Oscillations of the shoreline were caused by the building out of the land in the form of deltas at times of rapid supply of sediments and the sudden transgression of the sea over these deltaic sands perhaps due to sudden subsidence. The form typical of these regressive sandstone tongues which project into the marine shale facies is illustrated in Figs. 10–18 and 10–19. Bedding planes in the sandstone tongue are not parallel to its upper surface but slope gently seaward like the foreset beds of a delta. On the alluvium, coastal swamps formed and the trees left a carbonaceous residue as thin beds of coal.

Each episode of delta building closed with the sudden transgression of the sea over the swamp, killing the vegetation and setting the stage for the beginning of a new regressive cycle. These cyclical regressive deposits and their coal beds are comparable to the Pennsylvanian cyclothems.

During these transgressive–regressive cycles, a few feet, or tens of feet, of beds accumulated, but similar cycles exist on a larger scale. In the plains region the Upper Cretaceous Series can be divided into four sets of beds representing transgression and four sets representing regression. The regressive stratigraphic units of sandstone and shale are hundreds to thousands of feet thick and project eastward into the marine shale that accumulated on the cratonic shelf during much of the period.

On a still larger scale, the whole of the Cretaceous System is a regressive succession. The pattern of facies changes in cross-section is illustrated in Fig. 10–20. With many oscillations, the shoreline was driven eastward by the increasing supply of clastic sediments from the west until, by the end of the period, the whole epeiric sea had been converted into an alluvial plain 500 miles at its greatest width. Early in the epoch, the Late Cretaceous epeiric sea had extended from Utah to the Great Lakes and from the Arctic Ocean to the Gulf of Mexico (Fig. 10–17). Its eastward extent is established by small outliers of Cretaceous strata resting on the Precambrian Shield in the Mesabi district of Minnesota. By the end of the period, the sandstones of the Fox Hills, Hell Creek, and Lance formations and their equivalents had spread over the shale facies as far as the Dakotas. The Fox Hills Sandstone is the marine part of the regressive sandstone unit, but the succeeding Lance and Hell Creek formations are nonmarine. The non-marine sandstones of the clastic wedge continued to accumulate into the Paleocene Epoch with little change, and the lack of a break in sedimentation at the era boundary caused considerable uncertainty in locating the beginning of the Cenozoic beds in the stratigraphic succession. Detailed paleontological and paleobotanical re-

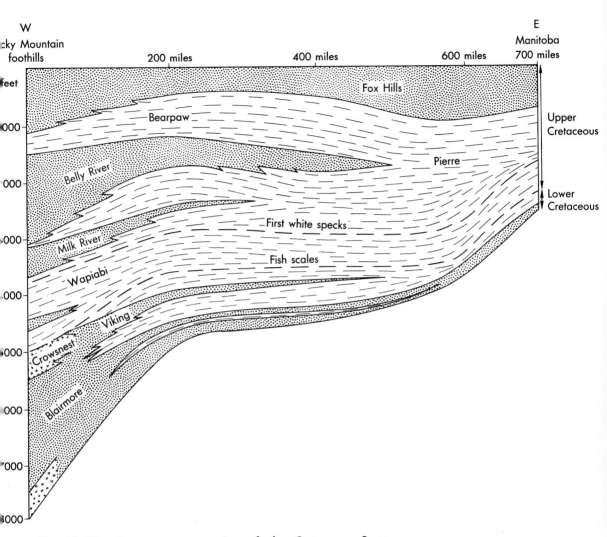

Fig. 10–20. East–west cross-section of the Cretaceous System along the 49th parallel (vertical exaggeration extreme). Note the flood of sandstone eastward at the beginning of the Cretaceous and at the end of the period. The white specks and fish scales zones are key beds used in subsurface correlation.

search was required to locate the boundary between the Mesozoic and Cenozoic beds in this succession of non-marine sandstones.

The fauna of the Cretaceous sandstones consists of fresh-water mollusks that lived in the rivers and lakes and dinosaurs that roamed the plains and swam in the lakes. The dinosaurs most characteristic of the Late Cretaceous, non-marine beds are the semi-aquatic duckbilled dinosaurs (p. 467). Their bones are found along with those of the greatest meat-eating dinosaurs, *Tyrannosaurus*, which preyed upon the smaller plant eaters. The uppermost beds of the Cretaceous System also contain the three-horned *Triceratops*, the last of these giant reptiles.

The load of sediments derived from the Cordilleran mountains depressed the edge of the craton into a complex, elongate basin stretching from the Arctic Ocean to the Gulf of Mexico. The Cretaceous part of this wedge reaches thicknesses of over 20,000 feet in western Wyoming, where the sands were deposited close to the Cretaceous mountain front. In Canada, a maximum of 10,000 feet of Cretaceous strata accumulated in the

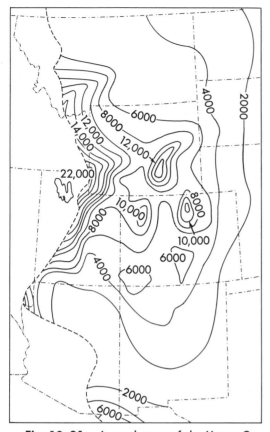

Fig. 10–21. Isopach map of the Upper Cretaceous Series in the western states. Contour interval is 2000 feet, except in the area of the Great Salt Lake. (After W. C. Krumbein and F. G. Nagel, courtesy of the *American Association of Petroleum Geologists Bulletin.*)

Peace River area of eastern British Columbia. In addition, about 5000 feet of early Cenozoic, non-marine sandstones form the final sediments of the clastic wedge along the foothills of the Canadian Rockies. The geometry of the Cretaceous part of the clastic wedge is illustrated in the isopach map of Fig. 10–21. Note that the wedge does not thin regularly eastward but thickens locally into basins along the edge of the craton and thins over the arches between these basins. The accompanying facies map (Fig. 10–22) shows that the coarser clastic sediments are near the Cordilleran mountains, where the wedge is thickest. Gaps in the lithofacies pattern mark ranges from which Cretaceous

rocks have been eroded after Cenozoic uplift. That the uplifted areas were not active during the Cretaceous is shown by the independence of the facies boundaries of the present borders of the ranges.

The regressive sandstone tongues of the Cretaceous clastic wedge are economically important not only because they are commonly associated with coal deposits but also because they serve as reservoirs for oil and gas. Large gas fields in the San Juan basin of southern Colorado and northern New Mexico have been discovered in the sandstone tongues of the Mesaverde Formation, which

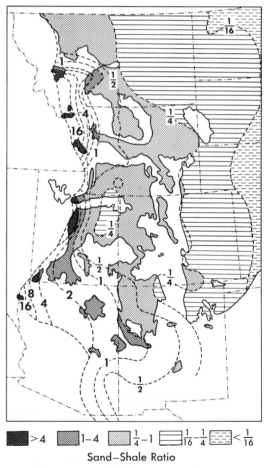

Sand–Shale Ratio

Fig. 10–22. Sand–shale ratio map of the Upper Cretaceous Series in the western states. (After W. C. Krumbein and F. G. Nagel, courtesy of the *American Association of Petroleum Geologists Bulletin.*)

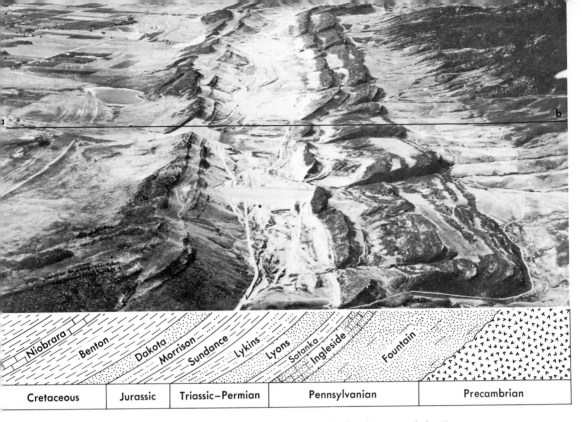

Niobrara	Benton	Dakota	Morrison	Sundance	Lykins	Lyons	Satanka	Ingleside	Fountain	
Cretaceous		Jurassic		Triassic–Permian		Pennsylvanian				Precambrian

Fig. 10–23. Aerial photograph of the hogbacks east of the Front Range at the site of the Horsetooth Reservoir in northern Colorado. The cross-section at the bottom shows the strata of the Mesozoic and upper Paleozoic successions along the line *ab* in the photograph. Note that the resistant sandstones, such as the Dakota, form prominent ridges and the shaly rocks underlie the valleys. (Official U. S. Bureau of Reclamation Photograph.)

extend out into the Mancos Shale. Farther north, the Dakota Sandstone near the base of the Cretaceous System has acted as a reservoir for petroleum in many fields in Colorado and Wyoming (Fig. 10–23). Lower Cretaceous sandstones such as the Viking, Bow Island, and "Glauconitic" yield both oil and gas in numerous fields in Montana and Alberta. The Cardium Sandstone lenses out eastward into the Upper Cretaceous shales and forms a stratigraphic trap for oil at the Pembina field, Canada's largest, with reserves of 750 million barrels.

Although volcanism is typical of geosynclines, during the Cordilleran orogeny it spread to the cratonic border. Volcanoes were in violent eruption in the Cordillera near the end of the Early Cretaceous Epoch. Ash from explosive volcanic vents to the west was carried by the wind over the interior

seas and deposited as a discrete bed of ash, or mixed with sand and mud. The latter was consolidated into a porcellaneous, siliceous rock (Mowry Shale) that is found covering large areas of Wyoming, Montana, Idaho, and northern Colorado to a thickness as great as 2000 feet.

Bentonites are distinctly light-colored, unconsolidated sediments consisting largely of the clay mineral montmorillonite and occurring in beds which are commonly less than 2 feet in thickness. Bentonites up to 25 feet in thickness are known but are rare. We can deduce from their distribution that the bentonites in the Mowry Shale of Wyoming represent ash ejected by violent eruptions of volcanoes. Isopach studies (Fig. 10–24) of these thin beds demonstrate an overlapping pattern of lobes and establish that each bed consists of a single set or multiple overlap-

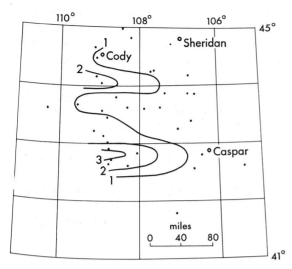

Fig. 10–24. Isopach map of the "Bed C" bentonite in the Mowry Shale of Wyoming. The outline of the map is the outline of the state of Wyoming. The contour interval is one foot. Note that the bed consists of two tongue-shaped bodies which thicken toward the west. (After J. W. Earley and M. Slaughter, courtesy of the Geological Society of America.)

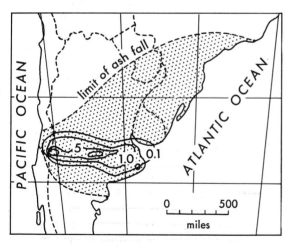

Fig. 10–25. Isopach map of the volcanic ash ejected from Volcán Quizapu in Chile. The extent of the ash fall is indicated by the stippled pattern, and the thickness of the deposit (in centimeters) by isopach lines. Compare the geometry of the deposit with that of the bentonite in Fig. 10–24. (After J. W. Earley and M. Slaughter, courtesy of the Geological Society of America.)

ping sets of tongue-like bodies, each of which represents an episode of eruption. The configuration of the bentonite beds is closely comparable with that of ash distributed from volcanic eruptions within historic times (Fig. 10–25). The elongate form of the bentonite bodies is due to the distribution of the ash eastward by high-altitude winds and is a confirmation that a westerly jet stream was as important in Cretaceous time as it is now.

The montmorillonite of bentonites seems to have been formed by the decomposition of the glassy ash particles on the ocean floor. When wet, this mineral swells to a gooey mass several times its dry volume. Bentonite may be used as a filler and to give "body" to drilling muds in oil wells. Because each thin layer of bentonite represents an episode of eruption which, geologically speaking, took place in an instant of time, such beds are invaluable in correlation, for they establish a time-parallel plane within a succession of facies that are generally time-transgressive.

Other Cretaceous volcanic deposits are found in the stratigraphic record of southern Alberta and western Montana.

SUMMARY

During the long process of orogeny, some segments of the geosyncline are uplifted to supply detritus, while other segments subside rapidly and accumulate volcanics and coarse detritus several miles in thickness.

Cordilleran batholiths are composed of many small intrusions emplaced over an interval that may span hundreds of millions of years. Individual igneous bodies within batholiths appear to have cooled in intervals of a few million years.

Batholiths intruded in the Cordilleran orogeny range in age from earliest Jurassic to early Cenozoic. Major periods of intrusion seem to have taken place in the late Jurassic and middle Cretaceous time.

The structure of the Rocky Mountains, which were formed from the sediments deposited along the cratonic edge, is characterized by:

1. Thrust faults and folds of the decollement type.
2. Lack of involvement of the basement in compressional movements.
3. Vertical uplift of basement rocks.
4. Lack of metamorphism and intrusion.

The pulses of an orogeny may be detected by cross-cutting relationships of faults, folds, and unconformities, and may be dated if sediments were deposited between the periods of deformation in intermontane valleys.

Orogeny in geosynclines brings about (1) a reversal in the direction of the supply of sediments to the margins of the craton, and (2) the formation of clastic wedges of sediments eroded from the rising mountains.

In clastic wedge deposits the constant oscillation of the shoreline produces a complex interfingering of offshore, near-shore, shoreline, and continental facies. Typically, the shoreline facies is represented by regressive sandstone tongues overlain by thin coal beds.

Ash from explosive volcanic eruptions was spread eastward into the clastic wedge by high-altitude winds, forming bentonite beds.

QUESTIONS

1. Using Figs. 10–21 and 10–22, construct a hypothetical cross-section of the Cretaceous clastic wedge from Salt Lake City to eastern Kansas, showing the geometry of the body of sediments, interfingering of facies, and the correct proportions of sandstone and shale indicated by the facies map.

2. How does the Cordilleran geosyncline illustrate the generalization made in Chapter 5 that orogeny is practically continuous in a geosyncline?

3. Why should the oceanic crust be more mobile and more easily deformed than the continental crust?

4. In a regressive sandstone tongue such as that illustrated in Fig. 10–18, why is the upper surface a time plane, but not the lower surface?

REFERENCES AND SUGGESTED READINGS

Alberta Society of Petroleum Geologists. *Geological History of Western Canada.* Calgary: 1965. The chapters in this atlas on the three Mesozoic systems clearly show the changing pattern of facies in the plains adjacent to the Cordillera.

CHILDS, O. E., and BEEBE, B. W. (Eds.). "Backbone of the Americas," *American Association of Petroleum Geologists Memoir 2,* 1963. A collection of papers describing segments of the Cordillera from Antarctica to Alaska.

DOTT, R. H., JR. "Mobile Belts, Sedimentation, and Orogenesis," *Transactions of New York Academy of Science,* ser. II, 27: 135–43, 1964. Many of the problems and generalizations that have been made concerning geosynclinal evolution are examined, particularly the relationship of geosynclines to the margin of the continental crust.

DOTT, R. H., JR. "Mesozoic–Cenozoic History of the Southeastern Oregon Coast in Relation to Cordilleran Orogenesis," *Journal of Geophysical Research,* 70: 4687–4707, 1965. The tectonic history of the Klamath Mountains illustrates the almost continuous orogeny in geosynclinal areas. The Mesozoic movements in this area should be grouped in the Cordilleran orogeny and the late Cenozoic fragmentation of the continental margin, called the Cascadian orogeny.

GABRIELSE, H., and RESSOR, J. E. "Geochronology of Plutonic Rocks in Two Areas of the Canadian Cordillera," *Royal Society of Canada Special Publication 8,* pp. 96–138, 1964. This study of the timing of intrusions in the

Nelson and Cassiar districts of British Columbia shows that intrusion and deformation took place during almost the entire Mesozoic Era.

GILLULY, J. "Volcanism, Tectonism, and Plutonism in the Western United States," *Geological Society of America Special Paper 80,* 1965. This review of the tectonic behavior of the American part of the Cordillera illustrates that volcanism is not necessarily connected with intrusion, and that the geosyncline may be formed on an oceanic rather than a continental crust.

MCKEE, E. D., *et al.* "Paleotectonic Maps of the Jurassic System," Map I–175, *U. S. Geological Survey, Miscellaneous Geologic Investigations,* 1956. The Jurassic System in the United States is summarized with correlation tables and isopach and lithofacies maps.

SLAUGHTER, M., and EARLEY, J. W. "Mineralogy and Geological Significance of the Mowry Bentonites, Wyoming," *Geological Society of America Special Paper 83,* 1965. A detailed mineralogical and stratigraphic investigation of the Mowry Formation of Cretaceous age allows the separation of individual ash falls carried eastward to the sea by high-altitude winds of that time.

WEIMER, R. J. "Upper Cretaceous Stratigraphy of the Rocky Mountain Area," *American Association of Petroleum Geologists Bulletin,* 44: 1–20, 1960. The strata are analyzed into four facies on the basis of six sections across the Rocky Mountain area of the United States.

11

Cenozoic Evolution of the Cordilleran Mountains

INTRODUCTION

The historical geologist systematizes and classifies the geological record of a continent in order to compare and contrast the behavior of its various parts with the tectonic divisions of other continents. In systematizing the record in the Cordillera, we have tried to describe its behavior in three phases: a preorogenic phase, an orogenic phase, and a postorogenic phase. In the geosynclinal cycle these phases should correspond to: first, subsidence and the accumulation of sediments and volcanics; second, the deformation of this filling and the formation of mountains; and third, the continued uplift of the mountains and their reduction by erosion. In the preceding chapter we have seen how difficult it is to separate the preorogenic from the orogenic phase; in this chapter we will discover that similar difficulties surround the separation of the orogenic from the postorogenic phase. As with the dating of the start of the Cordilleran orogeny, an arbitrary placement of the time of its end is forced on us.

The word orogeny means mountain making. The process can be thought of as having two components: the *deformation* of the rocks and the *elevation* of the deformed belt. Orogeny is used here to encompass horizontal movements and those vertical movements which are associated with deformation of the geosynclinal filling; the vertical movements that follow the main period of deformation are considered postorogenic.

On what basis can the boundary between the orogenic and postorogenic phases of the geosynclinal cycle be drawn? One criterion that might be used is the replacement of dominantly compressional earth movements by the largely vertical movements associated with the elevation of a mountain range. Although the cause of orogeny is in doubt, the deformation of the geosyncline *seems* to involve forces which shorten the earth's crust. When such apparent or real shortening stops, the orogenic phase may be said to end. To use such a criterion we must be able to determine unequivocally whether structures are due to horizontal or vertical forces. Unfor-

253

tunately, the structures of some mountains, such as the ranges of central Wyoming, have been interpreted as caused by either type of force.

Another criterion that might be used is the conversion of the geosyncline from a site of marine deposition to one of continental deposition. This change, however, took place progressively throughout the history of the Cordilleran geosyncline and cannot be dated at a particular time. Similar difficulties arise if the time of change from a phase of deposition to one of erosion is sought. Despite these difficulties, the postorogenic phase of the Cordilleran geosyncline, or of any geosyncline, can be imprecisely defined as that stage in the geosynclinal cycle when earth movements were dominantly vertical, when the mountain chain was above sea level and undergoing reduction, and when sedimentation, if any, was limited to continental deposits laid down in intermontane basins. Most of the North American Cordillera reached this stage in Oligocene time, but along the Pacific Coast orogenic deformation continues to the present day.

In Chapter 5, the general postorogenic behavior of geosynclinal mountain ranges was described and the following patterns were noted:

1. As the mountain ranges are uplifted, erosional agents attack the deformed rocks, wear them away, and either deposit the sediments in adjacent local basins or carry them to the sea.

2. Erosion surfaces are formed by the wearing down of the mountains; they may be uplifted when the mountains are rejuvenated.

3. Non-uniform elevation results in the breaking of the deformed belt into blocks tilted along normal faults that will form another generation of mountains.

4. Fracturing of the earth's crust along such faults opens conduits to deep-seated magma reservoirs, and basic lavas flow out on the surface from fissures and volcanoes.

Early Cenozoic Summary

During the Paleocene and Eocene epochs, the main movements of Cordilleran orogeny were taking place in the eastern Cordillera, but compressional movements had largely stopped in the central part of the mountain system. The principal deformation along the eastern ranges in Canada, Wyoming, and Colorado took place in Eocene time; the central Cordillera, however, was elevated in Cretaceous time and was not the site of extensive deposition during the early Cenozoic, although some continental sediments and lavas accumulated locally. Eocene beds several thousands of feet thick were laid down along the border of British Columbia and Washington, and flat-lying lavas of this age fill valleys over a large area of central British Columbia.

Each area of the Cordillera had a different Cenozoic history, but in the amount of space available we can only sample the regions. Pleistocene glaciation has obscured the Cenozoic events in the Cordillera north of latitude 49°N., and no detailed reconstruction of them has been made. In Wyoming, a fine record of postorogenic sedimentation in the basins and of erosion surfaces in the ranges has been preserved. In Nevada, Cenozoic sediments reveal the extent of explosive volcanism during the era and reflect the topographic evolution of the Sierra Nevada. In California, the Cenozoic basins record marine sedimentation, the persistence of orogenic processes to the present day, and the importance of transcurrent faulting. These three areas will form the basis of our discussion of the Cordillera during Cenozoic time.

WYOMING

By the end of the Cretaceous Period all the major ranges of the Wyoming–Colorado Rockies were in the process of formation, but they were of much lower relief than now. Pebbles of Precambrian rocks in the latest Cretaceous sediments of the Laramie basin are evidence that some of the ranges were

Fig. 11–1.   Shishaldin volcano, with Isanotski and Round Top peaks behind, Unimak, Aleutian Islands. These peaks are part of the line of volcanoes from which the Aleutian Islands were formed at the north end of the Cordillera in Cenozoic time. (Navy Department Photo 80–G–81322.)

so greatly elevated that the streams cut through the thick sedimentary cover, eroding the basement rocks. The Paleocene Epoch was a time of major deformation and uplift. The basins between the ranges received up to 11,000 feet of variegated sandstones and claystones eroded from the highlands. Most of these deposits are fine-grained, second-cycle sediments derived from the erosion of the uplifted Cretaceous sandstones and shales. On the alluvium in the basins, swamps developed in areas of poor drainage, and vegetation accumulated that was later consolidated into lignite. Many times during the Cenozoic, tilting of the basins or rapid sedimentation dammed streams and rivers to form lakes.

Eocene Sediments

Only recently have the Rockies had as great relief as in the Eocene Epoch. This was a time of extensive faulting, folding, and uplift along the length of the mountains. Most of the sediments derived from these orogenic pulses were deposited in the intermontane basins—as coarse conglomerates near mountain fronts, and as variegated sandstones and red-banded shales in the centers.

During Eocene time, a large lake in southwestern Wyoming and western Colorado filled the Green River basin (Fig. 11–2B). In this lake sediments of great variety, including kerogen shale, algal limestone, phosphate rock, anhydrite, salt, and sodium carbonate, were laid down (Fig. 11–3). **Kerogen shale** (sometimes called **oil shale**) is a light-brown to black shale that contains hydrocarbons in the form of waxy spores and pollen grains. Under proper treatment these hydrocarbons can be distilled and used to prepare petroleum products. The shales contain a large and generally untouched reserve of petroleum, and efforts have been made for many years to perfect an extractive process inexpensive enough to make the oil produced competitive with that obtained from drilling. The Eocene Wasatch Sandstone, which underlies and replaces the shales laterally, is a reservoir for oil in several fields in Wyoming.

The fine, regular laminations in these sedimentary rocks of the Green River Lake are believed to be annual deposits, or **varves**, similar in that respect to the banded structure of the anhydrite of the Permian basins of west Texas. By counting these layers in a representative section of the formation, one can calculate that 6½ million years were required to deposit the 2000 feet of Green River beds. Wilmot H. Bradley, who has studied the Green River Lake beds over a period of 30 years, has found beautifully preserved microfossils of soft-bodied animals, such as insect larvae, in these beds (Fig. 11–4). In addition, some of the most perfectly preserved fish fossils in the world are found here, pressed flat on the bedding planes of the calcareous mudstone. Bradley believes that the conditions in the lake are closely duplicated by those in some modern shallow lakes in Florida whose bottom is covered with a soupy, algal ooze which inexplicably does not decay as long as oxygen is present and provides a sterile environment in which soft-bodied animals can be preserved as fossils.

Although Eocene sediments are thick and widespread in the basins between the mountains, they are missing from the wedge of

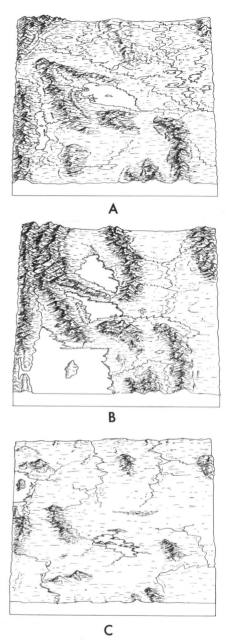

Fig. 11–2. Three reconstructions of the topography of Wyoming during the Cenozoic Era. A. Late Paleocene, when orogenic forces were still deforming the rocks and relief was high. B. Early middle Eocene, when relief was greatest and extensive lakes were formed by the westward tilting of the area. The Green River shales were deposited in the lake in the southwestern corner. C. Late Pliocene, when filling of the basins and erosions of the highlands brought the area to its lowest relief. (Modified from J. D. Love, D. O. McGrew, and H. D. Thomas.)

Fig. 11–3. Thin, even beds of the Green River Formation. View is north across the Bitter Creek Valley to White Mountain. Pilot Butte on the skyline is capped by a lava flow. (Courtesy of W. H. Bradley, U. S. Geological Survey.)

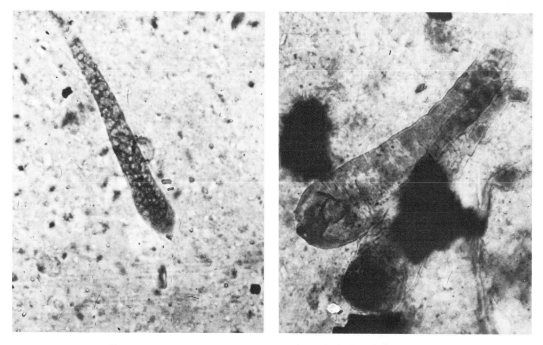

Fig. 11–4. Microorganisms from the oil shale of the Green River Formation. *Left:* An unidentified organism showing vesicular internal contents enclosed in a membrane. It may be a nematode or a motile spore of an aquatic fungus (magnification × 730). *Right:* Two larvae of a fly (midge) just after hatching. Their closeness suggests that they are part of a clump of larvae, possibly still in the gelatinous envelope of the egg mass. Black grains are pyrite (magnification × 1100). (Courtesy of W. H. Bradley and the Geological Society of America.)

sediments that spreads eastward into the plains. This absence may have been caused by a regional warping that changed the direction of the rivers draining the mountains, so that the rivers flowed with their burden of sediments southward or northward to the sea rather than eastward. The absence of sediments may also have been caused by the erosion of whatever Eocene beds were deposited, or by the failure of Eocene streams to leave sediment on the plains, whose high gradient would allow them to transport nearly all the detritus to the sea before depositing it.

Middle Cenozoic Sediments

During Oligocene and Miocene times, the agents of erosion lowered the mountains formed early in the Cenozoic Era, and streams filled the intermontane basins with sediment. The relief slowly decreased until, at the end of the Miocene Epoch, many of the ranges were buried completely in alluvium and the highest stood only a thousand feet above the plain. Oligocene rocks are largely claystones, and Miocene rocks, sandstones. Explosive volcanic activity contributed great thicknesses of tuffs to the clastic sediments filling the basins. Plant fossils in these sediments indicate that the climate was changing from semitropical at the end of the Eocene Epoch to temperate in mid-Cenozoic time.

When the mountains were almost buried in sediments (Pliocene), an erosion surface was cut on many ranges of the Wyoming–Colorado Rockies (Fig. 11–2C). This surface has different names in different ranges, but all have been referred to collectively as the Subsummit surface because some ranges have flat summits about 2000 feet higher than this broader surface. Some geologists have thought that the Subsummit surface is a remnant of a peneplain to which the Rockies were reduced in late Cenozoic time. More recently, other geologists have demonstrated that these erosion surfaces have the characteristics of pediments, or outward sloping surfaces eroded in the semiarid climates around mountain ranges. If the surfaces are the result of **pediplanation** (cutting of pediments) rather than peneplanation, we need not postulate that the Rockies were reduced close to sea level as implied by the peneplain concept, for pediplains can form at high altitudes. When these erosion surfaces were formed, they were continuous with the upper surfaces of the Cenozoic sedimentary rocks that filled the basins, but with the erosion of the basin fillings they have been isolated.

Pliocene Emergence

In late Pliocene time, the pattern of sedimentation of the early and middle Cenozoic Era was disrupted by regional uplift, normal

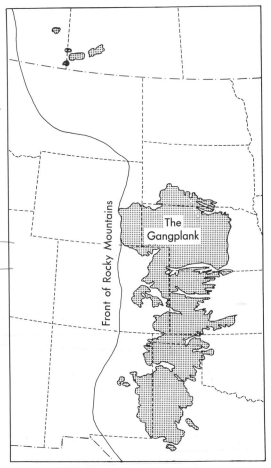

Fig. 11–5. Extent of the High Plains, the remnants of the apron of middle Cenozoic sediments that spread out from the Rockies after they had been dissected by late Cenozoic erosion.

faulting, and increased rainfall. Some geologists believe that the change was almost entirely climatic; others ascribe it to regional uplift. The streams that once deposited sediments in the basins began to erode them and excavated the poorly consolidated filling, bringing the buried ranges again into high relief. East of the Rockies, the quickened streams dissected the wedge of sediments formed in middle Cenozoic time and eroded most of the plains down to Cretaceous and Paleocene strata. The remnants of these Oligocene, Miocene, and Pliocene strata now constitute the "High Plains" (Fig. 11–5). If the surface of the High Plains is projected on a section westward into the mountains, it will coincide with the Sherman erosion surface of the Laramie Range, one of the Subsummit surfaces (Fig. 11–6). The former is a surface of deposition, the latter, a surface of erosion; but in Pliocene time they formed a continuous surface. At the "Gangplank," where the Union Pacific Railroad crosses the Laramie Range west of Cheyenne, a narrow salient of

the High Plains still lies against the mountains and the continuity of erosional and depositional surfaces has been preserved. So gentle is the slope of this surface that the railroad can cross this range at 8000 feet on a relatively low grade.

The rejuvenated streams in the mountains cut into the filling, removing most of the middle Cenozoic sediments and leaving the basins floored with Eocene and Paleocene rocks. However, some remnants of the Oligocene, Miocene, and Pliocene filling escaped erosion and are now found high on the mountainsides.

Normal faulting on a grand scale accompanied the rise of the mountains. Many of the normal faults that bound Wyoming ranges cannot be dated accurately, but those that have been dated are of late Pliocene and early Pleistocene age. In the northwest corner of Wyoming, the Teton Range was elevated at this time along normal faults, with a displacement of 10,000 to 20,000 feet. The east face of the Tetons is an impressive

Fig. 11–6. The Sherman erosion surface, cut on the granite rocks of the Colorado Front Range. Pikes Peak in the background rises above this surface. (Courtesy of the U. S. Geological Survey.)

Fig. 11–7. Aerial view of the Teton Range, western Wyoming, looking south along the trace of the fault which bounds the mountains on the east. (Photograph by John S. Shelton.)

fault-line scarp which rises 1½ miles over a horizontal distance of 3 miles to an altitude of 13,800 feet (Fig. 11–7).

Canyon Cutting

In the late Cenozoic, when the basins were filled with sediments, the stream courses were independent of the structures buried beneath the alluvium. As the alluvium that covered the ranges was carried away, several rivers maintained their courses across the resistant ridges of Precambrian rocks that emerged. Such rivers, "let down" across resistant ridges from which a cover of sediment has been eroded, are superposed.

The superposed rivers cut canyons into the ranges as deep as 3000 feet. One of the most spectacular of these is the Royal Gorge, cut by the Arkansas River where it crosses the Colorado Front Range (Fig. 11–8). Many other rivers in Wyoming and Colorado now follow similar routes totally out of adjustment with the structure and topography. The Bighorn River, instead of flowing eastward through the prominent gap in the Front Ranges of central Wyoming, turns northward and crosses the Owl Creek Mountains in a canyon 2500 feet deep; it then crosses the Bighorn Mountains before reaching the plains (Fig. 11–9). Perhaps nowhere in the world is there such a remarkable record of a superposed drainage system.

The Cenozoic sediments and ranges of Wyoming illustrate the postorogenic phase of the Cordilleran geosynclinal cycle: sedimentation and degradation decreased the relief; high-level erosion surfaces were formed; the ranges were again uplifted and

Fig. 11–8.   Basins and ranges of the central Rocky Mountains and Colorado Plateau.

Fig. 11–9. Aerial photograph of the Owl Creek Range, Wyoming (looking west), showing the canyon cut by the Bighorn River across the resistant core of the range during the canyon-cutting cycle. (Photograph by John S. Shelton.)

relief renewed; the crust was fractured along normal faults; and the drainage system was superposed across ranges emerging from an alluvial cover. To appreciate the part that explosive volcanism plays in the postorogenic phase, we must turn to the Basin and Range Province; and for effusive volcanism, to the Columbia Plateau.

THE BASIN AND RANGE PROVINCE

The Basin and Range physiographic province of the Cordillera is bounded on the north by the lava plateau of the Columbia and Snake rivers, on the west by the Sierra Nevada, on the east by the Colorado Plateau and the central Rockies, and on the south by the Sierra Madre Occidental of Mexico (Fig. 11–10). In the Basin and Range Province, high ranges of complex structure are isolated

from neighboring ranges by valleys filled with Cenozoic continental deposits. It is an area of low rainfall, a desert in the rain shadow of the Sierra Nevada. None of the streams or rivers in the northern section of the province (called the Great Basin) now reaches the sea. Infrequent, heavy rains feed torrential streams that carry detritus and dissolved salts into closed basins. When the water evaporates, the salts, dust, and sand are left on the basin floor (Fig. 11–11).

The Paleozoic and Mesozoic rocks of the ranges are folded, cut by thrust faults, and subsequently broken by normal faults into a mosaic of small blocks. (Their structure was formed in repeated orogenies, as discussed in Chapters 9 and 10.) Most of the compressional structures of this part of the Cordillera were formed before the close of the Cretace-

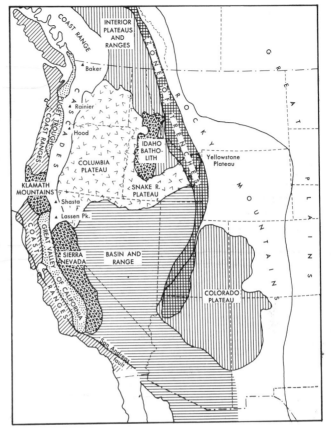

Fig. 11–10. Map of the major structural unit of the Cordillera active in Cenozoic time.

Fig. 11–11. Topography of the Basin and Range Province (aerial view) showing the flat basins filled with alluvium and the sharply defined ranges, many of which are bounded by fault scarps. (Courtesy of Fairchild Aerial Surveys.)

ous Period. The absence of early Cenozoic sediment in the Basin and Range Province suggests that it was a highland at this time. Drainage of the area at the close of the Cretaceous, and during most of the Cenozoic Era, was westward to the Pacific across the site of the Sierra Nevada, which was a region of low relief until the end of the era.

Mid-Cenozoic Volcanism

During the middle of the Cenozoic Era, a line of great volcanoes erupted violently along what is now the Sierra Nevada and Cascade mountains. In the western part of the Basin and Range Province, extensive flows of lava and agglomerates were contributed by the volcanoes; but in the eastern part the volcanic rocks in the basins were largely ash from explosive eruptions. This ash is the product of the Pelean type of volcanism, in which hot gases and steam are discharged with great force laterally from vents. The clouds, charged largely with pumice and ash, moved rapidly downhill and out onto flat country for many miles. Many of these *nuées ardentes* must have swept across tens of miles of the province, depositing their hot ash and pumice as their velocity decreased. The rocks so deposited are called **welded tuffs** (or **ignimbrites**) because the individual, glassy ash particles kept hot in a cloud of gas were still plastic when they came to rest and were welded to their neighbors to form a solid rock.

Flows from these volcanoes built a great lava plateau on the site of the Sierra Nevada during the middle of the Cenozoic, but the altitude of the plateau was less than 3000 feet and drainage was maintained westward through it to the sea. Paleobotanists can estimate the height of this plateau in the Miocene by a study of the plants in sediments of this age that were interbedded with the lavas and lifted to about 9000 feet·near the top of the Sierra Nevada. The fossil plants of the Miocene are similar to modern plants found only below an altitude of 2000 feet, and late Pliocene floras from altitudes near 10,000 feet resemble modern forests of only moderate altitudes.

Late Cenozoic Changes

Late Pliocene plants in the basin sediments of Nevada indicate a change from the warm, moist, subtropical conditions of early Cenozoic time to the dry, savannah climate characteristic of regions with less than 15 inches of rainfall per year. On the west, the Sierra Nevada began to rise along normal faults bounding its eastern side, a movement that in Pleistocene time carried it like a giant wedge 10,000 feet above the floor of the adjacent Owens Valley. The rising barrier placed Nevada in a rain shadow and initiated the aridity and interior drainage which now characterize the region. The history of the uplift is recorded in the valley profiles of the rivers that drain the gently sloping western flank of the range. The lower valley of the Merced River is a good example of a composite valley. The river now flows in a deep V-shaped valley cut into a wider valley whose remnant walls appear high above the river.

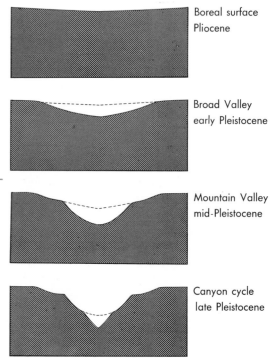

Boreal surface
Pliocene

Broad Valley
early Pleistocene

Mountain Valley
mid-Pleistocene

Canyon cycle
late Pleistocene

Fig. 11–12. Diagrammatic representation of one interpretation of the stages in the evolution of the transverse valley profiles in the Sierra Nevada.

Fig. 11–13. Aerial view northwestward from the main crest of the Sierra Nevada across the upper Kern basin to the Great Western Divide. Some geologists believe that an ancient erosion surface is preserved on the flat summit of Mount Whitney (14,495 feet) in the foreground; others attribute its flatness to high-altitude erosion processes. The surface of the Kern basin is another controversial erosion surface. (Courtesy of F. E. Matthes, U. S. Geological Survey.)

Traces of an even wider valley that was eroded into an upland surface remain above the other two (Fig. 11–12). From this profile and a study of the sediments that accumulated to the west, in the Great Valley of California, geologists have read the following history. During most of Cenozoic time, when the Sierra Nevada was less than 2000 feet above sea level, the oldest and now highest erosion surface, the Boreal surface, was formed. The first uplift of the Sierra Nevada in Pliocene time started a new cycle of erosion and caused the Merced to cut a wide valley into the Boreal surface, forming the Broad Valley surface. The Pleistocene uplift of the range to its present height took place in two steps: in the first, or Mountain Valley stage, a valley was cut into the Broad Valley surface; in the second, or Canyon stage, the gorge in which the river now flows was formed. The erosion surfaces are preserved only in the lower parts of the Merced Valley because the headwaters were deeply eroded by glaciers during the Ice Age, forming the picturesque scenery of the Yosemite Valley. The dating of these surfaces and others within the Sierra Nevada has been a problem of reconciling contradictory geomorphological, paleobotanical, stratigraphic, and geochronological evidence (Fig. 11–13). The "stepped" topography of the Sierra Nevada, ascribed by most geologists to a succession of erosion surfaces, has also been explained as a phenomenon of differential weathering and erosion.

As sediments continued to accumulate in the basins in late Cenozoic time, normal faulting took place, the relief increased, and the Basin and Range Province began to assume its present appearance. Early geologists assumed that each range was bounded on one or more sides by the normal faults along which it had been raised relative to the basins. After recent earthquakes, scarps several feet high appeared in the alluvium that obscures the base of many of these ranges. The scarps suggest that movement along the faults bounding the ranges still continues. However, further investigations have shown that the form of the ranges is controlled primarily by differential erosion in places along a normal fault in which the range side is upthrown, in places along a fault in which the displacement is downward, and in places where no fault exists.

EFFUSIVE VOLCANISM

Pyroclastic sediments are important constituents of the present basin fillings in Wyoming and Nevada, but lava flows are uncommon. However, flows played a major role in the Cenozoic history of the northwestern states, and volcanoes dotted the Colorado Plateau for much of the era. The dormant or recently extinct volcanoes of the Cascade Range, built on the deformed Paleozoic and Mesozoic volcanics of the Cordilleran geosyncline, remind us that volcanism remains a characteristic feature of geosynclinal areas from their inception until their ultimate peneplanation.

Columbia–Snake River Plateaus

Twenty-five thousand cubic miles of lava rose through fissures in Oregon, Washington, and southern Idaho to form the Columbia Plateau. The basaltic lava must have been a rapidly moving liquid of low viscosity when it emerged from the conduits, which are believed to have been fissures in the crust rather than volcanoes, because single flows a few hundred feet thick spread over 100 miles before they cooled enough to solidify. The first lava flowed out over a mountainous countryside with relief of at least 2500 feet. The bedrock of this mountainous area consisted of Paleozoic and Mesozoic metamor-

phic rocks deformed in the Cordilleran orogeny and of intrusions associated with this orogeny. Flow after flow of the molten basalt filled the valleys, until the mountains were entirely buried in lava. More lava welled up, ultimately covering an area of 200,000 square miles. The successive flows that built up this great volcanic plateau were 100 to 500 feet thick (Fig. 11–14). The total thickness of the flows is difficult to measure because the basement rocks are rarely exposed beneath the lava covering, but a well has penetrated over 10,000 feet of lava.

Continental sediments and tuffs interbedded with the lavas contain fossils which date the flows of the Columbia Plateau, for the most part, as of Miocene age. The Snake River Plateau of southern Idaho is composed of flows that seem to have been erupted from volcanic centers rather than fissures. They are more varied in composition and considerably younger than the Columbia Plateau flows. Extrusion in this area occurred in Pliocene and Pleistocene times, and the most recent flows may be only a few thousand years old.

Yellowstone National Park

At the eastern end of the Snake River lava plateau, in the northwestern corner of Wyoming, is Yellowstone National Park with its world-famous geysers. The Yellowstone Plateau is underlain by two or three "series" of breccia and agglomerate 6000 feet thick, covered by a flow of andesite. Fissure eruptions of basalt and rhyolite occurred later and filled the valleys cut during an interval of erosion in the former flows.

The park is famous for its geysers, more than 100 in number, which intermittently spray hot, mineralized water and steam into the air. Each time the geysers "play," a terrific amount of thermal energy is released. "Old Faithful," the most famous of these erupting springs, sprays 12,000 gallons of boiling water skyward about 24 times a day, year in and year out. This heat is supplied from below, where water seeping through cracks mixes with superheated steam from cooling igneous rocks. The heat may be de-

Fig. 11–14. Basalt flow showing columnar jointing, Columbia Plateau, Washington. This mass is an erosional remnant of a much more extensive flow. (Courtesy of F. O. Jones, U. S. Geological Survey.)

rived from the cooling of buried lava flows or from a large intrusive body just below the surface.

The Colorado Plateau

Although the Colorado Plateau was only slightly deformed during the Cordilleran orogeny, it was an area of volcanism in late Cenozoic time. Volcanic cones, only slightly dissected by erosion, are evidence that the extrusion of lavas continued until recently.

From his study of the Henry Mountains of Utah located near the center of the plateau (Fig. 11–8), G. K. Gilbert in 1877 coined the term "laccolith" to describe a type of sill that domes the overlying beds, making room for the molten rock. Later work has shown that the structure of the Henry Mountains is not as simple as Gilbert had conceived it, and

that each mountain is composed of many small, tongue-shaped laccoliths surrounding a central stock. Simple domed laccoliths similar to those mentioned in Gilbert's classic interpretation of the Henry Mountains intrusions occur in the La Sal and Abajo mountains to the east.

During Pliocene and Pleistocene times, a group of volcanoes known as the San Francisco Mountains was built by successive eruptions in the neighborhood of Flagstaff, Arizona (Fig. 11–15). Most of the volcanoes of the Hopi buttes and Navajo volcanic fields have been eroded, and only the resistant necks remain as buttes surrounded by radiating dikes, such as those at Ship Rock, New Mexico.

In addition to the minor intrusions mentioned above, a broad belt in central and

Fig. 11–15. San Franciscan volcanic field, north of Flagstaff, Arizona, looking southeast. An aerial photograph showing a recent, undissected lava flow that has issued from a small volcanic cone. (Photograph by John S. Shelton.)

southeastern Arizona, western New Mexico, and central Utah was intruded by a group of stocks ranging in composition from granite to diorite. Ore-forming fluids accompanying these intrusions deposited valuable copper ores in the host rocks of Paleozoic and Precambrian ages. Some of these ores are identical to those of the Colorado porphyry belt. The deposits at Bisbee, Arizona, have yielded 2¼ million tons of copper and large quantities of silver, gold, and other metals. The colossal open pit at Bingham, Utah, is the largest copper quarry in the world and yearly produces 370,000 tons of this metal. These are only the major producers among a host of smaller mines whose ores were formed during Cenozoic intrusions.

The Cascades

All other evidence of Cenozoic volcanism seems prosaic in the shadow of the majestic, snow-capped peaks of the Cascade Range of Washington, Oregon, and northern California (Fig. 11–16). The major peaks, such as Shasta (14,161 feet), Rainier (14,408 feet), Hood (11,253 feet), and Baker (10,750 feet), combine massive symmetry and graceful beauty with altitudes approaching the greatest in the American Cordillera. The Cascades are a series of volcanoes that were built on the western side of the Columbia lava plateau in Pleistocene time. The basement rocks are metamorphosed and intruded sediments of the Cordilleran geosyncline, overlain by marine Cretaceous and Eocene beds.

At the end of Eocene time, volcanic eruptions began to build up a thick plateau of lavas in the Cascade belt. Miocene crustal unrest opened north–south fissures, along which the basaltic volcanoes of the Cascades began to form in Pliocene time. The largest cones of the Cascade Range accumulated during Pleistocene time by the quiet extrusion of andesite flows. At the southernmost of these cones, Lassen Peak (10,453 feet), a Pelean type of eruption took place in 1914 and 1915. It is the only volcano known to be active within the continental United States exclusive of Alaska, but several other Cascadian peaks may only be dormant, not extinct. The internal structure of one of these volcanoes, whose summit has collapsed, is exposed at Crater Lake, Oregon.

The North American Cordillera is still the site of active volcanoes, such as Lassen Peak in California. A belt of active, dormant, and extinct volcanoes crosses Mexico at the latitude of Mexico City. The belt contains the highest peaks in Mexico, including the famous Popocatepetl (17,887 feet), which overlooks Mexico City. A belt of volcanoes bordering the Pacific Coast includes the recently born (1943) and recently dormant (1952) volcano Parícutin, the volcanoes of the Aleutian island arc, and the volcanoes in the Alaska Range, which are a continuation of that arc.

Fig. 11–16. Mount Rainier (14,408 feet), Washington. An aerial photograph looking toward other Cascade peaks: Mount Adams (12,307 feet) at left, Mount Hood in the center distance, and Mount St. Helens on the right. (Courtesy of H. Miller Cowling, 116th Photo Section, Washington National Guard.)

CENOZOIC BASINS OF THE PACIFIC COAST

The California Coast Ranges

A relief map of California (Fig. 11–17) shows two longitudinal highlands separated by a valley occupied by the San Joachin and Sacramento rivers. The eastern highland is the Sierra Nevada; the western one, the Coast Ranges. The valley between is commonly referred to as the Great Valley of California. The lowland areas, such as the Great Valley and the basins within the Coast Ranges, are floored with Cenozoic sedimentary rocks, some of which are folded and faulted. The highlands of the Coast Ranges owe their relief to more resistant folded and intruded Mesozoic rocks. The Late Jurassic and Early Cretaceous Franciscan, Knoxville, Paskenta,

and Horsetown groups consist of a clastic succession 25,000 feet thick which was derived from the erosion of the highland formed on the site of the Sierra Nevada by a Late Jurassic pulse of Cordilleran orogeny. A younger pulse, called the Santa Lucian, caused the deformation and intrusion of these rocks in Late Cretaceous time. After this orogenic event, the coastal highland was broken into a mosaic of fault blocks which define the present basins and ranges, and a new cycle of sedimentation in the basins began.

Basins of Southern California

In the Los Angeles area, the stratigraphy of the Cenozoic basins is known in great detail because their sedimentary fillings have been extensively drilled for oil. The basins, high-

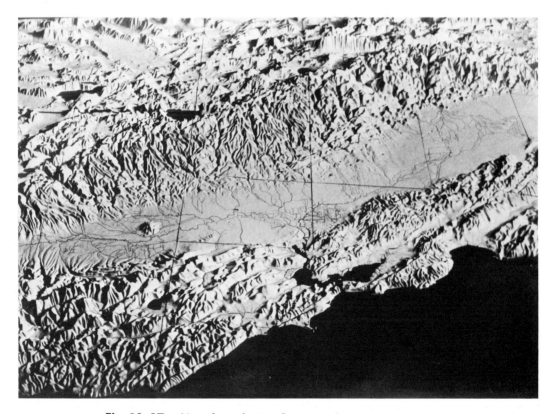

Fig. 11–17. View from the Pacific across the Coast Ranges at San Francisco to the Great Valley of California and the Sierra Nevada. In the left background, the Basin and Range Province can be seen. (From the relief map at the Babson Institute, courtesy of the Babson Institute.)

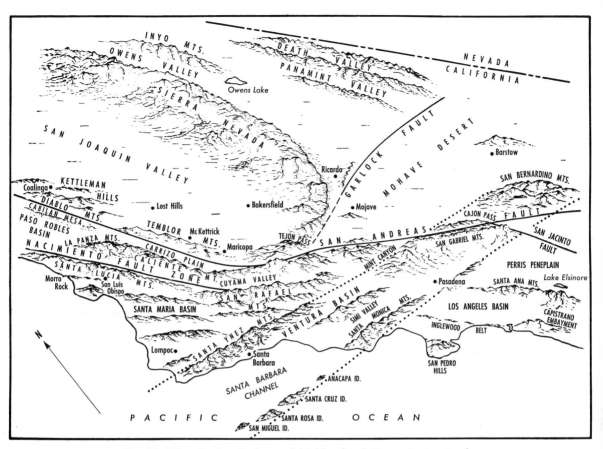

Fig. 11–18. Basins, faults, and highlands of Cenozoic time in the Coast Ranges of southern California. (From L. D. D. Reed and J. S. Hollister, courtesy of the *American Association of Petroleum Geologists Bulletin*.)

lands, and principal faults are shown in Fig. 11–18. At times the basins were open to the sea to the west; at other times they were filled by continental deposits. Sedimentation in the basins was rapid because subsidence and uplift along the bordering faults were rapid. In the Ventura basin, 46,000 feet of Cenozoic beds accumulated, of which 20,000 feet are of Eocene and Paleocene ages. In the middle of the basins most of the beds are marine, but at the margins they interfinger with clastic non-marine sediments that spread out as deltaic deposits from the Mesozoic highlands. In the deposits of these basins, rapid lateral and vertical facies changes reflect a varied and active tectonic history.

By comparing the foraminifera collected from these Cenozoic sediments with those now found off the California coast geologists can deduce the depth of the water in the basins millions of years ago. The similarity of the foraminifera in Miocene beds to those that now live at a depth of 4000 feet in the Pacific Ocean is taken to indicate that the depth of the water in some of the Miocene basins was also about 4000 feet. Only with relatively recent fossils are such determinations of depth of deposition accurate, because the older the fossils are the less they resemble living species, and the less certain we are that they lived in similar environments.

Folding and faulting of the Cenozoic sedimentary rocks took place several times during the Cenozoic Era and resulted in angular unconformities in the stratigraphic record. This deformation affected different basins at different times, but generally the movements reached a climax near the end of the era. In Pleistocene time, the Cenozoic beds were folded and cut by thrust faults. Numerous recent earthquakes indicate that the area is still in the throes of orogeny. Repeated land surveys that involve the determination of precise elevations show that parts of the crust are rising at appreciable rates. For instance, the western part of the Baldwin Hills is rising at a rate of 3 feet per century. If these rates of elevation were to persist over a period of 1 million years, mountains as high as the Himalayas could be built. The processes of orogeny are deforming the crust of this area today, but they act so slowly by man's standards that they are impressive only when some sudden movement along a fault shakes the earth and topples his fragile structures.

The folding and faulting of the basin sediments in southern California have produced many traps for petroleum in the porous sandstones of the Cenozoic succession. The reserves of the California oil fields are estimated at 4 billion barrels, making it one of the major oil regions in the continent.

Strike-Slip Faulting

The movement along Cordilleran faults so far discussed was largely perpendicular to the strike of the fault and roughly parallel to its dip. Along many of the faults in Cali-

Fig. 11–19. Trace of the San Andreas fault near the northern end of Temblor Range, California, looking north. Note the disruption of the drainage pattern caused by recent movements along the fault. (Photograph by John S. Shelton.)

fornia, the movement has been parallel to the strike. Such faults are called **strike-slip** or **transcurrent**. The most famous of these is the San Andreas fault, which can be traced for 600 miles from the Mexican border to 40 miles north of San Francisco (Fig. 11–19). Repeated movements and resulting earthquakes, the most famous of which destroyed San Francisco in 1906, have occurred along this zone. The San Andreas fault is the longest of a set of faults which branch throughout southern California and border many of the sedimentary basins. The Sierra Nevada is cut off on the south by the Garlock fault, a major branch of the San Andreas.

At its northern end, the San Andreas fault turns westward into the Pacific and seems to pass into a zone of irregular topography, including scarps, that extends along the ocean floor as far as Hawaii. This zone is the northernmost of four subparallel fracture zones of the western Pacific, which are called —from north to south—the Mendicino, Murray, Clarion, and Clipperton zones. On the Pacific floor, the bands defined by the remnant magnetism of the rocks (see p. 113) are displaced along the fracture zones in such a way that lateral movement is suggested.

In the San Francisco earthquake of 1906, the maximum displacement along the San Andreas fault was 21 feet in a right-lateral sense, i.e., the side of the fault opposite the observer seems to have moved to the right. Displacement of drainage lines and other topographic features indicates that this direction of movement has persisted for the last few thousand years. By locating stratigraphic and structural features that might have been continuous across the fault in the past but are now separated, the geologist can determine the movement of the fault back to the Mesozoic Era. John Crowell believes that Miocene features across the fault, which are now separated by 160 miles, can be matched. If the crustal block west of the fault were moved southward 350 miles, which some geologists believe would restore it to its Jurassic position, Baja California

would touch Mexico and the Gulf of California would disappear. Not all geologists agree that 350 miles of displacement occurred along the fault, and some have postulated that, despite recent lateral displacements, the main movement in the past was vertical. A right-lateral movement of 250 miles, however, is also suggested by the geology along either side of the Denali fault in southern Alaska. On a large scale, these faults imply a southward movement of the whole continent relative to the Pacific Ocean floor.

What was the effect of the hundreds of miles of displacement along the San Andreas fault on the sediments accumulating in the basins during the Cenozoic Era? This problem has not yet been solved. Some geologists believe that the deformation of the basin sediments can be explained as a response to the shearing stress set up by the strike-slip faults. Others believe that Pleistocene and Recent deformation can be explained by the rise of the adjacent Mesozoic highlands. These geologists propose that Cenozoic orogeny in California has been largely the result of vertical forces related to underground movements of magma, and not the result of lateral displacements. California offers a unique opportunity for the study of orogeny, for not only have folding and faulting taken place within the last million years, but earthquakes, raised terraces along the coast, precise leveling surveys, and recent volcanism all indicate that the processes of mountain building are still at work and can be observed firsthand. In California, the Cordilleran orogeny continues to this day.

SUMMARY

The postorogenic phase of the geosynclinal cycle can be considered to have replaced the orogenic phase when structures, such as thrust faults, indicative of compression are largely completed and the structures that are forming can be largely attributed to vertical forces.

The Cenozoic history of Wyoming illustrates:

1. Filling of intermontane basins by fluvial deposits eroded from the ranges.
2. Ponding of drainage in intermontane lakes resulting from the tilting of the land surface.
3. The formation of erosion surfaces, possibly at relatively high altitudes, by pediplanation.
4. Normal faulting during the second elevation of the mountainous area.
5. Excavation of the basin fillings and superposition of the drainage system across the emerging ranges.

The Cenozoic history of the Basin and Range Province illustrates:

1. The intense, explosive volcanic activity that characterizes the postorogenic phase.
2. Reconstruction of the geological history of uplifts on the basis of the fossil flora of the highland; and on the basis of the effect of the highland on the climate and, therefore, on the flora of areas in its rain shadow.

3. The possibilities and difficulties of reconstructing the history of uplifts from erosion surfaces in composite valleys.
4. Importance of normal faulting to the late history of a geosynclinal mountain range.

Plateau basalt flows welling out of fissures and central vents are also a feature of the postorogenic phase of a geosynclinal mountain system.

Smaller intrusions of great diversity may occur in the craton adjacent to the deformed geosyncline.

Parts of the geosynclinal area may break into fault basins that are filled with marine and non-marine sediments. In California, deformation in these basins has been almost continuous from early Cenozoic time to the present.

Strike-slip or transcurrent faulting seems to play an important role in the postorogenic phase of geosynclinal development, but geologists disagree as to the extent to which it is responsible for the minor structures of the geosynclinal belt.

QUESTIONS

1. On the basis of the information and diagrams in the text, draw three diagrammatic cross-sections across Wyoming from the Utah border to Cheyenne, showing the topography and basin fillings during the Eocene, Miocene, and Pleistocene epochs.

2. The canyons in the Wyoming ranges are described as superposed. In what other ways can rivers cut valleys across resistant ridges?

3. What famous recent eruptions have been of the Pelean type?

4. Explain how the rise of the Sierra Nevada in Pliocene time caused increasing aridity in the Basin and Range Province to the east.

5. Make a chart similar to that of Fig. 5–11, showing the times of deformation, uplift, and deposition in California since the beginning of the Cambrian Period.

REFERENCES AND SUGGESTED READINGS

AXELROD, D. I. "Post-Pliocene Uplift of the Sierra Nevada, California," *Geological Society of America Bulletin,* 73: 183–98, 1962. A summary of the author's work on the paleobotany of the Sierra Nevada and a discussion of the confusion concerning the various erosion surfaces.

BRADLEY, W. H. "Tropical Lakes, Copropel, and Oil Shale," *Geological Society of America Bulletin,* 77: 1333–38, 1966. Conditions in some lakes in Florida and Africa are compared with those under which the Green River oil shales were deposited.

CHRISTENSEN, M. N. "Late Cenozoic Deformation in the Central Coast Ranges of California," *Geological Society of America Bulletin,* 76: 1105–24, 1965. Recent deformation in the Cenozoic sediments can be explained by vertical uplift of the highlands and not by transverse faulting.

CROWELL, J. C. "Displacement Along the San Andreas Fault," *Geological Society of America Special Paper 71, 1962.* The case for the displacement of 160 miles along the fault since Miocene time is presented.

KING, P. B. *Evolution of North America.* Princeton, N.J.: Princeton University Press, 1959. Pp. 111–31. A description of the Cenozoic development of the Rocky Mountains.

LOVE, J. D. "Cenozoic Sedimentation and Crustal Movement in Wyoming," *American Journal of Science,* 258A: 204–14, 1960. This and a similar article in the *Backbone of the Americas* volume published by the American Association of Petroleum Geologists (1963) outline the history of the Wyoming Rocky Mountains.

THORNBURY, W. D. *Regional Geomorphology of the United States.* New York: John Wiley & Sons, Inc., 1965. Chaps. 17–26. A brief and clear summary of the geomorphic history of the Cordillera in the United States.

VAN HOUTEN, F. B. "Maps of the Cenozoic Depositional Provinces, Western United States," *American Journal of Science,* 259: 612–21, 1961. A brief discussion of a group of maps of the American Cordillera showing the extent of continental and volcanic sediments.

IV

THE APPALACHIAN GEOSYNCLINE

12

The Appalachian Geosyncline in the Early Paleozoic

When James Hall proposed and James Dana shaped the geosynclinal theory, their model was the Appalachian geosyncline. Their generalizations concerning the sequence of events that leads to the formation of a folded mountain chain arose from their knowledge of the geology of the Appalachian Mountains. This mountain system borders the east side of North America from Newfoundland to New York, but from New York to Alabama it is separated from the ocean by a narrow coastal plain. In Alabama the structures of the folded belt are covered by Cretaceous strata but emerge to the west in the Ouachita Mountains of Arkansas and Oklahoma. They plunge again beneath the unconformable cover and emerge in the Marathon Mountains of west Texas. From the Marathon region to Newfoundland, the Appalachian mountain system is almost as long as the North American Cordillera. Much of the southwestern half of the Appalachian deformed belt is covered by Cenozoic and Mesozoic sediments or by a deep regolith of weathered material that makes investigation difficult. Although the rocks of the Appalachian geosyncline have been studied for over 100 years, many questions remain to challenge geologists to find new ways of unlocking the history of this area (Fig. 12–1).

THE REGIONAL SETTING

The Appalachian Arcs

From Alabama to Newfoundland the Appalachians are arranged like giant earth waves from the Atlantic breaking against the American craton (Fig. 12–2). Three nodes divide the chain into four arc-shaped seg-

279

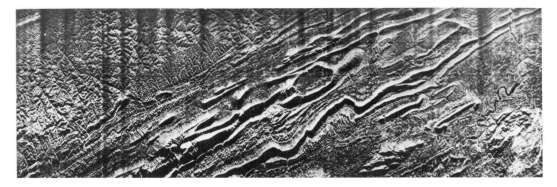

Fig. 12–1. Radar image, taken from an airplane, of the Appalachians of southern Virginia. The topography of the Appalachian Plateau, Valley and Ridge, and Blue Ridge provinces is shown from upper left to lower right. The area pictured is about 160 miles along the base. (Courtesy of the National Aeronautics and Space Administration.)

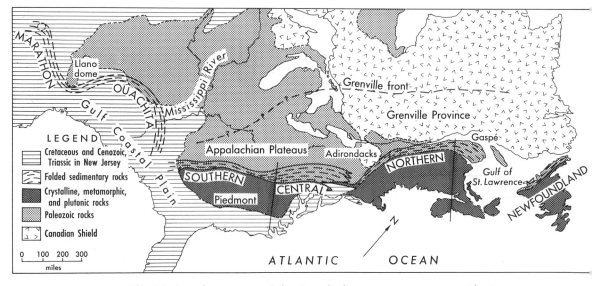

Fig. 12–2. The six arcs of the Appalachian mountain system. The two transverse lines mark the cross-sections discussed in the text.

ments convex toward the continent. The nodes between these arcs are marked by changes in structure and strike of the folded rocks near Roanoke, Virginia; at the Hudson River; and in the Gulf of St. Lawrence. The arcs have been called the southern Appalachians (Alabama to Virginia), the central Appalachians (southern Virginia to New York), the northern Appalachians (the New England states, the Maritime Provinces, and parts of New York and Quebec), and the Newfoundland Appalachians (the island of Newfoundland). The two small segments of the Appalachian system that emerge from covering sediments in Oklahoma and Arkansas, and in Texas, define the Ouachita and Marathon arcs. The nature of two of the nodes which seem to have held back the northwestward push of the folds is unknown, because they are covered by younger sedimentary rocks between the Ouachita and southern Appalachian arcs and by water between the Newfoundland and northern Appalachian arcs. The nodes between the northern and central arcs and between the Ouachita and Marathon arcs may be caused by the restraining action of prominences in the Precambrian basement; in the first by the Adirondack axis, and in the second by the Llano dome of central Texas. The boundary between the central and southern Appalachians is associated with a change in manner of deformation from folding to faulting and with changes in the stratigraphy of the deformed sediments, but the problem of the deflection of the strike of the Appalachians needs further investigation.

Two Traverses

To scan the structure and rocks of the Appalachian system we can take imaginary traverses; in the southern Appalachians from North Carolina to West Virginia, and in the northern Appalachians from Nova Scotia to eastern Quebec (Fig. 12–2).

From the coastal lowlands of the Carolinas underlain by flat-lying Cenozoic sediments, our traverse crosses a belt of low relief, called the Piedmont, developed on schists, gneisses, and plutonic rocks (Fig. 12–3). The metamorphic and igneous rocks are weathered to depths of several hundred feet between the stream valleys. Fossils are almost unknown in the Piedmont and the age of the rocks remains a subject of controversy after a hundred years of investigation. On the west

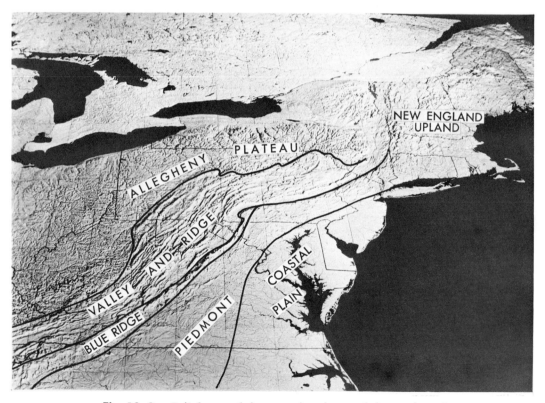

Fig. 12–3. Relief map of the central and part of the northern Appalachians showing the boundaries of the physiographic units. (Courtesy of the Babson Institute.)

Fig. 12–4. Topography of the Valley and Ridge Province. The contrast between the resistant rocks of the ridges and the shales and carbonate rocks in the valleys is emphasized by the trees growing on the former and the fields in the latter. Aerial photograph looking southwest, about 25 miles west of Harrisburg, Pennsylvania. (Photograph by John S. Shelton.)

side of the Piedmont an escarpment with up to 4000 feet of relief marks the boundary of the Blue Ridge Province. The bedrock is better exposed in this area of mountains and is composed of metamorphic rocks like those of the Piedmont and slightly metamorphosed Cambrian and late Precambrian sedimentary rocks involved in complex structures. The southern part of the Blue Ridge Province includes the Great Smoky Mountains, the highest peaks in the Appalachian system (Mt. Mitchell has an altitude of 6684 feet). West of the Great Smokies is a belt of lesser altitude and relief characterized by long ridges

composed of resistant sandstones and valleys floored with shale and limestones (Fig. 12–4). These Paleozoic rocks are broken by numerous thrust faults into complex structures. Beyond the Valley and Ridge Province lies the Cumberland Plateau, founded on gently folded late Paleozoic sedimentary rocks, deeply incised by stream valleys. The folding dies out westward in the rocks of the plateau.

If our traverse were to start a thousand miles north at the coast of Nova Scotia (Fig. 12–2), we would first cross rocks not unlike those of the Piedmont—schists, gneisses, slates, and granitic batholiths. Scattered and poorly preserved fossils in these rocks demonstrate that they are of early Paleozoic age. Set within this metamorphic belt are fault-bounded basins containing less deformed and unmetamorphosed sedimentary rocks of late Paleozoic and Triassic age. Similar bedrock and rolling topography continue northwestward from the Nova Scotia coast for 300 miles across that province and New Brunswick. When our traverse crosses into the Gaspé Peninsula of southeastern Quebec, the plutonic and metamorphic rocks are replaced by sandstones, siltstones, and limestones of middle Paleozoic age, folded into open anticlines and synclines. In eastern Quebec the northwestern edge of the Appalachian deformed belt is covered by the St. Lawrence estuary, but in western Quebec a lowland of gently folded Paleozoic rocks separates the mountains from the Canadian Shield.

The gross distribution of rocks in these two traverses is similar to that established in the Cordillera: an intensely deformed, plutonic–metamorphic belt occupies the oceanic side of the mountains, and a broadly folded and faulted belt of sedimentary rocks adjoins the craton. Like the Cordillera, the Appalachian Mountains include the deformed, intruded, and metamorphosed rocks of the geosyncline, and the folded and faulted shelf sediments of the cratonic margin.

The maps (Figs. 12–2 and 12–3) show the distribution of the Piedmont, Blue Ridge, Valley and Ridge, Plateau, and New England Upland provinces. The rocks of the Piedmont, Blue Ridge, and New England Upland were deposited in the Appalachian geosyncline; the rocks of the Valley and Ridge and Plateau provinces were deposited along the edge of the craton. The sector of the Appalachian geosyncline north of New York has been called the Acadian geosyncline, after an early name used for this region by settlers, but as the similarity between the history of the New England Upland and the Piedmont has been revealed by isotopic ages, the distinction has become less useful.

THE BASE OF THE GEOSYNCLINE

Precambrian Rocks

The oldest rocks in the southern Appalachians are gneisses and intrusives, about 1 billion years old, which form a narrow belt along the west side of the Blue Ridge Province. Rocks of similar age and lithology occupy the core of the Green Mountains of Vermont. These rocks seem to be part of the Grenville structural province of the Canadian Shield, which was deformed about 1 billion years ago, and are probably continuous with this part of the Shield beneath the younger platform sediments (see Fig. 16–12).

The lowest beds exposed on the eastern or Atlantic side of the Appalachians are great thicknesses of Precambrian sedimentary rocks and lavas. Eastern Newfoundland presents a good example of the thickness and complexity of the Precambrian record in the northeastern end of the Appalachian geosyncline. Lavas and tuffs 6000 feet thick are overlain by 7000 feet of marine slates and graywackes and were intruded by a granite dated as about 575 million years old before being overlain by Lower Cambrian strata. Similar thick late Precambrian successions of lavas and graywackes are found at several other places along the Canadian Atlantic coast. These rocks, the oldest in the northern Appalachians, tell us that the cycle of sedimentation and orogeny that produced the mountain system of today started in late Precambrian time.

Basal Clastic Sediments

In the Blue Ridge Province, a great thickness of late Precambrian and Early Cambrian clastic rocks that crosses the boundary between Paleozoic and Precambrian time is exposed. The abundant feldspar in the 30,000 feet of Ocoee Group sandstones in the Great Smoky Mountains indicates rapid erosion of a granitic terrane. This thick Ocoee succession is unconformably overlain by 6000 feet of quartzites and shales of the Chilhowee Group. The boundary of the

Paleozoic Era has been placed by some geologists at the occurrence of the index fossil *Olenellus* near the top of the Chilhowee Group and by some at the basal unconformity of the group (see p. 134).

The compositions of the Chilhowee and Ocoee sandstones indicate that they were derived from the erosion of cratonic rocks. They appear to have been built out from the west as a wedge of coastal plain sediments on the folded rocks of the Grenville belt in late Precambrian time. Although no volcanics occur in either of these two groups, farther north, in the Blue Ridge of Virginia and Maryland, lava flows record the presence of volcanoes in the embryonic geosyncline. In the northern Appalachians, late Precambrian and Cambrian volcanics and graywackes leave little doubt that a pattern of island arcs and deep basins was established before the beginning of the Paleozoic Era.

ORDOVICIAN UNREST

The slates, schists, gneisses, and granites of the Piedmont are a barrier to our understanding of the early Paleozoic history of the Appalachian geosyncline, for although the times of metamorphism of the sedimentary rocks and intrusion of the igneous rocks can be determined by isotopic methods, the time of deposition of the sediments cannot be determined without fossils. Events in the southern part of the Appalachian geosyncline were impressed on the sedimentary record deposited in a long, deep basin at the east margin of the craton. This basin, which stretches from New York to Alabama, will be called the Allegheny basin in this book because its west limb underlies the Allegheny Mountains and Plateau of Pennsylvania. Its eastern side has been folded into the Valley and Ridge Province of the Appalachians. The sedimentary sequence in the Allegheny basin and isotopic ages from the Piedmont allow us to reconstruct the tectonic history of the southern segment of the Appalachian geosyncline. Fossiliferous lower Paleozoic rocks in the northern Appalachians make interpretation of this segment much simpler.

Black Shales and Megabreccias

Ordovician rocks of the northern Appalachian geosyncline are dark shales unlike the limestones that accumulated at the same time on the shelf to the west. Along the St. Lawrence Valley these shales contain beds of limestone breccia in which the fragments range from the size of pebbles to the size of a house. These enigmatic breccias have been studied intensely along the south shore of the river in Quebec, in western Newfoundland, and in New York. The limestone blocks at Levis, Quebec, contain fossils which show that limestones of Early Cambrian, Late Cambrian, and Early Ordovician ages contributed detritus to the megabreccias. At first, the breccias were thought to occur at a single stratigraphic level, but detailed paleontological and structural work has shown that in Newfoundland and New York they are distributed throughout the succession from Cambrian to Middle Ordovician rocks. The limestone blocks must have been eroded from part of the shelf on the cratonic side of the geosyncline, elevated along faults, and then introduced by sliding or slumping into the shales that were accumulating in deeper water. The breccias are evidence of continuing instability along the margin of the geosyncline from Cambrian into Ordovician time.

The Middle Ordovician Clastic Wedge

The eastern edge of the craton from Middle Cambrian to Early Ordovician time was the site of deposition of limestones which point to the low relief of the Shield to the west and the geosyncline to the east. In Middle Ordovician time this pattern of sedimentation changed, as rapid erosion of highlands in the geosyncline introduced coarse clastic sediments into the Allegheny basin, forming a wedge of sandstone and shale that reaches its greatest thickness of 7000 feet in eastern Tennessee. Figure 12–5, a cross-section of this clastic wedge, shows coarse clastic sediments derived from the southeast pushing the site of limestone deposition on the shelf westward during Middle Ordovician time. These same facies changes are found in the Middle Ordovician Series of central New York and in the St. Lawrence lowlands, where the clastics are the dark marine shales of the Utica Group and the limestones are of the Trenton and Black River groups. A pulse of orogeny at the beginning of Late Ordovician time dis-

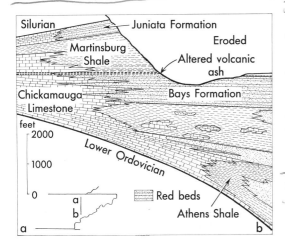

Fig. 12–5. Facies changes in the Middle and Upper Ordovician Series of Tennessee. Note the interfingering of the limestone facies deposited on the shelf with the shale deposited in marginal basins; the shale facies spreads progressively northward, while the limestone decreases. (After J. Rodgers.)

tributed shale over the whole of the adjacent shelf as far west as Lake Huron (Fig. 12–6). This pulse is called the Vermontian orogeny because the Green Mountain axis was elevated at this time. It is one of the few accurately dated pulses of the Taconic orogeny, which affected the Appalachian geosyncline during the Ordovician Period.

Thin, highly persistent layers of clay occur within Middle and Upper Ordovician limestones and shales along the margin of the Appalachian geosyncline. Although these beds are only a few inches thick, they can be traced for tens of miles through the clastic wedge and across the facies change to carbonates. Because they are independent of facies they make excellent "key beds" for establishing correlations. These clay beds, like the Late Cretaceous water-absorbing bentonites of the western plains, are believed to be the product of volcanic eruptions in the geosyncline that spread ash into the surrounding seas. But because this clay has lost the ability to absorb water and swell, it is called **metabentonite.**

Evidence of Ordovician volcanism in the geosyncline recorded in the cratonic rocks to the west is confirmed by the geosynclinal rocks themselves. Many beds of pillow lava

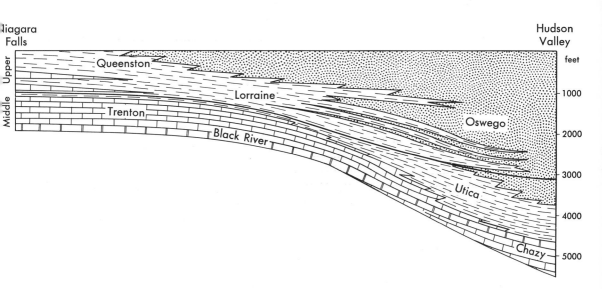

Fig. 12–6. Restored and simplified cross-section of the facies changes in the Middle and Upper Ordovician Series of New York.

extruded under the sea occur in the 20,000 feet of Ordovician rocks in central New-foundland. Thousands of feet of lavas that poured out onto the geosynclinal floor in Ordovician time occur in New England.

The Queenston Clastic Wedge

The sedimentary rocks in the Allegheny basin testify that orogeny in the Appalachian geosyncline intensified in Late Ordovician time, for an increasing volume of sediments was eroded from geosynclinal highlands and deposited to the west in a vast compound delta. Some idea of the size of the Ordovician mountains in the geosyncline can be obtained from the estimate of Marshall Kay that 200,000 cubic miles of sediments were eroded from them during Late and Middle Ordovician time and deposited in the Allegheny basin. The Middle Ordovician clastic wedge was thickest in the southern Appalachians, but the Late Ordovician wedge was thickest in New York and Quebec, where streams from the rising highlands in the geosyncline pushed the shoreline steadily westward with an increasing supply of sand and silt, building a compound delta and spreading red sediments as far as Lake Huron, 500 miles from the front of the mountains. This Ordovician apron of red sediments is called the Queenston delta because the red muds now constitute the Queenston Formation of the Niagara Gorge; the mass of sediments that accumulated constitute the Queenston clastic wedge. Figure 7–17 shows the maximum extent of the deltaic sediments and the distribution of sedimentary facies in Late Ordovician time. The apron was a broad alluvial plain rising gently eastward to the mountains along the present site of the Hudson Valley and the edge of the Piedmont. Over this slope rivers and streams flowed out toward the sea, depositing sand and gravel. Unlike modern deltas, the Queenston delta was barren, because there was as yet no vegetation on land. Only here and there might a patch of yellow or green lichen on a boulder have relieved the monotonous, dull red of the sediments deposited by the flooding rivers.

THE TACONIC OROGENY

The major orogeny that affected the Appalachian geosyncline in Ordovician time is called the Taconic orogeny, after the Taconic Range of eastern New York, western Massachusetts, and Vermont, which was thrust westward at this time. Both the northern and Newfoundland Appalachians were then intensely deformed, but the extent of the deformation in the central and southern Appalachians is problematical. The obscurity of Taconic structures in most of the Appalachian Mountains is caused by later folding and metamorphism of the geosynclinal rocks in Devonian and in late Paleozoic time.

Structures formed during the Ordovician orogeny can be identified with certainty only where they are overlain unconformably by Silurian or Devonian strata, or along the northwest edge of the geosyncline, which was not affected by later orogeny. Taconic deformation was restricted to geosynclinal rocks, and in only a few places were rocks of the margin of the craton involved.

Structures and Unconformities

In the northern Appalachians the most spectacular result of the Taconic orogeny was the thrusting of geosynclinal sediments for many miles northward and westward along the edge of the craton. The limit of the westward extent of the folded rocks is called "Logan's Line," after Sir William Logan, who was the first to recognize its significance. This major fault zone has been traced northward from Pennsylvania up the Hudson Valley through Lake Champlain, and northwestward along the border of the Appalachians in Quebec to Quebec City, where it passes under the waters of the St. Lawrence estuary toward Newfoundland. Geosynclinal graywackes and volcanics were carried at least 30 miles along the fault and have come into contact with the shelf limestones and shales. The Taconic Range itself is composed of Lower Cambrian and Ordovician graywackes which slid and were thrust westward over the limestone and shale succession

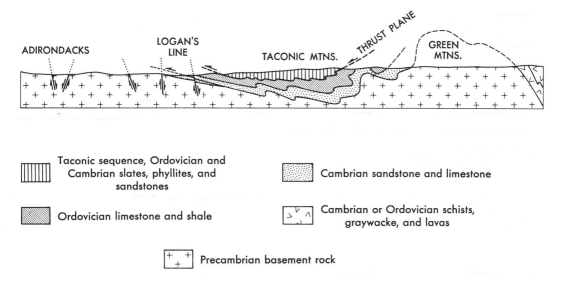

	Taconic sequence, Ordovician and Cambrian slates, phyllites, and sandstones		Cambrian sandstone and limestone
	Ordovician limestone and shale		Cambrian or Ordovician schists, graywacke, and lavas
	Precambrian basement rock

Fig. 12–7. Cross-section of the Taconic Range of western New York. The phyllites and graywackes of this range were transported for miles along the surface of a low-angle thrust fault during the Taconic orogeny. (After M. P. Billings, J. B. Thompson, and J. Rodgers.)

at the cratonic margin. This massive succession of folded sedimentary rocks 150 miles long and 30 miles wide is believed to have been thrust upward and westward from the east side of the Green Mountain uplift. The front part of the overthrust block is believed to have become detached from the back part and slid westward down a low slope into the Ordovician sea (Fig. 12–7). A similar block of geosynclinal rocks may be present in western Newfoundland, and although the time of the emplacement of the Taconic block in New England cannot be determined from stratigraphic relations, some evidence suggests that the thrusting which occurred in Newfoundland took place in Middle Ordovician time.

Widely scattered unconformities show that the Taconic deformation affected the whole exposed width of the Appalachian geosyncline in Canada, although Taconic folds and faults are clearly exposed only along the south bank of the St. Lawrence River, where the overprint of Acadian folding has not obscured them. Structures formed in Ordovician orogeny cannot be identified in the southern and central Appalachians, but iso-

topic ages (discussed below) and the stratigraphic evidence already presented indicate that much of the Piedmont was involved in the deformation.

The approximate time of some of the Taconic movements—which may have been numerous—is indicated by unconformities along the western edge of the geosyncline. Along the Hudson Valley, Middle Ordovician shales are highly contorted, metamorphosed to slate, and overlain by Upper Silurian limestone that has been gently folded by later earth movements. Such unconformities indicate the time of folding only within the wide limits of the Middle Ordovician and Late Silurian epochs. Farther south, the stratigraphic break between the beds bounding the unconformity diminishes. At Shawangunk Mountain, New York, the upper beds are Lower Silurian, while in central Pennsylvania they are Late Ordovician. Orogeny there apparently occurred within the later part of the Ordovician Period. The unconformity can be traced northward into the Lake Memphremagog region of Quebec, where Middle Silurian conglomerate covers the Middle Ordovician contorted slates.

Intrusions and Isotopic Ages

Identification of Taconic intrusions by their field relationships to Ordovician and younger rocks or by isotopic ages has proved to be difficult because of the obscuring effects of the subsequent and more intense Acadian orogeny. Some of the problems may be solved by a combination of rubidium–strontium and potassium–argon determinations on the same sample in order to estimate the amount of argon released by the reheating of a metamorphic rock in a subsequent episode of orogeny. Potassium–argon studies on rocks north of New York City reveal that a metamorphic event occurred in an interval 460–480 million years ago (mid-Ordovician?). Increasing numbers of rocks from the northern and Newfoundland Appalachians are being dated by isotopic methods as 400–500 million years old; this range includes both Silurian and Ordovician periods on current scales. In the southern Appalachians, a few age determinations have established a metamorphic event 450–470 million years ago (Late to Middle Ordovician?). Many of these ages can be interpreted as recording either Taconic metamorphism or partial removal by Devonian metamorphism of the argon content of Precambrian rocks, so that isotopic analyses give intermediate ages. Studies of the Appalachians are disclosing more and more isotopic ages that fall between the times indicated by structural and stratigraphic evidence as orogenic (for example, Middle and Late Ordovician). These ages can be interpreted either as evidence for more or less continuous orogeny in the geosyncline, or as products of the modification of older rocks by later metamorphic events.

Two kinds of igneous rocks were intruded during the Taconic orogeny. In New England, granitic and dioritic bodies were emplaced in Ordovician time; however, farther north in Canada and farther south in the Piedmont, granitic intrusives of early Paleozoic age have been hard to identify. Two belts of small peridotite bodies which can be followed from Newfoundland to the southern Piedmont seem to be Taconic in age. In the Piedmont these intrusives cannot be accurately dated, but in the northern Appalachians they are nearly everywhere associated with Ordovician sedimentary and volcanic rocks, and where they seem to penetrate younger strata, they appear to have been remobilized in a later earth movement. These ultrabasic rocks are comparable to those intruded in the Cordilleran geosyncline in the Permian Period (see p. 223). The Appalachian peridotites are important commercially because they have been altered locally to serpentine; and from the southern Quebec deposit of serpentine alone comes 37 per cent of the world's asbestos.

THE SHRINKING CLASTIC WEDGE

Over most of the eastern side of the continent, a break in the sedimentary record occurred in Late Ordovician and Early Silurian time. The mountainous condition of the Appalachian geosyncline did not allow marine sedimentary rocks to accumulate permanently. West of the geosyncline, the sea apparently withdrew for a short time from the center of the continent at the end of the Ordovician Period.

The Taconic Mountains

At the beginning of the Silurian Period the Taconic mountain system, 2000 miles long, bordered the North American continent. The only evidence for the height of the mountains comes from the coarseness of the sedimentary rocks eroded from them, but such evidence, as discussed earlier, must be used with care. The coarsest particles, presumably deposited near the highest part of the range, are quartz pebbles that accumulated to a thickness of 1400 feet in southern New York, forming the Shawangunk Conglomerate.

The correspondence of the coarsest sedimentary particles with the greatest thickness of the clastic wedge confirms the view that this was the high point of the system. The basal part of the formation, of Early Silurian age, can be traced westward and southward

Fig. 12–8. Silurian rocks at Black Cape, on the south shore of the Gaspé Peninsula. In the foreground is the cape itself, formed of about 2000 feet of dark lavas; the cliffs in the background are made of vertically dipping Middle Silurian strata 8000 feet thick.

into pure quartz sandstones. During the Early Silurian Epoch, rivers from the northern Taconic Mountains continued to spread red sandstone and shale westward across New York State into Ontario, forming the red beds of the Cataract Group. Westward, away from the supplying streams, the Cataract sandstones pass laterally into the red shales of the Cabot Head Formation, and finally, on the margins of the Michigan basin, into the limestones characteristic of shelf sedimentation (see Chapter 1).

In a geological sense, geosynclinal mountain ranges are short-lived features of the earth's crust, although the geosynclines from which they arise may persist for half a billion years or more. The absence of earliest Silurian marine sediments and the coarseness of the non-marine sediments of this age in intermontane basins suggest that the geosyncline was mountainous in the early part of the period, but that by Middle Silurian time large segments of the trough were downwarped sufficiently to receive the sea, and geosynclinal sedimentation and volcanism resumed.

Middle Silurian marine strata are found in widely separated areas in the folded rocks of New England, southern Quebec, the Maritime Provinces, and Newfoundland. The geosyncline was rapidly sinking and bristling with volcanoes, for the sedimentary rocks everywhere are very thick and contain great quantities of ash and lava flows. At Eastport, Maine, the Silurian strata, 17,000 feet thick, are mostly water-laid ash with intercalated lavas of various kinds. On the north shore of Baie des Chaleurs, Quebec, the total thickness of Silurian rocks is nearly 10,000 feet, of which over 2000 feet is lava poured out onto the ocean floor (Fig. 12–8). Some of the lava flows covered corals on the sea floor.

Eastward Transgression
of the Epeiric Sea

Middle Silurian rocks deposited in the Allegheny basin record the transgression of the epeiric sea eastward toward the Taconic Mountains as the supply of sediments from their erosion dwindled. The regressive facies changes in a growing clastic wedge are well illustrated by the stratigraphy of the Great Plains, but these beds do not record the transgression of the sea as the sediment supply diminished. At the end of the Early Silurian Epoch, mud, sand, and gravel were still delivered by streams to the sea west of the Taconic highlands, but the area in which these sediments were deposited was much smaller than it had been at the beginning of the Silurian Period. Middle Silurian sedimentary rocks of this area are divided into a lower Clinton Group and an upper Albemarle Group. Near the mountains the Shawangunk Conglomerate was still accumulating in Clinton time, and a tongue of it spread westward as far as Lake Oneida, New York (Fig. 12–9). The Clinton Group of western New York State is predominantly shale, but the proportion of limestone increases as the group is traced westward and the proportion of sandstone increases toward the east. In eastern Tennessee and Alabama, the Clinton Group consists largely of interbedded sandstone and shale which pass into limestones a short distance to the west. The narrowness

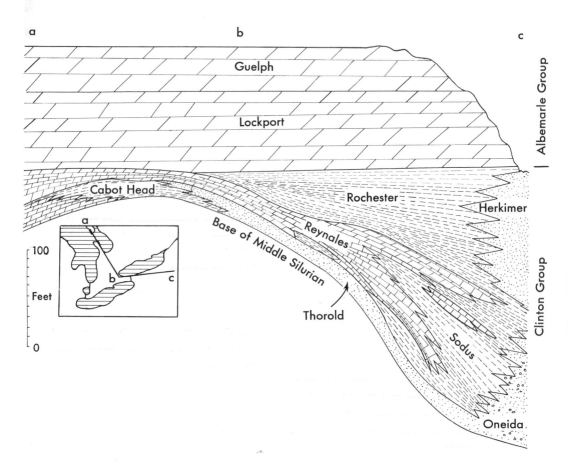

Fig. 12–9. Facies changes in Middle Silurian rocks of the Niagara escarpment from central New York to Manitoulin Island along the section shown in the index map.

of the Silurian belt of clastic rocks in the southern Appalachians is evidence of the low relief of the Taconic highlands in this latitude, but Silurian sandstone in the Ouachita Mountains suggests that the relief increased still farther southward (see Fig. 7–19).

Beds of sedimentary iron ore are widespread in the Clinton Group. The ore consists of hematite (Fe_2O_3) in the form of sandlike pellets, a replacement of oolitic limestone; in the form of fossil shells, a replacement of fossiliferous limestone; or in the form of a fine, intergranular matrix. The iron ore beds thicken southward from New York, where they are less than 5 feet thick, to about 25 feet near Birmingham, Alabama. In the north the ores were capable of supplying local forges only, but at Birmingham they supply a thriving steel-making industry.

Through the later part of Middle Silurian and all of Late Silurian time, only fine gray and red mud was supplied to the eastern side of the Allegheny basin from the lowlands in the geosyncline. In the western part of the basin, away from the geosyncline, beds of Albemarle age are largely limestones. In the southern part of the basin they are missing because of either non-deposition or later erosion. During late Silurian time evaporites accumulated in the northern part of the Allegheny basin in New York State, as described in Chapter 7. These salt deposits grade eastward into the red Bloomsburg mudstones, the last clastic sediments supplied from the Taconic generation of mountains. By the end of the Silurian Period the supply of clastics from the east was so low that limestone was deposited along the site of the present Hudson Valley, where, in the preceding period, the Taconic Mountains had risen. The limestone overlies the contorted Ordovician shales at several localities along the valley, forming an unconformity that attests the end of 40 million years of erosion of the highlands raised in the Taconic orogeny.

We have seen in this chapter how the Taconic Mountains were heralded by tec-tonic unrest along the cratonic side of the geosyncline; how the events of the orogeny are recorded in overthrust structures and isotopic ages; how the relief of the mountains was reflected in a growing clastic wedge; and how their destruction by erosion was recorded in a dwindling supply of detritus and in the transgression of the sea over the deltaic, orogenic sediments of the clastic wedge.

SUMMARY

Like the Cordilleran mountain system, the Appalachians can be divided into an ocean-side belt of metamorphic, volcanic, and plutonic rocks derived from the geosyncline; and a cratonside belt of deformed sedimentary rocks derived from the shelf.

The oldest rocks in the Appalachian geosyncline show that its western side was underlain by the eroded roots of the Grenville orogenic belt and that geosynclinal sedimentation and volcanism was established on the eastern side before the beginning of the Paleozoic Era.

Large blocks of shallow-water limestone, emplaced as a breccia in shale deposited in a deep-water environment, are evidences of faulting, erosion, and slumping on the margins of the geosyncline.

Clastic wedges of mid-Ordovician time in the southern Appalachians and of Late Ordovician time in the northern and central Appalachians show the shifting locale of Ordovician uplift.

Structures formed in the Taconic orogeny are obscured by later episodes of folding and metamorphism, except along the northwestern border of the geosyncline, where thrusting carried geosynclinal rocks over the cratonic facies.

Diminution of the argon content of metamorphic and igneous rocks by later reheating may cause confusion in dating early periods of metamorphism in a geosyncline.

Decrease in supply of detritus reaching the marginal cratonic basins and continuance of subsidence lead to shrinkage of the clastic wedge and transgression of the sea.

QUESTIONS

1. On thin tracing paper, draw a map showing the major features of the Appalachian mountain system. Turn the paper over and beside the map of the Appalachians draw a similar map of the Cordilleran mountain system, making the maps about the same length by manipulating the scale. Describe the geographic similarities and differences between the two systems when the mirror image of one is compared with the true image of the other.

2. Discuss the erosion, transport, and deposition of sediments on the Queenston delta, considering the probable effects of the absence of vegetation on these processes, as compared with the same processes on a modern delta.

3. Make a table to compare and contrast the Appalachian and Cordilleran geosynclines with respect to time of origin, times of principal orogeny, nature of border with the oceans, present elevation and relief, etc.

4. If the westerly winds of the Cretaceous carried the Mowry bentonites eastward, what winds carried the volcanic ash westward from the Appalachian geosyncline to form mid-Ordovician metabentonites?

5. Proponents of the continental drift theory say that the Atlantic Ocean was not in existence in the early Paleozoic. Discuss how this situation might be reflected in the sedimentary and volcanic record of the Appalachian geosyncline.

REFERENCES AND SUGGESTED READINGS

FAUL, H., *et al.* "Ages of Intrusion and Metamorphism in the Northern Appalachians," *American Journal of Science*, 261: 1–19, 1963. Results of isotopic dating in Maine and parts of other New England states are described.

KAY, G. M. "Development of the Northern Allegheny Synclinorium and Adjoining Regions," *Geological Society of America Bulletin*, 53: 1610–58, 1942. The history of sedimentation in the Allegheny basin is described with the aid of maps.

KING, P. B. "Geology of the Central Great Smoky Mountains, Tennessee," *U. S. Geological Survey Professional Paper 349–C,* 1964, 148 pp. A description of the Ocoee and Chilhowee groups and a discussion of their origin.

LONG, L. E., and KULP, J. L. "Isotopic Age Study of the Metamorphic History of the Manhattan and Reading Prongs," *Geological Society of America Bulletin,* 73: 969–96, 1962. Most of the rocks in the vicinity of New York City are dated at about 360 million years, but some are of Grenville age and others seem to have been affected by Taconic metamorphism.

LOWRY, W. D. (Ed.). "Tectonics of the Southern Appalachians," *Virginia Polytechnic Institute Department of Geological Sciences Memoir 1,* 1964. A volume of six papers on various aspects of the geology of the southern Appalachians.

NEALE, E. R. W., *et al.* "A Preliminary Tectonic Map of the Canadian Appalachian Region Based on Age of Folding," *Canadian Institute of Mining and Metallurgy Bulletin,* 54: 687–94, 1961. A concise summary of the history of the Canadian Appalachians accompanies maps of the area.

POOLE, W. H., KELLY, D. G., and NEALE, E. R. W. "Age and Correlation Problems in the Appalachian Region of Canada," *Royal Society of Canada Special Publication 8,* 1964, 61–84. A summary of isotopic ages and the problems they raise in the Canadian part of the Appalachians.

RODGERS, J., and NEALE, E. R. W. "Possible 'Taconic' Klippen in Western Newfoundland," *American Journal of Science,* 261: 713–30, 1963. The writers postulate that structures similar to those of the Taconic Range are present in western Newfoundland.

WOODWARD, H. P. "Reappraisal of Appalachian Geology," *American Association of Petroleum Geologists Bulletin,* 45: 1625–33, 1961. A summary of older concepts and newer ideas concerning the history of the Appalachian geosyncline.

13

The Acadian and
Appalachian Orogenies

The orogenies in which the Appalachian geosyncline was consolidated took place in the latter half of the Paleozoic Era. As in the Cordillera, the climactic orogeny took place at different times in different parts of the geosyncline. The northern sector, referred to as the Acadian geosyncline, was most intensely deformed in the Devonian Period; the southern and central Appalachians, although affected by Devonian orogeny, were again compressed against the craton in late Pennsylvanian and Permian time. The first of these movements is called the Acadian orogeny and the second, the Appalachian orogeny. In the Appalachian orogeny the sedimentary succession on the edge of the craton was caught up in the folding, and formed the Valley and Ridge Province. This chapter describes the sediments eroded from the mountains and the structures produced in the Acadian and Appalachian orogenic episodes.

THE CATSKILL CLASTIC WEDGE

Devonian Sedimentation in the Gaspé Peninsula

The end of the Gaspé Peninsula where the Appalachian folds strike out into the Gulf of St. Lawrence has been eroded, creating spectacular coastal scenery (Fig. 13–1). The high cliffs that contribute to the beauty of the coastline are composed of Lower Devonian limestones that reach a thickness of 10,000 feet in the center of the peninsula. The wide distribution of Lower Devonian limestones in the northern Appalachians indicates that the highlands in the geosyncline that resulted from the Taconic orogeny had by this time been so reduced that they supplied little detritus. From Newfoundland to New Hampshire, calcareous and argillaceous sediments and, locally, volcanics accumulated in the Appalachian geosyncline.

Fundamental changes in this pattern of

293

Fig. 13–1. Percé Rock at the end of the Gaspé Peninsula, composed of massive Lower Devonian limestone deformed in the Acadian orogeny. (Courtesy of the Province of Quebec Film Bureau.)

tectonic behavior and sedimentation in the geosyncline are reflected in the stratigraphy of the Devonian System of the Gaspé Peninsula. Figure 13–2 is a graphic representation of the Devonian succession in this area. Upper Silurian strata consist of calcareous siltstone and limestone which reach thicknesses of several thousand feet and contain volcanics locally. The Lower Devonian Grande Grève and Cape Bon Ami limestones are very impure, silty, and argillaceous. Bentonites in Gaspé and thick lava flows in rocks of this age in northern New Brunswick show the persistence of volcanism in the geosyncline. At the end of Early Devonian time the supply of coarse sediments steadily increased, forming the 10,000 feet of sandstones called the York River Formation. At its base this thick clastic succession is of marine origin, but the sandstones at the top of the succession were deposited in a deltaic environment. Abundant feldspar grains in the York River sandstones show that rapidly eroded granitic rocks were the source of the formation. The youngest strata in the central part of the Gaspé Peninsula are red siltstones and sandstones, a typical continental deposit. Plant fossils from these beds make up the famous *Psilophyton* flora, the first plants to populate the land. Upper Devonian non-marine sandstones and coarse conglomerates that were probably deposited in intermontane basins are exposed along the south shore of the peninsula. These Upper Devonian sandstones in some places overlie tilted and truncated Lower Devonian and Silurian strata unconformably. Upper Devonian sandstones, and conglomerates believed to be of Mississippian age, show that the Acadian orogeny took place in at least two pulses. The deltaic sediments of Gaspé were folded in late phases of the Acadian orogeny, then extensively eroded so that only isolated remnants of the clastic wedge were left. The Devonian rocks of New York that are exposed in a wide belt from the Hudson Valley to Lake Erie offer an opportunity to study the facies relationships of these orogenic sediments in an undisturbed area (Fig. 13–3).

The Devonian of New York

If a stratigrapher in New York were to measure three sections, one at the Catskill Mountains near the Hudson River, a second at the Finger Lakes in the center of the state,

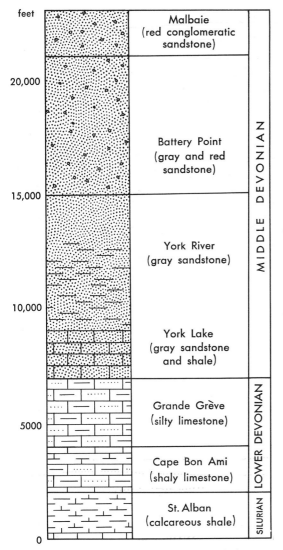

feet

	Malbaie (red conglomeratic sandstone)
20,000	Battery Point (gray and red sandstone)
15,000	York River (gray sandstone)
10,000	York Lake (gray sandstone and shale)
5000	Grande Grève (silty limestone)
	Cape Bon Ami (shaly limestone)
0	St. Alban (calcareous shale)

MIDDLE DEVONIAN

LOWER DEVONIAN

SILURIAN

Fig. 13–2. Stratigraphic section of the Devonian rocks at the eastern end of the Gaspé Peninsula, showing the effects of the growing highlands in the geosyncline during the Acadian orogeny.

and a third at Lake Erie, he would record a similar succession of lithologies in each section. At the base of these sections is a thin, coral-bearing formation, called the Onondaga Limestone, which extends from one side of the state to the other. Above the limestone each section passes into marine shale, the eastern ones continuing upward through estuarine sandstones into red, deltaic sandstones. The thickness of these facies varies from section to section, but the succession of lithologies is the same. Until early in this century, stratigraphers correlated shale with shale, sandstone with sandstone, and red bed with red bed (Fig. 13–4).

Detailed lithologic and paleontological studies by George W. Chadwick and G. Arthur Cooper showed that time surfaces are not parallel to boundaries between the major lithologies but cross them; and that the lithologic boundaries slope eastward but time surfaces slope westward (Fig. 13–4). The reconstructed cross-section shows a vast clastic wedge from which the younger beds have been eroded, the remnants of a deltaic apron which stretched in Late Devonian time from the present site of the Catskills to Lake Erie (Fig. 13–5). As the supply of detritus from the mountains in the geosyncline grew, the delta surface pushed westward and the facies belts moved westward with the shoreline. In central New York, the marine Middle Devonian shales and limestones of the Hamilton Group contain some of the most abundant and beautifully preserved fossils on the continent. Along the Hudson Valley, rocks equivalent to the Hamilton Group are red and gray sandstones of continental origin, the oldest of the deltaic beds that were to cover the northern Allegheny basin before the close of the Devonian Period. Freshwater fish and plant remains indicate the environment in which these beds were deposited. During the excavation of a Catskill reservoir for the city of New York, a buried forest of the tree fern *Aneurophyton* and the scale tree *Protolepidodendron* was discovered in these sandstones. The stumps of the trees were preserved as they were buried by sand washed in by streams more than 350 million years ago. Slabs of the sandstone with the fossil tree trunks were quarried and set up at the New York State Museum with a reconstruction of the forest in which these Middle Devonian trees grew (Fig. 13–6).

Coarse, red, deltaic sandstones of Upper Devonian age cap the Catskill escarpment, which rises abruptly 3000 feet on the west side of the Hudson Valley. As these Catskill sandstones are traced westward, they pass

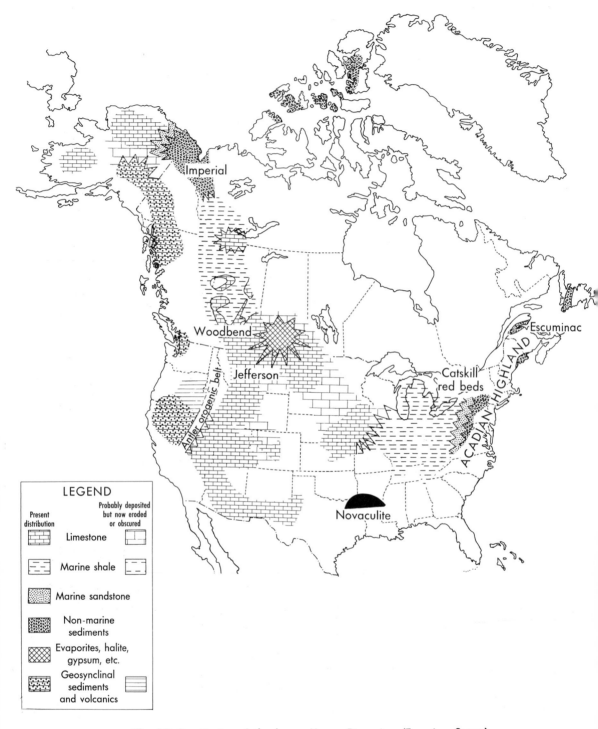

Fig. 13–3. Facies of the lower Upper Devonian (Frasnian Stage) in North America, showing particularly the clastic wedge from the Acadian mountains in the east and the clastic wedge from the mid-Paleozoic mountains in Alaska and northern Canada.

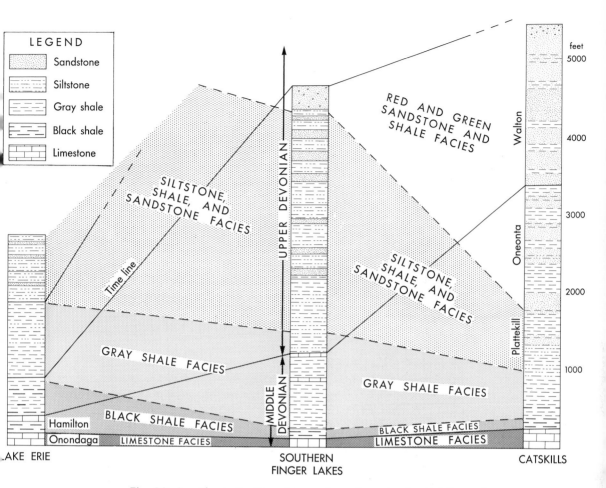

Fig. 13–4. Three stratigraphic sections through the Middle and Upper Devonian strata of New York at Lake Erie, the Finger Lakes, and the Catskill Mountains. Only the major facies are represented.

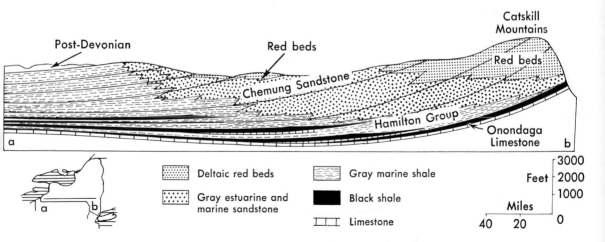

Fig. 13–5. Facies changes in the Middle and Upper Devonian strata of southern New York State. (Modified from the work of Chadwick and Cooper, after C. O. Dunbar and J. Rodgers, *Principles of Stratigraphy*. New York: John Wiley & Sons, Inc., 1957).

Fig. 13–6. Reconstruction of the Gilboa Forest. In the foreground of this exhibit, blocks from the reservoir containing the stumps of trees have been mounted. In the background is a reconstruction of the forest in which the trees grew. (Courtesy of the New York State Museum and Science Services.)

Fig. 13–7. Thin-bedded Upper Devonian siltstones and fine-grained sandstones at Watkins Glen, New York. (Courtesy of the U. S. Geological Survey.)

into an estuarine facies of silty, fine-grained sandstones which contain a rich fauna of clams and brachiopods (Fig. 13–7). Farther westward, in the Great Lakes area, these sandstones pass laterally into black marine shales that contain the giant fossil fish *Dinichthys* and *Cladoselache*.

The clastic sediments of the Middle and Late Devonian Series form a wedge of detritus that spread westward from highlands in the northern and central sectors of the Appalachian geosyncline. The red beds accumulated subaerially; the thin-bedded sandstones represent an estuarine facies; and the black shale is a marine facies formed where the fine mud settled in a still sea. As the supply of sand and mud from the erosion of the geosynclinal highlands grew, the red sandstones were swept by flooding streams over the marine sandstones and over the black shales until, at the end of the period, red beds were deposited 300 miles west of the mountains and the shoreline of the Catskill delta was in the area that is now Lake Erie.

The geometry of the Devonian clastic wedge may be illustrated by an isopach map (Fig. 13–8). The thickest and coarsest parts of both the Catskill and Late Ordovician Queenston clastic wedges are in eastern Pennsylvania and New York. The similar geometry of the two wedges suggests that the major drainage and greatest height of both the Taconic and Acadian mountains were just east of these states. The wedge thins southward along the Appalachian front, as well as westward. In Tennessee, Late Devonian sediments are thin and largely limestone, and still farther south, no Devonian sediments are present in the Valley and Ridge or Plateau areas. The shape of the clastic wedge indicates that the Acadian uplift did not extend to the southern Appalachians.

In summary, the sand and mud shed from the Appalachian geosyncline to the north and west show that a highland was built in the northern and central Appalachians, beginning in the Middle Devonian and reaching its greatest height in the Late Devonian Epoch. Only in the Gaspé area does the stratigraphic evidence allow us to distinguish multiple pulses in this orogeny; but from what we have learned of the nature of orogeny in the Cordillera, we deduce that the deformation and uplift must have taken place in a series of earth movements. In the Gaspé area, the main movement was at the end of the Early Devonian Epoch and was accompanied by the intrusion of granite; later movements of lesser intensity at the end of the Middle and Late Devonian epochs are recorded by unconformities. From the stratigraphic evidence outside the geosyncline, we now turn to the structures and intrusions of the geosyncline itself to see what evidence they provide of the nature of the Acadian orogeny.

THE ACADIAN OROGENY

Structures

The structures of the Devonian deformation are more easily identified than are those of the Late Ordovician deformation because throughout the northern and Newfoundland Appalachians, the Acadian orogeny was the most intense of several movements that affected the geosyncline, and its structures were only slightly obscured by later earth movements. As in the Taconic orogeny, the geosyncline was thrust northward and westward, and its sedimentary filling was crumpled against the stable block of the craton. Generally, the deformation was restricted to the geosyncline, but unconformities and isotopic ages suggest that some of the rocks of the Valley and Ridge area were folded at this time. The potassium–argon method dates minerals recrystallized in a crushed zone along the Tuscarora thrust in southern Pennsylvania at 340 million years, and points to Acadian movements on this fault. In the anthracite basin of Pennsylvania, angular unconformities between the Upper Devonian and Pocono conglomerates are good evidence of the deformation of cratonic rocks in the Acadian orogeny. The regional metamorphism that produced gneisses and schists

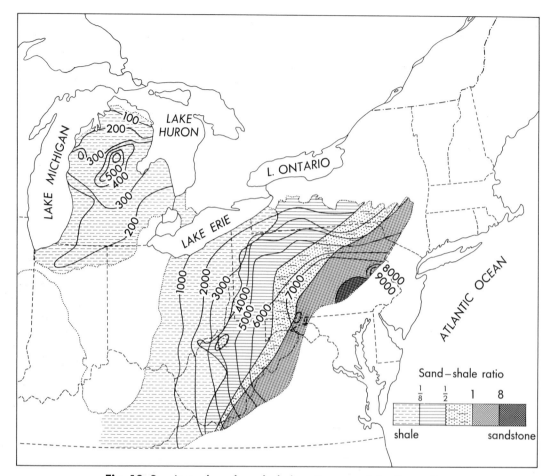

Fig. 13–8.   Isopach and sand–shale ratio map of the Upper Devonian Series of the eastern United States, showing the geometry of the upper part of the Catskill delta. (After W. Ayrton, courtesy of the Pennsylvania Geological Survey.)

from the Lower Paleozoic rocks of the Maritime Provinces and northern New England took place during the Acadian deformation. Thrust faults cut the geosynclinal rocks. In New England, the youngest beds that were folded are the Lower Devonian Littleton schists, and the oldest beds overlying them are the supposedly Mississippian Moat volcanics. In Nova Scotia the Late Mississippian McAras Brook Conglomerate overlies folded Silurian and Lower Devonian strata.

Intrusion and Isotopic Ages

During the orogeny, the depths of the Appalachian geosyncline were mobilized and

granites formed in the Maritime Provinces and New England (Fig. 13–9). The emplacement of the igneous rocks seems to have been accomplished in a number of pulses whose dates range from Early Devonian to Mississippian. In New Hampshire three groups of intrusions have been recognized.

Isotopic ages in Appalachian metamorphic rocks indicate the extent of Acadian deformation, where stratigraphic evidence is lacking. Figure 13–10 shows the frequency distribution of about 400 age determinations made in the American Appalachians. Ordovician (Taconic) ages are common in the central and southern Appalachians but surprisingly rare in the northern Appalachians. The greatest number of ages throughout the Appalachians fall within the Devonian Period, generally between 340 and 360 million years ago. In the Piedmont, dates indicative of Devonian metamorphism are found in a zone 100 miles wide along the western edge of the province. Intrusion of granite batholiths and pegmatites accompanied this metamorphic event. In the northern and central Appalachians, age determinations are commonest in the range of the Acadian orogeny, but ages in nearly all parts of the late Paleozoic have been recorded. As explained on page 288, not all of these ages represent times of metamorphism and orogeny; some of them are taken from samples whose argon content has been modified by recrystallization, fracturing, and weathering. In the Canadian Appalachians also, frequency distributions of age determinations show a grouping at about 350 million years, near the end of the Devonian Period (Fig. 13–11). The distribution of Acadian ages across the Appalachians from southern Quebec to eastern Newfoundland

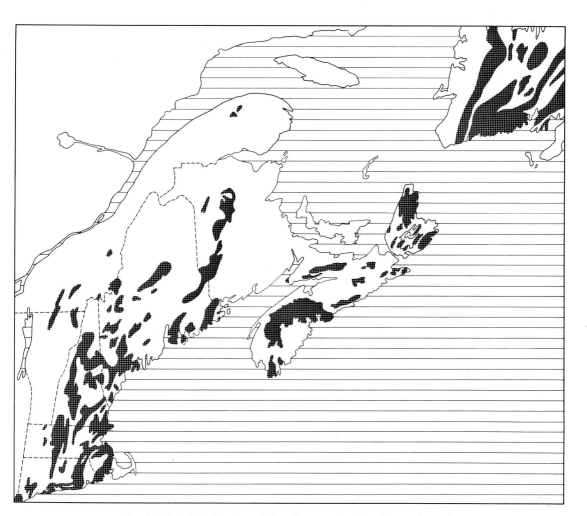

Fig. 13–9. Distribution of Acadian granites in the northern Appalachians. Some of the batholiths plotted here may have been intruded during the Appalachian orogeny, but most seem to be of Devonian or Mississippian age.

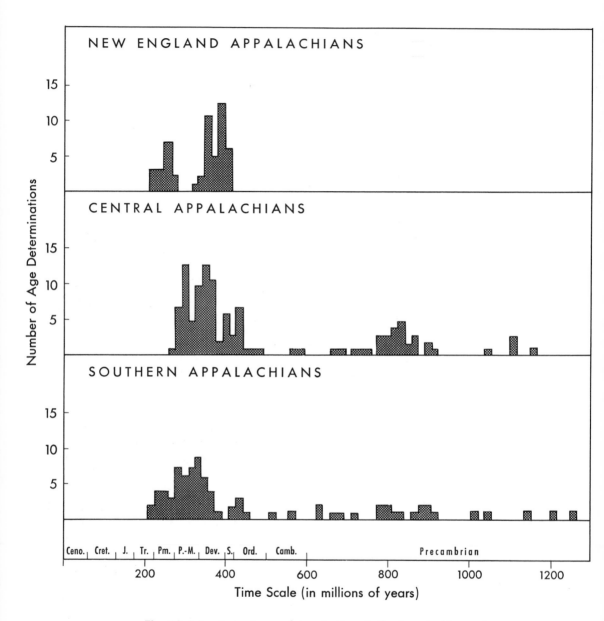

Fig. 13–10. Isotopic age determinations in the Appalachian region of the United States. The frequency of age determinations that were published between 1958 and 1963 is plotted in intervals of 1.7 million years. The greatest frequency, or concentration, of ages should mark periods of most intense orogeny. (After J. B. Hadley, courtesy of the Department of Geological Sciences, Virginia Polytechnic Institute.)

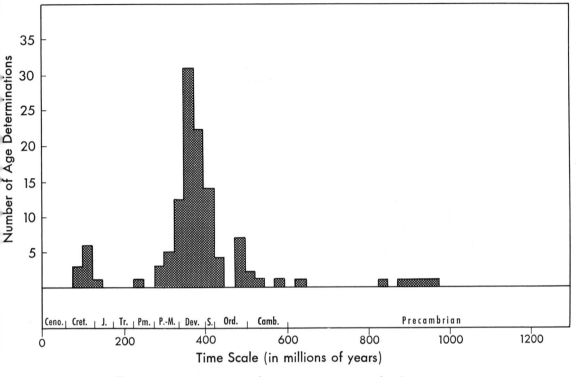

Fig. 13–11. Frequency of potassium–argon and rubidium–strontium age determinations in the Canadian Appalachians. (After Poole, Kelley, and Neale, from *Geochronology in Canada*, F. Fitz Osborne, ed. Used by permission of the University of Toronto Press.)

confirms that the whole width of the Appalachian geosyncline was metamorphosed in the Devonian orogeny. These dates suggest that the Acadian was the most intense of several orogenies that affected the Piedmont and northern Appalachians. They deepen the mystery of the absence of the Catskill clastic wedge in the southern Appalachians and force us to re-examine our assumptions about the temporal relationship between uplift, metamorphism, and intrusion.

Postorogenic Fault Basins

After the phase of intense metamorphism has passed, many mountain chains are cut by sets of nearly vertical faults. In blocks that have been thrown down, basins like those of the Cenozoic of California, described above (p. 270), collect clastic sediments. Similarly, the north end of the Appalachian geosyncline was faulted into a series of basins separated

by highlands of intrusive and metamorphic rocks in Mississippian time (Fig. 13–12). The uplifted blocks were eroded, supplying coarse sand, silt, and gravel to the basins, and were continually re-elevated by resumption of movement along the old faults. During the Mississippian Period these basins were at times above sea level and received deposits of red and gray non-marine sandstones and shales; at those times when they contained arms of the sea, limestone was deposited; and when the connection with the sea was restricted, salt, anhydrite, and gypsum accumulated.

The Pennsylvanian sediments are a non-marine, coal-bearing succession interrupted by numerous unconformities which reflect the crustal instability of the fault-bounded basins. The rapid deposition of certain beds is indicated by the 13,000-foot section of Pennsylvanian strata exposed at Joggins,

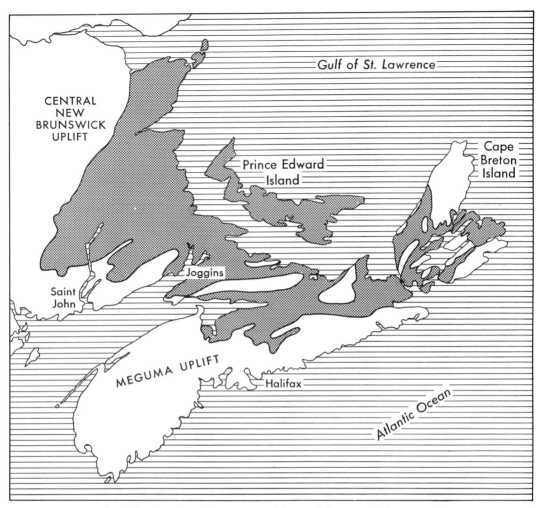

Fig. 13–12. Late Paleozoic uplifts and basins of the Canadian Maritime Provinces. (After W. A. Roliff.)

Fig. 13–13. Two trunks of *Calamites* buried upright in the Pennsylvanian sediments at Joggins, Nova Scotia. Some of the stumps in this section contain a fauna of the earliest reptiles and amphibians, which were trapped in the hollows during Pennsylvanian time. (Courtesy of the Geological Survey of Canada.)

Nova Scotia. At several levels, hollow tree stumps of the coal swamps were buried upright (Fig. 13–13). Within the stumps are found fossil bones of small amphibians and a reptile that were trapped in the hollow when the stump was buried in accumulating sands.

Two isolated basins containing late Paleozoic sedimentary rocks occur in southern New England. In the Boston basin the succession is 7000 feet thick and consists of conglomerates and argillaceous sediments. The only evidence for dating these strata is two poorly preserved fossil tree trunks that may be as old as Devonian or as young as Permian. In this non-marine succession are lenses of the Squantum Formation, a coarse, unsorted conglomerate consisting of boulders and cobbles of various lithologies set in an argillaceous matrix. For many years the conglomerate was thought to have been a till deposited by valley glaciers from the Acadian mountains, but recent investigations by Robert H. Dott suggest that the lenses are mudflows and cannot be interpreted as a record of either cold climate or extreme elevation. The Pennsylvanian sedimentary rocks of the Narragansett basin, in Rhode Island, consist of 12,000 feet of coal measures, conglomerate, sandstone, and shale deposited in an intermontane environment. Metamorphism at the end of Pennsylvanian time raised the coal beds beyond the anthracite grade, forming graphite and making them unsuitable for use as fuel.

LATE PALEOZOIC CLASTIC WEDGE

Mississippian sedimentary rocks in the Allegheny basin are similar in facies to those of the Devonian System. Acadian uplifts in the northern Appalachians must have been renewed during the period, continuing to supply detritus to the west. In Pennsylvania the Mississippian deltaic rocks are divided into two formations. The lower Pocono Formation consists of gray sandstone with interbeds of conglomerate which, because of their resistance to erosion, underlie many of the ridges in the Valley and Ridge Province. The systematic decrease in maximum size of pebbles in the Pocono conglomerates northwestward across Maryland and Pennsylvania shows that the source area for this formation was the Appalachian highlands in New Jersey (Fig. 13–14). The upper Mauch Chunk Formation is composed of less resistant red siltstones and shales. Southward along the Allegheny basin the clastic content of the system decreases, and in Tennessee, Mississippian rocks are mostly limestones like those

of the Mississippi Valley (see Fig. 8–11). Mississippian facies patterns confirm the evidence of Devonian sediments that during mid-Paleozoic time the Piedmont of the southern Appalachians did not supply clastic sediments in quantity.

During Pennsylvanian time detritus from the Appalachian highlands and from the Canadian Shield continued to keep the subsiding Allegheny basin full and its surface largely above sea level. The patterns of the distributary channels on the deltas (Fig. 13–15) show clearly that the major source of sediment was southeast of the basin and the minor source north of it. This was a time of crustal or sea level instability, when the cyclothems were formed in cratonic successions and the shoreline moved back and forth hundreds of miles across the platform. When the shore was withdrawn to the southwest, detritus from the geosyncline and Shield formed a vast coastal swamp stretching westward a thousand miles from the mountains. The dominance of the non-marine sandstones in the cyclothems of the Allegheny basin shows that the supplying highlands must have been repeatedly renewed in the Appalachian geosyncline from Middle Devonian time until the end of the era in order to keep the basin full. Neither Mississippian nor Pennsylvanian geosynclinal sediments are known in the Appalachian Mountains.

THE APPALACHIAN OROGENY

Late Paleozoic earth movements in the Appalachian Mountains have for many years been called the Appalachian orogeny, but some geologists have recently used the term "Allegheny orogeny." The deformation took place chiefly in the Permian, but may have begun in the Late Pennsylvanian and continued into the Triassic. Not only the area of the geosyncline, but parts of the Allegheny basin at the edge of the craton were involved. In the northern and Newfoundland Appalachians, this orogeny is recorded in the gentle folding and faulting of the intermontane late Paleozoic sediments.

The Structures of the Valley and Ridge Province

Paleozoic sediments of the Valley and Ridge Province in Pennsylvania are bent into open folds and cut by a few thrust faults (Figs. 13–16 and 13–17). Northward, the amplitude of these folds decreases and the fold axes turn toward the east. The intensity of the deformation in the Valley and Ridge Province increases toward the southeast. In a belt parallel to the boundary of the Piedmont, shales have been metamorphosed into slates and coal has been turned into anthracite, but generally the Valley and Ridge rocks are unmetamorphosed.

The belt of deformed sediments narrows in the southern Appalachians and the strata are cut by many thrust faults into partly overlapping slices (Fig. 13–18). Some of the thrusts were folded after the major displacement, and windows have been eroded through the overthrust sheet into the footwall. The faults probably decrease in dip downward

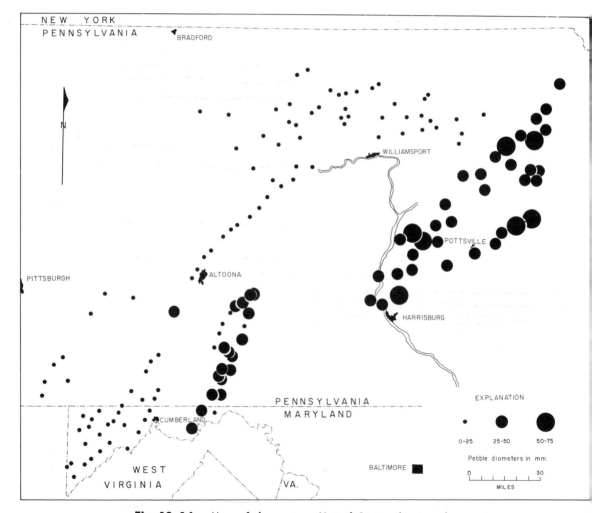

Fig. 13–14. Map of the eastern United States showing the maximum size of pebbles in the Pocono conglomerates. The westward decrease in size of pebbles indicates an eastern source in the Appalachian geosyncline and suggests the area where the source had greatest relief. (From B. R. Pelletier, courtesy of the Geological Society of America.)

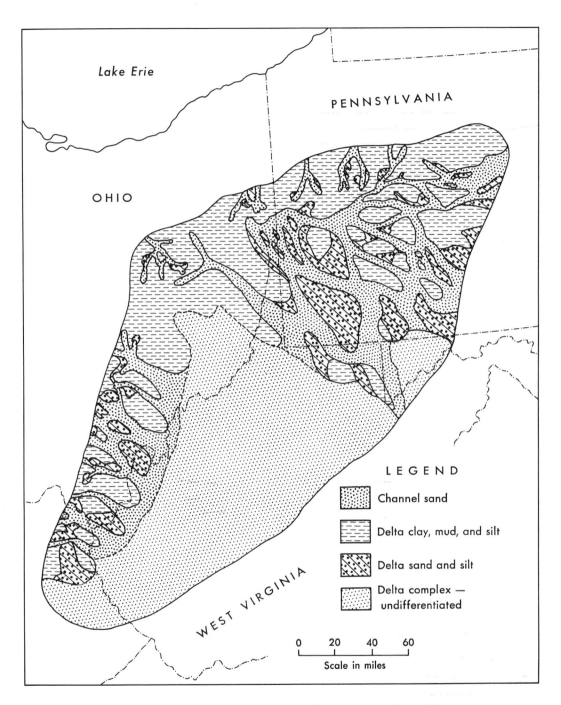

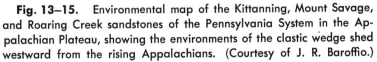

Fig. 13–15. Environmental map of the Kittanning, Mount Savage, and Roaring Creek sandstones of the Pennsylvania System in the Appalachian Plateau, showing the environments of the clastic wedge shed westward from the rising Appalachians. (Courtesy of J. R. Baroffio.)

Fig. 13–16. View of large synclinal fold in the Valley and Ridge Province of Pennsylvania, looking southwest over Trevorton toward the Susquehanna River. (Photograph by John S. Shelton.)

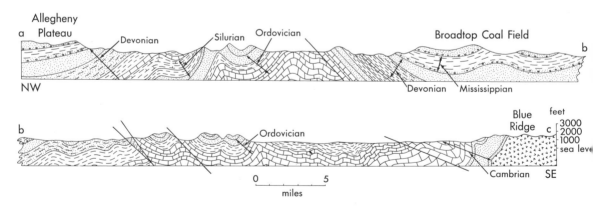

Fig. 13–17. Cross-section of the Valley and Ridge Province in southern Pennsylvania (vertical exaggeration × 3). Modified from G. W. Stose.)

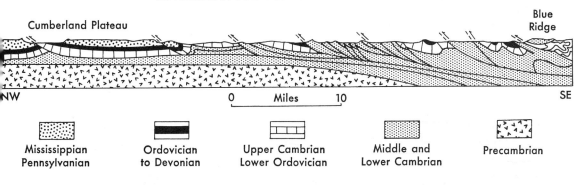

Fig. 13–18. Cross-section of the Valley and Ridge Province in Tennessee, showing the abundance of thrust faults. (After J. Rodgers, courtesy of the Kentucky Geological Survey.)

and are probably localized along weak shales and evaporites in the stratigraphic succession, where fault movement would have been relatively easy. The contact between the Valley and Ridge and Blue Ridge provinces is a zone of intense overthrusting and folding in the southern Appalachians, whereas in the central Appalachians the Precambrian rocks to the east, at the edge of the Blue Ridge, are folded sharply downward beneath the Paleozoic rocks to the west.

Only the surficial structure of mountain ranges can be directly observed by the geologist; the structure in depth can be investigated indirectly by geophysical methods, but the resulting data must be interpreted. Two interpretations of the deep structure of the southern Appalachians have been proposed. They are sometimes called the "thick-skinned" and "thin-skinned" or the "basement" and "no-basement" hypotheses. According to the "thick-skinned" geologists, the folds and faults in the Valley and Ridge Paleozoic rocks extend down into the Precambrian basement rocks under the basin; and these basement rocks were involved in the late Paleozoic deformation. To confirm basement involvement, they have shown that stratigraphic sections measured in the axes of synclines are thicker than correlative sections in neighboring anticlines, and that the anticlinal sections contain facies suggestive of shallow-water deposition belonging to times when the synclinal sections had

deeper-water sediments. The "thick-skinned" geologists believe these differences show that the folds were not structures formed at the close of the Paleozoic Era, but were growing in the basin, steadily increasing in amplitude, since the beginning of the era. In the Hurricane Ridge syncline in Virginia, Mississippian strata in the center of the fold are not only thicker than equivalent beds on the limbs, but they contain coarse conglomerates composed of fragments of rocks of lower Paleozoic age eroded from the limbs. Directional structures in the axial sediments confirm that the syncline was in existence in Mississippian time and erosion was attacking the anticlines on either side.

The "thin-skinned" geologists believe that the sedimentary layers were sheared off the basement and lower strata in the succession, along bedding plane surfaces lubricated by evaporites or weak shales. In this theory of decollement (see p. 236) the faults, which at the surface cut across bedding, are postulated to join a few major zones of displacement along weak sedimentary layers in the basin filling. John Rodgers has used the analogy of a pile of crumpled rugs (the sedimentary strata) overlying floor boards (the basement) to illustrate these two viewpoints. The "thick-skinned" geologists believe the folds in the rugs were caused by differential movement between the floor boards below, but the "thin-skinned" geologists believe they were caused by the pushing of the pile of rugs from the edge so that they slid over the floor boards. Detailed stratigraphic, structural, and geophysical investigations will be needed before either of these two hypotheses can be rejected.

The different styles of deformation in the Valley and Ridge Province of Pennsylvania and Tennessee have caused considerable speculation on their origins. The change in structure coincides with the southward extent of the Catskill clastic wedge. Possibly, confinement during deformation of early Paleozoic strata beneath this great thickness of sandstone made the sediments more plastic, so that they bent into broad folds. In the south, where they were not buried so deeply, they yielded by breaking along thrust faults. Perhaps the structures of the two areas are the same but appear to be different because they have been eroded to different levels. If the folds of Pennsylvania were eroded to a lower level, according to this theory, we would see a structure like the Valley and Ridge Province of Tennessee.

The Structures of the Plateaus

The Appalachian plateaus are underlain by Pennsylvanian rocks that are thrown into gentle, open folds whose limbs dip at only a few degrees. Although the structure of the plateau rocks seems simple at the surface, drilling has shown that more complex structures may lie beneath. In Tennessee, a plate of the Cumberland Plateau 25 miles by 120 miles has slid westward 5.8 miles along the Pine Mountain thrust. Wells drilled on simple anticlines at the surface in Pennsylvania and West Virginia have encountered complex structures with thrusts dipping away from the anticlinal axis at the level of the Lower Devonian (Fig. 13–19). The disturbance of the strata in depth seems to have been caused by a bedding-plane thrust fault, or decollement, at the level of Upper Silurian evaporites (see p. 154), under a wide area of the Plateau Province. The different forms of deformation of the Valley and Ridge, eastern Plateau, and western Plateau may be the result of the westward stepping up of the plane of decollement from the Middle Cam-

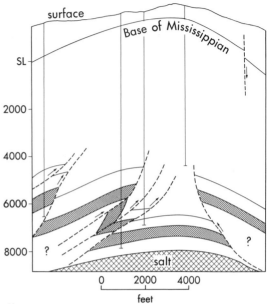

Fig. 13–19. Structure of the Griffin dome, Pennsylvania, showing the contrast between the gentle anticline at the level of the Mississippian and the complexly thrust structure in the lower part of the Devonian System just above the decollement plane on Late Silurian salt. The stippled layer represents the Onondaga–Oriskany–Helderberg unit. (After V. E. Gwinn, courtesy of the Geological Society of America.)

brian Rome Shale to the Upper Ordovician Martinsburg Shale, and then to the Upper Silurian evaporites.

The Blue Ridge, the Piedmont, and New England

The complex structure along the western side of the Blue Ridge shows that the rocks of this province were thrust strongly westward over the Valley and Ridge rocks at the end of Paleozoic time. The metamorphic rocks consolidated in the Precambrian, Taconic, and Acadian cycles of orogeny seem to have acted as a plunger, shoving the little metamorphosed sediments of the Valley and Ridge Province against the continental interior. The extent to which the deformation affected the rocks of the Blue Ridge and the Piedmont is revealed only by isotopic age studies, for no late Paleozoic rocks have been identified in these areas.

In a belt along the east boundary of the Piedmont in Alabama, Georgia, and South Carolina, potassium–argon ages of about 250 million years are common. These and similar ages from rocks in the central Appalachians indicate a period of widespread metamorphism in Early Permian or Late Pennsylvanian time. The Appalachian orogeny in the Piedmont may have been accompanied by the intrusion of granitic batholiths but, at present, criteria have not been set up to distinguish among the intrusions of the various orogenic cycles.

Two relatively large basins in which late Paleozoic rocks are preserved and several scattered outcrops permit the tracing of the Appalachian deformation eastward across southern New England. In addition, isotopic ages of about 250 million years indicate that late Paleozoic metamorphism affected the southern half of Maine and New Hampshire, and the southern New England states. The metamorphic Pennsylvanian rocks of the Narragansett basin in Rhode Island are intruded by granites that accompanied the Appalachian orogeny, and isotopic dating of intrusions in many places in Connecticut and Massachusetts proves that they were emplaced at the same time.

Dating the Appalachian Orogeny

The stratigraphic evidence for dating the Appalachian orogeny is poor. The youngest folded beds in the Valley and Ridge Province are Late Pennsylvanian coal measures, but in the Plateau Province, Early Permian beds of the Dunkard Group are gently flexed. In Alabama, Cretaceous rocks of the Coastal Plain overlie the Valley and Ridge folds unconformably, establishing an upper limit to their time of deformation. Triassic red beds in fault basins within the Piedmont and New England highlands indicate an earlier limit to the time of deformation of these rocks. Isotopic dating does not allow a precise placement of the orogenic event, but distributions like that in Fig. 13–10 indicate that metamorphism may have extended over a considerable interval from late Pennsylvanian to Triassic time. From all this evidence we can conclude that the Appalachian orogeny was a complex earth movement spanning probably several millions, perhaps several tens of millions, of years between the end of Pennsylvanian and the middle of Triassic time.

TRIASSIC FAULT BASINS

Speculation on the height of the late Paleozoic Appalachians is useless, since no unequivocal evidence has been discovered. In the Middle Triassic Epoch, the metamorphic rocks of the Piedmont and New England highlands were cut from Nova Scotia to Georgia by a set of normal faults, and some segments formed fault-bounded basins in which a thick succession of continental sediments accumulated. By this time the Permian Appalachians had been reduced to a low, rolling plain, today represented by the surface of the unconformity between the Triassic rocks and the metamorphic basement. The pattern and displacement of the faults suggest that they resulted from a vertical uplift of the mountain system and crustal tension resulting from the uplift. In Chapter 5 such uplift was ascribed to isostatic rebound of the thick, light prism of geosynclinal sediments when the compressive forces of orogeny ceased to hold the mountain belt down. Episodes of normal faulting and the formation of intermontane basins are part of the evolution of all mountain systems, and comparisons can be drawn between the Appalachian Triassic basins, the late Paleozoic basins of the Maritime Provinces, and the Cenozoic basins of California.

The intermontane basins were filled with sediment eroded from the uplifted blocks that bordered them. The sedimentary fillings of the Connecticut and New Jersey basins are now wedge-shaped in cross-section, bounded on one side by a normal fault and on the other by the tilted, pre-Triassic erosion surface. These two basins appear to represent the flanks of a wide rift valley which occupied the site of the Hudson Valley. After Triassic deposition, the axis of the valley was arched and eroded until basement rocks were exposed and the margins were isolated as separate basins. Triassic sediments in this trough may have attained thicknesses as great as 30,000 feet, but only 10,000 feet in the Connecticut Valley and 20,000 feet in New Jersey have been preserved from erosion. Throughout the thickness of the Triassic rocks in the Connecticut basin, coarse conglomerates along the faulted side indicate that movements along the fault maintained the degree of relief between mountain and valley in spite of erosion and fill. The sedimentary basins remaining after 150 million years of erosion now occupy a belt extending along the eastern side of the Appalachian Mountains from the Bay of Fundy to North Carolina (Fig. 13–20). Deep drilling through the younger sediments that cover the eastern margin of the Appalachian structures has indicated that similar Triassic basins are preserved as far south as Florida.

Sedimentary Rocks of the Newark Group

The sedimentary rocks of Middle and Late Triassic age that filled these intermontane troughs are known as the Newark Group. The group consists of three sedimentary facies: arkose and the red shales associated with it, black shales, and coarse conglomerates. Arkose is a sandstone in which more than a quarter of the grains are feldspar. Usually, although not always, it is colored deep red by the reddish feldspars orthoclase and microcline, and by the iron oxides staining the clayey matrix. The shales normally contain the impressions of land plants and fresh-water fish, but very few fossils have been found in the arkose. In the southern basins, thin coal beds occur in the Newark Group. Coarse conglomerates form a border facies along the fault margin of several of the basins and represent indurated alluvial fan sediments dropped where fast-flowing streams from the highlands were discharged onto the valley floor.

The fresh feldspar and mica in the arkose were derived from the granites and gneisses of the Piedmont area and New England upland, which formed the surrounding highlands. Only under conditions of considerable relief, rapid stream erosion in the mountains, and rapid deposition where the streams discharged into the plain could unstable minerals such as plagioclase feldspar be preserved to enter the accumulating arkose. The red iron oxides that color the matrix of the arkose indicate accumulation under oxidizing conditions on land. Red sediments are today being produced by the weathering processes of warm climates with marked seasonal rainfall, and we can infer that the same conditions produced the red arkose of the Triassic Period (Fig. 13–21). Where drainage in the valleys was interrupted, lakes were formed and black clays were laid down, with interbeds of coal recording the luxuriant vegetation. Dinosaurs walked and ran over the lake and river flats, leaving their footprints behind in the drying mud. These fossil footprints, found covering the bedding planes at some localities, are the best evidence that reptiles were abundant, because only a few reptilian skeletons have been found in the Newark Group.

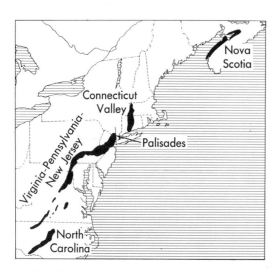

Fig. 13–20. The basins containing Triassic rocks of the Newark Group in eastern North America.

Volcanic Rocks of the Newark Group

The deep-reaching normal faults formed channels along which basic igneous magma

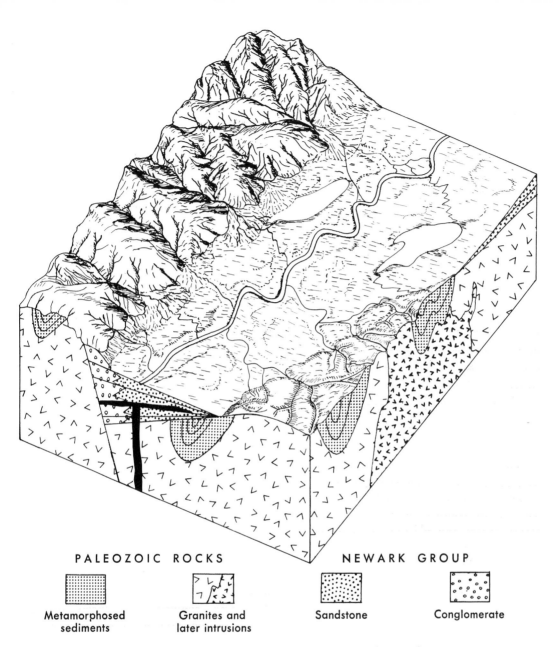

PALEOZOIC ROCKS   NEWARK GROUP

Metamorphosed   Granites and   Sandstone   Conglomerate
sediments   later intrusions

Fig. 13–21. Block diagram of a typical Triassic basin of eastern North America. Note the contrast between the side of the basin that was continuously uplifted along the bounding normal fault and the low hills on the opposite side. Conglomerates forming alluvial fans against the mountains interfinger with the sandstone accumulating in the valley. In the front of the block, a dike feeds a sill in the Newark strata.

from depth approached the surface to form dikes, sills, and pipes, or poured out onto the surface as lava flows. These diabase (a dike rock of intermediate composition like a diorite) intrusions and basalt extrusions now form hills and ridges within the Triassic basins because igneous rock is more resistant to weathering and erosion than arkose and shale. Most of the flows welled up quietly from fissures, but some evidence of explosive volcanic activity has been found in the Connecticut Valley. The most famous of the intrusions, the Palisade Sill, about 1000 feet thick, is grandly exposed on the bank of the

How rationalize island arcs if cont. dr. is true?

Hudson River west of New York City. The resemblance of the cliff to a palisade comes from the conspicuous columnar jointing.

Strike-Slip Faulting

In the Cenozoic history of the western Cordillera, strike-slip faulting played an important role. Although the presence of faults with tens of miles of displacement, such as the San Andreas, has been suggested in the Appalachian mountain system, their influence on the structure and the time of their movement require further study.

The Brevard zone is a narrow belt of steeply dipping schists and slates that extends for 350 miles from Alabama to North Carolina along the eastern edge of the Blue Ridge Province. Some geologists have suggested that a right-lateral strike-slip movement of 135 miles occurred along this zone toward the end of the Paleozoic Era.

Herbert Woodward postulates that separation of the Blue Ridge from the Reading Prong of the New England Upland where Triassic rocks cross the crystalline Appalachians (see Fig. 12–2) occurs along a strike-slip fault with a right-lateral movement of about 70 miles. Others have postulated strike-slip movement along the western margin of the Blue Ridge Province. J. Tuzo Wilson suggests that the Cabot fault, which crosses western Newfoundland and may continue southward across the Cabot Strait and through Nova Scotia to the Bay of Fundy, is a major zone of strike-slip movement. If the North Atlantic Ocean was closed in late Paleozoic time, as postulated by the continental drift theory, the Cabot fault is aligned with a well-documented strike-slip fault of northern Scotland, the Great Glen fault (see Fig. 6–6). The direction of movement along the Cabot fault is unknown, but the Great Glen fault is a left-lateral fault. The movement along these major faults probably had a profound influence on the fault basins of late Paleozoic and Triassic time in the Appalachians. Geologists continue to study the mechanics of these extensive strike-slip movements and their bearing upon our knowledge of the nature of the crust and mantle and upon the theory of continental drift.

THE OUACHITA AND MARATHON ARCS

Although the Ouachita and Marathon sectors of the Appalachian system have been traced for 1300 miles along strike, only 275 miles of their folded rocks are exposed. The outlines of the rest of the belt have been followed by extensive drilling for oil through the post-Paleozoic strata that cover it in Texas, Arkansas, and Mississippi (Fig. 13–22). Only where the deformed rocks are exposed

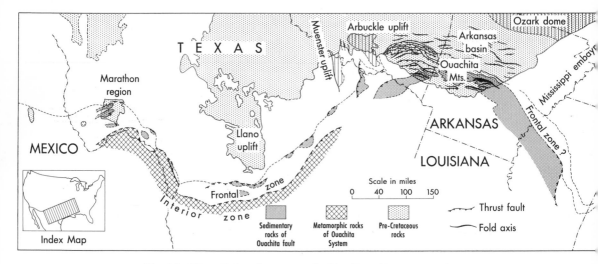

Fig. 13–22. Major features of the Ouachita mountain system. (Simplified from P. T. Flawn and others.)

at the surface—in the Ouachita Mountains of southern Oklahoma and Arkansas, in west Texas, and in small, scattered areas of northern Mexico—can detailed structural and stratigraphic studies be made. Even in the Ouachita Mountains the bedrock is not exposed extensively, and the limited nature of the outcrops has led to controversy concerning the structure.

Lower Paleozoic Siliceous Facies

Twenty-six thousand feet of Paleozoic sedimentary rocks filled the Ouachita geosyncline, but of this thickness only about 6000 feet were deposited before the end of the Devonian Period. The other 20,000 feet were poured into the rapidly subsiding trough in the relatively short interval from Early Mississippian to mid-Pennsylvanian time (Fig. 13–23). The pre-Mississippian sedimentary rocks are of a puzzling facies of bedded chert, black shale, and sandstone.

The siliceous rocks contain poorly preserved fossils of organisms such as radiolarians and sponges that secreted siliceous hard parts, but these fossils do not seem to be present in nearly sufficient quantity to account for the amount of silica in this succession. The thickest (up to 950 feet) of the siliceous units is the Arkansas Novaculite of Early Devonian to Early Mississippian age. Novaculite is an almost white, bedded sedimentary rock like chert, but slightly coarser in grain. Its very fine and even grain, great hardness, and abrasive qualities make it suitable for the manufacture of grindstones and whetstones. Unlike the bedded cherts of the Cordilleran geosyncline, those of the Ouachita facies are relatively thin and not interbedded with lava flows, although bentonites are common. Nevertheless, the processes of explosive volcanism and submarine weathering of volcanic ash on the ocean floor are the most satisfactory explanations yet proposed to account for these rocks. The volcanoes supplying this ash must have been on an island arc south of the present outcrops where Paleozoic rocks are now deeply buried beneath the Coastal Plain. Sandstones that thicken in this direction are further evidence

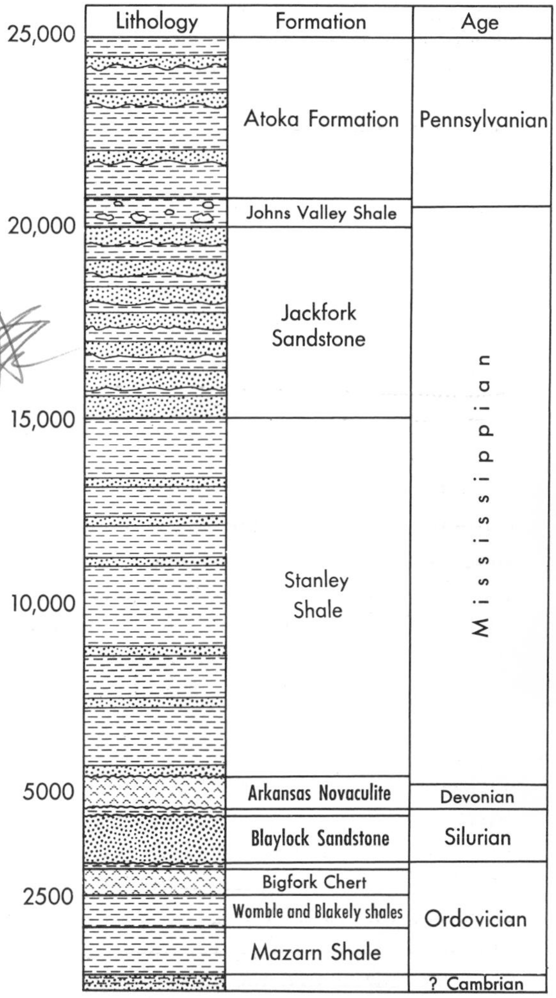

Lithology	Formation	Age
25,000	Atoka Formation	Pennsylvanian
20,000	Johns Valley Shale	
	Jackfork Sandstone	Mississippian
15,000		
10,000	Stanley Shale	
5000	Arkansas Novaculite	Devonian
	Blaylock Sandstone	Silurian
2500	Bigfork Chert	Ordovician
	Womble and Blakely shales	
	Mazarn Shale	
		? Cambrian

Fig. 13–23. Diagrammatic stratigraphic section of the sedimentary sequence in the Ouachita Mountains. Thicknesses are only approximate and change from place to place. (From information of P. T. Flawn and others.)

that the relatively small volume of clastic sediments in the early Paleozoic succession came from the south. The thickest of these, the Blaylock Sandstone of Early Silurian age, may reflect an orogeny of Taconic date in the oceanward side of the Ouachita geosyncline.

The siliceous facies of the Ouachita Mountains records an environment unknown in other geosynclines in the continent. Black shales, abundant organic matter in the sediments, and graptolitic faunas suggest that the floor of the geosyncline was stagnant and the water was probably deep. During the early Paleozoic, the Ouachita geosyncline was "starved" for sediments and deposition was slow; but its continuation, the Appalachian geosyncline, was well supplied and accumulated a great thickness. The continuation of subsidence with little sedimentation may have carried the sea floor into deep water.

The Late Paleozoic Clastic Wedge

At the beginning of the Mississippian Period the tempo of sedimentation in the Ouachita geosyncline changed abruptly. Great thicknesses of shales and sandstones deposited rapidly in the trough overlie the cherts and fine shales of the pre-Mississippian succession. The Stanley Shale, which succeeds the Arkansas Novaculite, may be as thick as 12,000 feet, but its complex folding makes stratigraphic measurements difficult. The Jackfork Sandstone is up to 7000 feet thick and was deposited in the rapidly filling trough from highlands south of the present exposures. Sandstone beds in these Ouachita formations have irregular lower surfaces which are molds of irregularities in the top surface of underlying shale layers (Fig. 13–24). These irregularities are believed to

Fig. 13–24. Flute marks and groove casts on the lower surface of a sandstone bed in the Atoka Formation (Pennsylvanian), Hodgen, Oklahoma. (Courtesy of G. deV. Klein.)

have been eroded by turbidity currents that carried the sand down the flanks of the geosynclinal trough into the deeper water. The orientation of these **sole markings,** as they are called, indicates that the turbidity currents flowed parallel as well as transverse to the length of the trough. The transverse and longitudinal trends show that turbidity currents flowed down the side of the geosyncline, then turned along its length at the axis.

The Johns Valley Shale is a relatively thin formation of peculiar lithology. The notable feature of this shale is the presence of large blocks surrounded by a fine-grained, argillaceous matrix. The blocks are as large as 370 feet across and consist of sedimentary rocks ranging in age from Late Cambrian to Early Pennsylvanian. Limestones of Late Cambrian and Early Ordovician age form the majority. The blocks are not of the geosynclinal facies but were deposited in a shelf environment north of the Ouachita trough. One hypothesis accounts for their emplacement in the shale by uplift of the shelf along faults at the geosynclinal margin and the slipping and slumping of the blocks eroded from the fault escarpment down the shaly slope into the geosyncline. The suggestion that the blocks may have been frozen in icebergs and rafted to their places has also been made.

Sedimentation ended in the Ouachita segment of the geosyncline in the middle of the Pennsylvanian Period, but continued in the Marathon sector until the end of the period. Thereafter, orogeny lifted the Ouachita area into the zone of erosion until it was covered by the first transgression of the seas depositing the Mesozoic rocks of the Coastal Plain (see Chapter 14).

History and Structure

The major change from the slow sedimentation in the "starved" basin of the early Paleozoic to the rapid filling of the geosynclinal trough must have been caused by orogeny on the oceanward (now buried) side of the Ouachita geosyncline at the beginning of Mississippian time. Highlands just south of the present edge of the Coastal Plain must have supplied the detritus for the late Paleo-

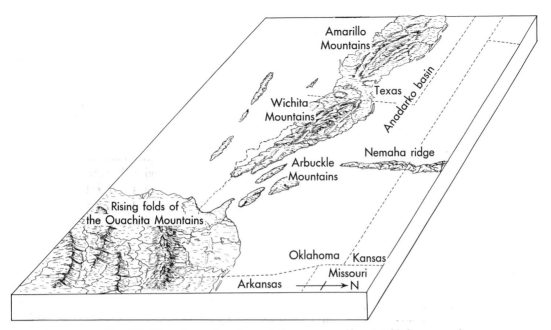

Fig. 13–25. Reconstruction of the geography of Oklahoma and adjacent areas in Middle Pennsylvanian (Des Moines) time. Clastic sediments derived from the domed uplifts of the Oklahoma Mountains were deposited in the Anadarko basin. Most of the Ouachita geosyncline had been deformed into the zone of erosion and the growing folds contributed more sediment to the basin. (After C. W. Tomlinson and W. McBee.)

zoic clastic wedge (Fig. 13–25). In Middle Pennsylvanian time the sedimentary rocks of the Ouachita Mountains moved northward against the continental platform and were folded and broken by thrust faults in what is called the Ouachita orogeny. In the Marathon region, the final orogeny in the geosyncline was delayed until Early Permian time.

The rocks in the Ouachita Mountains are cut by a few major thrust faults and by many faults of minor displacement. They have been intensely folded locally, but in the exposed part of the deformed belt metamorphism is weak or non-existent. The Ouachita Mountains resemble the Valley and Ridge Province of the Appalachians, but the sedimentary section there, unlike the rocks of the Valley and Ridge Province, is a mixture of geosynclinal rocks and rocks transitional to the shelf facies. In the Marathon region the rocks are similarly folded and cut by thrust faults (Fig. 13–22). Subsurface studies in western and central Texas show that a belt of metamorphic rocks—phyllites, slates, and schists—lies south and east of the deformed

sedimentary rocks in a position similar to that which the Blue Ridge and Piedmont provinces occupy with respect to the Valley and Ridge Province. South of the Ouachita Mountains in Arkansas this metamorphic belt has not been identified below the Coastal Plain, where its junction with the Blue Ridge Province was anticipated.

Much of the Ouachita–Marathon belt remains hidden from direct observation, and its history remains unknown. New techniques developed for "seeing through" the covering sediments and continued drilling will probably reveal that the history of this fascinating mountain system is as complex as that of the Appalachian geosyncline to the northeast.

SUMMARY

Orogeny in a geosyncline is revealed in the sediments of the basins at the edge of the craton by an increase in the clastics derived from the geosyncline and their eventual change from marine to non-marine deltaic beds.

In a clastic wedge, correlation on the basis of gross lithology leads to error because the facies boundaries move seaward as the delta extends.

The most intense and areally extensive earth movement in the Appalachians (the Acadian) preceded the folding of the basins at the edge of the craton by at least a full period, as was the case in the Cordillera.

Frequency distributions of potassium–argon ages in metamorphic belts may be interpreted by the geologist as showing (1) almost continuous orogeny, or (2) various degrees of modification of the argon content of very old rocks by a single period of metamorphism.

Metamorphic events recorded in isotopic ages may not necessarily be correlated with uplifts producing clastic wedges.

At the close of the Acadian orogeny the northern part of the Appalachian geosyncline was fragmented into fault-controlled basins in which coal formed during the Pennsylvanian Period.

The cyclothems and coal measures of the late Paleozoic clastic wedge are thickest in the southern Appalachians.

The different methods of deformation in the northern and southern segments of the Valley and Ridge Province may be caused by (1) the varying response to deformation of rocks loaded differently by overlying sediments, or (2) the different levels to which similar structures have been eroded.

The thinning of sedimentary units over the crests of anticlines in a folded belt suggests that the structures were forming during deposition.

The Triassic basins of the Appalachians are the product of postorogenic normal and strike-slip faulting, but the part played by each is not clear.

The Ouachita geosyncline in Cambrian to Mississippian time was a "starved basin" in which sedimentation did not keep up with subsidence; the sediments are largely chert (probably derived from volcanic ash) and black shale.

Uplifts in the now buried part of the Ouachita geosyncline changed the pattern of sedimentation in Mississippian time and introduced clastic sediments, largely through turbidity currents and slumping, into the rapidly subsiding trough.

QUESTIONS

1. Compare the geometry and facies changes of the Catskill delta with those of the Queenston delta.

2. Formulate several alternative hypotheses to account for the absence of Devonian clastic wedge sediments in the southern Appalachians, although isotopic ages indicate an orogenic event in the geosyncline.

3. Discuss the application of the "thick-skinned" and "thin-skinned" theories of Appalachian structure to the origin of the Rocky Mountain structures of Alberta and Wyoming.

4. What area of the world today resembles in climate and relief the Triassic fault basins of the Appalachians?

5. Compare and contrast the Levis Shale (p. 284) with the Johns Valley Shale with respect to age, lithology, age and size of the blocks, conditions of deposition, position in the geosynclinal cycle with respect to orogeny, etc.

REFERENCES AND SUGGESTED READINGS

COOPER, B. N. "Relation of Stratigraphy to Structure in the Southern Appalachians," *Virginia Polytechnic Institute Department of Geological Sciences Memoir No. 1*, 81–114, 1964. Stratigraphic measurements show that Appalachian folds were growing in the Valley and Ridge throughout the Paleozoic.

COOPER, G. A. "Paleoecology of the Middle Devonian of the Eastern and Central United

States," *Geological Society of America Memoir No. 67*, 249–78, 1957. Conditions under which the Middle Devonian fauna lived in the eastern part of the United States.

DOTT, R. H. "Squantum 'Tillite,' Massachusetts —Evidence of Glaciation or Subaqueous Mass Movements?" *Geological Society of America Bulletin*, 72: 1289–1306, 1961. The "tillite" is distributed in several horizons in the Boston basin succession and probably represents sediments which have slumped on the sea floor.

FLAWN, P. T., *et al.* "The Ouachita System," *University of Texas Bureau of Economic Geology Publication 6120*, 401 pp., 1961. A valuable summary of the stratigraphy and structure of the Ouachita and Marathon arcs at the surface and in the subsurface.

GWINN, V. E. "Thin-skinned Tectonics in the Plateau and Northwestern Valley and Ridge Provinces of the Central Appalachians," *Geological Society of America Bulletin*, 75: 863–900, 1964. A decollement on the horizon of the Cayugan salt underlies much of the plateau of Pennsylvania.

PELLETIER, B. R. "Pocono Paleocurrents in Pennsylvania and Maryland," *Geological Society of America Bulletin*, 69: 1033–64, 1958. Thickness, lithofacies, cross-bedding, and other primary structures are used to reconstruct the environment of deposition of early Mississippian time.

RODGERS, J. "Basement and No-Basement Hypotheses in the Jura and the Appalachian Valley and Ridge," *Virginia Polytechnic Institute Department of Geological Sciences Memoir No. 1*, 71–80, 1964. Supports the "thin-skinned" hypothesis of Appalachian structure and compares the Valley and Ridge to the Jura Mountains of France.

SANDERS, J. E. "Late Triassic Tectonic History of the Northeastern United States," *American Journal of Science*, 261: 501–24, 1963. The Connecticut and New Jersey Triassic basins are remnants of a large rift valley which was subsequently bowed into an anticline and breached along the axis.

WILSON, J. T. "Cabot Fault, an Appalachian Equivalent of the San Andreas and Great Glen Faults, and Some Implications for Continental Displacement," *Nature*, 195: 135–38, 1964. Major lateral displacement on the Cabot fault in Newfoundland and its extension eastward to join the Great Glen fault of Scotland are postulated.

WOODWARD, H. P. "Structural Elements of the Northeastern Appalachians," *American Association of Petroleum Geologists Bulletin*, 41: 1429–40, 1957. The crossing of the Acadian and Taconic structural trends by late Paleozoic folds in southern New England is postulated.

WOODWARD, H. P. "Central Appalachian Tectonics and the Deep Basin," *American Association of Petroleum Geologists Bulletin*, 48: 338–56, 1964. The fold axes of the central Appalachians are concentric with the gneiss domes of the Baltimore region and symmetrical about an axis trending N40°W from them.

The Atlantic and Gulf
Coastal Plains

The eastern and southern coastal areas of the United States are underlain by Cenozoic and Mesozoic sedimentary rocks which dip gently toward the Atlantic Ocean and the Gulf of Mexico. The surface of this coastal plain is broken only by low escarpments that mark the outcropping of resistant strata or by terraces that mark the former positions of the sea or the abandoned banks of a river (Fig. 14–1). The plain is conveniently divided into an Atlantic segment from New England to Florida, and a Gulf segment from Florida to the Yucatan Peninsula. The surface of the plain and the strata below it extend out beneath the sea to form the continental shelves. The position of the shoreline and consequently the relative widths of the emerged and submerged parts of the Atlantic and Gulf coastal plains have changed constantly since middle Mesozoic time.

The beds of sedimentary rock beneath the coastal plains dip seaward at less than 1 degree and consist largely of sand, silt, and clay eroded from the continental interior and the Appalachian highlands. Although the sedi-

mentary strata are poorly exposed, the stratigraphy of these rocks is known in great detail, for they have been penetrated to depths as great as 4 miles by tens of thousands of holes drilled in search of oil. Each sedimentary unit beneath the coastal plains thickens, slowly at first and then more rapidly, as its distance from the continent increases. Information from drilling, supplemented by geophysical evidence, indicates that the Cenozoic and Mesozoic sedimentary succession is 40,000 feet thick beneath the present coastline of the Gulf of Mexico and may continue to thicken seaward. This great wedge of sediments is comparable in thickness to that which accumulated in the Appalachian or Cordilleran geosynclines during the Paleozoic; the thickness has suggested to many geologists of the Gulf Coast region that this is the site of a developing geosyncline. Certainly rates of subsidence and sedimentation in the Gulf region during the Cenozoic must have been comparable to those in the geosynclines we have studied so far, but these alone do not make a geosyncline. At

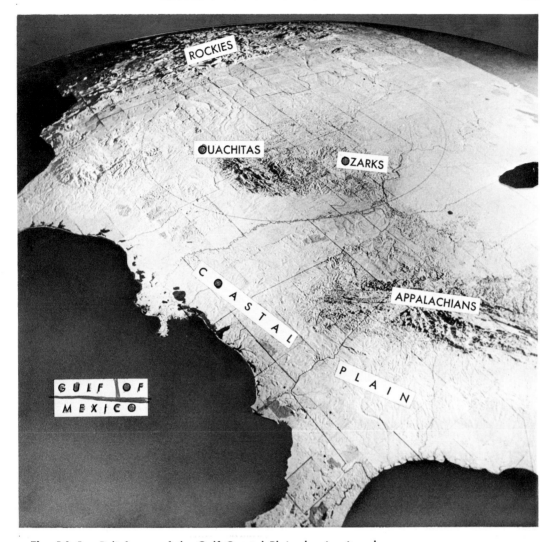

Fig. 14–1. Relief map of the Gulf Coastal Plain showing its relationship to the neighboring mountains of the continent. (Courtesy of
the Babson Institute.)

the end of this chapter, the problem is discussed in the light of the information on the
geology of the province reviewed in the following pages.

BASEMENT ROCKS OF THE GULF COASTAL PLAIN

The overlapping strata of the Gulf and
Atlantic coastal plains conceal the Paleozoic
geology of the southern and eastern sides of
North America and confront geologists with

tantalizing problems concerning the continuity of Appalachian structures and the
nature of the oceanward side of the Appalachian geosyncline.

Beneath the Mississippi Embayment

The tongue of coastal plain sediments that
extends 500 miles up the Mississippi Valley to
Cairo, Illinois, covers the junction between
the structures of the Ouachita Mountains,
which strike east–west, and the southwest-
striking structures of the southern Appala-

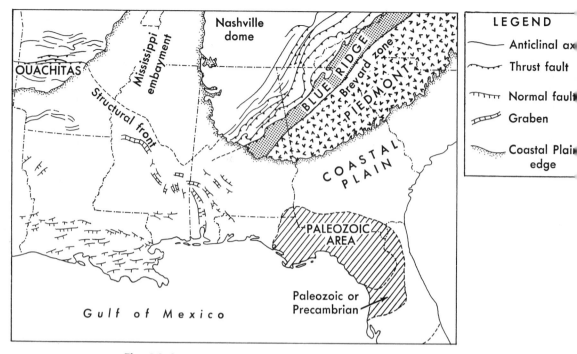

Fig. 14–2. Structures of the eastern Gulf Coastal Plain related to the extension of the Ouachita and Appalachian mountain systems. The zone of normal faults and graben which follows the Ouachita front seems to continue across the trend of the Appalachians into southern Alabama.

chians. Although this area has been extensively drilled and the two belts of deformed rocks have been followed beneath the Mesozoic cover until they approach within 50 miles of one another, the nature of their junction remains a mystery. Instead of turning northward to join the Appalachian folds, the strike of the folds of the Ouachita system curves southward, so that where the two deformed belts are closest, beneath the state of Mississippi, the trends of their folds and faults are at right angles (Fig. 14–2). A zone of graben and normal faults downthrown toward the Gulf follows the Ouachita folds across the Mississippi embayment. Its continuation across the strike of the Appalachian folds suggests that the Ouachita structures with which it seems to be associated truncate the Appalachian ones. In the critical area, pre-Mesozoic rocks occur at depths of more than 15,000 feet and have not been penetrated. Whether the Ouachita belt crosses the Appalachian, turns to merge with it, or is separated from it by a major fault will only be decided by deeper drilling and more geophysical research.

Beneath Northern Florida

Although the southeastern side of the Appalachian System is deeply buried beneath coastal plain sediments, a glimpse of its geology is provided by a few deep wells drilled on the Ocalla arch of northern Florida. Although no stratigraphic sequence can be constructed because each well has penetrated only the top of the pre-Mesozoic basement sequence, fossils show that Ordovician sandstone and shale, Silurian shale, and Devonian sandstones and shales are present. The southern part of the arch is underlain by Precambrian rocks and a sequence of pyroclastic rocks of unknown age.

THE GEOMETRY OF THE COASTAL PLAIN SEDIMENTS

Although the gross structure of the coastal plains is that of a simple wedge of strata dipping and thickening seaward, anticlines, domes, basins, and faults are important locally. The position of these smaller structures is influenced by the buried Paleozoic mountain belt.

Where the sedimentary rocks are depressed into regional synclines, the Coastal Plain widens into the Rio Grande, East Texas, and Mississippi embayments (Fig. 14–3). Between them it narrows into the San Marcos, Sabine, Monroe, and Decatur arches. The embayments of the Coastal Plain are located behind the salients of the Appalachian mountain system, and the arches behind the nodes between the arcs. A prominent feature of the Atlantic Coastal Plain is the Cape Fear arch on the border between the two Carolinas and in line with the node between the southern and central Appalachians. A broad syncline known as the Salisbury embayment occurs in the neighborhood of Chesapeake Bay.

A thousand-mile zone of normal faulting in the coastal plain sediments can be traced from the Rio Grande to the northern boundary of Florida above the trend of the buried Ouachita mountain system (Fig. 14–2). Most of these faults are downthrown toward the Gulf, but some have the opposite displace-

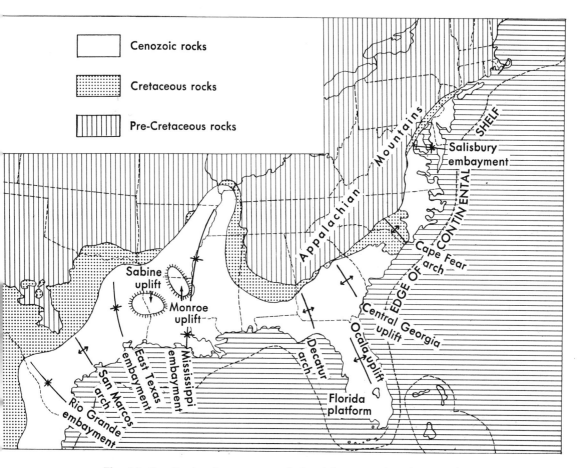

Fig. 14–3. Regional structures of the Atlantic and Gulf coastal plains.

ment and form horsts and graben. A second major zone of normal faults occurs along the coastline in the Rio Grande and East Texas embayments. That movement on most of these faults has been repetitive is shown by the increasing displacement of stratigraphic horizons on either side of the faults as they are followed downward. These faults are commonly ascribed to the subsidence of the Gulf basin under the weight of accumulating sediments. The part of the coastal plains cut by the faults corresponds to the area underlain by Mesozoic salt beds and the edge of the salt corresponds to the line of graben which overlies the buried Ouachita folds. Ernst Cloos has suggested that the faults are caused by the slipping toward the Gulf of the whole plate of sediments lubricated by the salt layer. If this hypothesis is correct, then the graben follow the edge of the salt and are not directly connected with the buried Ouachita Mountains; but these highlands may have determined the edge of salt deposition in the early Mesozoic.

THE STRATIGRAPHY OF THE COASTAL PLAIN WEDGE

During much of Permian and all of Triassic time the agents of weathering and erosion attacked the Appalachians, reducing first the Paleozoic mountains and then the Triassic fault-block mountains to low relief. Along the Atlantic Coast this interval of erosion may have continued until Early Cretaceous time, for the first evidence of marine transgression over the eroded surface is Cretaceous in age. Farther south, the sea began its advance northward from the Gulf of Mexico over the eroded roots of the Ouachita mountain system late in the Triassic Period. By Late Jurassic time, it had reached southern Arkansas.

Triassic–Jurassic Sedimentation

The climate of the middle Mesozoic in the area of the Gulf must have been arid, because at times the whole of the Gulf of Mexico acted as an evaporating pan, concentrating the waters from the Atlantic

Ocean. The basal deposit on the margin of the Gulf is the Eagle Mills Formation, a salt-bearing sedimentary succession up to 1000 feet thick. Only a small area of the salt has been penetrated by the drill because its southward dip rapidly carries it far below the surface; but the presence of structures believed to be salt domes beneath the central part of the Gulf (Fig. 14–8) is good evidence that the salt extends throughout this area. Study of the spores in the salt beds has dated them as Late Triassic and Early Jurassic in age.

When the waters of the Jurassic sea approached normal salinity late in the period, lime mud was deposited to a thickness of 2000 feet. These muds have now consolidated into the brown, chalky Smackover Limestone, named after an oil field in southern Arkansas that produces from this interval. The rest of the Jurassic System consists of sandstones, shales, and siltstones that accumulated along an oscillating shoreline.

Cretaceous Chalk and Greensand

The general pattern of facies changes along the Gulf Coast shoreline was established in Mesozoic time and continues to the present day. Red and gray silts and muds were deposited in estuaries near the shoreline and sands and muds accumulated in deltas. Farther inland, alluvial sands and clays were laid down in the flood plains of rivers or in lakes. Offshore, marine clays accumulated and consolidated into shale; farther from the land and the source of clastics, marls, limestones, and chalk were deposited. These facies zones shifted back and forth across the Coastal Plain as the shoreline oscillated. After a Late Jurassic withdrawal, the sea slowly advanced on the Gulf sector of the Coastal Plain in Early Cretaceous time, but beds of this age in the Atlantic sector are all non-marine except at their extreme outer edge.

In Late Cretaceous time the sea flooded the downwarped edge of the continent on a front extending from New Jersey to Mexico and advanced inland along the Mississippi embayment as far as southern Illinois. This tilting of the continental margin was synchronous with the general depression of the western part of North America, a depression that admitted the latest of the great epeiric seas to the continental interior (see p. 246).

Upper Cretaceous marine sediments of the Gulf Coastal Plain contain several formations composed of chalk. Although this type of limestone is common in beds of Cretaceous age all over the world, it is uncommon in sedimentary successions of other ages. The predominance of chalk in the Upper Cretaceous Series in Europe is reflected in the name of the system. **Chalk** is a soft, white, very fine-grained, remarkably pure limestone composed largely of fragments of disintegrated shells and whole shells of micro-organisms. Comminuted molluscan shells, small platelets of calcium carbonate (**coccoliths**) secreted by floating algae (Fig. 14–4), and Foraminifera are the main organic constituents. The lack of sedimentary structures attributable to currents or waves and the abundance of planktonic marine life suggest that chalk was deposited below the zone agitated by the waves, but the fossils of organisms that live in water of moderate depth indicate that deposition was not abyssal.

While chalk accumulated along the Gulf Coastal Plain, another unusual sediment, greensand, was deposited along the Atlantic Coast, interbedded with quartz sandstones and clays. **Greensand** is composed largely of

Fig. 14–4. Electron photomicrograph of a coccolith from the Cretaceous Taylor Chalk of the Gulf Coast area (approximate magnification × 20,000). (Courtesy of S. Gartner, Jr., and William W. Hay, University of Illinois.)

the dark green pellets of **glauconite**, a complex silicate mineral rich in iron and potassium and related to the micas and clays. Like chalk, greensand is an important constituent of the Cretaceous type section of the English Channel; but, unlike chalk, it is common in beds of other ages, most notably those at the base of the Cambrian System. It has been quarried for use as a fertilizer and as a water softener.

Chalk and greensand raise the question of whether certain sediments are characteristic of certain times in the earth's history. Some geologists have thought that iron formation, the finely laminated hematite and chert combination described more fully in Chapter 16, was deposited only under conditions peculiar to Precambrian time. The abundance of chalk in Cretaceous rocks may reflect physical conditions ideal for the multiplication of coccoliths and for the appearance and rapid increase in the number of planktonic Foraminifera at about this time. The conditions responsible for the formation of greensand are not fully understood, but its deposition occurred in shallow, agitated, marine water.

The tectonic unrest that marked Late Cretaceous time in the western part of North America is reflected in igneous action in the Gulf Coastal Plain. An alkalic suite of igneous rocks intruded the Ouachita deformed belt as stocks and dikes. Syenite intrusions of this age have weathered, producing the bauxite deposits of Arkansas. A Late Cretaceous ultrabasic stock in the same state has furnished the only diamonds ever mined on this continent. Volcanic ash beds, dikes, and sills have been penetrated by many wells in the central Gulf region. A weathered igneous rock forms the reservoir of several oil fields in the vicinity of Austin, Texas. Pilot Knob, south of Austin, is believed to be the relic of an eroded volcano. These igneous rocks are insignificant components of the 1½ million cubic miles of coastal plain sediments and volumetrically are not comparable to the volcanics of Paleozoic and Mesozoic geosynclines.

CENOZOIC SEDIMENTATION

Sedimentary Cycles in the Gulf Coastal Plain

The Cenozoic sediments of the Gulf and Atlantic coastal plains consist of sands, marls, clays, and shales; many of these are still unconsolidated and crumble in one's hands. The complex facies changes that take place down the dip and along the strike in this sedimentary prism are known in great detail from well records. Downward along the dip, each stratigraphic unit grades, with much interfingering, from a near-shore or continental facies to a marine facies. In addition to small-scale oscillations of the shoreline, a broad, cyclical change in its position can be recognized. Each cycle of sedimentation started as the advancing sea deposited calcareous marls, glauconitic sands, or dark clays. As the recessional phase of the cycle began, marine deposits were overlain by gray sands and, as the shoreline moved still farther outward, by non-marine and estuarine sands and lignite. These recessional deposits are deltaic in nature and were formed as the rivers from the interior of the continent built out the shore. Subsidence was apparently more rapid during the recessional phases of the cycle, for these strata are much thicker than are the strata of the transgressional, marine phase. The greater thickness of the recessional phase of deposition in the coastal deltaic environment contrasts with the greater thickness of the transgressional succession in cratonic environments, where the recessional deposits may be missing entirely. Figure 14–5 illustrates two such cycles from the Eocene Series of the Gulf Coast. The thick, non-marine sand wedges of the recessional phase are represented by the Sparta and Yegua formations. The Crockett and Cane River shales belong to the thinner, transgressional phase. Throughout the Cenozoic, the shoreline moved generally seaward as each transgression fell short of the northward extent of its predecessor, and each delta was built farther out into the Gulf.

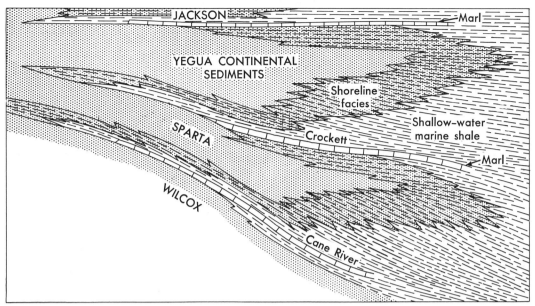

Fig. 14–5. Cross-section showing the facies changes in the Eocene Claiborne Group of central Louisiana. The Sparta and Yegua sands are regressive deposits separated by marine shales that were laid down during transgressions of the sea. (After S. W. Lowman, courtesy of the American Association of Petroleum Geologists.)

The first Cenozoic transgression deposited beds of Paleocene age known as the Midway Group. The recessive phase of the Midway cycle is formed by 5000 feet of deltaic Wilcox sandstones, which are among the most important reservoirs for oil and gas on the Gulf Coast. The next two cycles constitute the Claiborne Group and are illustrated in Fig. 14–5. The sea advanced and retreated again before the close of Eocene time, depositing the Jackson Group. The recessive phase of an Oligocene cycle is represented by the thick, oil-bearing Frio Sand (Fig. 14–6). The cyclical movement of the shoreline was poorly defined in Miocene and Pliocene times, but the largely deltaic sediments of these epochs reach a thickness of more than 15,000 feet in the region of the Mississippi delta. This sedimentary record shows that the rapid sedimentation and concomitant subsidence, which are features of the delta region today, have been in progress since the beginning of Miocene time. Pleistocene deposits of this area are alluvial silts, gravels, and sands.

Thickness

The formations of the Gulf Coastal Plain thicken seaward irregularly; locally they increase rapidly in thickness. Grover Murray has compared the pattern of thickness variations in stratigraphic units along the strike to a chain of flattened link sausages. The sausages represent basins, or what he calls "depocenters"; the links represent the thin areas between them. An average thickness of 2500 feet of sediments accumulated in each of these basins before the site of rapid subsidence shifted laterally. The normal fault, which bounds many of the basins on the inland side, may have been either the cause or an effect of their subsidence.

The deepest wells in the Coastal Plain have penetrated to nearly 25,000 feet, but at this depth they were still in Cenozoic sediments. The thickness of the wedge of coastal plain sediment, therefore, cannot be measured directly. Geophysical measurements suggest that the depth of unconsolidated sediments at the shoreline is about 40,000 feet, and that

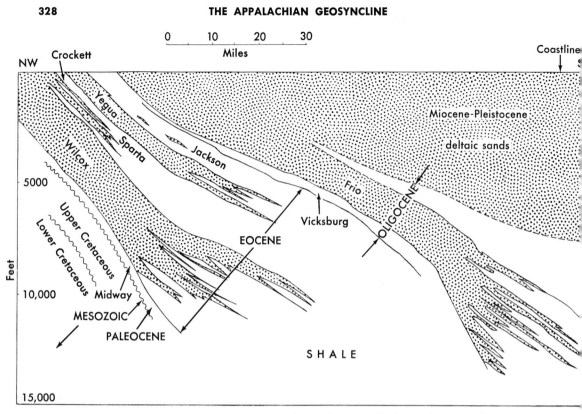

Fig. 14–6. Cross-section of the sediments of the Gulf Coastal Plain along the Colorado River, Texas. The alternation of sandstone and shale units is illustrated, as is the over-all spread with time of the sand facies toward the Gulf. The stippled areas are interbedded sandstone and shale (vertical exaggeration × 25). (After J. O. Colle and others.)

this wedge thins toward the center of the Gulf of Mexico. Almost three-quarters of this great thickness of sediment accumulated in Miocene, Pliocene, and Pleistocene times. The Sigsbee Deep of the central part of the Gulf is underlain by a thick sedimentary succession lying on oceanic crust.

Micropaleontology

Rapidly changing facies make the Cenozoic and Cretaceous sediments difficult to correlate. This problem became acute when many oil wells were drilled in which accurate location of stratigraphic horizons was required. In the drilling process, minute shells of Foraminifera are brought up with the waste rock cuttings by the circulating mud that lubricates the bit. The use of these minute fossils for dating and correlating the

rocks of the Gulf Coastal Plain was refined during the 1920's and 1930's by J. A. Cushman. As a result of his research and that of other micropaleontologists, the Cenozoic and Mesozoic beds of this province are divided into many foraminiferal zones that can be recognized by a field paleontologist at the drilling site as the cuttings are collected.

The Atlantic Coastal Plain

The stratigraphy of the Atlantic Coastal Plain cannot be resolved into cycles as easily as can that of the Gulf Plain, but, in general, the times of marine transgression after the Early Cretaceous were the same in both areas. These invasions of the coast in Eocene time resulted in the accumulation of more greensand. The extensive Oligocene transgression of the Gulf region did not affect the Atlantic Coastal Plain north of Georgia. Miocene seas spread widely over the eastern seaboard, depositing marls in which the fossils, although 25 million years old, are so well preserved that they might have been collected from a modern beach. Pliocene and Pleistocene gravels and sands form marine and river terraces.

Carbonates

Although Cenozoic sediments in the coastal plains are largely sandstone and shale, limestone and dolomite were deposited through much of Cenozoic and Mesozoic times at opposite ends of the Gulf Coastal Plain. Florida is underlain by thick, flat-lying carbonate sediments of Cretaceous and early Cenozoic age. The Bahama Islands, although separated by a deep channel from Florida, are part of this carbonate province; here limestones are forming today, and the lime muds are dolomitized in some shoreline environments. The peninsula of Yucatán is

underlain by Mesozoic and Cenozoic limestone, and the formation of limestone continues to the present day offshore, to the northwest, in the reefs of the Campeche Bank.

PETROLEUM RESOURCES

Oil wells in the Gulf Coastal Plain produce about 42 per cent of the petroleum output of the United States, or about 1 billion barrels annually. The most productive of the Gulf states are Texas and Louisiana; smaller quantities of oil come from Arkansas and Mississippi, and only a trickle from Alabama and Florida.

Salt Domes

While drilling for salt on a low hill in the Mississippi delta, Anthony Lucas noticed that the drill penetrated many pockets of gas. In 1901 he moved his drill over the border from Louisiana into Texas to test for oil in the

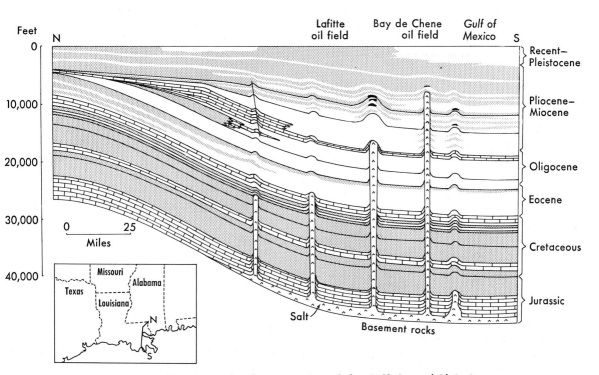

Fig. 14–7. Generalized cross-section of the Gulf Coastal Plain in southern Louisiana, showing the relationship of the salt domes to the sediments. (Modified from J. B. Carsey, courtesy of the *American Association of Petroleum Geologists Bulletin*.)

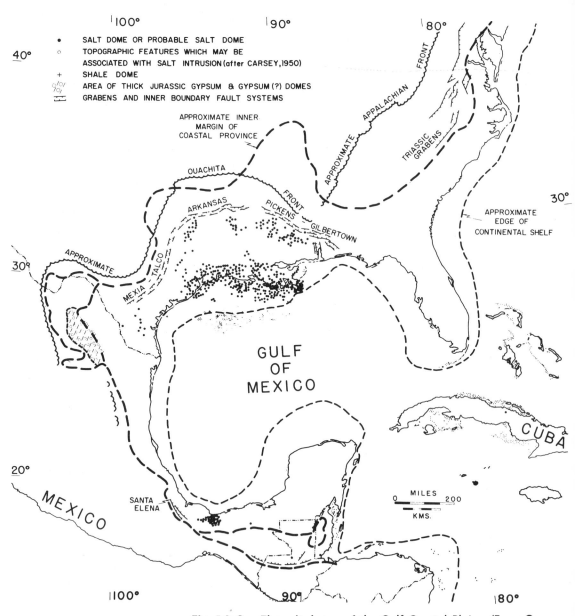

Fig. 14–8. The salt domes of the Gulf Coastal Plain. (From Grover E. Murray, *Geology of the Atlantic and Gulf Coastal Province of North America.* New York: Harper & Row, 1961.)

rocks below a low mound, called Spindletop, similar to the one he had drilled in Louisiana. His first well was a "gusher," and 64 others drilled on the same hill each yielded 75,000 barrels a day. The hill at Spindletop was pushed up by the intrusion of rock salt into the sedimentary strata about 1000 feet below the surface. After Lucas' success, the search was begun for similar structures; in 65 years, this search has resulted in the discovery of more than 300 other domes. The **salt domes** of the Gulf of Mexico are stocks of halite from ½ mile to 6 miles in diameter which have penetrated as much as 30,000 feet of sedimentary rocks. The salt of the column has flowed plastically through the strata from the Eagle Mills Formation at the base of the Gulf Coast succession, under the confining pressure produced by the great weight of overlying sediments (Fig. 14–7). The movement of the light salt with respect to the denser sediments around it may be a response to the differences in density between the two substances. The moving mass of salt punctured beds low in the succession, dragging them upward along its flank; higher beds may have merely been domed above the advancing salt.

The domes do not occur on the San Marcos arch or the Sabine and Monroe uplifts (Fig. 14–8). The largest area of domes, along the eastern Texas and Louisiana coastlines, extends out across the continental shelf (Fig. 14–7). Smaller areas occur in the Rio Grande, East Texas, and Mississippi embayments and on the isthmus of Tehuantepec, Mexico. The domes may be absent from regional uplifts because salt was not deposited there or because after deposition it flowed off the high areas into the basins. The movement of the salt into the domes accompanied the subsidence of the Gulf, as the latter received the great weight of sediments; this movement may still be taking place.

The top of the salt pillar is commonly composed of a cap rock of cavernous calcite, dolomite, gypsum, and anhydrite. It was this highly porous cap rock that held the oil at Spindletop. Native sulfur is an interesting constituent of the cap rock of some of these domes. It is extracted by pumping superheated steam down bore holes to melt the sulfur and bring it to the surface through another hole. The anhydrite of the cap rock is an accumulation of the insoluble material in the salt which was left as percolating water dissolved the top of the rising salt column.

The salt of some domes reaches almost to the surface; that of others remains beneath thousands of feet of sediments; and that of still others is too deep to be penetrated by the drill, but is betrayed by the arching of strata above it.

Petroleum Traps

The formation of an oil field depends on the availability of (1) a source rock that can supply the hydrocarbons, (2) a migration route, (3) a porous reservoir rock, and (4) a trap. The alternating sands and shales of the Gulf area form ideal source and reservoir beds, respectively; the structures associated with the salt domes form many traps, some of which are illustrated in Fig. 14–9. Porous beds domed into anticlines, the porous cap rock, beds truncated against the upthrust salt, and porous beds sealed off by faults or unconformities on the flanks of the domes may all form reservoirs for Gulf Coast oil fields. The largest trap in the Gulf region, at the East Texas field is formed by the truncation of the gently dipping Upper Cretaceous Woodbine Sandstone and is sealed by the impervious Austin Chalk. The field has produced 3.6 billion barrels of oil and is expected to produce 1.4 billion barrels more before being exhausted.

Petroleum may also be trapped by facies changes. Where beds of sand in such formations as the Yegua or Frio wedge out or become less porous upward along the dip, this change of facies traps oil and gas in many Gulf Coast fields. Reefs that became established on the Monroe dome of Louisiana and the Jackson dome of Mississippi during the Late Cretaceous later became porous limestone reservoirs for natural gas fields.

A GULF COAST GEOSYNCLINE

What criteria learned from our study of the Appalachian and Cordilleran geosynclines can we apply to judging the geosynclinal nature of the Gulf Coastal province? Both the Appalachian and the Cordilleran geosynclines were characterized by subsidence for a long time—at least 350 and 600 million years, respectively. During this period of subsidence, they trapped great thicknesses of a particular facies of sediments characterized by graywacke, chert, shale, and tuff. Effusive and explosive volcanism was an important feature of the history of both geosynclines. Finally, they were marked by a tectonic mobility expressed in frequent episodes of orogeny, rapid subsidence, and extensive intrusions.

The Gulf Coastal province is a linear area of subsidence which has acted as a trap for a

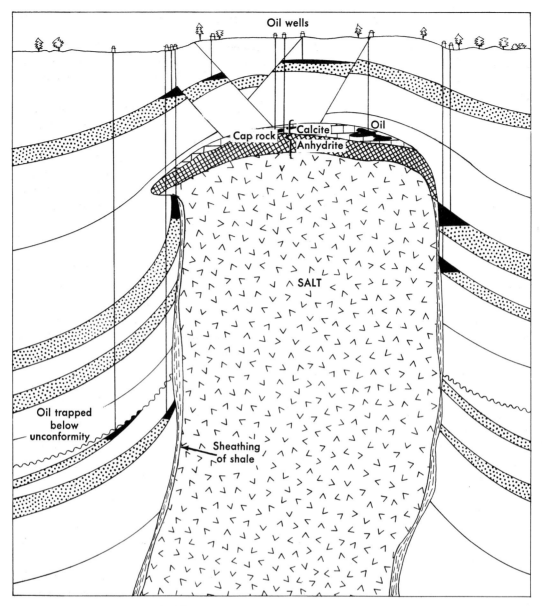

Fig. 14—9. Oil traps that may develop around a salt dome. In this cross-section of an ideal dome, the various positions in which petroleum can accumulate have been indicated.

great thickness of sediments for at least 100 million years. These rocks are not, however, of geosynclinal facies, but are largely shales, sandstones, and limestones. Igneous rocks, both extrusive and intrusive, are insignificant compared with the great tuff beds and outpourings of lava in the geosynclines. The slight warpings that controlled the spread and retreat of the seas and the structures associated with the subsidence and salt intrusion are not evidence of the sort of mobility that characterizes a geosyncline. Measured by these standards, the deposits cannot be termed a Gulf Coast geosyncline.

The Coastal Plain wedge is similar to other deltaic deposits that accumulated on the edge of the craton from highlands in the Appalachian and Cordilleran geosynclines. Unlike them, it was derived from the interior of the continent, not from geosynclinal highlands adjacent to the ocean. We have studied similar sedimentary wedges in the Precambrian and Cambrian sandstones that accumulated at the edges of the craton to thicknesses of tens of thousands of feet during the early history of the Appalachian and Cordilleran geosynclines.

Traverses with seismic instruments across the North Atlantic continental shelf have revealed that the coastal plain sediments fill a trough located under the shelf and a parallel one under the continental slope. The geophysicists who discovered this configuration suggest that the outer of these troughs is the modern counterpart of the Appalachian geosyncline and the inner is analogous to a marginal basin on the edge of the craton. Perhaps this is evidence for the development of a new geosyncline beneath the continental shelf on the oceanward side of the old Appalachian geosyncline.

EROSION OF THE APPALACHIAN MOUNTAINS

Evidence that the structures of the Appalachian mountain system were formed in the late Paleozoic was reviewed in Chapter 13; that the deformation was accompanied by uplift is shown by the clastic sediments deposited west of the geosynclinal area. By Triassic time these ranges had been eroded to low relief and a new generation of fault-block mountains was uplifted. That the Triassic mountains were eroded enough to be covered by the transgressing Cretaceous sea is shown by the truncation of the Triassic structures by the basal marine sediments of the Atlantic Coastal Plain. The erosion surface between the Piedmont crystalline rocks and Triassic sediments below and the coastal plain sediments above is called the Fall Zone peneplain. The evolution of the Appalachian landscape to its present form is open to two interpretations, neither of which can yet be rejected.

The summits of the ridges of the Appalachians are remarkably smooth and level, except where they are cut by major rivers (water gaps) or by valleys formerly occupied by rivers (wind gaps). The accordance of the summit levels has suggested to many geomorphologists—beginning with William Morris Davis, at the end of the nineteenth century—that the summits are remnants of a peneplain whose surface would be restored if the valleys between the ridges were filled in. This erosion surface has been commonly referred to as the Schooley peneplain. Monadnocks are hills that have escaped erosion in the process of peneplanation and rise conspicuously above the peneplain surface. Some mountains, such as the Great Smokies of Tennessee and the White Mountains of New Hampshire, rise above the Schooley surface and are considered to be monadnocks, a name derived from Mt. Monadnock in New Hampshire, which rises above the New England Upland surface. The Schooley surface could have been eroded only during late Mesozoic and early Cenozoic times, because it cuts the Fall Zone surface, which is of early Cretaceous age. The modern topography of the Appalachians is believed to have resulted from the dissection of the surface in later Cenozoic time.

The concept of the Schooley peneplain offers a convincing explanation for the water gaps which the major rivers cut through the ridges of the Appalachian Mountains. Rivers such as the ancestral Potomac, Susquehanna, and Shenandoah are thought to have flowed in early Cenozoic time toward the Atlantic on alluvium that covered the peneplained bedrock surface, uninfluenced by the structure of the folded sediments beneath. The uplift of the Schooley surface cannot be dated exactly, but it could have occurred in mid-Cenozoic time and could have been responsible for the coarsening of coastal plain sediments in the Miocene Epoch. The rivers, quickened by uplift, started cutting into the alluvial covering and then into the bedrock beneath the Schooley plain. As the land was worn away, differential resistance to erosion caused the more resistant beds to be left as ridges and the valleys to be cut out of the more easily removed shales and carbonates. The major streams that had flowed across belts of resistant rock on the plain continued to erode their courses, cutting water gaps through the ridges as they were uncovered, somewhat like a rotary saw cutting a log. The discontinuous nature of the uplift is believed to have allowed time for the cutting of such smaller and lower surfaces of planation as the Harrisburg and Somerville surfaces. The drainage was thus superposed across a topography whose relief had been first almost eliminated by peneplanation and then re-established by uplift.

Some geologists do not believe that such erosion surfaces as the Schooley, Harrisburg, and Somerville are the remnants of peneplains or partial peneplains. They explain the present landscape as the result of continuous erosion since Permian time and believe that the different levels of topography are the results of the responses of different lithologies to the processes of weathering and erosion. The uniformity of altitude of the summits of the Appalachian ridges reflects the similar response of resistant beds of sandstone in a particular structural position to a particular set of weathering conditions. The lower erosion surfaces, such as the Harrisburg, are developed on softer rocks. The altitude of these surfaces can be no lower than the channels of the master streams, whose gradients, in turn, are controlled by the grain size of the sediments they carry. Streams transporting coarse, resistant particles, such as sandstone derived from the Appalachian ridges, must maintain steep gradients. When the supply of this size particle is removed, the river adjusts to its new environment by cutting down through the non-resistant rocks, leaving them, for a time, as broad terraces (for example, the Harrisburg surface) to be dissected by later erosion. This theory has been called the theory of dynamic equilibrium, for it proposes that the landscape features are lowered by mass wasting and stream erosion at about the same rate; thus the relief does not eventually decrease to an ultimate peneplain but is maintained as the area is lowered by erosion, until the equilibrium is disturbed.

The Appalachian Mountains are the net result of the forces of deformation, uplift, and erosion at work for over half a billion years since the inception of the Appalachian geosyncline. Deformation of the crust has shaped the structure; uplift has kept the rocks within the zone of erosion; and erosion and weathering have etched the weaker rocks from around the more resistant ones to produce the mountains that we see today.

SUMMARY

Coastal plain sediments cover the enigmatic junction of the Ouachita and Appalachian mountain systems and a puzzling area of unmetamorphosed Paleozoic rocks in northern Florida.

The wedge of coastal plain sediments thins over transverse arches and thickens into broad troughs which are situated behind the nodes and arcs of the Ouachita and Appalachian mountain systems. The sediments are cut by normal faults caused by the subsidence of the Gulf.

Chalk and greensand are sediments particularly widespread in Cretaceous rocks.

The Coastal Plain clastic wedge is composed of thick recessive sandstones and thin transgressive beds. The shoreline shifted back and forth across the area during the Cenozoic, but the transgressions became progressively less extensive after the beginning of the era. Microfossils allow correlations to be made in the complexly interfingering facies.

Salt domes, structures characteristic of the Gulf Coastal Plain, have risen from the Mesozoic salt beds, puncturing, doming, and fracturing the overlying strata and forming traps for oil. Many kinds of structural and stratigraphic traps for petroleum have been found in the Gulf Coastal Plain.

The Gulf Coastal Plain has a great thickness of sediments in common with the Appalachian and Cordilleran geosynclines.

The evolution of the Appalachian landscape can be explained in terms of (1) a succession of peneplains and partial peneplains that record standstills in the process of uplift, or (2) a dynamic equilibrium in which the various topographic levels are determined by the interaction of lithology, structure, weathering, and erosion.

QUESTIONS

1. Draw a series of cross-sections to show the development of a normal fault in which the stratigraphic displacement increases downward.

2. Under what special conditions might one kind of sediment be confined to a single time in the geological past?

3. Compare the geomorphic evolution of the Appalachian mountain system since the mid-Jurassic with that of the Cordilleran Mountains of Wyoming during the Cenozoic Era.

4. Outline the future history of the Atlantic Coast region if the trough beneath the continental slope is the beginning of a new geosyncline.

REFERENCES AND SUGGESTED READINGS

Bornhauser, M. "Gulf Coast Tectonics," *American Association of Petroleum Geologists Bulletin,* 42: 339–70, 1959. Most of the structures of the Gulf Coastal Plain can be explained on the basis of downbuilding or subsidence of the Gulf and the flow of weak sedimentary beds downslope.

Drake, C. L., Ewing, M., and Sutton, G. H. "Continental Margins and Geosynclines: The East Coast of North America North of Cape Hatteras," *Physics and Chemistry of the Earth,* 3: 110–98, 1960. Evidence for two troughs—one under the shelf and one under the continental slope—is discussed, and the troughs are compared to ancient geosynclines.

Hack, J. T. "Interpretation of Topography in Humid Temperate Regions," *American Journal of Science,* 258(A): 80–97, 1960. The concept of dynamic equilibrium is proposed and contrasted with Davis' theory of the geomorphic cycle.

Murray, G. E. *Geology of the Atlantic and Gulf Coastal Province of North America.* New York: Harper & Row, 1961. A summary of aspects of the geology of the Coastal Plain.

Murray, G. E. "Salt Structures of the Gulf of Mexico Basin," *American Association of Petroleum Geologists Bulletin,* 50: 439–78, 1966. A summary, with many illustrations, of recent investigations of the salt domes.

Richards, H. G. *Record of the Rocks.* New York: The Ronald Press Co., 1953. A textbook of historical geology concerned largely with the history of the Gulf Coastal Plain.

Complete flat erosion

OR

just "lowered" by erosion

V

CONTINENTAL NUCLEUS AND NORTHLAND

15

The Arctic Islands

Beyond Cape Columbia, the northernmost part of the continent, the Arctic Ocean forms a frozen cap over the world. Between the ocean and the mainland of North America the continental platform breaks up into peninsulas and islands. The straits between the islands seem to define an ancient, drowned river system, and bathymetric measurements of the shape of the ocean floor support the hypothesis that a rise of sea level has formed the islands. The flooding of the river valleys and the conversion of the northern end of the continent into a series of islands probably took place within the last few million years.

Although climatic conditions are rigorous in this part of the world and the season during which the bedrock is free of snow is rarely more than 2 months, geologists have shown within the last 15 years that the geology of the Arctic Islands is as complex, varied, and interesting as that of any region in North America. An ancient mountain system traverses the islands, comparable in complexity to the Appalachian or Cordilleran systems. Rocks representing all the geological systems, from Precambrian to Recent, have been found in the Arctic Islands. De-

vonian, Mississippian, Pennsylvanian, and Cenozoic episodes of orogeny created a belt of deformed rocks called the Innuitian mountain system, which, along with the Appalachian and Cordilleran mountains, closes the ring around the Canadian Shield.

The first step in the exploration of the Arctic wasteland was instigated by the search for a northwest passage around the end of North America, which was stimulated by a prize of £20,000 offered by the British government to the first ship to sail through the passage. The second stage of exploration followed the disappearance of Sir John Franklin and two ships in 1846. Several expeditions were sent during the next decade by the government, and by Lady Franklin, to explore these desolate coasts for traces of the explorer. Incidentally, these search parties charted the coasts of the islands, plotted the outlines of the geology, and brought back fossil collections. With the discovery in 1857 that Franklin and his men had abandoned the ships in the ice and had died of starvation trying to reach civilization by land, this phase of exploration came to a close. Not until after World War II were systematic geological surveys made of the islands, and the Geological Survey of Canada instituted the program of mapping which continues to the present day.

Within the Arctic Islands is the last major onshore sedimentary basin in the world to be explored for oil. All other major sedimentary areas have been extensively tested by the oilman's drill, but the numbers of wells drilled in the Arctic can be counted on one's fingers. Yet enthusiastic geologists have predicted that vast reserves of oil exist in the Arctic and have envisioned its transportation to market by atomic submarines pulling plastic "sausages" filled with oil. In this chapter we shall examine the sediments and structures of the Arctic Islands to see how the geologist is able to assess the potentialities of a region for petroleum exploration.

PETROLIFEROUS BASINS

Most of the oil discovered so far has come from basinal areas of the earth underlain by great thicknesses of sedimentary rocks. Potential reservoirs must be covered with an adequate thickness of impermeable rocks or the oil will leak to the surface and be dissipated. Thus, in regions where the sedimentary covering of the basement rocks is less than 2000 feet thick, oil and gas are missing or present only in small quantities. The sedimentary filling must be unmetamorphosed, for oil is not found in strata that have been affected by regional metamorphism.

Although regional metamorphism generally precludes the accumulation of oil in quantity, deformation of the strata by faulting and folding often forms structural traps in which petroleum accumulates. The inner edges of marginal cratonic basins, where sediments have been slightly disturbed by the movements in the geosyncline or by the instability of the cratonic margin, are among the most favorable places for the accumulation of oil. Examples of states with large production from such accumulations are Pennsylvania, Oklahoma, and Wyoming. Petroleum may be trapped in both flat-lying and folded sedimentary rocks by facies changes, such as the sealing of porous sand

lenses by shale or the transition of limestone reefs into shales. Study of recent sediments shows that they contain only infinitesimal amounts of hydrocarbons, which can be flushed out with a great quantity of trapped water into adjacent porous beds as the sediments are compacted. If petroleum is to accumulate in quantity, the sedimentary basin must have a great volume of the source beds (probably dark shales) to supply the necessary hydrocarbons, because hydrocarbons are in such low concentrations in the source sediments.

Keeping these characteristics of other oil-bearing basins in mind, let us now examine the geology of the Arctic Islands to assess their potential for petroleum exploration.

TECTONIC DIVISIONS OF THE ARCTIC ISLANDS

The Platform

The Precambrian rocks of the Canadian Shield extend out into the sedimentary basin of the Arctic Islands in two promontories (Fig. 15–1). One crosses Victoria Island (Minto arch) and the other extends up the Boothia Peninsula (Boothia arch). From these promontories the surrounding Paleozoic strata dip away, forming anticlines in which Precambrian basement rocks are exposed along the crests. These folds are cratonic arches similar to the Cincinnati arch or the Transcontinental arch, and they separate basins floored with a thin succession of early Paleozoic sedimentary rocks. Typical of such basin successions are the Cambrian, Ordovician, and Silurian limestones, dolomites, and sandstones of Banks and Victoria islands. Although some of the sandstones are porous enough to act as reservoirs, the whole succession is flat-lying and about 3,000 feet thick, and is therefore not a "prime target" in the search for petroleum. Reef carbonates in similar platform successions produce oil in some basins, but the only positively identified reefs in the Arctic basins are at the top of the sedimentary section, where any oil they may have contained has since leaked out.

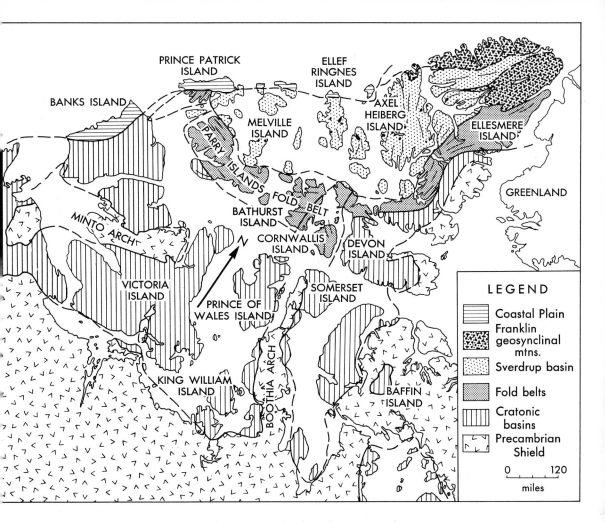

Fig. 15–1. Tectonic map of the Arctic Islands. The structural trends in the fold belts are shown by short lines. The gypsum intrusions in the Sverdrup basin are represented by dark blobs.

The Marginal Basins

North of the cratonic basins, with their thin sections of lower Paleozoic rocks, are the folded rocks of the Parry Islands fold belt of Bathurst and Melville islands, and the Central Ellesmere fold belt of southern Ellesmere Island (Fig. 15–2).

The rocks of Melville Island, which is the second island from the west in the Parry group, will serve to illustrate the geology of the marginal basins. The rocks of Melville Island are largely Ordovician, Silurian, and Devonian in age. Cambrian rocks are rare in the Arctic Islands and are absent entirely in the Parry Islands fold belt. Ordovician and Silurian sedimentary rocks are represented by two facies: a thin black shale facies

and a thicker limestone and dolomite facies. The Ibbett Bay Formation is a good example of the former (Fig. 15–3). It is about 3,000 feet thick and contains graptolite zones that span the interval from the Early Ordovician Epoch to the beginning of the Devonian Period. These shales grade southward into the limestones deposited in the shelf seas of the cratonic basins, but they grade northward into limestones and dolomites that seem to represent reefs constructed on areas of the sea floor above the muddy bottom. The abrupt transition from carbonates to black shales can be observed all along the Parry Islands fold belt (Fig. 15–4). On Cornwallis Island, the facies change is from the Cape Phillips graptolitic shales (8500 feet thick) to vuggy, light-gray dolomites with a coral-

Fig. 15–2. Aerial photograph of the Judge Daly Peninsula on the eastern coast of Ellesmere Island. On the right of the fiord, the folded Paleozoic rocks of the Ellesmere Island fold belt strike eastward toward Greenland along the horizon. (Courtesy of the Department of Energy, Mines and Resources, Canada.)

Fig. 15–3. Aerial photograph of the Canrobert Hills, a section of the Parry Islands fold belt on the western side of Melville Island. The dark shales of the Lower Paleozoic Ibbett Bay Formation form the cores of anticlines at the left and right. In the center and background, the lighter colored Pennsylvanian Canyon Fiord Formation overlies the shales unconformably. (Courtesy of the Department of Energy, Mines and Resources, Canada.)

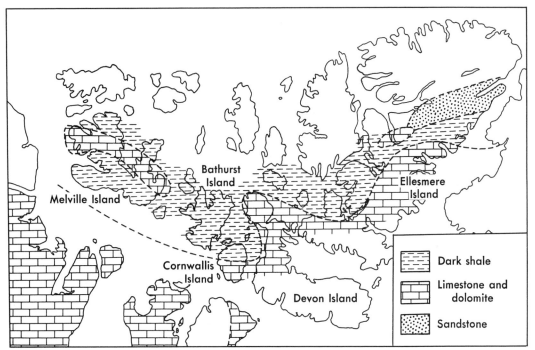

Fig. 15–4. Distribution of Ordovician and Silurian facies in the Arctic Islands. (After R. J. W. Douglas and others.)

stromatoporoid fauna and fossiliferous lime-stones (combined thickness of 13,500 feet). The dolomites are generally impregnated with solid bitumen and give off a smell of oil when broken.

The structures of Melville Island are much like those of the Valley and Ridge Province of the Appalachians. As vegetation is sparse at these latitudes, the anticlines and syn-clines stand out dramatically in an aerial view (Fig. 15–5). The folded rocks are also cut by steeply dipping thrust faults, usually near the crests of the anticlines. William Logan observed 125 years ago that oil seeps in the Gaspé Peninsula of Quebec were located on the crests of anticlines, and since that time geologists have found most of the world's petroleum resources by drilling such struc-tures. Today 80 per cent of the oil in the major oil fields of the free world comes from anticlinal traps.

In the Parry Islands fold belt, the geology is favorable to the accumulation of oil. The thick black shales are excellent source beds; the dolomites and limestones are porous enough to absorb hydrocarbons squeezed by compaction from the shales; and the gentle folding of the beds provides many structures in which migrating oil could be trapped. That some of the porous dolomite now at the surface did contain oil is confirmed by the presence of a bituminous residue, which forms when the more volatile constituents of oil evaporate. To find oil in a promising reservoir such as this, the geologist must locate his well where the porous bed has been covered since the time of migration with a layer of impermeable sediment that seals in the oil.

The first "oil" well was drilled in the Arctic Islands in the winter of 1961–62 to test the hypothesis that oil had accumulated in Silurian reef carbonates below a gentle anticline on the south shore of Melville Island. The well passed through nearly 8000 feet of Devonian sandstones and shales be-fore entering the shale succession containing Silurian graptolites. After drilling through about 4000 feet of these shales, geologists abandoned the well as a dry hole at 12,543

Fig. 15–5. The open anticlines and synclines of the Parry Islands fold belt on Melville Island. Most of the rocks in the photograph are Upper Devonian sandstones and shales of the Hecla Bay and Gripper Bay formations. (Courtesy of the Department of Energy, Mines and Resources, Canada.)

feet, where dolomites and anhydrites of uncertain age were found. The well had apparently missed the porous reefs and passed through the shale facies without encountering any reservoirs in which oil might have accumulated. This failure to find reservoir beds illustrates the difficulties of predicting facies changes in this type of basin, for, although the general pattern of facies was known, the specific changes could not be accurately predicted below the surface; the only way to make sure was to drill and test. The geologist picks the best location based on the geological facts available, but the occurrence of oil depends on many factors, some as yet unknown. Each hole drilled is a risk, and in the United States only one in ten of these exploration or "wildcat" wells results in a new discovery. (The ratio is about 2 in 10 in Canada, where exploration for petroleum is at a younger stage.) Whether or not oil is found, however, these test holes contribute stratigraphic information. The well at Melville Island showed that adjustments must be made in the facies maps to reduce the chances of making a similar miscalculation when the next hole is drilled.

The succession of strata in the Parry Islands fold belt tells a familiar story that need not be elaborated here. The marine limestones and shales of the Ordovician and Silurian systems and the Lower Devonian Series are succeeded by thick, non-marine sandstones and siltstones of the Middle and Late Devonian Series. These clastics indicate that orogeny was taking place in a geosyncline north of the fold belt in late Devonian and Mississippian times. In Mississippian time, the deformation in the geosyncline crumpled the basins along the margin of the craton, forming the Parry Islands and Central Ellesmere fold belts. The Mississippian age of the deformation and subsequent uplift is indicated by the general absence of Mississippian sediments throughout the fold belts and the angular unconformity between Devonian and Pennsylvanian beds. The late Devonian clastic wedge of the Arctic Islands was almost certainly continuous southwestward with the Devonian deltaic sediments in the northern Cordillera, and the highlands raised in mid-Paleozoic time in the Cordilleran geosyncline (see p. 221) may have continued northeastward, joining those in the Franklin geosyncline.

Cornwallis Fold Belt

On eastern Bathurst Island, the gentle folds of the Parry Islands end against the western side of the older Cornwallis fold belt and either turn northwesterly or abut northwesterly strike-slip faults. The Cornwallis belt includes northwest-trending folds that were formed by the vertical movement of the northern extension of the Boothia arch beneath this sedimentary basin. The structures of the Cornwallis belt were formed in Paleozoic time but were influenced by structures formed in the basement rocks in Precambrian time. Stratigraphic evidence shows that the Boothia arch was raised in at least six episodes from Precambrian to Cenozoic time. The three episodes of folding and faulting that were most important in the deformation of the Cornwallis fold belt took place in the Devonian Period. The first is dated as Early Devonian by the 2000 feet of red conglomerates and sandstones of the Lower Devonian Peel Sound Formation, whose fragments were eroded from the crest of the Boothia arch. The formation records the raising of this structure and the stripping of its Paleozoic cover to its Precambrian core in Early Devonian time.

The gentle folds of the strata on Cornwallis Island and the facies changes between the shales and dolomites tempted petroleum geologists to drill the second Arctic Island well on this island. Although the well penetrated a thick section of the porous Allen Bay Reef Dolomite, no oil was found. The difficulties of predicting facies changes in a relatively unknown sedimentary basin were illustrated by a third unsuccessful well that was drilled on Bathurst Island near the junction of the Cornwallis and Parry Islands fold belts. Again the target was porous Silurian dolomite, but although dolomite was found it was not porous. This well encountered 4000 feet of evaporites in the Ordovician succession, which are represented in outcrop by 200 feet of gypsum and gypsiferous shales.

The Franklin Geosyncline

The Ordovician, Silurian, and Devonian rocks of the Parry Islands cannot be traced farther north, for they become covered by a great thickness of relatively undeformed younger beds that occupy the Sverdrup basin. However, in northern Ellesmere Island, the carbonates and shales of the marginal basins are in contact with rocks of equivalent age but of geosynclinal facies. These sandstones and volcanics were deposited in the Franklin geosyncline, named after the District of Franklin in Canada's Northwest Territories.

The northern part of Ellesmere Island is mountainous, and the relief is as great here as anywhere in the Arctic Islands. In this rugged country, where the bedrock is largely covered with ice, great thicknesses of lower Paleozoic rocks of geosynclinal facies have been discovered. Typical of the rocks of the Franklin geosyncline is the M'Clintock Group, probably of Ordovician age, which consists of at least 10,000 feet of closely folded volcanic flows, greenish tuffs, graywackes, slate, and sandstone. Similar groups of indefinitely dated geosynclinal rocks can be traced along the coast of the Arctic Ocean to the northern tip of Axel Heiberg Island, but farther west the entire geosynclinal facies has been buried beneath younger sediments. The regional unconformity between the folded early Paleozoic geosynclinal rocks and the Pennsylvanian beds at the base of the Sverdrup basin succession, as well as isotopic age determinations on granitic intrusions within the geosynclinal terrane, places the major deformation of the Franklin geosyncline in Late Devonian or Early Mississippian time, connecting this orogeny with the Devonian clastic wedge of the Parry Islands.

Geosynclinal sediments do not attract the petroleum geologist. Sandstones of the graywacke type are relatively "tight" or nonporous because their clay matrix fills the potential pore spaces between the larger grains. The degree of metamorphism of most geosynclinal rocks indicates that temperatures are reached in deformation that would volatilize or destroy any oil that might accumulate. Although oil is not found in geosynclinal rocks, some sedimentary basins that are built on geosynclines, such as the Gulf Coast region and the Cenozoic basins of California, are major sources of oil and gas.

The Sverdrup Basin

The spoon-shaped mass of the late Paleozoic, Mesozoic, and Cenozoic sediments that covers the whole westward extension of the

Franklin geosynclinal rocks accumulated in the Sverdrup basin. In the deepest part of the "spoon," the basin filling may reach a thickness of 40,000 feet. The sediments of the western end of the basin dip into a shallow syncline, but those in the thick eastern end were deformed by Cenozoic orogeny into complex structures.

The Pennsylvanian and Permian strata at the base of the Sverdrup basin are sandstones and shales containing local, porous limestone masses that may have been reefs; the portions of the strata that are sealed by impermeable beds would make excellent reservoirs (Fig. 15–6). Mesozoic formations of marine and non-marine sandstones and shales include many porous beds that are potential reservoirs. That oil may be trapped in Triassic sandstones in the Sverdrup basin is suggested by the occurrence of oil-saturated sandstone of this age along the edge of

the basin on Melville Island. Cenozoic beds are non-marine sandstones and shales.

The rocks of the Sverdrup basin have been compared to those of the Gulf Coastal Plain, for both are thick accumulations of Mesozoic and Cenozoic sandstones and shales that were deposited on the edge of the continent and derived from sources within the continent. Like the sediments of the Gulf region, the Sverdrup basin sediments are intruded by columns of evaporites; but the intruding material is gypsum and anhydrite, not salt. Along the axis of the basin from Melville to Ellesmere Island, gypsum intrusions have risen through thousands of feet of strata from a source bed in the Pennsylvanian System. In the western part of the basin the domes are usually round; but in the folded and faulted eastern part the shape of the intrusions has been controlled by the structure, and some are oblong or linear at the

Fig. 15–6. Reef mass of limestone in thin-bedded Pennsylvanian limestones and shales, northern Ellesmere Island. Note how the beds bend upward over the limestone mass. (From R. L. Christie, courtesy of the Geological Survey of Canada.)

Fig. 15–7. Gypsum intrusive in the folded rocks of the Sverdrup basin on Axel Heiberg Island. The syncline at the left is in Mesozoic strata. (Courtesy of the Department of Energy, Mines and Resources, Canada.)

crests of anticlines or along fault traces (Fig. 15–7). Around the margins of the gypsum masses, bedding in sediments as young as Cenozoic has been dragged upward by the force of the rising intrusion. Although nothing is yet known about the geometry of these gypsum domes below the surface, because no drilling has taken place around them, geologists assume that the structure of the penetrated beds is much like that around the salt domes of the Gulf Coast; that is, the porous beds are turned up and truncated against the gypsum to form traps. If this is so, then these structures will be targets for petroleum exploration. By surveys of the surface and aerial photographs, geologists have so far discovered about 100 of these strange intrusions, but many more may be hidden beneath the surface and discovered only by geophysical methods and drilling.

At the eastern end of the Sverdrup basin the structures in the Mesozoic and Cenozoic beds strike northeast, parallel to the Paleozoic folds of the Central Ellesmere fold belt (Fig. 15–1); but in the central part of the basin they strike northwest. These northwest-striking anticlines formed in Cenozoic time are in line with the similarly oriented folds of the Cornwallis belt formed in the Devonian Period. Evidence of Early Devonian folding at the northern tip of Axel Heiberg Island supports the hypothesis that the orientation of the folds in the middle part of the Sverdrup basin may be controlled by northwest-trending structures of mid-Paleozoic age that are now deeply buried.

Deformation near the Silurian–Devonian boundary was widespread in the Arctic and affected not only Cornwallis Island but the East Greenland geosyncline, Great Britain and Spitzbergen, Norway. In Europe, this period of deformation is called the Caledonian orogeny. The spatial relationship of the deformation in these areas to that in Cornwallis and Axel Heiberg islands is one of the problems of Arctic geology. Parts of the Arctic Islands were deformed in Devonian, Mississippian, late Pennsylvanian, and Cenozoic times. The problem of linking these belts of orogeny with those in northern Europe and the Soviet Union which strike out into the Arctic Ocean basin continues to concern geologists, particularly those with an interest in continental drift. The placement of Europe and North America close together in the Paleozoic, as suggested in Chapter 6, almost closes the Arctic Ocean and would locate the Arctic Islands close to the Soviet Union. The orogenic belts which now pass into the Arctic Ocean basin must then have been continuous from one continent to the other.

CONCLUSION

We have seen that the hopes of petroleum geologists for the Arctic Islands are based on sound reasoning and comparisons with other oil-rich regions of the world. Source beds, porous reservoir beds of various types, a great volume of sediments from which hydrocarbons could be concentrated, a diversity of structures that could trap the migrating oil, and signs, such as oil sands and bitumen, that oil exists or has existed within the basin sediments are all present. The geologist can weigh all these factors and suggest the best sites for exploratory wells, but the decision to drill is primarily an economic one. If the world's supply of petroleum had been inadequate for our needs, the petroleum potential of the Arctic would have been thoroughly investigated long ago; but oil can be found and transported cheaply from the Middle East and the Caribbean, while drilling in the Arctic is expensive and transportation of the crude oil from harbors that are ice-locked for 10 months of the year would be difficult.

As the world's supply of petroleum and other raw materials dwindles, man will be forced to turn to less accessible sources such as the Arctic, and the information that geologists are gathering about the geological evolution of the region will begin to yield dividends. Geological investigation and evaluation of the Arctic Islands are just beginning, but they promise to be as interesting and rewarding as the investigations of the Appalachian or Cordilleran regions.

SUMMARY

Petroleum has been found in sedimentary basins in which thick sections of fine-grained clastic sediments act as source beds, porous sandstones or limestones act as reservoirs, and gentle structures or facies changes form traps.

Cratonic basins which have thin sections of flat-lying carbonates rarely contain oil in quantity.

The Central Ellesmere and Parry Islands fold belts are favorable areas for oil exploration, but the facies distributions which control the occurrence of reservoir rocks are difficult to predict below the surface; even when such reservoirs are found, they may have lost or never contained petroleum.

The uplift of the Boothia arch in Early Devonian time formed northwest-trending folds on Cornwallis Island which perhaps extend as far north as the Arctic Ocean. These buried folds may have influenced the deformation of Mesozoic and Cenozoic sediments in the Sverdrup basin.

The sedimentary facies and degree of metamorphism of folded geosynclinal rocks make them unfavorable as targets for oil exploration.

Gypsum and anhydrite intrusions closely resembling salt domes penetrate about 40,-000 feet of Mesozoic and Cenozoic strata in the Sverdrup basin.

The rocks of the Arctic Islands record periods of orogeny in Devonian, Mississippian, Pennsylvanian, and Cenozoic times. The most intense deformation in the Franklin geosyncline took place in the late Devonian and Mississippian periods.

QUESTIONS

1. Compare the structures produced in the Appalachian geosyncline by the Llano and Adirondack extensions of the Shield with the structures produced in the Cornwallis fold belt and the Sverdrup basin by the Boothia extension of the Shield.

2. Construct a table comparing the Sverdrup basin with the Gulf Coastal Plain under as many headings as possible.

3. Briefly describe the geology of a hypothetical basin with optimum geological conditions for the occurrence of oil and gas.

4. What kind of stratigraphic evidence could be used by the stratigrapher to show that the Boothia arch has been uplifted six times?

REFERENCES AND SUGGESTED READINGS

CHRISTIE, R. L. "Geological Reconnaissance of Northeastern Ellesmere Island, District of Franklin," *Geological Survey of Canada Memoir 331,* 1964. A description of the geosynclinal facies in the Franklin geosyncline of northern Ellesmere Island.

DOUGLAS, R. J. W., *et al.* "Geology and Petroleum Potentialities of Northern Canada," *Geological Survey of Canada Paper 63–31,* 1963. A highly condensed summary with facies and isopach maps of the geology of the Arctic Islands and the whole area of sedimentary rocks in Canada above 60°N latitude.

FORTIER, Y. O., *et al.* "Geology of the North-Central Part of the Arctic Archipelago, Northwest Territories," *Geological Survey of Canada Memoir 320,* 1963. A comprehensive treatment of many of the Arctic Islands with geological maps of most of them.

RAASCH, G. O. (Ed.). "Geology of the Arctic," *Alberta Society of Petroleum Geologists,* 1961. 2 vols. A symposium volume of many papers covering all the countries that border the Arctic Ocean.

THORSTEINSSON, R., and TOZER, E. T. "Banks, Victoria and Stefansson Islands, District of Franklin, Northwest Territories," *Geological Survey of Canada Memoir 330,* 1962. A description of the sediments in the cratonic basins at the edge of the Canadian Shield.

TOZER, E. T., and THORSTEINSSON, R. "Western Queen Elizabeth Islands, Arctic Archipelago," *Geological Survey of Canada Memoir 332,* 1964. A description chiefly of Prince Patrick and Melville islands, with valuable discussion of the structure and stratigraphy of the Parry Islands fold belt.

16

The Canadian Shield

Only with the lithology, structure, and history of the Mesozoic and Paleozoic mountain-built areas of the continent in mind can the older, more complex rocks of the Canadian Shield be understood. The interpretation of Precambrian sedimentary rocks is made difficult by their lack of guide fossils, the incompleteness of the record they preserve, and the intense deformation and metamorphism that they have undergone. Without fossils, the geologist must rely either on lithologic methods of doubtful validity or on isotopic dates to correlate sediments from one basin of deposition to another. Compared with the younger record, less of the older sedimentary record is available for study because it has been exposed longer to destruction by erosion, and because the older the sediments are the more likely they are to be hidden by later sedimentary layers. Older rocks are also more likely to have been affected by metamorphism in the many periods of orogeny that have deformed the earth's crust. Although gneisses and schists are the most common Precambrian rocks, some of the Precambrian record is preserved in sedimentary rocks as "fresh" as the Paleozoic rocks of the North American platform. Most of the rocks of the Shield are similar in degree of metamorphism and in structure to those of the younger geosynclinal mountains, such as the Piedmont of the Appalachians or the western Cordillera, and their interpretation presents similar problems. As in the younger mountain systems, isotopic ages have provided a key which in the last twenty years has removed some of the major barriers to our understanding of the Canadian Shield.

Five-sixths of geological time and the second and third quarters of earth time are represented by the rocks of the Canadian Shield. Such a span included many eras as long as the Paleozoic, but the virtual absence of fossils prevents differentiation into eras on the basis of life. Recently, this vast time span has been divided into eras on the basis of major episodes of orogeny, as defined by isotopic age determinations. In the oldest of these rocks, geologists look for evidence of the condition of the crust and atmosphere when the planet was young. This information is relevant to theories of the origin of the earth and the solar system. Geologists can test the hypothesis that the original atmos-

350

phere of the earth was different from the present atmosphere by looking for unique features in the type of sediment deposited during early Precambrian time. One theory for the frequent association of chert and iron oxides in many Precambrian iron deposits, and for the rarity of this association in younger iron ores, postulates that the lack of oxygen in the early atmosphere produced geochemical conditions that were never again duplicated.

Through intensive exploration of the United States and Canada, geologists, prospectors, and geophysicists have brought to light the great mineral wealth of the Shield. Some of the world's richest deposits of iron ore, copper, nickel, gold, silver, and many other metals have been found in these Precambrian rocks. The search for these mineral riches has stimulated scientific investigation of the Shield and has yielded profits both in dollars and in new knowledge of the earth's early history.

The Continental Nucleus

Each of the continents of the world has a nucleus (or core) of Precambrian rocks that is either exposed as a shield area or covered thinly with sedimentary layers. The shield areas outside North America include the African, Arabian, Brazilian, Guianian, Patagonian, Indian, Fennoscandian, and Siberian shields.

The Canadian Shield is an irregular, elliptical area of Precambrian rocks of about 1.86 million square miles that spans Greenland and most of eastern and central Canada, and extends into the United States in New York, Minnesota, Wisconsin, and Michigan. The center of the ellipse is a depression occupied by the shallow waters of Hudson Bay and by Paleozoic and Late Precambrian rocks that geophysical surveys show may reach a thickness of 10,000 feet.

Precambrian rocks form the nucleus of North America. On all sides of this nucleus younger sediments were laid down and geosynclines and mountain systems were formed. By the end of the Precambrian it had become a stable area, an unyielding buttress against

which younger peripheral geosynclines were crumpled during orogenies. Post-Precambrian fault movements and volcanism occurred within the Shield, but these events affected only a small part of this vast, generally stable area.

Topography

A large part of the Canadian Shield is a low, flat, glaciated peneplain dotted with innumerable lakes that were formed either in depressions scoured out of rock or in areas dammed by glacial drift (Fig. 16–1). Along its eastern and southeastern margins, the Shield has been elevated and dissected into mountains over 3000 feet high, but relief of more than 300 feet is uncommon in the rest of the Shield. The topography generally reflects the structure and lithology of the bedrock. Valleys follow belts of rock less resistant to erosion, and high ground is underlain by resistant rocks. The perfection of this adjustment of drainage to bedrock resistance could have been attained only through a long period of erosion. The similarity of the topography of the unconformity surface beneath the Paleozoic strata on the edges of the Shield to that of the Shield itself suggests that the present topography is essentially the same as that buried by early Paleozoic transgressing seas.

GEOLOGY OF A TYPICAL AREA

The study of a typical area provides an introduction to the nature of the rocks of the Shield. The region from Timmins, Ontario, to Val d'Or, Quebec, geologically well known because it contains many gold mines, will serve as a model.

Gneiss, Graywacke, and Greenstone

The geological map in Fig. 16–2 shows a pod or trough of metamorphosed volcanic and sedimentary rocks surrounded by granite gneiss. Similar gneiss covers about 80 per cent of the Canadian Shield. Geologists first thought that this gneiss represented the original crust of the earth and crystallized as the molten planet cooled. Late in the nineteenth

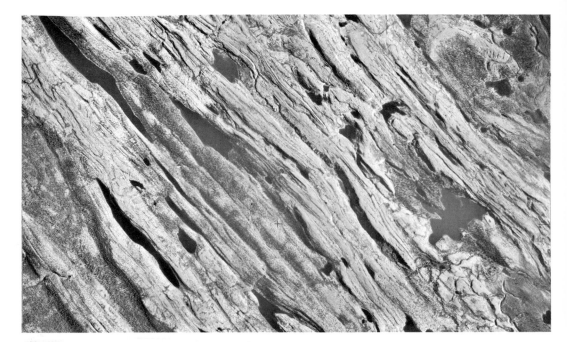

Fig. 16–1. Vertical aerial photograph of the folded rocks of the Labrador trough in the Canadian Shield near Shefferville, Quebec. Note the correspondence between the outlines of the lakes (dark areas) and the structure of the rock. (Courtesy of the Department of Mines and Technical Surveys, Canada.)

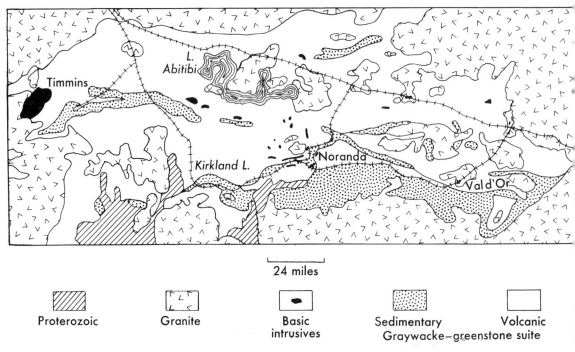

24 miles

Proterozoic   Granite   Basic intrusives   Sedimentary Graywacke–greenstone suite   Volcanic

Fig. 16–2. Simplified geological map of the Temiskaming greenstone belt in Ontario and Quebec, showing the position of the graywacke–greenstone "pods" surrounded by granite and overlain unconformably by Proterozoic rocks.

century, however, Andrew Lawson discovered that the granite gneiss had been intruded into the sedimentary rocks and lavas and was not the basement rock upon which they rested; therefore, it could not be the original crust of the earth. No geologist since Lawson's time has tried to identify the original crust or to set up criteria on which it might be recognized. Like the Mesozoic batholiths of the Cordillera, the sea of granite gneiss in which the volcanic and sedimentary rocks "float" was obviously not emplaced in a single episode, but represents the union of countless individual intrusions.

The sedimentary and volcanic rocks have been folded into a complex syncline and metamorphosed into schists of various kinds. The most common sedimentary rock is the highly indurated, poorly sorted, clay-rich sandstone known as graywacke. In this rock grains of quartz, feldspar, and mica, and fragments of metamorphosed and igneous rocks are embedded in a matrix of fine-grained chlorite. Many graywackes show repeated graded bedding, a sedimentary structure in which the size of the particles in each bed grades from coarse at the base to fine at the top (see Fig. 5–3). These beds, like those in the Paleozoic successions in other parts of the continent, are believed to be the deposits of turbidity currents that flowed down the flanks of the geosyncline and out on its floor.

In the conglomerates, which also occur frequently in the sedimentary pod, the pebbles include a great variety of volcanic, sedimentary, and intrusive rocks. Particular tectonic importance has been attached to conglomerates that contain granite pebbles, for geologists have suggested that they record a whole sequence of orogeny, intrusion by batholiths, exposure to deep erosion, and deposition of the granite fragments in an adjacent basin.

The most remarkable of Precambrian sedimentary rocks in the greenstone belts are **iron formations.** In their most common form, these rocks consist of alternating thin beds of red chert (jasper) and an iron oxide, either magnetite or hematite (Fig. 16–3). Pyrite, iron carbonate (siderite), and several iron

Fig. 16–3. Highly contorted banded iron formation, Beresford Lake, Manitoba. (From C. H. Stockwell, courtesy of the Geological Survey of Canada.)

silicates occur less commonly. Iron formations have been extensively studied because they are the sources of most of the iron ore mined in this continent, but no agreement has been reached on the chemical conditions that permitted their deposition. The suggestion that the disappearance of atmospheric conditions unique to Precambrian time may have precluded their deposition in later periods has already been mentioned.

The infolded lavas are called greenstones because they have been metamorphosed into secondary green minerals. The pillow structure (Fig. 16–4) of many of these lavas developed when they were extruded under sea water. Petrographic study shows that most of the greenstones were once andesites and basalts, but rhyolites are also common. Beds of tuff and agglomerate were laid down during the explosive phases of volcanism.

Fig. 16–4. Pillow structure in lavas, Northwest Territories. Shapes indicate that the tops of the flows face the upper left-hand corner. (Courtesy of the Geological Survey of Canada.)

Thickness and Structure

Measurement of the thickness of these sedimentary and volcanic successions is difficult because they are intensely deformed and metamorphosed. However, structural and geophysical estimates indicate that as much as 35,000 feet of strata are present in some belts.

The deformation of most of these infolded pods was so intense that the limbs of the folds were tilted vertically and sediments were converted to schists and, in some places, gneisses. Extensive zones of contact metamorphism were formed near intrusive igneous bodies. In determining the structure of the sedimentary beds, the geologist is aided by primary features which indicate the side of the bed that was originally on top. If such features as cross-bedding, graded bedding, scour marks, and ripple marks show that the tops of vertical beds in two outcrops face each other, then the geologist knows that the structure between them is a syncline; if the beds face away from each other, it is an anticline (Fig. 16–5).

In the Timmins–Val d'Or region two groups, separated over a considerable area by an angular unconformity, can be distinguished in the downfolded pod (Fig. 16–6). The older group, called the Abitibi, consists largely of volcanic rocks; the younger group, called the Temiskaming, consists largely of sedimentary rocks.

The granite-pebble conglomerate at the base of the upper group reaches a thickness of thousands of feet in places and seems to indicate that a major orogeny occurred near the basin of deposition. However, the absence of any intrusions of granite that can be definitely assigned by stratigraphic relationships or by isotopic dating to such an orogeny has suggested that the granite pebbles were derived from an uplift of an older granitic terrane not yet identified.

After the deposition of the Temiskaming Group, the belt of sediments and volcanics was intensely deformed, metamorphosed, and intruded in the Kenoran orogeny of 2.5 billion years ago. How much earlier the Temiskaming and Abitibi groups were deposited is difficult to determine, for the metamorphism

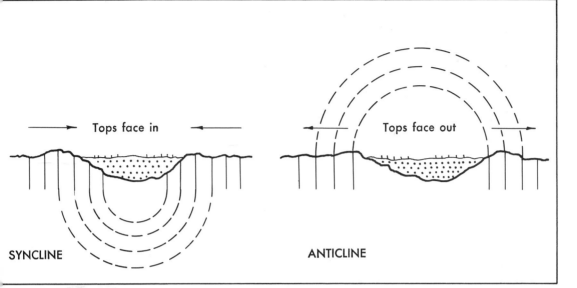

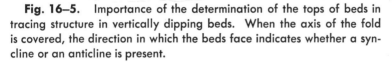

Fig. 16–5. Importance of the determination of the tops of beds in tracing structure in vertically dipping beds. When the axis of the fold is covered, the direction in which the beds face indicates whether a syncline or an anticline is present.

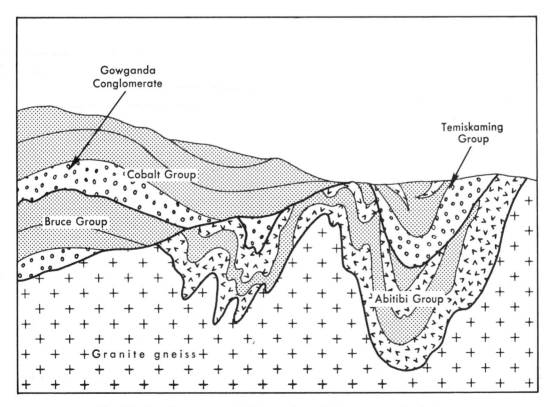

Fig. 16–6. Diagrammatic cross-section of the structural relationships of the stratigraphic units in the Temiskaming area.

accompanying the Kenoran orogeny destroyed the evidence of older events that might have been recorded in the isotopes of these igneous rocks.

Flat-lying and Gently Folded Rocks

In the southern part of the Timmins–Val d'Or area (Fig. 16–2), the greenstones and graywackes are unconformably overlain by less deformed sedimentary rocks of the Cobalt Group (Fig. 16–6). These rocks consist largely of quartzites, with some conglomerates, limestones, and dolomites. The basal formation of the Cobalt Group is the Gowganda Conglomerate. It consists of 3500 feet of unsorted and unbedded conglomerate overlain by finely bedded graywacke (Fig. 16–7). Some of the cobbles in this conglomerate have striated facets similar to those abraded in a modern glacier, and locally the

conglomerate rests on a smoothed surface of older rocks that resemble those cut and polished by the movements of modern glaciers. The evidence shows that the Gowganda Conglomerate is in part a Precambrian tillite, and its continuation for at least 200 miles in one direction suggests that a large area of the Shield may have been glaciated at this time. The banded graywackes which overlie this ancient tillite may represent varved clays that were deposited in glacial lakes (see p. 375). Above the Gowganda Conglomerate, the Cobalt Group consists largely of quartzite about 7000 feet thick.

Near Timmins, Ontario, the Cobalt Group unconformably overlies the Temiskaming graywackes; but along the north shore of Lake Huron the Bruce Group intervenes between the highly deformed basement rocks and the Cobalt Group. The quartzites, lime-

Fig. 16–7. Gowganda Conglomerate, Cobalt District, Ontario. The lack of sorting and the variety of boulders in this conglomerate suggest that it is an ancient glacial till. (Courtesy of the Ontario Department of Mines.)

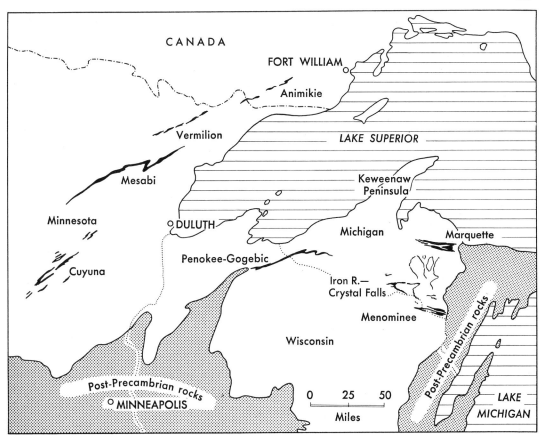

Fig. 16–8. Iron ranges in the Lake Superior area.

stones, dolomites, and conglomerates of the Bruce Group are similar in lithology to those of the Cobalt Group. The conglomerate at the base is notable for the diversity of its pebbles, its lateral persistency, and the presence of two uranium minerals, brannerite and pitchblende. The uranium minerals may have been either concentrated in the conglomerate as a placer deposit during Precambrian time or introduced by hot solutions later.

Flat-lying and Gently Folded Rocks of Other Areas

In addition to the rocks of the Bruce and Cobalt groups, northeast of Lake Huron, sedimentary rocks that are only slightly folded and metamorphosed underlie other large areas of the Shield. One of the largest of these is the area south and west of Lake

Superior in Minnesota, Wisconsin, Michigan, and adjacent Ontario. The iron formations of this region have been North America's main source of iron ore for more than half a century. Although the richest ores are nearing depletion, the mines continue to produce more than 133 million tons yearly—75 per cent of the ore produced in the United States. The most productive mines in this district are located in the Mesabi Range (Fig. 16–8), where the basement rocks are composed of granite gneiss within which small patches of metamorphosed sediments and volcanics closely resembling the Abitibi and Temiskaming groups of the Timmins–Val d'Or area are tightly downfolded. Gently dipping quartzites overlie the basement rocks unconformably and are succeeded by the iron formations. The cherty iron oxides, iron silicates, and iron carbonates of the iron

Fig. 16–9. Sherman open-pit mine in the Mesabi Range of northern Minnesota. The taconite ore is loaded on railroad cars for shipment to the concentrator. (Courtesy of the U. S. Steel Corporation.)

Fig. 16–10. Thin section of finger-like stromatolites from the Precambrian rocks of Marion Lake, Labrador (magnification × 4.5). (Courtesy of the Geological Survey of Canada.)

formations were weathered during Precambrian time under climatic conditions that favored the dissolution of silica by groundwater and the concentration of iron oxides. Until a few years ago only the iron formation that had been enriched by weathering was mined at Mesabi, but mining of the leaner, silica-rich iron formation (taconite) has now begun (Fig. 16–9). The ores are overlain by a thick sequence of slates, and the whole succession is intruded by gabbro but is only gently folded. Similar sedimentary rocks were deposited at the other iron ranges shown in Fig. 16–8. The iron-bearing rocks of the Lake Superior area and the Huronian rocks of the Lake Huron area were folded about 1.6 billion years ago along southwest–northeast axes during the Penokean orogeny. The limestones in these gently deformed successions usually contain concentric structures called stromatolites, which were probably formed by lime-trapping algae (Fig. 16–10).

The Keweenawan Group is the youngest Precambrian sedimentary unit in the Lake Superior region. The lavas, feldspathic sandstones, quartz sandstones, and shales of this group were laid down after the Penokean orogeny to a thickness of up to 50,000 feet, in a basin that occupied the present site of Lake Superior. The lavas were largely gas-charged basalts that flowed repeatedly from fissures in the earth, building up thousands of feet of vesicular and amygdaloidal flows. The red color, cross-bedding, and mud cracks in the sediments interbedded with the basalt flows indicate that the group was deposited in the environment of a subaerial delta. The remarkable deposits of metallic copper within the flows and conglomerates of the Keweenawan Group were worked by the Indians long before the white man arrived. Copper production from the mines of the Keweenawan Peninsula reached a peak of 115,000 tons in 1905, and has since declined to 15,000 tons per year. The youngest beds of the Keweenawan Group are so similar to the overlying Upper Cambrian sandstones that the boundary between them is difficult to determine, even though a disconformity representing all of Early and Middle Cambrian time, and perhaps some of late Precambrian time, separates them.

INTERPRETATION OF THE PRECAMBRIAN RECORD

Generally, the rocks of the Canadian Shield consist of a basement succession of infolded greenstones and graywackes that are partly engulfed by granite and overlain unconformably by gently deformed or flat-lying sandstones and limestones. This record can be interpreted by comparing the Precambrian rocks with their counterparts in the Mesozoic, Paleozoic, and Cenozoic successions of the rest of North America, and by applying the principle of uniformitarianism. Application of this principle to the oldest Precambrian sediments must be made with the reservation that conditions on the earth in early Precambrian time, when the crust was thin, the atmosphere strange, life absent or rudimentary, and sea water probably warm, were much different from conditions of today. How much different these conditions were, and when conditions comparable with those on the present surface of the earth began, we shall not know until we can date

the time of deposition of Precambrian sedimentary rocks rather than the time of metamorphism.

Greenstone and Graywacke Belts

Rocks similar to those in the greenstone and graywacke belts can be found in the axes of the younger mountain systems of this continent. The Precambrian volcanic and sedimentary rocks are closely matched by the Upper Jurassic Franciscan Group of California, by the lower Paleozoic rocks in the Acadian region, and by the Paleozoic rocks of the north coast of Ellesmere Island. The association of volcanics, chert, and graywacke with rapidly sinking geosynclinal troughs bordered by complex volcanic highlands has been discussed in previous chapters and does not need elaboration here. The pods of graywacke and greenstone are interpreted as synclinal remnants of geosynclines that were downwarped in orogeny and almost engulfed by the granite gneiss that surrounds them.

In deeply eroded geosynclinal mountain ranges, the granitic batholiths that intruded the geosyncline are exposed. Many geologists believe that these igneous rocks are derived from the sediments of the geosynclinal filling that were changed—by solutions, gases, and high temperatures deep in the crust—first to plastic, then to molten, and finally to intrusive igneous rocks. In the upper part of the crust, the distinction between igneous and sedimentary rocks is clear. However, we would have to dissect a mountain chain at various levels to see all the stages in the transition—from distinct intrusions and country rock, through sedimentary and igneous phases intimately intermixed (migmatites), to gneiss and granite. In young mountain systems, only the tops of the batholiths are exposed and most of the mountains consist of deformed sedimentary or metamorphic rocks; but the deeper a mountain chain has been eroded, the more the gneissic and granitic rocks are exposed, and most of the rocks are of this nature at the keel of the deformed geosyncline.

The ubiquity of granite and gneiss in the Canadian Shield indicates that deep erosion has exposed the roots of the orogenic belts that have been welded together to form the Shield. Erosion, largely in Precambrian time, has carried away the bulk of the geosynclinal sediments, leaving only the keels of the deepest synclines at the roots of the mountain chains.

Structural Trends and Provinces

The strike of the belts folded into the gneiss of the Timmins–Val d'Or area is east–west, and the general trend of the structures in adjacent areas is similarly oriented. However, west of Hudson Bay the pods of infolded sediments and volcanics strike northeast–southwest, and in the area of the Adirondacks the sedimentary rocks are folded into complex swirling patterns. The different trends of the basement rocks reflect both the different directions from which deforming forces acted on the rocks and the depth to which erosion has dissected the ancient geosynclinal mountains. These define the structural provinces, which are illustrated in Fig. 16–11. At present, the Bear, Slave, Churchill, Superior, Southern, Grenville, Nain, and Central provinces are recognized, but further work will doubtless lead to the recognition of greater structural complexity.

In each of these structural provinces, the metamorphic rocks are of approximately the same ages. We can conclude that each province represents a mountain system roughly equivalent in dimensions to the Appalachian or Cordilleran systems with a history that is probably as complex as either of these systems. Each province was affected by one major orogeny, but many parts of the

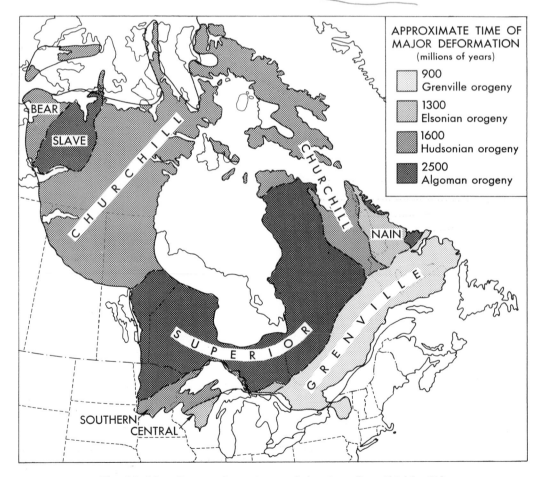

Fig. 16–11. Structural provinces of the Canadian Shield. (After C. H. Stockwell, courtesy of the Geological Survey of Canada.)

Shield were involved in several orogenies and have complex histories which can be deciphered only by detailed structural and isotopic studies. The Superior and Slave provinces, and part of the Nain Province, were metamorphosed in the Kenoran orogeny about 2.5 billion years ago. The Churchill, Southern, and Bear provinces were subjected to the Hudsonian orogeny (called the Penokean in the Superior area) about 1.6 billion years ago. The rocks of the Nain Province in Labrador record the Elsonian orogeny of 1.3 billion years ago, and those of the Grenville Province record the Grenville orogeny of about 900 million years ago.

Within any one province most isotopic ages lie close to those given above, but for several reasons a wide range of values is usually measured. For example, in the Churchill Province most of the isotopic ages range from 1.6 to 1.7 billion years, but a few values around 2.5 billion years have been found. The ages found in the Appalachian mountain system ranged from approximately 1 billion to 200 million years, because some metamorphic rocks are not remetamorphosed in later orogenies and retain in their isotopic compositions a record of previous orogeny. Just as Precambrian rocks in the Blue Ridge retained a record of their age through the late Paleozoic orogeny, so in the Churchill Province rocks that were first metamorphosed in the Kenoran orogeny retained their isotopic composition through the succeeding Hudsonian orogeny, when the surrounding rocks had their radioactive "clocks" reset. Because each of these Precambrian orogenies was as complex an event as the Cordilleran orogeny and included many pulses spread over at least 100 million years, a comparable range of ages is to be expected in any one province.

Division of Precambrian Time

Geologists have long sought a reliable method for dividing Precambrian time. Local divisions of time were made on the basis of major unconformities in the Precambrian record, but such divisions could not be applied over the whole Shield because the absence of fossils prevented the correlation of these unconformities from province to province. Only when isotopic dating became readily available could any given rock samples be placed in a time scale. Isotopic dating determines the time of metamorphism, whereas fossils on which the post-Precambrian scale is based determine the time of deposition.

The frequency distribution of age determination in the Canadian Shield reveals four major orogenies: the Kenoran, Hudsonian, Elsonian, and Grenville. These episodes have been used to divide Precambrian time into four eras. Geological time older than the Kenoran orogeny (2.5 billion years ago) is called the Archean Era. The rest of the Precambrian is called Proterozoic time and is divided into Early, Middle, and Late Proterozoic eras by the Hudsonian (1.6 billion years ago) and Grenville (900 million years ago) orogenies. The Elsonian orogeny (1.3 billion years ago) can be used to separate the Middle Proterozoic Era into early and late subdivisions. Although names have been proposed for these subdivisions, they have not as yet been widely accepted.

The presence of granite-pebble conglomerates in Archean rocks suggests a pre-Kenoran orogeny or orogenies whose effects have been masked by later periods of metamorphism.

Cratonic Rocks

If the greenstone and graywacke belts represent the remnants of Precambrian geosynclines, where are the rocks that were deposited in marginal and cratonic basins, and on the adjacent shelves, when the geosynclines were active? In lithology (clean sandstones and carbonates), lack of metamorphism, and structural attitude, the flat-lying and gently folded sediments, such as the Bruce and Cobalt groups or the iron-bearing successions of the Southern Province, are similar to Paleozoic rocks deposited in cratonic environments. In the Paleozoic Era, rocks of this type were deposited at the same time as the geosynclinal facies but in a different tectonic environment—one that had a lower rate of subsidence and was farther removed from supplies of clastic sediments. It would be logical, therefore, if in the Shield each cycle of geosynclinal deposition were accompanied by a succession of cratonic rocks. However, nearly all the rocks of cratonic facies in the Shield are Proterozoic in age, and the largest areas are Middle and Late Proterozoic.

One or both of the following may account for the absence or rarity of earlier Precambrian cratonic rocks in the Canadian Shield:

1. The sediments deposited on the shelves and in intracratonic and marginal basins have been completely eroded. Shelf sediments and sediments in intracratonic basins are deposited in a thin veneer on cratonic areas and are, therefore, particularly susceptible to removal by erosion when the continent is elevated. Sediments of marginal basins are not as thick as the geosynclinal prisms of sediments, nor are they intensely folded into the earth's crust during orogeny.
2. Conditions early in earth history may have been such that these sediments were not deposited. Limestones, quartzose sandstones, and clay shales are formed only when subsidence is moderate to slow, the source area is far away, and waves and currents sort the sediment. If both subsidence and sedimentation were rapid throughout early Precambrian time, the quartz sandstones and limestones associated with the shelf environment of the Paleozoic and later eras would never have been deposited.

In younger mountain systems the gradation of sediments of the geosynclinal facies into those of the cratonic facies can rarely be traced, for the geosynclinal rocks are separated from the adjacent basinal rocks by thrust faults. Fossils prove that the two facies were deposited at the same time. In the Shield the matching of the two facies is made difficult by the absence of fossils, and, for many Proterozoic groups isolated on the highly metamorphosed basement rocks, no correlative geosynclinal facies can be identified. However, in the Labrador trough of Quebec, the cratonic facies of Early Proterozoic age can be traced eastward into a geosynclinal facies that is intruded and more highly metamorphosed.

Keweenawan rocks are among the most interesting of Late Proterozoic strata, for they are comparable to the sediments and lavas laid down in the late stages of the geosynclinal cycles of both the Appalachian and Cordilleran regions. The flows of Keweenawan basalt are the counterparts of the Columbia Plateau lavas (see p. 266) and the Triassic lavas (see p. 312) of the Piedmont. In many areas of the Shield, the last event in the cycle was the intrusion of dikes of diabase. Most of these are only a few feet wide, but some are up to 800 feet in width and can be traced for 25 miles. Isotopic dating shows that these dikes are of many different ages and probably were intruded at the close of each orogeny.

Structural Provinces Beneath the Platform Sediments

To determine the boundaries of the Precambrian structural provinces beneath the covering younger rocks, the geologist can date the small fragments of basement rocks brought up in the deepest oil wells and can plot the structural trends in these basement rocks as revealed by geophysical surveys at the surface. Some of the buried boundary between the Churchill and Central provinces can be traced by anomalies in the gravitational field of the earth. The subsurface trace of the Grenville–Superior boundary has been traced southward through Michigan and Indiana on the basis of earthquake epicenters.

Figure 16–12 is a map of the present state of our knowledge of the provinces beneath the platform. The Grenville Province continues along the eastern and southern sides of the United States, parallel to the Appalachian mountain system. Much of the central part of the United States is underlain by the Central Province, which has a limited outcrop in the Shield itself and was deformed between 1.2 and 1.5 billion years ago in the Elsonian orogeny. The Superior Province,

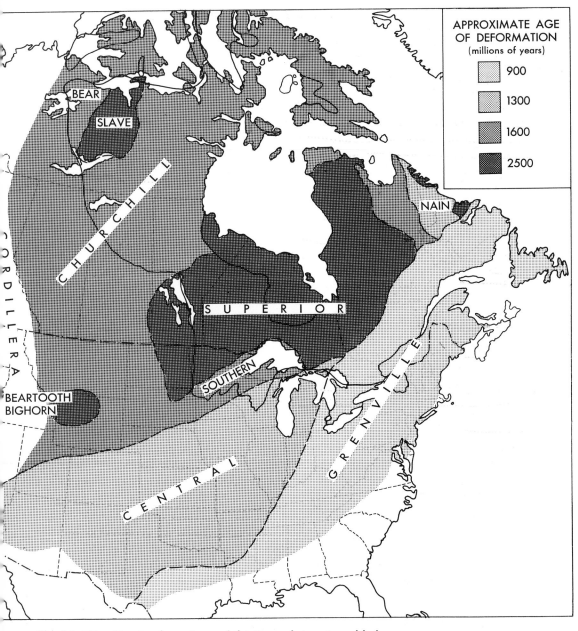

Fig. 16–12. Structural provinces of the Precambrian, traced below the overlying sedimentary strata in boreholes and in uplifts of the basement rocks through the younger cover.

with its Archean rocks, does not extend much farther than the southwestern boundary of the Shield, but a small area in northern Wyoming called the Beartooth–Bighorn Province is also composed of Archean rocks metamorphosed in the Kenoran orogeny. The western side of the platform is almost entirely underlain by the basement rocks of the Churchill Province.

Accretion of the Continent

James Dana postulated, as a corollary to the geosynclinal theory, that continents grow by the acquisition of geosynclines welded on the periphery during mountain building. If this theory is correct, the continents must have been considerably smaller in early Precambrian time than they are now. The original crust of the earth is believed to have been andesitic or basaltic in composition and not sharply differentiated into oceans and continental platforms. From scattered nuclei each continent began to grow by the accretion of successive geosynclinal belts. Because geosynclinal sediments are always more silicic than the rocks from which they are derived, the transformation of the roots of these geosynclines when they were thrust deep into the crust during mountain building resulted, after one or two cycles, in the formation of granite. The granitic continents stood higher than the surrounding ocean basins because granite is a lighter rock than basalt and "floats" higher on the denser layers that lie beneath and around it. According to this hypothesis, each continent should have a nucleus of great age away from which the successive, consolidated geosynclinal belts become younger.

Much of what has been learned recently about the distribution of isotopic ages does not support this hypothesis. For example:

1. The oldest Archean rocks are not located at the center of the continent but are distributed in at least four nuclei; one of these is at the continental periphery (East Nain) and another is next to a Cenozoic mountain system (Beartooth–Bighorn).

2. A concentric arrangement of increasingly younger mountain belts away from the nuclei is not regularly developed. Provinces of decreasing age lie southeast (Grenville, Appalachian) and south (Central, Grenville, Ouachita) of the Superior Province; but to the southwest, east, and northwest, the isolated Archean nuclei of the Beartooth–Bighorn, Slave, and East Nain provinces destroy the concentric pattern.

3. The mountain systems represented by several structural provinces were established, at least partially, on the sites of older mountain belts and do not, therefore, represent new additions to the continental crust. Most of the northern part of the Grenville Province seems to have been deformed previously in the Kenoran orogeny, and part of the Appalachian Province seems to have been involved in the Grenville orogeny.

Have these objections destroyed the theory of continental accretion? They have certainly shown that the theory cannot be accepted in its simplest form. Although the extensive overlapping of mountain systems has been proved by isotopic methods, the possibility that successive orogenies added new continental crust to the craton along the outside of each province is almost impossible to disprove. For example, although the northern part of the Grenville Province consists basically of remetamorphosed Archean rocks, the southern part, which now underlies the Appalachian Mountains, may have extended the size of the continent in late Precambrian time. Despite its deficiencies, the theory of continental accretion seems to contain a kernel of truth, for the Precambrian mountain systems are generally in the center of the continent; the Paleozoic, Mesozoic, and Cenozoic mountains circle the Precambrian systems; and new geosynclines are believed to exist beneath the continental margins.

Metallogenetic Provinces

The distribution of mineral deposits in the Canadian Shield is not random. Each province is characterized by the presence of certain suites of elements or minerals. Knowledge of these distributions allows the exploration geologist to focus his attention on an area in which the chances of finding the minerals he seeks are good.

The mineral typical of the Bear Province is pitchblende. The uranium deposits at Great Bear Lake have been known for many years, but thousands of small deposits of similar mineralogy also dot this province. Although several base metals have been found, gold is the mineral typical of the Slave Province to the south, where uranium is almost unknown. The Superior region is Canada's richest structural province, and contains many mines from which a wide variety of precious and base metals has been extracted. The Grenville Province is noted for its deposits of magnetite, particularly a variety rich in titanium. Since the provinces

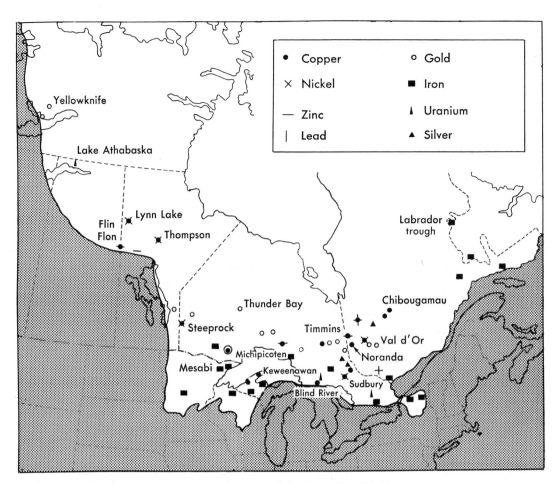

Fig. 16–13. Map of the major ore deposits of the Canadian Shield.

differ in history and structure, it is not surprising that they are characterized by different suites of ore minerals (Fig. 16–13).

SUMMARY

The Canadian Shield consists of mountain systems that have been welded together to form a continental nucleus which acted as a stable block during post-Precambrian time.

The adjustment of topography to bedrock resistance, and the similarity of the surface emerging from the covering platform sediments to that of the central part of the Shield, indicates that most of the deep erosion occurred in Precambrian time.

Older rocks of the Shield consist of belts of greenstone and graywacke deformed into vertical-limbed folds and engulfed in a "sea" of granite and gneiss.

The flat-lying and gently folded sedimen-

tary rocks that overlie the greenstone and graywacke belts unconformably consist of quartzite, limestone, dolomite, and conglomerate. Major deposits of iron ore are found in these rocks in the Lake Superior area and the Labrador trough.

The greenstone and graywacke belts can be interpreted as the synclinal remnants of geosynclines that were downwarped in orogeny, extensively granitized, and deeply eroded.

The Canadian Shield and its extension under the platform can be divided into provinces on the basis of structural trends and isotopic ages. At present, nine such provinces are recognized.

Precambrian time can be divided into the Archean Era and the Early, Middle, and Late Proterozoic eras by three major orogenic periods: Kenoran (2.5 billion years ago), Hudsonian (1.6 billion years ago), and Grenville

(900 million years ago). The Elsonian orogeny (1.3 billion years ago) divides the Middle Proterozoic Era into early and late subdivisions.

The Proterozoic age of most cratonic rocks may be a result of either different conditions of deposition in early Precambrian time or erosion of the older cratonic deposits.

Although older mountain systems are near the center of the continent and younger ones encircle the continent on all sides, no single nucleus surrounded by progressively younger concentric orogenic belts exists in North America.

The Shield can be divided into metallogenetic provinces on the basis of the occurrence of suites of minerals and metals. Mines in the Shield are major suppliers of gold, nickel, copper, iron, uranium, and many other metals.

QUESTIONS

1. How would you identify the original crust of the earth?

2. Compare, in area, width, and length, the Precambrian structural provinces of the Shield with the Cordilleran and Appalachian mountain systems.

3. Draw a series of maps and cross-sections to show the development of an ideal continent according to the theory of continental accretion.

REFERENCES AND SUGGESTED READINGS

AMBROSE, J. W. "Exhumed Paleoplains of the Precambrian Shield of North America," *American Journal of Science*, 262: 817–57, 1964. The topography and drainage of the Shield are shown to have been formed in pre-Paleozoic time and to have changed little since.

ENGEL, A. E. J. "Geological Evolution of North America," *Science*, 140: 143–53, 1963. A discussion of the accretion hypothesis in North America in the light of isotopic ages from the Shield and platform areas.

LANG, A. H. "On the Relation of Metal Occurrences to Tectonic Divisions of the Canadian Shield," *Royal Society of Canada Special Publication*, 4: 16–21, 1962. A preliminary account of the metallogenetic provinces of the Shield.

STOCKWELL, C. H. "Fourth Report on Structural Provinces, Orogenies, and Time Classification of the Canadian Precambrian Shield," *Geological Survey of Canada Paper 64–17*, 1964 (part II). A summary of the structural provinces recognized in Canada and an attempt to divide Precambrian time on the basis of four major episodes of orogeny.

STOCKWELL, C. H. "Tectonic Map of the Canadian Shield," *Geological Survey of Canada Map 4*, 1965. This map shows the important structures, the structural provinces, and the various times of deformation in the Canadian Shield.

17

The Great Ice Age

INTRODUCTION

Much of northern Europe and North America is covered with gravels, sands, alluvium, and boulders set in a clay matrix. These surficial deposits are collectively known as drift, and were named by geologists of the early nineteenth century who believed that the sediment either was swept over the land in a great submergence or was dropped from icebergs melting in a sea which covered much of the continent. Some thought that the drift was the sediment laid down in the biblical flood. The true nature of the surficial deposits of northern Europe was explained by three Swiss geologists who applied to the problem their knowledge of the behavior and deposits of the glaciers of the Alps.

The evidence for the recent expansion of glaciers in the Alps down their valleys and onto the plain was recognized by geologists before the turn of the nineteenth century. J. Charpentier and I. Venetz-Sitten were the first to postulate that all of northern Europe had once been covered with an immense ice sheet, beneath which the "drift" had been deposited. Louis Agassiz, a young Swiss professor at Neuchâtel, went even further and

declared (in 1838) that the earth had recently passed through a great ice age in which the glaciers had extended in an unbroken sheet over Europe and Siberia. Skepticism was the immediate reaction of most geologists to such an imaginative concept, but before the end of the century the theory of the glacial origin of the drift and the "ice age" received widespread acceptance.

In 1846, Agassiz settled in North America, where he recognized the drift deposits, polished and striated bedrock, and erratic boulders as unmistakable signposts of continental glaciation. In their discovery of the Ice Age, Agassiz and his co-workers applied the principle of uniformitarianism, championed a generation before by James Hutton, which states that a study of modern processes (in this case the glaciers of the Alps) is the key to an understanding of ancient deposits.

GROWTH OF THE GLACIERS

Determining Cenozoic Temperatures

The glaciation of the Northern Hemisphere was the outstanding event of the Pleistocene Epoch. The cause of the Ice Age is not clear, but most authorities agree that a mean an-

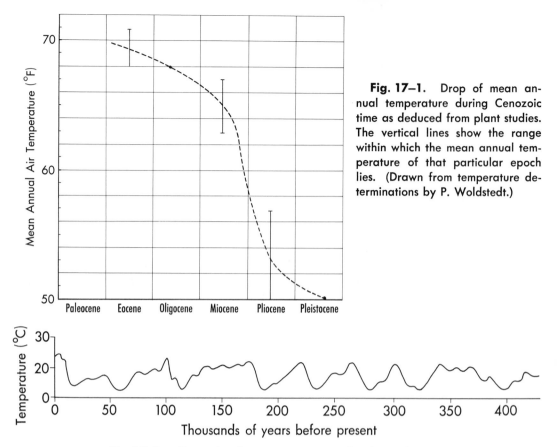

Fig. 17–1. Drop of mean annual temperature during Cenozoic time as deduced from plant studies. The vertical lines show the range within which the mean annual temperature of that particular epoch lies. (Drawn from temperature determinations by P. Woldstedt.)

Fig. 17–2. Generalized temperature curve for the surface waters of the central Caribbean constructed from the oxygen-isotope ratios of Foraminifera in deep-sea cores. The time scale beyond 200,000 years is extrapolated and may need revision. (After C. Emiliani, courtesy of the University of Chicago Press.)

nual temperature about 8 degrees Centigrade (14 degrees Fahrenheit) lower than at present would initiate continental glaciation. The history of Late Cenozoic climate is recorded in the fossils of the animals and plants that adapted themselves to it and in the isotopic composition of the sediments deposited in the sea at that time.

Late Cenozoic plants are so similar to modern plants that accurate estimates can be made of the ecological conditions under which a given fossil flora grew. Studies such as the one summarized in Fig. 17–1 show that the mean temperature in the Northern Hemisphere decreased from Eocene to Pleistocene time. The gradual chilling of the air resulted in the southward migration of floras and faunas in later Cenozoic time. On the West Coast of the United States, an Eocene

and Oligocene subtropical flora gave way first to a Miocene temperate flora of redwoods and then to a boreal Pleistocene flora. These changes record the steady southward movement of the climatic zones and the cooling of the air temperatures.

Two methods have been used to detect recent temperature changes in the ocean. Both methods use the minute shells of the foraminifer *Globigerina* recovered from drill cores of the sediment that is accumulating on the ocean floors. The deep parts of the oceans probably preserve a relatively complete sedimentary record of geological time, but by present sampling methods we can examine the stratigraphy of only the upper 30 feet of these sediments—a stratigraphic record representing the last half million years. The ecological requirements of the Foramini-

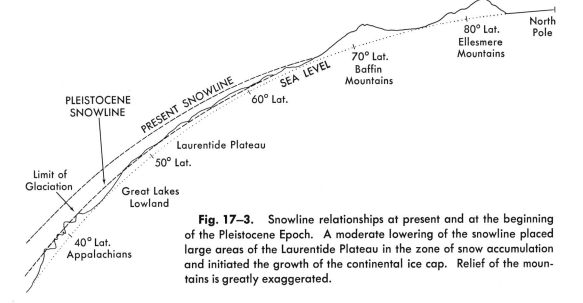

Fig. 17–3. Snowline relationships at present and at the beginning of the Pleistocene Epoch. A moderate lowering of the snowline placed large areas of the Laurentide Plateau in the zone of snow accumulation and initiated the growth of the continental ice cap. Relief of the mountains is greatly exaggerated.

fera found in successive layers of these cores can be determined by comparison with living species, and the oscillation of water temperature they record can be plotted for the last few hundred thousand years. The isotopic composition of the calcite secreted by these animals in building their shells depends on the temperature of the water in which they lived. The ratio between the O^{18} and O^{16} in the calcium carbonate decreases 0.02 per cent for each drop of 1 degree Centigrade in the temperature of the water. The paleontologist separates from the successive strata of the core a species of *Globigerina* whose depth range in modern oceans is known. Variations in the isotopic composition of the carbonate of the shells will reflect changes in the temperature of the water. A curve constructed by this method (Fig. 17–2) shows an almost rhythmic oscillation of the temperature of the sea water during the last half million years. It indicates also that the difference in sea-water temperature between the present non-glacial period and the last ice advance of 11,000 years ago is 5 to 6 degrees Centigrade, and that changes in temperature throughout the last half million years have been in this range. When longer cores are obtained from the ocean depths by improved drilling methods, we will be able to determine the temperature of the sea throughout the Pleistocene Epoch and perhaps for older epochs of the Cenozoic Era.

The Laurentide Ice Cap

Snowline is the altitude above which more snow accumulates in winter than melts in summer. At present, this line is near sea level at the poles and rises to 16,500 feet at the equator. The decrease in the mean annual temperature that took place near the end of the Cenozoic Era in the Northern Hemisphere lowered the snowline over a wide area. When the snowline reached an altitude of about 3000 feet in central Quebec, the broad Laurentide Plateau of this area began to receive more snow in winter than melted in the summer (Fig. 17–3). Permanent snowfields appeared and steadily grew in thickness. Under the weight of the accumulating snow, the base of the snowfield recrystallized to ice. The Laurentide ice cap was "born" when the ice reached a thickness of about 200 feet and flowed radially outward under its own weight. In the north and east the ice cap calved into the sea as icebergs, but in the south the ice advanced steadily toward the central lowlands of the continent.

Several factors favor a rapid increase in the size of an ice cap from its embryonic stage. The smooth, white, snow-and-ice surface of the glacier reflects more of the sun's heat than does the darker soil. The reflection of solar energy lowers the temperature of the air above the ice and favors a greater expansion of the glaciers and a further increase in reflection. By chilling the masses of humid air along its advancing front, the ice sheet induces snowfall and storms along its margins. As more snow is supplied, the ice cap expands, chilling more air and inducing more snowfall. Both atmospheric phenomena act together, creating a rapid increase in the rate of expansion of the ice cap.

Cordilleran Glacier Complex

As the snowline was lowered, valley glaciers formed and thickened in the northern Cordillera. South of Washington and Idaho no further stage of glaciation was reached during the Ice Age; but in Canada, where the climate was colder, the glaciers moved down valleys, incorporating tributaries and eventually flowing out of the mountains to calve into the Pacific Ocean in the west and to push out into the plains in the east. Moist air masses from the Pacific that were carried eastward over the icy mountains by westerly winds continued to feed the glaciers with snow, filling the valleys until only a few peaks projected above the gently convex dome of ice, like the nunataks that rim the Greenland ice cap today.

The failure of the Pleistocene glaciers to cover large areas of Alaska and a small part of the Yukon (Fig. 17–4) was apparently a result of the lack of precipitation in these areas. Conditions in which the temperature is low enough for glaciers to form but the amount of snow falling is not great enough to support their growth are found today in the Arctic Islands and seem to have existed in the northwest corner of the continent during much of Pleistocene time. Because the glaciers did not reach the western part of the Yukon, the rich gold placers of Klondike Creek, whose discovery led to the famous Gold Rush of 1898, were preserved from glacial erosion.

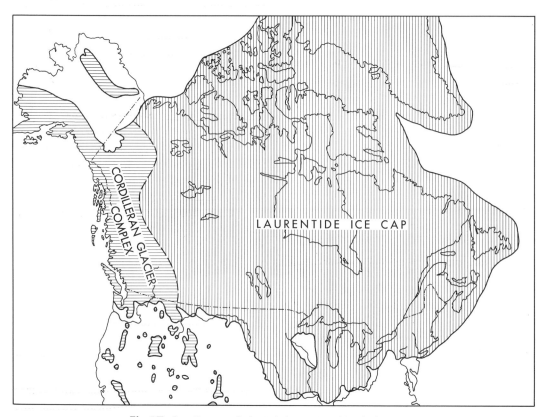

Fig.17–4. Extent of glacial deposits in North America.

The Advance of the Ice Sheet

The advance of the first ice sheet across the North American countryside was probably slow and halting. The rate of the first advance is difficult to determine because the record of earliest glacial times has been obliterated or covered by later events. However, radiocarbon determinations (see p. 57) on a group of pinewood samples from a sheet of glacial till in Illinois indicate that the late Pleistocene ice front of 20,000 years ago advanced at about 320 feet per year. Although the effects of the advancing ice and the changing climate on the plants and animals of North America were profound, they were slow. Occasionally, the ice advanced rapidly enough to overwhelm forests, and trees were smashed down and incorporated in the till beneath the glacier. The animals did not literally flee before the advancing ice, but followed the environment to which they were adapted as the climate moved slowly southward. An Arctic fauna moved into the northern United States and the temperate fauna moved toward the tropics.

Beneath the glaciers, the ice eroded and incorporated the soil and scoured the surface of the bedrock. When the ice moved over hills and mountains, it smoothed and rounded the peaks, leaving a subdued topography. Although the erosion of the bedrock of the Canadian Shield was not deep, the impression left by the passage of the ice can be seen in the streamlined form of hills and knobs of resistant rock.

CONDITIONS AT THE GLACIAL MAXIMUM

Thus far, we have been concerned with the expansion of the continental ice sheet until it covered one-third of North America. But the glacier did not expand indefinitely. The position of a glacial terminus is governed by rates of wastage (largely melting) and flow. When flow exceeds wastage, the ice front advances; when wastage exceeds flow, the ice front retreats. The front is stationary when wastage and flow are balanced; but, like a conveyor belt, the moving ice brings clay and boulders with it and deposits them at the terminus as moraines (Fig. 17–5).

When the terminus of the continental glacier in its advance southward reached a climate in which the average rate of wastage at the front exceeded the average rate at which more ice was accumulated by glacial flow, the glacier began to retreat. At every stage of the growth and shrinkage of the ice cap, minor local variations in climate resulted in limited retreats and advances of the different lobes. Although an over-all picture of glacial advance and retreat appears simple, in detail it was extremely complex.

Extent of Glaciation

At its greatest stage of expansion, the Laurentide ice cap calved into the Atlantic Ocean from the Baffin Sea to Long Island (Fig. 17–4). The ice pushed out along the broad continental shelf east of the Maritime Provinces and New England until it reached the edge of the ocean basin. Westward from Long Island, the ice margin extended through central Pennsylvania. The ice flowed as a broad lobe into the lowlands formed by the drainage basin of the Mississippi River and reached St. Louis, as far south as latitude 40°N. West of this lowland, the ice did not push as far south, for the land surface rises slowly toward the mountains. The front of the Laurentide ice cap followed an irregular course about 100 miles south of the 49th parallel, through western North Dakota and Montana.

The Cordilleran glaciers pressing eastward from the Rockies met the Laurentide ice cap along the foothills from the 49th parallel to Alaska. The margin of the Cordilleran ice in Washington and Idaho was deeply lobate, for the glaciers flowed south from the main ice cap into valleys and lowlands. South of the main ice front, valley glaciers in the major Cordilleran ranges, such as the Sierra Nevada and the Colorado Front Range, moved into lower altitudes but did not reach the plains.

At the same time, another ice cap covered Scandinavia, northern European Russia, and most of northern Germany. Northeastern

Fig. 17–5. Moraine on Victoria Island, Arctic Islands. The ice sheet advanced from right to left, spreading a thin sheet of till over the countryside on the right. The moraine marking a temporary position of the ice terminus is the low ridge of irregular topography dotted with kettle lakes which stretches away on the left side of the aerial photograph. (Courtesy of the Department of Mines and Technical Surveys, Canada.)

Asia was largely free of ice because, although the climate was cold enough, snowfall was not adequate to support continental ice caps. The expanded glaciers of the Alps came within a few miles of joining the Scandinavian ice sheet advancing from the north. England as far south as the Thames was also glaciated.

Nature of the Ice Margin

The terminal position of the ice margin in North America is marked by festoons of terminal moraines. These were deposited from the melting glacier at times when a balance between wastage and flow stabilized the front. The moraine system farthest from the glacial center is not necessarily the largest, for the ice may have occupied this advanced position only a short time.

The front of the continental ice sheet was not a towering cliff; like that of modern glaciers, it rose at an angle of 7 to 9 degrees at the margin and decreased in slope to 2 to 4 degrees within a mile. In the central part of the ice cap, the slope of the surface was probably a fraction of a degree. Although the thickness of the Laurentide ice cap at its center is difficult to determine, the heights of mountains overridden near its margins provide some evidence of the thickness of the peripheral ice. In the Appalachian sector the ice must have been more than 6000 feet thick to cover such mountains as the Catskills (4200 feet), the Adirondacks (5344 feet), and the White Mountains (6288 feet), all of which show evidence of the passage of the ice at their summits. At its southwestern margin in the plains, the ice cap was probably thinner, but estimates are difficult to make because the relief is less than a few hundred feet. The ice is estimated to have been 1500 to 2500 feet thick along the 49th parallel during the climax of glaciation. Comparisons with modern ice caps suggest that the maximum thickness of the ice at the center of the Laurentide ice cap was 10,000 feet.

Pluvial Lakes

The world-wide change in climate brought surges of cold polar air 1000 miles farther south than they now reach. The zone of westerly winds, in which the polar and low-latitude air masses interact to produce cyclonic storms, moved nearer the equator. The shift of climatic belts brought more rain to the mid-latitude deserts of the world, such as the Sahara and the Basin and Range Province. In these areas, existing lakes expanded during glaciation, and dry, closed basins were filled by new lakes (Fig. 17–6). Although the Pleistocene was an epoch of glaciation in high latitudes, it was a stormy time of increased rainfall in the low and middle latitudes. The Pleistocene is said to be a **pluvial epoch** (that is, characterized by rain) in these latitudes, and the lakes that were formed or enlarged are known as **pluvial lakes**.

The largest of the pluvial lakes in North America was Lake Bonneville, which occupied several of the coalescing basins around the present site of Great Salt Lake in Utah. Its maximum extent can be traced in shoreline features, especially the wave-cut terraces that were left high on the slopes of the basins when the water level dropped. At its highest level, the lake had an area of 20,000 square miles (similar to Lake Michigan) and a depth of 1100 feet. The lake level fluctuated with the rainfall, rising during pluvial intervals, when the glaciers expanded, and falling when they retreated. At times the lake had no outlet and became saline as the water evaporated. About 30,000 years ago, the water was high enough to overflow through Red

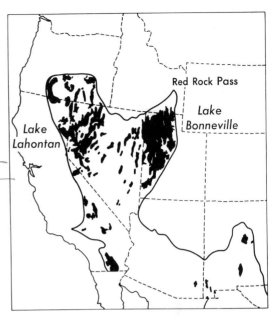

Fig. 17–6. Pluvial lakes of the southwestern states. (From W. D. Thornbury, *Principles of Geomorphology.* New York: John Wiley & Sons, Inc., 1954.)

Rock Pass in northern Utah into the Snake River Valley and to the Pacific. Huge boulders strewn along the abandoned spillway suggest that a great volume of rapidly moving water once passed through, and geologists deduce that initially the water flowed over an alluvial dam which rapidly gave way, causing a catastrophic flood which moved the boulders down the Snake River Valley. The bedrock sill that now floors the pass is of the same elevation as a prominent shoreline in the lake basin, showing that, once the alluvium was swept away and the resistant bedrock exposed in the spillway, the level of the lake was stabilized for some time while the shoreline features were formed. At the close of the Ice Age, Lake Bonneville shrank by evaporation to its present stage, now called the Great Salt Lake.

In northwestern Nevada, the expansion of lakes in several intermontane valleys formed Lake Lahontan at the peak of the pluvial epochs. The history of this lake's fluctuations is probably as complex as that of Lake Bonneville.

EARLY WISCONSIN	Sand
	Till and varved clay
SANGAMON ?	Scarborough Clay
	Don beds
? ILLINOIAN	Till
ORDOVICIAN	Shaly limestone

Fig. 17–7. Section of the glacial and interglacial sediments at Toronto, Ontario. (Courtesy of A. K. Watt, Ontario Department of Mines.)

STRATIGRAPHY OF THE DRIFT

The debris deposited directly from glacial ice is known as **till.** If meltwater has moved and sorted the debris before deposition, it is called **stratified drift.** Meltwater is almost always present in places where till is being deposited, so that the distinction between these two types of drift is not everywhere sharp. Tills form a highly varied group of sediments and have in common only their lack of sorting and stratification. They may be rich in boulders set in a clay matrix, or almost entirely clay with a few pebbles, or composed entirely of silt, sand, or boulders.

Soon after geologists recognized the drift of northern Europe and North America to be of glacial origin, they discovered that in many exposures two layers of till are separated by sediment deposited in a warm climate. Such exposures could only be interpreted as indicating that the glaciers advanced more than once and that non-glacial sediments were deposited between these advances.

The Toronto Interglacial Section

The nature of interglacial sediments is illustrated by exposures at Toronto, Ontario. The beds of this succession are shown in Fig. 17-7. Two main till horizons occur, one above the Ordovician bedrock and the other at the top of the section. Between these tills lies a series of clays, sands, gravels, and peat overlain by a thick series of banded clays with till zones at three horizons. The lower beds of the interglacial sequence (the Don beds) contain a remarkable assemblage of interglacial fossils of trees, fresh-water snails, clams, and mammals. The vertebrate fossils include the bones of woodchuck, deer, bison, bear, and an extinct giant beaver. Study of these fossils has led paleontologists to the conclusion that the plants and animals lived in a climate 3 degrees Centigrade warmer than the present climate of Toronto. The Scarborough beds, above this lower assemblage, contain 14 species of trees and 72 species of beetles, which indicate a climate slightly cooler than the present one.

These fossils provide the key to the problem of the extent of withdrawal of the ice sheet during interglacial times. Because the fossils of the Don beds indicate a climate warmer than the present one at Toronto, the climate all over the continent was probably warmer, and therefore less permanent ice was present in North America during the interglacial age represented by the Don beds than there is today. The interglacial succession at Toronto is proof that the ice cap melted and was reconstituted at least once in Pleistocene time, and other sections of similar stratigraphy record two additional interglacial episodes and two additional ice advances.

Interglacial Sediments

The interglacial sediments at Toronto were laid down in a lacustrine depression that protected them from the erosion of the next ice advance. They consist of lake clays and sands, peat, and layered or varved clays. Trees fell into the lake from the margins or were carried to it by streams and sank to the bottom when they became waterlogged. The shells of fresh-water clams and snails accumulated in the mud and sand, and insects that fell into or lived in the water were covered by layers of mud and preserved.

Peat is a common interglacial and postglacial sediment found over wide areas in the higher latitudes. It is formed in bogs, under cool climatic conditions, by the partial decomposition of vegetable matter, such as trees, leaves, and moss. Although the larger parts of plants are difficult to identify botanically in the tangled mass of decayed vegetation, pollen grains can be identified in peat deposits. A record of the peat strata in a bog can be obtained by forcing a tube through the dead vegetation and retrieving the core in the tube. The pollen grains are extracted from the core and identified under a high-power microscope. Because we know the conditions in which many of the species whose pollen is found in the peat grow today, the changes in climate during the accumulation of the bog can be estimated from the changing proportions of the various types of pollen along the length of the core (Figs. 17–8 and 17–9).

The laminated clays found in interglacial deposits consist of alternating dark and light layers. The light layers are coarse-grained and silty; the dark layers are fine-grained and carbonaceous, and contain more clay. Each pair is the deposit of a single year and is called a **varve.** The varved clays were laid down in lakes near the ice front. In the thaw of the spring and in the early summer, the streams brought much silt and clay to the lakes. The coarse silt settled quickly to form a light layer, while the fine clay and suspended organic matter settled more slowly, largely in the autumn or in the winter, when the lake surface was frozen, to form a dark layer (Fig. 17–10). The intercalation of thin till layers with the varved clays at the top of the Toronto succession indicates that the ice advanced several times over the glacial lake in which the clay was being deposited.

Since each varve represents a yearly deposit, the rate of sedimentation in these glacial lakes can be determined by counting the layers. In Sweden, the time since the ice withdrew from certain moraines has been estimated by counting the number of varves in the lake deposits formed during the withdrawal of the ice. In North America this method has not been as successful, for the sedimentary record preserved by glacial lakes is less complete.

Between till sheets in the Mississippi Valley a silty, unconsolidated sediment called loess is frequently found, characterized by its silt-sized particles, lack of stratification, and blocky, vertical fracture that allows it to stand in almost vertical banks. Loess is thought to be deposited primarily by the wind from the fine sediment blown out of desert areas and outwash plains. The Pleistocene loess of North America was derived from silt spread out by meltwater streams at the margin of the ice and dried by the sun.

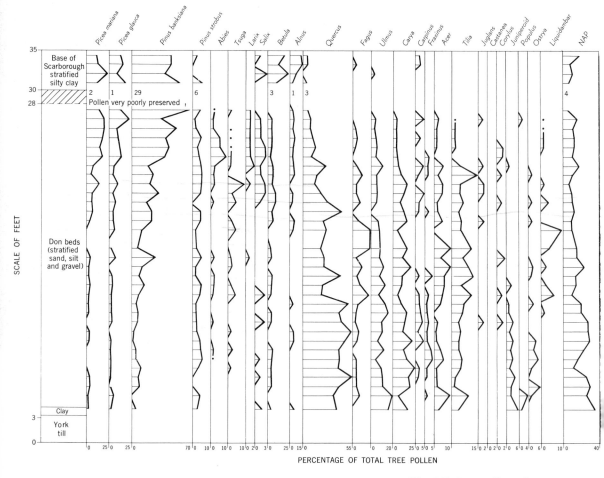

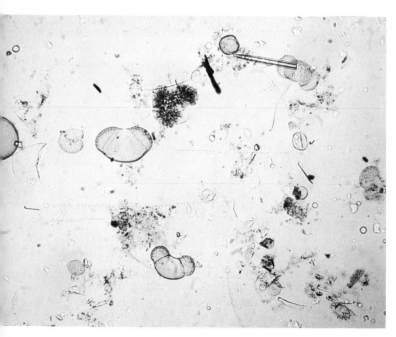

Fig. 17–8. Pollen diagram of the Don Valley Brickyard section at Toronto. The changing proportion of the various kinds of tree pollen through the Don beds and into the Scarborough beds is shown by the graphs. *NAP* is the non-arboreal (not tree) pollen. (From J. Terasmae, courtesy of the Geological Survey of Canada.)

Fig. 17–9. Photomicrograph of pollen grains from Pleistocene lake sediments (magnification × 200). (From J. Terasmae, courtesy of the Geological Survey of Canada.)

Fig. 17–10. Varved clays of the Pleistocene section at Toronto. (Courtesy of P. F. Karrow, Ontario Department of Mines.)

Loess from the last glaciation now covers most of the central United States, from the Rocky Mountains to Pennsylvania. Loess is not indicative of a specific climate, because only moderately strong winds and a continually renewed supply of dry silt are necessary for its formation, but the land snails and other fossils contained in loess may provide data on past climates.

Weathered Zones and Soils

Conditions during the interglacial ages are revealed by the soils developed by weathering after the ice withdrew. Ancient soils (**paleosols**) of the Pleistocene Epoch were developed through the weathering of till, interglacial loess, or clay. The weathering of this drift proceeds in a regular manner. First, the colorless iron compounds are oxidized to red and brown ferric compounds. Because oxidation is the most rapid weathering process, it penetrates deepest into the drift; therefore, the oxidized zone is the thickest in the soil profile (Fig. 17–11). The

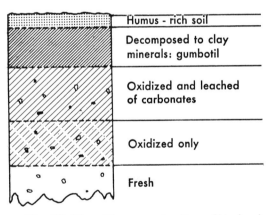

Fig. 17–11. Diagram of soil profile developed in till.

Humus - rich soil

Decomposed to clay minerals: gumbotil

Oxidized and leached of carbonates

Oxidized only

Fresh

next process, the dissolution or leaching by groundwater of the finely divided carbonate grains and the limestone pebbles in the drift, is shown. Hence, leached and oxidized drift forms an intermediate zone in the soil profile. In the last phase of weathering, the resistant silicate minerals are decomposed chemically to stable clay minerals. Appropriately, this zone is sometimes called gumbotil. Recently, the residual nature of all gumbotils has been questioned, and some Pleistocene geologists believe that this sticky clay was formed in depressions on the till plains not by decomposition but by the inwashing of clayey particles derived from soil-forming processes in poorly drained areas and by the addition of loess.

In the standard soil profile shown in Fig. 17–11, the upper, humus-rich layer is the "A" horizon; the decomposed zone is the "B" horizon; and the oxidized and leached zones are the "C" horizons. This soil profile may be completely or only partially developed and the soil zones may be thick or thin, depending on the length of time the drift was exposed to weathering agents, the climate under which the weathering took place, and the composition and texture of the drift from which the soil was developed. The extent of the weathering in interglacial soils has been used to estimate the lengths of the interglacial ages. This method, however, is based on the oversimplified assumption that the depth of weathering is dependent only on the length of time the till was exposed.

Glacial and Interglacial Ages

In only a few localities can more than two till sheets be identified, but a composite section, such as that of Fig. 17–12, can be built up by correlating separate outcrops. From such correlations geologists have discovered that at least four major advances of the ice occurred during Pleistocene time and that three interglacial periods intervened, during which the continent was largely free of ice. The advances took place during the Nebraskan, Kansan, Illinoian, and Wisconsin glacial ages and were separated by the Aftonian, Yarmouth, and Sangamon interglacial ages, respectively.

The Wisconsin drift, representing the last major ice advance, covers most of the glaciated parts of North America; but in the Mississippi Valley the Wisconsin advance fell short of earlier glaciations, leaving Kansan and Illinoian tills exposed. The Nebraskan, Kansan, and Illinoian tills can be studied in detail only in the Mississippi lowlands, for farther north the fourth advance of the ice (Wisconsin) incorporated the older drift into its own deposits. Because the Wisconsin

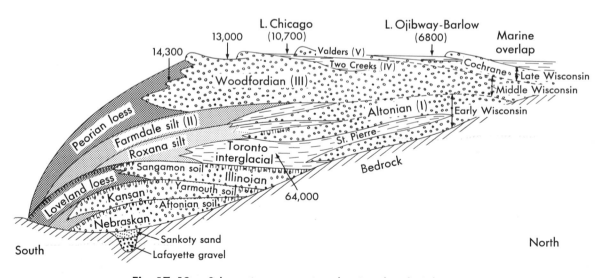

Fig. 17–12. Schematic cross-section showing the glacial sequence in the Great Lakes region of North America. Note the interbedding of glacial and interglacial deposits and the position of the loess formations. The section is about 1000 miles long and the thicknesses are immensely exaggerated. The figures represent numbers of years before the present, as determined by radiocarbon analysis. (Prepared by J. A. Elson.)

drift is extensively exposed and has not been disturbed by the advance of later ice sheets, regional study of its stratigraphy and morphology has been possible. In the upper Mississippi Valley, five main divisions of the Wisconsin stage are recognized (Fig. 17–12). The persistent Farmdale silt (II) separates a lower group of several Altonian tills (I) from the upper Woodfordian group (III). Woodfordian tills are separated from the Valders till (V) by an intensely studied interglacial deposit, the Two Creeks beds (IV). During the Wisconsin glaciation, retreats were local, covering perhaps a few hundred miles; they did not involve the disappearance of the ice from the continent, as the extensive interglacial deposits indicate.

PLEISTOCENE CHRONOLOGY

Before 1950, the timing of the glacial advances and retreats was estimated on the basis of varve counts or on rates of weathering or erosion. Many of these estimates have been proved unsound and are now only of historical interest. The discovery that radioactive isotopes of carbon, uranium, and potassium could be used for dating events in the recent past has revolutionized Pleistocene research.

Radiocarbon

In Chapter 3, the principles governing the use of carbon 14 for dating shells, peat, or wood—or almost anything that contains carbon and was once living—were described. Unfortunately, the relatively short half life of the isotope (5730 years) limits the usefulness of the method to dating of events within the last 40,000 years, although some laboratories have been able to date samples as old as 70,-000 years. Through this method, however, a detailed history of the last retreat of the glaciers has been compiled.

Deep-Sea Cores

Recent variations in temperature of the seas can be determined from the species of fossil microorganisms preserved in deep-sea cores and from the isotopic composition of the oxygen in their shells (Fig. 17–2). Before these oscillations of ocean temperature can be correlated with the fluctuations of the glaciers, however, the sediments in the cores must be dated. Several methods of using the elements of the uranium series have been tried.

The isotopes of uranium decay with a very long half life (see p. 53), but the isotopes which form a series of intermediate steps between uranium and lead decay much faster (see Fig. 3–2). A relatively short time after uranium is deposited in a rock and begins to decay, an equilibrium amount of each of the daughter isotopes is produced; that is, the amount of each isotope decaying is balanced by the amount being created. The decay series can be likened to a series of jars with outlets at the bottom whose size is proportional to the half life of the isotope represented by the jar. When the first jar is filled, some of the liquid passes into the second, the second into the third, and so on. When the liquid is flowing through all the jars, the amount of liquid in any one of them is constant, although there is a steady transfer of liquid from the first to the last jar. The jars with smallest outlets (isotopes with the longest half lives) contain the most fluid. Disturbances in the equilibrium result during sedimentation because uranium has a greater solubility than its daughter isotopes, protactinium and thorium. Detrital sediments deposited in the sea, therefore, will be rich in the insoluble daughter products and relatively poor in the parent uranium, which has remained in solution. As the isotopes decay, the equilibrium quantities characteristic of this disintegration series will eventually be established; but before this happens, in an interval depending on the half lives of the isotopes involved, the age of the sedimentary layer can be determined by how close the series has come to this equilibrium condition. Several variants of this method have been tried on deep-sea cores, with some successes and some failures. The method promises to provide a key to the dating of the climatic changes that occurred in the Ice Age, when more cores and longer cores have been analyzed.

Other Methods

In the relatively rare places where volcanic rocks are interbedded with tills, potassium–argon ages of the volcanic rocks can be related to climatic events in the Pleistocene. For instance, the Bishop Tuff in California, which overlies the second oldest till in the Sierra Nevada, has been dated as 700,000 years old.

Reversals of the earth's magnetic field can also be used to define time intervals in the Pleistocene Epoch (see p. 113). Measurements of the direction of magnetism of Pleistocene sediments and volcanics define a recent epoch of normal polarity that has lasted for a million years, preceded by an epoch of reversed polarity extending to 2.5 million years ago, an earlier epoch of normal polarity between 2.5 and 3.4 million years ago, and so on. These epochs can be used to correlate beds containing marine invertebrate and vertebrate faunas with deposits which contain neither.

Beginning of the Pleistocene

The Pleistocene Series was defined from the Tertiary succession of Sicily by Charles Lyell. Lyell's criterion for separating the Pleistocene beds from the Pliocene was the greater similarity of the fauna of the upper beds to modern fauna. When the drift of the Northern Hemisphere was recognized to be of glacial origin, European and American geologists began to think of the Pleistocene Epoch as equivalent to the Ice Age and to recognize its beginning on the basis of the arrival of the ice sheets, not correlation with the type section. Although in the type section of the Pleistocene in Italy the arrival of the Pleistocene fauna seems to have been a response to the chilling of the climate, the correlation between this marine section and the glacial sequences of the Alps, Scandinavia, and North America has been difficult to establish and is still open to revision. The time of the arrival of the ice in any area depended on its latitude and on the local climatic and topographic conditions. This criterion for establishing the time of the beginning of the epoch, therefore, is not satisfactory. At present, the boundary can be drawn only at some faunal or physical indication of a marked chilling of the temperature.

How long ago was this chilling? For many years geologists have estimated the length of Pleistocene time, by means of rates of erosion or weathering, to be one million years. With the improvement of isotopic methods of dating, these older methods have been abandoned; however, not enough new dates have been determined to establish a revised chronology for the entire epoch. Unfortunately, no method has yet been found of establishing the date of the Pliocene–Pleistocene boundary at its type locality, but indirect methods of correlation with other sections containing materials that can be dated suggest that the epoch began between 2 and 3 million years ago. When further dating methods have been developed and correlations have been refined, the Pleistocene as defined by Lyell may turn out to be considerably longer than the Ice Age in the Northern Hemisphere.

DEGLACIATION

Retreat of the Ice

At least four times during the Pleistocene Epoch the continental ice cap retreated, thinned, and eventually melted away. Very little is known of the first three episodes of deglaciation because the succeeding glacial advance redistributed the deposits laid down by the retreating ice. Much is known about the retreat of the Wisconsin glaciers, however, because the record of this retreat is written in the till and stratified drift spread across Canada and the United States.

About 18,000 years ago, the mean annual temperature in the northern latitudes began to rise. The melting of the ice cap quickened, the snowfall lessened, and the southward flow of the ice diminished. When the flow of ice to the terminus was exceeded by the rate of wastage, the ice front retreated northward. The retreat was a slow and halting process interrupted by many readvances. Rising of temperatures and shrinkage of the ice sheet were accompanied by the rise of the regional snowline. The events of glaciation were repeated in reverse.

Ice-Margin Lakes

Deglaciation in North America involved the melting of a mass of ice 6 million square miles in area and possibly 2 miles thick at the center. The amount of water released staggers the imagination (about 8 million cubic miles) and certainly would have resulted in world-wide catastrophe had the melting occurred rapidly. Instead, it extended through a period of more than 10,000 years. Although the melting lasted for a long time, the south-flowing rivers still carried prodigious quantities of water to the sea, because the ice blocked most of the northerly drainage systems until deglaciation was practically complete.

As the ice retreated from elevated areas, water was ponded between the ice and the drainage divide, forming giant ice-margin or **proglacial lakes**. Most proglacial lakes discharged southward, but some discharged along the margin of the ice front. As the glacier retreated from these ice-margin lakes, it uncovered successively lower outlets, and the lake levels dropped to the altitude of the new threshold. Some outlets were abandoned when the isostatic rebound of the crust caused by the ice recession (see later discussion, p. 386) raised the threshold and backed up the lakes until they overflowed through a formerly abandoned spillway. In other lakes, erosion of the outlet changed the level of the water. Each ice-margin lake had many such changes in level, and at each level shoreline features such as cliffs, beaches, and deltas were formed.

Some of these lakes were drained completely when the retreating ice uncovered an outlet lower than the floor of the lake basin; others still exist as remnants of the ice-margin bodies of water, even though the ice no longer forms their northern shore. We can recognize the past extent of these lakes by their abandoned beaches and the lake-bottom deposits of sand, silt, and clay.

Lake Agassiz was the largest of the proglacial lakes in North America. Meltwater began to collect when the Laurentide ice sheet uncovered the basin of the Red River. The deposits of Lake Agassiz extend from central Manitoba to central North Dakota and from the Lake Nipigon area to Saskatchewan. The "first" Lake Agassiz was formed at the close of the Woodford stage of the Wisconsin glaciation and drained southward through the Mississippi River system. As the ice retreated north of Lake Superior, it was drained completely eastward. The second lake was initiated by the Valders readvance, which blocked the eastern discharge channels. This lake originally overflowed through the Minnesota River to the Mississippi Valley, but as the Valders ice retreated the water was again discharged eastward through spillways into the Superior basin (Fig. 17–13). A third phase began when the ice advanced to the Nipigon moraine. Even lower outlets were then opened by the waning ice sheet and Lake Agassiz was drained almost completely, leaving only the present Lakes Winnipeg, Winnipegosis, and Manitoba as remnants.

The Great Lakes

Before the first ice sheet advanced over the central lowlands of the continent, the Great Lakes region was the drainage basin of a large river. The Laurentide glacier deepened this lowland by erosion, scoured the five lake basins, and depressed the segment of the crust under thousands of feet of ice.

As soon as the ice of Late Wisconsin time had melted north of the Mississippi watershed, water was ponded in the Lake Michigan and Lake Erie basins. The two resulting lakes, Lakes Chicago and Maumee, drained southward into the Mississippi River through the valleys of the Maumee and Wabash rivers, and through the valley of the Des Plaines River south of Chicago (Fig. 17–13). Early in this period of deglaciation, water was ponded in the Finger Lakes basins of central New York and drained southward along the valley of the Susquehanna. Another spillway used by the ancestor of Lake Erie led eastward along the margin of the ice immediately south of Syracuse to the Mohawk Valley, the Hudson River, and the sea.

When the water first accumulated in the Superior basin, it was separated from the rest of the lakes by ice and drained southward

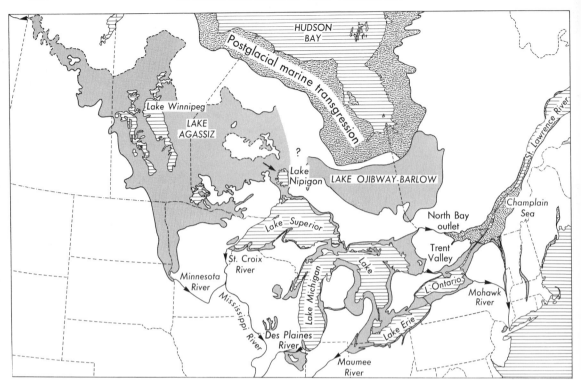

Fig. 17–13. Major glacial lakes of the Great Lakes area showing the major spillways through which the lakes drained. The shaded areas along the shores of the Great Lakes represent the areas flooded by the predecessors of the lakes. (Outline of Lake Agassiz after J. A. Elson.)

through the St. Croix Valley to the Mississippi River system. The ancestor of Lake Ontario, Lake Iroquois, drained into the Mohawk Valley at Rome, New York. At one time, the upper lakes drained from Georgian Bay across the Trent Valley outlet into Lake Ontario. The position of this channel shifted progressively northward as the ice margin retreated, until the channel lay in the neighborhood of North Bay and the Ottawa River (Fig. 17–14). The threshold of the North Bay channel was so close to sea level when it was uncovered that nearly all the water in the upper lakes drained through it to the sea. The threshold was gradually raised to its present altitude of 600 feet by the isostatic recoil of the crust, and the lake basins again were filled and discharged southward through the Mississippi Valley. As soon as the ice withdrew from the St. Lawrence Valley, an embayment of the ocean called the Champlain sea flowed in almost as far as

the fresh water of Lake Ontario. The present discharge of the Great Lakes down the St. Lawrence began only a few thousand years ago as the Champlain sea retreated.

Meltwater Channels

Many of the valleys which extend southward from the glaciated part of the continent are much too large to have been cut by the small streams that now occupy them. These streams are said to be **underfit,** because they do not fill the valleys they occupy. Other great channels that once led from moraines and from the abandoned shorelines of glacial lakes are now dry. From the gradients and cross-profiles of these valleys, geologists have deduced that the valleys were channels along which great volumes of meltwater charged with gravel, sand, and silt reached the sea. Near the ice margin, where the water was filled with debris, the streams built up the valley floors with thick deposits of sand and

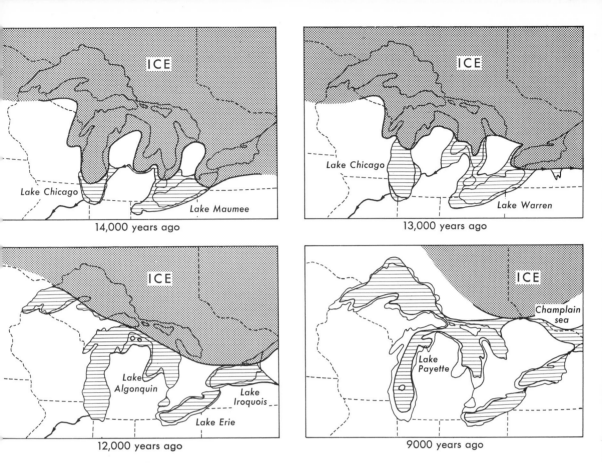

ICE

Lake Chicago

Lake Maumee

14,000 years ago

ICE

Lake Chicago

Lake Warren

13,000 years ago

ICE

Lake Algonquin

Lake Iroquois

Lake Erie

12,000 years ago

ICE

Champlain sea

Lake Payette

9000 years ago

Fig. 17–14. Four stages in the complex development of the Great Lakes during deglaciation. Note that when the outlet was higher, the lakes were larger than at present; when the outlet was lower, as in the last map, they were smaller than at present. (After J. L. Hough, courtesy of *American Scientist*.)

gravel. As the ice retreated and the sediment supply was trapped upstream in glacial lakes, the streams cut into the valley fillings and left terraces which in places may now be hundreds of feet above the valley floors.

Some of the most striking of these abandoned meltwater channels are found in the middle of the state of Washington, in an area known as the Channeled Scabland (Fig. 17–

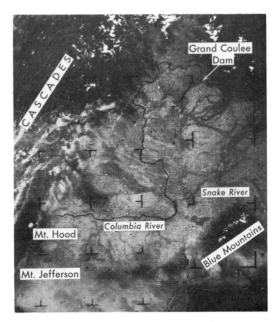

CASCADES

Grand Coulee Dam

Snake River

Mt. Hood

Columbia River

Blue Mountains

Mt. Jefferson

Fig. 17–15. Television photograph of northern Oregon and southern Washington taken from the weather satellite Nimbus I at a height of about 400 miles. The course of the Columbia River has been emphasized. The white patches are the snowcapped Cascades and Blue Mountains. The meltwater channels of the Channeled Scabland are on the right. (Courtesy of the National Aeronautics and Space Administration.)

15). A series of ice lobes extended southward along major north–south valleys at the edge of the Cordilleran glacier complex in northern Washington and Idaho, and dammed the drainage to the Pacific of such rivers as the Clark Fork, Spokane, and Columbia. Behind these lobes great volumes of meltwater were impounded in Glacial Lakes Columbia, Spokane, Coeur d'Alene, and Missoula (Fig. 17–16). Glacial Lake Missoula, in the valley of the Clark Fork River, was the largest of these and held 500 cubic miles of water. Some evidence suggests that the ice dam which held back Lake Missoula formed and collapsed several times before the last catastrophic event about 20,000 years ago. With the disintegration of the ice dam, water burst down the valleys of the Spokane and Columbia rivers, spreading coarse debris that marked its passage high on the valley walls. From the height of the flood deposits, the size of the pebbles in them, and a cross-section of the valley, the maximum flow of the flood has been estimated at 10 cubic miles an hour.

When the path of the flood was blocked across the Columbia Valley by the Okanagan ice lobe, the water spread southward across the Columbia Plateau and cut a complex of anastomosing, broad channels, called coulees, through the loess soil and into the resistant basalt. The discharge along the margin of the Okanagan lobe eroded the Grand Coulee, spilling over the famous Dry Falls in a cataract whose reconstruction staggers the imagination (Fig. 17–17). Through these channels the water found its way back into the valleys of the lower Columbia and Snake rivers, and eventually flowed out to sea. In spite of his attachment to the principle of uniformitarianism, the geologist should not overlook the occurrence of such catastrophic events in the history of the earth.

Sea Level Changes

When temperatures fell and the ice age began, precipitation in the northern latitudes was not returned to the sea by streams because it accumulated on the ground as snow

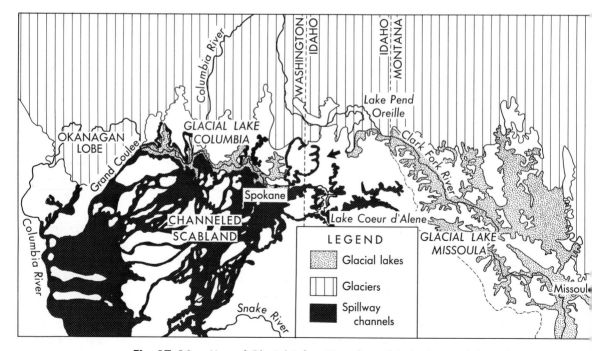

Fig. 17–16. Map of Glacial Lakes Missoula and Columbia and the Channeled Scabland of Washington. The arrow in the center represents the direction of the main discharge when the ice dam broke at Lake Pend Oreille. (Modified from G. M. Richmond and others.)

Fig. 17–17. Dry Falls in the Grand Coulee area, Washington. This aerial view is toward the north and shows the flat-lying lava flows of the Columbia Plateau, the lip of the Dry Falls, the plunge pool now occupied by Perch Lake, and the Grand Coulee, down which the diverted Columbia River flowed in the background. (Official U. S. Bureau of Reclamation Photograph.)

and ice. As more and more water that had evaporated from the oceans was trapped in ice and snow on the continents, the amount of water in the ocean basins decreased. Sea level continued to fall, until about 12 million cubic miles of ice had built up on the continents. When glacial ice reached its greatest extent and thickness, sea level had fallen about 350 feet below its present position, and much of the continental shelves was exposed. Shoreline features, cliffs, beaches, river valleys, and sand dunes were formed at this low-water stage but have since been inundated. The fall of sea level affected not only the northern latitudes but the coastlines of the world. Sediments deposited in deeper water before the fall of sea level were churned up when the zone of wave motion reached the top of the continental slope. Land bridges emerged from the receding waters, and animals from formerly isolated continents were able to cross and mix. For

North America, the most important of these land bridges crossed what is now the Bering Sea. Siberian and Alaskan mammals were interchanged by means of this corridor, and man probably reached the New World by this route.

As temperatures rose and the ice melted, water was returned to the sea, and its level rose. This fall and rise of the oceans must have taken place at least four times in the Pleistocene Epoch. Fossils show that the climate of some of the interglacial ages was warmer than the present climate, and we infer from this that less ice existed on earth then than now.

During warm interglacial ages, sea level was higher than at present and deltaic deposits were laid down by rivers along these higher shorelines. Along the Gulf of Mexico, these Pleistocene deltaic formations have been mapped and correlated with terraces cut in the river valleys farther inland. In southwestern Louisiana, where these deposits are best developed, four formations have been recognized in the Pleistocene sequence. Similar deltaic deposits and river terraces exist along the Atlantic Coastal Plain. South of New Jersey, two cliffs cut by the waves during interglacial times (when sea level was higher) can be traced parallel to the coast for 800 miles at altitudes of 20 and 100 feet above sea level. The lower cliff may be Sangamon in age, and the higher one belongs to an earlier interglacial age.

The altitudes of marine shoreline features suggest that the fluctuations of sea level caused by the waxing and waning of glaciation have been superimposed on a steady decrease in sea level since Pliocene time. This phenomenon has not been satisfactorily explained, but it could be due either to a deepening of the ocean basins or to the freezing of large quantities of water in the growing Antarctic ice cap. A. J. Eardley has summarized the evidence for a polar rise in sea level, and an equatorial fall in sea level of about 600 feet since the Cretaceous Period.

Today, sea level is rising at a rate of about .04 inch per year and glaciers are receding, but this is not the continuation of a trend started 10,000 years ago (Fig. 17–18). Climate and glaciers have fluctuated many times since then, and the earth has been both warmer and cooler than at present. If the present warming trend were to continue and all the ice in Greenland, the Arctic, and the Antarctic were to melt, sea level would rise almost 100 feet and the great seaport cities of the world would face serious flooding problems.

Isostatic Recoil

Geophysical measurements and comparisons with modern ice caps indicate that the ice was 10,000 feet thick beneath the center of the Laurentide ice cap during the glacial maxima. How far the weight of such a great thickness of ice depressed the crust can be easily calculated from the relative densities of ice and of the subcrustal material displaced, assuming that isostatic adjustment to the load was perfect. Since the ratio of the two densities was 1:3, the crust was probably depressed about 3000 feet below the ice. Geological evidence to confirm this estimate, however, is difficult to obtain. The plastic substratum below the crust must have flowed laterally to make way for the downbulging

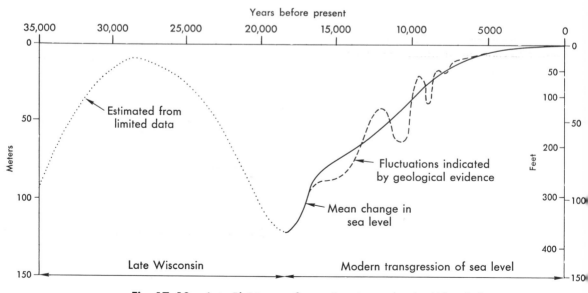

Fig. 17–18. Late Pleistocene fluctuations in sea level. (After J. R. Curray, from *Quaternary of the United States*, H. E. Wright and D. G. Frey, eds. Princeton, N. J.: Princeton University Press, 1965.)

Fig. 17–19. Raised beaches on the shores of the Arctic Ocean at Victoria Island. (Courtesy of J. G. Fyles, Geological Survey of Canada, Ottawa.)

crust. As the ice melted and the load was removed, this material flowed back slowly at depth and the crust recoiled upward to its former position, restoring the isostatic equilibrium before glaciation. Although the ice melted relatively quickly, the response of the earth was much slower and the recoil continues to the present day.

This postglacial recovery is recorded in the raising and warping of postglacial marine and lacustrine shoreline features. Marine beaches in the Arctic 900 feet above the sea level (Fig. 17–19) could not have been created by a fall of sea level, for evidence from the unglaciated parts of the world shows that sea level has risen during the last 20,000 years (Fig. 17–18). The beaches, therefore, must have been elevated by the isostatic recoil of the land as the ice load melted. They record the uplift only since the ice disappeared from the Arctic region and the sea came in. They do not indicate how much recoil accompanied the thinning of the ice cap. Radiocarbon dating of these beaches shows that the rate of uplift was rapid immediately after the load was removed but has been steadily decreasing since that time. Tide-gauge readings, which have recorded the

position of the land with respect to mean sea level over many years, can be used to prove the slow rise of the land north of the limit of glaciation.

Geologists have found that shoreline features formed in proglacial lakes, such as cliffs and beach ridges, slope downward away from the glaciated area but are horizontal farther from the old glacial margin (Fig. 17–20). In addition they have found that the beaches formed in the older lakes were tilted more than those of the younger lakes. The tilted shoreline features must have been horizontal when they were formed at the surface of a proglacial lake, and their tilting can be explained by the recoil of the land from its ice load.

The line along which this tilting begins is called the **hinge line,** and its position is related to the margin of the ice at the time the shoreline features are formed. As the ice recedes, the hinge lines of the beaches of successively younger lakes are formed nearer the glacial center (Fig. 17–20).

The Ice Age has supplied us with an illuminating experiment in the rate of response of the crust to large stresses and in the workings of isostasy.

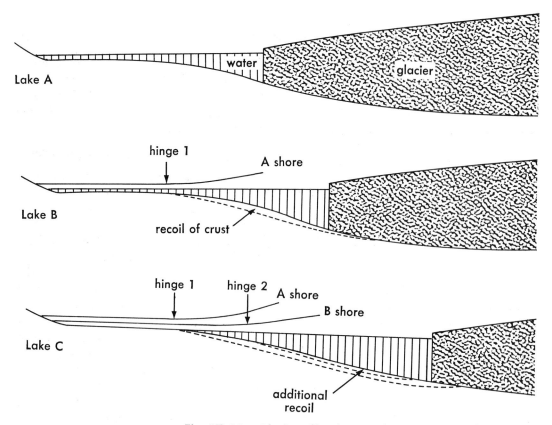

Fig. 17–20. Ideal profiles showing the upwarping of the crust during deglaciation. As lakes form at lower levels in successive stages, the beaches of former lakes are abandoned and bent upward by the rebound of the crust as its load is removed. (Courtesy of R. F. Flint.)

CAUSES OF GLACIATION

Since the recognition that much of the Northern Hemisphere was glaciated during the Pleistocene Epoch, geologists have proposed many theories to account for this extraordinary event in earth history. Only one similar event is well documented in the geological record—the glaciation of the Southern Hemisphere during the Permian Period (see p. 107). A few of these theories will be reviewed here. Most, but not all, of them attribute glaciation to a general decline in temperature.

A decrease in the amount of radiation received by the earth from the sun might have been caused by changes in the relative positions of the sun and the earth in space, by changes in the earth's atmosphere, or by changes in the sun itself. If carbon dioxide or water vapor, both of which insulate the earth, were partly removed from the atmosphere, the amount of heat radiated by the earth into space would increase and the temperature of the earth would fall. An increase in the dust content of the atmosphere, such as might be caused by an episode of volcanic eruptions, would block some of the radiation that the earth receives from the sun and would also cause a drop in the temperature. The position of the earth with respect to the sun varies periodically as a result of the interaction of three cyclical motions affecting the orientation and eccentricity of the earth's orbit and the angle of its axis of rotation. These three motions influence the distribution of solar radiation on the earth's surface and could conceivably produce enough cooling of the Northern Hemisphere to bring on glaciation. Neither the atmospheric nor the astronomic hypothesis alone completely explains the facts of Pleistocene glaciation.

Some geologists have postulated that an increase in radiation from the sun, rather than a decrease, could have been responsible for glaciation, because additional radiation would stimulate the circulation of the atmosphere and lead to increased precipitation in the form of snow in northern latitudes. An increase in precipitation in the northern latitudes is as important to a theory of the Ice Age as a lowering of the temperature.

Paleomagnetic evidence of the movement of the poles has suggested that glaciation began not long ago when the poles reached a position which placed the continental masses in a climate favorable for glaciation. When the poles were in the Pacific and South Atlantic oceans (Fig. 6–9) the world climate was equable and mild, but their migration to the Arctic Ocean and the Antarctic continent caused a division of world climates into various zones and brought on glaciation.

Maurice Ewing and William Donn have used polar movement to explain the onset of glaciation, and they account for the advances and retreats of the ice sheet by the repeated freezing and thawing of the Arctic Ocean. They believe that the present retreat of the glaciers is caused by the frozen condition of the Arctic Ocean, which prevents it from supplying Arctic Canada with the moisture necessary to nourish a continental ice cap. If the Arctic Ocean were free of ice, as they postulate it was at the start of the Ice Age, its water would mix with that of the North Atlantic Ocean over the threshold between Greenland and Scandinavia. The Atlantic would be cooled and the Arctic Ocean warmed. Evaporation from the Arctic Ocean would then so increase snowfall in northern Canada that the accumulation and advance of a continental ice sheet would begin. As water is withdrawn from the sea and accumulates as glacial ice, sea level would drop to a point at which the. interchange of Arctic and Atlantic water across the shallow sill would be impossible and the Arctic Ocean would freeze. The removal of the source of moisture by this freezing would start the retreat of the glaciers and the rising of sea level, to a point where the cycle could start again.

Many objections have been raised to this theory, and discussion of its merits continues. Perhaps the most damaging evidence is the lack of glacial features in areas that immediately adjoin the Arctic Ocean, for the effect of increased precipitation should have been most marked and the ice sheet should have been thickest in these areas.

Are We Living in the Pleistocene Epoch?

Although man would like to think that he is living in a postglacial epoch at a time quite separate from the Ice Age, there is little evidence to support this idea. We know that the continental ice sheets left the northern latitudes only a few thousand years ago. Thirty per cent of the land surface of the world was covered with ice at the glacial maxima, and 10 per cent is still covered. Several of the interglacial ages had warmer climates than at present, and several appear to have been of longer duration than the time elapsed since the Wisconsin glaciation. The mean annual temperature has not been steadily rising since the last glaciation; it reached a maximum 5000–6000 years ago and has been fluctuating since. If the present climate and geography are typical of interglacial times, we can only conclude that we still live in the Pleistocene Epoch.

SUMMARY

The steady decrease of Cenozoic temperatures is reflected in systematic changes in the fossil floras of a given latitude. Recent changes in the temperature of the sea can be detected in the oxygen isotopes and microfauna of deep-sea cores.

Growth of an ice cap, once started, is speeded by the chilling of the moist air above it, which induces storms and increases precipitation on glacial margins.

At its glacial maximum, the Laurentide ice cap advanced from central Quebec as far south as St. Louis, Missouri, and abutted on the west a complex of valley glaciers in the Cordilleran area thick enough to bury most of the mountains north of the 49th parallel.

Festoons of moraines were left along the successive ice margins because of the conveyor-belt action of retreating glaciers.

A comparison of the shape of modern ice caps with the dimensions of the Laurentide ice cap and evidence of glaciated mountains near its southeastern margin suggest that the ice cap was 10,000 feet thick in the center and about 6000 feet thick near the margin.

The increase in rainfall in the middle latitudes of the world during glacial advances caused pluvial lakes, whose presence is recorded in abandoned shoreline features and lacustrine sediments separated by evaporites, to form in desert regions.

In the upper Mississippi Valley, four groups of till sheets (Nebraskan, Kansan, Illinoian, and Wisconsin) represent four major advances of the glaciers. They are separated by interglacial sediments such as peat, clay, sand, varved clay, and loess, whose fossil fauna and pollen content indicate that climates as warm, or warmer, than the present one intervened between the glaciations. Interglacial weathering of tills to form a soil profile is also evidence of the retreat of the glaciers.

A detailed subdivision of the Wisconsin drift showing many minor advances and retreats is possible because the record of the retreat of the Wisconsin ice has not been destroyed by a later readvance.

The chronology of Pleistocene sediments can be established on the basis of radiocarbon measurements, uranium series disequilibrium relationships in deep-sea cores, and potassium–argon measurements in tuffs and intercalated lavas.

The interval of time defined by the Pleistocene Series at its type locality in Italy may not correspond to the interval of glaciation in the Northern Hemisphere as defined by glacial deposits.

During deglaciation, ice-margin lakes temporarily trapped meltwater and underwent complex changes in level as the ice withdrew and uncovered lower outlets and the land rose closing off other outlets. Occasionally, when ice or alluvial dams broke in catastrophic floods, the meltwater discharged down highly enlarged river valleys.

The storage of precipitation in the ice caps resulted in a drop in sea level of about 350 feet during glacial advances and a rise of over 350 feet during interglacial intervals. These changes are recorded in shoreline and submarine features all over the world.

The weight of the ice cap should have depressed the crust beneath it several thousand feet. The slow recovery of the crust can be studied in the raised marine beaches and tilted shorelines of glacial lakes.

Some of the theories that have been proposed to account for the glaciation of the Pleistocene Epoch are: decrease in atmospheric carbon dioxide or water vapor, increase in atmospheric dust, variations in the positions of the earth and sun, changes in the radiation emitted by the sun, shift of the poles, and freezing and thawing of the Arctic Ocean.

QUESTIONS

1. From the information provided in this chapter, summarize the evidence that temperature changes alone were responsible for the onset of glaciation in Pleistocene time. What are the alternatives to this theory of chilling?

2. Using an atlas and other sources of geographical information, compare the modern condition of Antarctica with respect to climate, thickness and size of the ice cap, topography, etc., with northern North America during a glacial maximum.

3. What program of research would you design to find evidence that more than four major

ice advances took place during the Ice Age? Where would you look for the deposits of such an advance?

4. Explain the methods that could be used to date and interpret the environment of deposition of a specific layer in a deep-sea core.

REFERENCES AND SUGGESTED READINGS

EMILIANI, C. "Paleotemperature Analysis of Caribbean Cores P6304–8 and P6304–9 and a Generalized Temperature Curve for the Past 425,000 Years," *Journal of Geology*, 74: 109–26, 1966. Oxygen-isotope analysis of long cores from the Caribbean is combined with similar analyses to give a general curve for temperature changes in the sea.

EWING, M., and DONN, W. L. "A Theory of Ice Ages," *Science*, 123: 1061–66, 127: 1159–62, 129: 463–65, 131: 99; 1956–60. The first of these references is to the initial paper presenting the theory that the freezing and thawing of the Arctic Ocean controlled the advance and retreat of Pleistocene ice. The other references are to elaborations and discussions of the theory.

FARRAND, W. R. "Postglacial Uplift in North America," *American Journal of Science*, 260: 181–99, 1962. Radiocarbon dating of uplifted beaches enables geologists to plot the rate of their uplift since deglaciation.

FLINT, R. F. *Glacial and Pleistocene Geology.* New York: John Wiley & Sons, Inc., 1957. A standard text on the glacial geology of the Pleistocene Epoch.

HOUGH, J. L. *Geology of the Great Lakes.* Urbana: University of Illinois Press, 1958. The origin of the Great Lakes basins and the complex evolution of their levels and drainages during deglaciation are discussed in detail. A later discussion of the succession of Great Lakes level changes can be found in "The Prehistoric Great Lakes of North America," *American Scientist*, 51: 84–109, 1963, by the same author.

TANNER, W. F. "Cause and Development of an Ice Age," *Journal of Geology*, 73: 413–30, 1965. The initiation of glaciation in North America was caused by polar wandering, and the retreats and advances of the ice were caused by a self-starving process.

VI

THE EVOLUTION OF LIFE

18

Precambrian and Cambrian Life

INTRODUCTION

The question might be asked, "Why, in a book devoted to the evolution of a continent, is so much space devoted to the evolution of life?" Several good answers can be given to such a question, one of which is that fossils *are* geological objects: they *do* occur in sedimentary rocks of all post-Proterozoic ages, and in places they make up 100 per cent of certain formations. Merely as geological objects they should receive due attention.

In many places in the first part of this book, fossils have been mentioned and illustrated—especially when their abundance or peculiar characteristics have a bearing on our understanding of the nature and origin of the rocks concerned. However, this is not the chief reason for including a treatment of the origin and development of life in this book.

If we are to write a history, that history must have a timetable to which the events can be referred. As explained in Chapter 2, species of animals and plants were not immortal: many lived through only a fraction

of a period. By applying the principle of contemporaneity of beds containing the same fossils, we can date rocks and correlate strata in time. To do this requires detailed studies in paleontology, and every historical geologist should be well acquainted with those index fossils without which the dating and correlating of post-Precambrian rocks would be as unsatisfactory as the dating and correlating of Precambrian formations.

In addition to their use in correlation, fossils give strong support to the doctrine of organic evolution. The evolution of life has resulted in an almost infinite number of species of animals and plants as time has proceeded; from these we have selected for discussion those which help solve problems in correlation. In the following pages, two concepts will be emphasized—the use to which fossils can be put in dating rocks, and the ways in which fossils aid in establishing the truth of organic evolution.

The paleontological record is far from complete or representative. Any fossil collection is likely to be heavily biased by several factors: an unusual local abundance or scarcity of some particular species; the disappearance of some shells by solution, either by groundwater or by weathering; a collector who selects particular kinds or sizes of shells; the nature of the outcrop; etc. Nevertheless, as further collections are made under other conditions by other collectors, many of these factors cease to be of importance. Still more important is the fact that neither any single fossil collection nor the total number of fossils so far collected truly represents the faunas and floras of the past, for the collections are biased in their lack of soft-bodied organisms. This latter bias will be referred to in many places in the text, and because of its importance in assessing Cambrian and Precambrian biotas, it deserves a preliminary note here.

Modern soft-bodied animals are largely confined to four taxa (Table 18–1). In

Table 18–1

Approximate Numbers of Living Soft-bodied Animal Species, with Period of First Appearance of the Phyla

"Worms"	25,000	Cambrian (Precambrian ?)
Protozoa	7000	Cambrian
Coelenterata	3300	Cambrian (Precambrian ?)
Chordata	2000	Ordovician (graptolites in Cambrian)
Bryozoa	550	Ordovician (Cambrian ?)
Porifera	500	Cambrian

Chapter 2 we established the extreme unlikelihood that a shelled animal will leave a fossil behind. There is, therefore, a much greater improbability that we will have a truly representative fossilized biota of soft-bodied forms. This is a disadvantage that the paleontologist must accept and work with. Minor adjustments in our total knowledge of soft-bodied animals will probably be made, but on the whole, paleontologists must depend upon fossilized shells and skeletons. Although a tremendous variety of organisms has been produced since the formation of the earth, the preservation of these forms has been sufficient to enable men to learn a great deal through the study of fossils.

The main outlines of the progress of life through time are well known (see end papers). Two chief criticisms have for some time been leveled at such charts and phylogenies. First, the lack of a visible, direct, lineal relationship makes the charts hypothetical. With this we cannot quarrel; but we can say that a certain group of fossils shows characteristics that undeniably indicate its descent from some other group. Second is the "missing link" criticism. Darwin in his *Origin of Species* (1859) recognized that the paleontological data available provided no compelling evidence of genetic relationship between two taxonomically related phyla or classes. If a fossil or living form could be found embodying some of the features of each of such taxa, it could be considered as a link between them, thus establishing a close genetic relationship. For the rest of the nineteenth century, after the publication of Darwin's theory, these hoped-for organisms were called "missing links," and the term became crystallized in the popular mind as the form intermediate between apes and man. Since the beginning of this century the term has lost much of its early significance, as link after link has been found in an intermediate position between high-ranking taxa.

With very few exceptions, classes and orders of the chordates are linked by fossil or living forms. Among invertebrates, *Neopilina* combines characteristics of both mollusks and annelids, and *Aysheaia* links the annelids and arthropods. However, such genetic links between many presumably closely related invertebrate phyla are not often found. Because all the main zoological phyla have Cambrian representatives, we infer that the differentiation of the phyla probably took place before that time, when shells and skeletons were not yet widely developed. If so, the chance of finding a fossil link between two phyla in the largely unfossiliferous Precambrian rocks is slim, and the possibility of finding a living representative of that link is still more remote.

A spectacular exception to our expectations is the living genus *Peripatus*, considered to be closely allied to the Middle Cambrian genus

Aysheaia from the Burgess Shale (discussed below). These two genera are assigned to the phylum ONYCHOPHORA, which combines the characteristics of annelids and arthropods and may well represent the group from which both annelids and arthropods diverged in Precambrian time. The discovery of *Neopilina* on the abyssal oceanic floor has called attention to the survival since early Paleozoic time of a group of gastropods known as the monoplacophorans; moreover, the internal anatomy of *Neopilina* points to a relationship between annelids and mollusks. But the more remote the separation in time between two taxa, the less the likelihood of our finding a link between them. This is another reason for the rarity of such forms among invertebrates and fish, and their frequent presence among the higher and later vertebrates.

TAXA KNOWN ONLY AS FOSSILS

The Burgess Shale

Scattered in the geological record are fossils of animals bearing no known close relationships either to other fossils or to living forms. The fauna of the Burgess Shale on Mount Wapta, British Columbia, contains examples. Here, in a thick section of shales (Stephen Formation) possessing a normal Middle Cambrian fauna, is a band of fine-grained shale 7 feet thick containing an astounding biota of algae and soft-bodied animals whose remains were pressed flat upon the bedding planes and are represented by the merest film of carbonaceous material. So faithful is the preservation that in many specimens the outlines of internal organs and delicate appendages not normally preserved are depicted. None of the fossils shows a trace of a hard shell; the only hard substances preserved are spicules of siliceous sponges. In a restricted area of the Middle Cambrian sea floor, the normal marine circulation must have been locally inhibited to such an extent that euxinic conditions prevailed: products of bacterial decay, such as hydrogen sulfide, were not dispersed by currents, and the oxygen content of the water was not renewed when depleted by bacterial action. No normal benthonic scavengers would enter such a lethal area; hence, carcasses of free-swimming plankton and nekton dying naturally or poisoned by emanations from the foul water below and falling upon the sea floor would remain intact. The exceedingly fine sediment that covered these accumulated remains preserved both their internal and their external anatomy. More than seventy genera of plants and animals have been identified in this biota, and of these not more than a half-dozen are known elsewhere. New families and even orders had to be designated to accommodate these genera.

Other Invertebrate Fossil Taxa

In addition to the groups of animals and plants represented in the Burgess Shale and the Ediacara Quartzite (see p. 406), there are many groups of invertebrates represented only by fossils. Among these there is only one phylum, the ARCHAEOCYATHA. Of lesser taxa there are many examples, such as the class STROMATOPOROIDEA and the subclasses TETRACORALLIA and TABULATA among the COELENTERATA; two of the five orders of BRYOZOA; the subclass AMMONOIDEA of the molluscan class CEPHALOPODA; the class TRILOBITA and the order EURYPTERIDA among the ARTHROPODA; and several classes of the ECHINODERMATA, including the CYSTOIDEA and the CARPOIDEA. The enrichment of the fossil fauna by the above taxa counterbalances the lack of fossils of most "worm" phyla, of the OCTOPODA among the CEPHALOPODA, and of a few lesser taxa.

PRECAMBRIAN LIFE

By means of fossils the evolution of the modern fauna and flora can be traced back in time toward their beginnings. The record of life is satisfactory enough back to the Cambrian Period, but prior to the beginning of the Paleozoic Era it is so scant as to be almost useless. Nevertheless the origins of all of the phyla, and hence of life itself, took place during Precambrian time, and we must look for the solutions of the major problems of the early evolution of life in rocks of that age.

Two of the most perplexing of those problems are the origin of life itself and the remarkable fact that, though the rocks of the Cambrian and later periods are richly endowed with fossils, Precambrian rocks are all but devoid of them. Even though these rocks have been the object of intense search by scores of geologists for more than a century, only a handful of unequivocal fossils has been discovered. One of the most assiduous of these geologists was Charles Doolittle Walcott (1850–1927), who did succeed in finding a very few primitive Precambrian fossils during a lifetime of paleontological research. Many objects hopefully claimed by their discoverers to be Precambrian fossils have been found to belong to younger rocks or are better explained as having been formed by inorganic processes.

Despite the frustrating paucity of fossils something is known and much can be inferred about Precambrian life. Information leading to a partial reconstruction of the life of the Precambrian Era comes from four sources: (1) deductions from chemical, physical, and biological evidence about conditions under which life originated on the primitive earth; (2) traces of organic matter in Precambrian rocks; (3) the type of life that should have been ancestral to the Cambrian fauna and flora; and (4) recognized Precambrian fossils.

The Origin of Life

The kindling of the spark of life in lifeless matter was among the most important events in the history of the earth. The gulf that stretches between even the most complex of man-made synthetic organic compounds and the simplest glob of living protoplasm is profound; and, despite decades of investigation, man has not yet been able to bridge it.

Living matter comprises a multiplicity of highly organized and integrated chemical systems; some of these are engaged in synthesizing complex compounds from simpler ones; others break down the complex to simpler compounds; and still others are concerned with the collection of energy derived from the sun and its transformation and storage for many different kinds of work. Hundreds of the great variety of compounds that compose living protoplasm have been isolated, characterized, and even synthesized in the laboratory. But man's partial success in performing these feats of synthesis is far from the creation of living systems. Even if he could synthesize the innumerable compounds, he would still be faced with the insuperable task of organizing them into viable systems; for, in addition to its chemical composition, protoplasm possesses four attributes missing *in toto* from non-living matter: growth, reproduction, response to external stimuli, and evolutionary change. Each of these activities is controlled by some particular component of a protoplasmic cell, whether it be a nucleic acid, an enzyme, a hormone, or some other complicated molecule, thus making the problem of duplicating living protoplasm much more complex.

Life as we know it today demands, among other things, sunlight and carbon dioxide for plants, and free oxygen for animals. Conclusions concerning the earth's first atmosphere indicate that neither of these two chemicals was present. Instead, the chief constituents were gases of the dust cloud from which the earth's protoplanet emerged. The high temperature of the earth's surface induced the light hydrogen and helium atoms to reach and to exceed the velocity of escape from the earth's gravitational field, and most of them passed into space, leaving the heavier, slower molecular gases behind.

Degassing of the planet at that time, probably nearly 4 billion years ago, brought gases to the surface of the earth, consisting, as today, mainly of water vapor, nitrogen, sulfur, and carbon dioxide; the result was that the atmosphere, still retaining much of the hydrogen not yet lost to space, became diluted with these new materials. When free hydrogen is in excess, the nitrogen, oxygen, sulfur, and carbon are thermodynamically most stable in the form of their hydrides,

NH_3 (ammonia), H_2O (water vapor), H_2S (hydrogen sulfide), and CH_4 (methane)—gases present in Jupiter's atmosphere today. Cooling resulted in an inability of the atmosphere to hold all its water vapor; the vapor condensed, producing the first rains, which fell on the hot surface of the earth and rose again as steam. Ultimately, however, as the earth's surface cooled still further, the hollows and irregularities of the surface could hold pools of water.

S. L. Miller has shown experimentally that in an atmosphere of CH_4, NH_3, H_2O, and H_2, in the absence of oxygen, an induced electric spark will produce a number of compounds, including some of the amino acids (the chemical basis of proteins), sugars, phosphoric acid, etc. Short ultraviolet rays, to which a hydrogen-rich atmosphere would be transparent, or lightning, or even high temperatures within the limits of thermodynamic stability could achieve the same effect, and the evidence is strong that in the early atmosphere simple organic compounds were spontaneously formed under these conditions and were carried by rain to the weathered surface of the earth, and by rivers to freshwater bodies or to the sea itself. "The waters of seas and lakes held in solution an unimaginably complicated mixture of mineral salts, acids, alkalis, colloidal particles of clay and other materials, and a vast hodge-podge of carbon compounds."* In developing this hypothesis, J. H. Rush supposes that into these waters the rivers continued to pour new supplies of like compounds, replacing the gradual decline of the early arrivals to the state of lowest energy or chemical equilibrium, so that a continuous situation arose, with equilibrium never being reached. "In a system that was in riotous disequilibrium for long ages, the opportunities for unlikely chemical events were sustained and practically infinitely varied."†

The amino acids combined with one another in chains and in many orders and sequences to give a variety of relatively stable protein molecules, some of which were large enough to be colloidal particles. At the same time, interaction between hot rain water and the exposed rocks produced soluble salts such as sodium and potassium carbonates, and inorganic colloids consisting of silica, aluminum silicates, etc. The sea soon became changed into a solution of salts and colloids. From this hot, dilute "soup" of organic and inorganic compounds there resulted the formation of **coacervate** globules—associated jelly-like, colloidal aggregates of large molecular weight—each surrounded by a relatively thin layer of electrically bonded water and the whole distinct from the water in which they floated. These may have associated with each other or with other gels held in aggregates by forces such as positive and negative charges, or by hydrogen bonding, or even by covalent linkages, if these may be formed at high temperatures. The solubility of these materials may have been influenced greatly by the concentration and kind of salts (ions) in solution. The coacervates were able to take up ions and organic compounds from the "soup" and retain them by means of chemical affinities. The interface between the coacervates and the surrounding medium constituted the most primitive form of membrane. Any substance which tends to lower the surface tension of water will become more concentrated at such an interface than in the solution; and any substance that raises the surface tension tends to be reduced in concentration at the interface. These differences in concentration of certain substances at the interface tend to make it still more like a membrane.

Probably there were hundreds, even thousands, of different kinds of such "hungry" aggregates, each specifically acquisitive of certain ingredients in the broth. Those which, by the accidental attachment of natural catalysts, could either speed up the "digestive process" or make use of other molecules in the nutrient medium would have their life expectancy thereby increased. The first catalysts are supposed to have been finely divided materials such as silica or sili-

---

* From *The Dawn of Life*, p. 148, by Joseph H. Rush. Copyright © 1957 by Joseph Harold Rush. Reprinted by permission of Doubleday & Company, Inc.
† *Ibid.*

cates, etc., which could promote or facilitate chemical reactions that would not occur in the absence of the catalysts. Now and then, as more complex organic molecules were formed, certain ones came into being which possessed catalytic properties or the properties of forming complexes with heavy metal ions, producing more powerful or more specific catalytic agents. Thus there was an evolution of catalysts leading to ever increasing potentialities for promoting the organic chemical evolution. Among these catalysts was porphyrin, a thermodynamically very stable compound which has a strong affinity for metals such as magnesium, iron, and vanadium. Magnesium prophyrin is a powerful catalyst which can transfer the energy of light to chemical reactions, for instance, in the manufacture of chlorophylls.

Such a molecule possessing appropriate catalysts fulfills three of the four necessary attributes of a living organism. Only the power of reproduction remained to be achieved. The "living" part of the material in cells apparently resides in the long, chain-like nucleic acids, especially in the DNA (desoxyribonucleic acid) molecules of the chromosomes and genes in the nucleus of the cell, and to a lesser extent in the RNA (ribonucleic acid) of the nucleus and the cytoplasm. In the DNA of the chromosomes lies the "memory" that directs the replication process and the capacity for training or adaptation. DNA directs the process of replication or reproduction, which involves the directed synthesis of the multiplicity of enzymes and highly specific protein biocatalysts. These, in turn, bring about the syntheses of the proteins and other structural materials of the cell.

The DNA directs the synthesis of specific molecules of RNA which have the property of serving as templates for lining up and joining together, in particular arrangements and sequences of types, the amino acids which make up the innumerable enzymes and other proteins in the cell. When a protein chain is fabricated, it separates from the template, and the process is repeated over and over again.

Each DNA molecule in a particular chromosome consists of two long, parallel chains twisted in the form of a spiral and held together by chemical (hydrogen) bonds. Each chain is made up of units called nucleotides, and the individual chromosomes differ in the kinds and the order of the nucleotides in the chain. The types and sequence of these units impart to the chromosome its characteristic properties.

Few of the processes outlined above could have proceeded without the consumption of energy. Some of the simplest methods of obtaining energy were probably derived from the oxidation of iron, sulfur, etc., by primitive organisms of which only a very few bacterial representatives have escaped extinction. Some more complex molecules were catalytically degraded to compounds of lower energy content, and the released energy was not wasted but collected and stored in the form of higher energy compounds such as adenosine triphosphate (ATP), or perhaps, in the beginning, as iron pyrophosphate. The energy thus stored could be released again to promote other metabolic syntheses or to do osmotic work. Or, in much later times, the energy could have been utilized also for production of heat, for doing mechanical work, or for transformation into electricity (as in the electric eel).

The experiments of Miller and many others have demonstrated that numerous simple organic compounds can be formed from excited gaseous molecules within the short space of two weeks. Furthermore, in other experiments that started with quite elaborate organic molecules, e.g., nucleotides, still more elaborate compounds were formed. The formation of these initial materials in the process of organic (chemical) evolution may have had to await the evolution of better catalysts, and thus may have taken a long time. It is apparent, however, that the nucleotides and their component parts—ribose (in RNA) or desoxyribose (in DNA), phosphoric acid, and one or another of the purine or the pyrimidine nitrogenous bases, including ATP (adenosine triphosphate, found in all organisms and fundamental to the transfer of energy)—must have appeared before the high degree of chemical integration and organization known as life occurred.

From the inanimate, primitively organized glob possessing some of the attributes of life, to the simplest living cell we know today, there is a vast gap; but, granting the validity of the chemical steps outlined above, the gradual assumption of the attributes of life by an aggressive molecule surrounded by a nutrient-rich medium would be inevitable. However, the formation in the sea of myriads of compounds probably depleted the medium of nutrients to such an extent that never again could the conditions be duplicated within which another "living" compound could be initiated. Life, once established, prevented the formation of any new compound capable of living.

In some such manner living matter might have originated. Hypothetical as the outlined process may seem, it makes the best scientific sense today. The chief objection is to the extremely unlikely grouping of molecules to form a substance resembling an organic compound. However, with both unlimited resources and a billion years' time, the objection of unlikelihood loses all force.

Two aspects of this hypothesis have geological implications: the time of initiation of life, and the uniqueness of the event of life's origin. The only direct evidence bearing on the time of the beginning of life is the age of the earliest rock with traces of organic remains or structures. Stromatolites in rocks whose age is determined to be more than 2.7 billion years have been reported from Rhodesia. The age of the oldest rock of sedimentary origin, which presupposes processes involving running and standing bodies of water, is about 3.3 billion years. Estimates of the time when the earth's surface was capable of bearing bodies of water are not securely based, but a figure of 4 billion years has been suggested. These estimates suggest that life originated certainly between 4.0 and 2.7 billion years ago, and probably between 4.0 and 3.3 billion years ago.

One of the concerns of paleontologists is the question of the monophyletic or poly-

phyletic origins of phyla, classes, etc. Mammals were without doubt polyphyletic in origin; that is, they arose, early in the Mesozoic Era, from at least three, and possibly four, separate reptilian stocks. Reptiles, on the other hand, are monophyletic, being descended from a single amphibian group. Life itself probably sprang from the successful compounds whose "descendants" eventually consumed all the nutrients in the "soup," including all competing molecules. According to this view, life is monophyletic and, once started, prohibited any further origins. No trace of this hypothetical early biota remains. Bacteria, which are the oldest actual fossils found (the stromatolites being indirect deposits telling us nothing about the organism responsible for the deposits), are much more complex organisms than the living molecules in which life began.

The evolution of the process of photosynthesis probably took place between 2.7 (if the Rhodesian age is definitely determined) and 1.0 billion years ago. From that time on, that is, during the Proterozoic Era, fossilization of lime-secreting algae was possible. Fossils of diverse kinds abruptly become plentiful in Early Cambrian strata and are found in abundance in the strata of all subsequent periods.

Graphite in Sedimentary Rocks

The second source of information about Precambrian life is the disseminated and layered graphite found in rocks of Precambrian age. That all carbon in the earth can be traced back to igneous emanations is reasonably certain. Such carbon, originating as gases, found its way into the atmosphere and the hydrosphere. Until photosynthesizing organisms evolved, it could not be released from CH_4, CO, and CO_2. When photosynthesis had become an established organic process, plant life began to exert a steady drain on the CO_2 of the atmosphere, exchanging O_2 for it so that for the first time free oxygen appeared on the earth. The carbon was incorporated in primitive alga-like plants, some of which were buried in accumulating mud. Black Paleozoic sediments generally owe their color to bituminous compounds derived from organic matter. Precambrian schists contain comparable amounts of carbon, largely in the form of graphite, presumably the residue after metamorphism of plant remains entombed in the original muds. The occurrence in one or two places in Precambrian rocks of bedded graphitic hydrocarbons, essentially like anthracite, corroborates the supposed organic origin of sedimentary graphite. One bed, 6 feet thick, of combustible hydrocarbons known as shungite occurs in the East Baltic region. Another occurrence is of combustible anthracite from Upper Huronian beds of northern Michigan 700 million years old.

The Cambrian Stage of Evolution

The third source of information on Precambrian life is the stage of evolution of animals in the Cambrian Period. The Cambrian fauna contains all of the major invertebrate phyla, represented not only by their most primitive members, but by some in an advanced stage of evolution. The complexity of the Cambrian fauna demonstrates that well over half the road of evolution from non-living matter to the modern fauna had already been traveled by the close of Precambrian time. G. Evelyn Hutchinson has estimated that multicellular life must have begun no less than 1 billion years ago in order for the complexity of the Cambrian fauna to have been attained by the opening of the Paleozoic Era, and unicellular life may have existed 1 billion years before that.

Precambrian Fossils

The fourth source is the fossils of animals and plants found in Precambrian rocks. Fossils have been reported from Precambrian rocks for a century or more. Each one has sooner or later been scrutinized carefully, and many have failed to qualify. Some are not now recognized as Precambrian; other supposed fossils have subsequently been identified as rill marks, bubble marks, feather fractures, concretions, etc. A few, such as the sponge spicules reported from the Grand Canyon and the radiolaria from Brittany,

cannot be considered critically for they have been lost. In another category are some that resulted from the metamorphism of limestone, such as *Eozoon canadense* (see Fig. 2–13), a layered structure of serpentine and calcite whose origin caused much discussion at the end of the nineteenth century.

THE PAUCITY OF PRECAMBRIAN FOSSILS

Introduction

The stage of evolution of the Cambrian fauna, chemical and physical considerations concerning the origin of life, and Precambrian graphite indicate that life in Precambrian time was probably rich and varied, and that it contained representatives of all the major animal groups. At the opening of the Paleozoic Era complex forms of life must have been in existence for more than half a billion years. Why is it, then, that the only common Precambrian fossils are primitive plants, and that among animals only coelenterates and annelids have been identified with certainty? These outstanding paleontological problems have stimulated much speculation, but there is yet no final answer.

Many solutions have been proposed for the problem of the sudden appearance of abundant fossils at the base of the Cambrian System. They fall into variations of three main generalizations: first, that there was no Precambrian life; second, that Precambrian life existed and was fossilized; and third, that Precambrian life existed, and was not fossilized. The first is a relic of the time when no Precambrian fossils were known, or at least accepted, and when there was still considerable dependence upon the doctrine of special creation, i.e., that life was specially created at the beginning of the Cambrian Period. Such a view is untenable today in the light of our knowledge of Precambrian animals and plants extending back through at least one billion years of Precambrian time.

The second solution grants the existence of Precambrian life and proposes that fossils might have been freely made but are unknown to us because they have been destroyed by either metamorphism or erosion, or both. Many Precambrian fossils may have been destroyed by metamorphism, but in many parts of the world, abundant unmetamorphosed Precambrian beds exist, such as the Belt Group, which contain no fossils of complex life. Walcott suggested that life began, or was largely developed, in an interval of time between the deposition of the youngest Precambrian rocks and the oldest Cambrian rocks. Because, by definition, no rock representing this interval of time remains, at least on our continents, Walcott named this the **Lipalian Interval** (Greek: left out). He postulated that during this interval the almost universal unconformity between Precambrian and younger rocks was developed, and that any sediments recording this time would have been deposited either on the continents, from which they were certain to be eroded, or far from the present continental margins, because the continents were extended beyond their present shorelines in this world-wide period of erosion and marine withdrawal. However, in many places in the world no unconformity separates Precambrian and Cambrian strata, yet the remarkable paleontological difference between the strata of the two ages remains.

The hypothesis that Precambrian life was present but consisted of soft-bodied animals that could not normally be preserved provides a more satisfactory solution to the sudden appearance of the Cambrian fauna. Today this is the accepted explanation, but differences of opinion have arisen as to the reason for the soft-bodied condition of the fauna. It has been suggested that the ocean was too acid to allow animals to extract calcium carbonate from the sea, but abundant stromatolites and both limestone and dolomite formations in Proterozoic rocks refute this.

Explosive Evolution

When the rate of evolution of animals increases severalfold at some point in a group's history, the group is said to undergo **explosive evolution.** Such explosions are generally related to the exploitation by the animals of a new way of life, the entry of the group into a new environment, or the removal of some deterrent factor. One of the most spectacular of these explosions occurred at the beginning of the Cenozoic Era, when the mammals diversified rapidly as they filled all the available environments on land, in the sea, and in the air left free by the near extinction of their reptilian competitors. This phase of the explosion is frequently referred to as an **adaptive radiation.** In such an explosion at the beginning of the Paleozoic, with accompanying adaptive radiation, complex life with preservable hard parts evolved from the previous soft-bodied biota. Such a spectacular explosion must have been caused by a radical change in the physical or biological environment of the whole fauna that opened new opportunities for life. What was this radical change?

Brooks's Hypothesis

The biologist W. K. Brooks postulated that late Precambrian life was complex but soft-bodied, and consisted largely of pelagic animals that floated or swam in the aerated waters near the surface of the sea. In such an environment, animals would find a rigid skeleton both unnecessary and cumbersome. After perhaps hundreds of millions of years, crowding of this environment may have occurred and led to the discovery that the shallow ocean floor was an environment with food and oxygen in abundance, unoccupied except by algae. Occupation and competition for the limited but very desirable space began at once among the late Precambrian species, and an advantage would have been held by those able to stand either the buffeting of the waves and currents or competition within a burgeoning benthonic population, some of whose members had developed predaceous habits. The first materials used for protection, in Early Cambrian time, were external coverings of chitin by the active animals (trilobites), and calcium phosphate or calcium carbonate by the sessile (rooted or cemented) forms (brachiopods, archaeocyathids). Sessility as a mode of life became common in succeeding epochs, so that by

Late Cambrian time and throughout the remainder of the Paleozoic, calcareous shells and skeletons became the rule, and chitin was restricted almost wholly to arthropods, annelids, and graptolites. The discovery of new ways of life and new environments, together with the stimulus of competition, gave rise to one of the greatest evolutionary explosions in the history of life on earth.

Plant Fossils

Universally accepted as fossils are concentric limestone structures known as stromatolites (Fig. 18–1). They occur in sediments of the Proterozoic type in all the shield areas of the world, as well as in Paleozoic, Mesozoic, and Cenozoic beds, and in recently deposited sediments. In many places they are common enough to form reefs. So abundant and so diversely built are these stromatolites that I. N. Krylov in the U.S.S.R. and Richard Rezak in the U.S. have attempted to show that they have

definite stratigraphic value. However, the dependence of the shapes and sizes of such stromatolites on the conditions of their growth casts some doubt on their use for paleontological zonation. These structures are today being built by slimy blue-green algae which extract lime from the water or trap small lime particles on their gelatinous surfaces. Most of the organic matter of these fossil algae has long since decomposed, but what are interpreted as algal filaments have been discovered in some Proterozoic cherts of Minnesota by J. W. Gruner. These filaments, encased in silica, have even retained some of the organic compounds formed by primitive plants about 1.7 billion years ago. Stromatolites have been reported from Precambrian rocks in Rhodesia with an age of 2.6 billion years.

S. A. Tyler and E. S. Barghoorn have reported rod-shaped and coccoid bacteria with filaments of blue-green algae and possibly fungi (Fig. 18–2) beautifully preserved in

Fig. 18–1. Huronian stromatolites. *Left:* From Lake Mistassini, Quebec. *Right:* From the Labrador Trough (about ½ actual size).

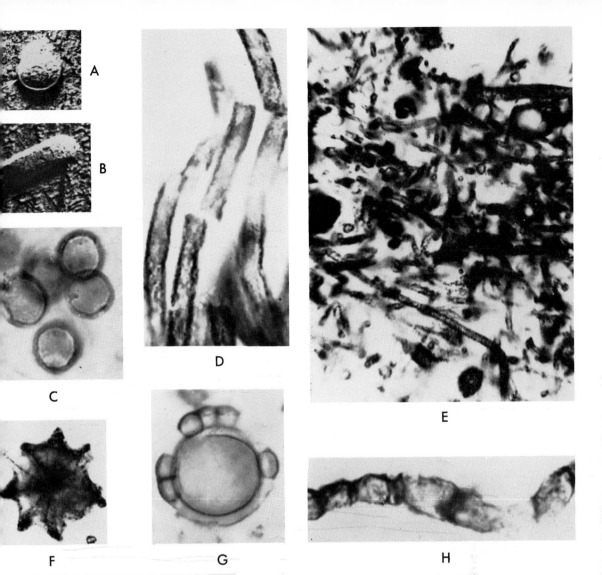

Fig. 18–2. Precambrian fossils. *A, B. Eobacterium* from the Fig Tree Series, South Africa, 3.1 billion years old (approximate magnification × 5000). *C, D.* Late Precambrian algal filaments and single algal cells from Bitter Springs Limestone, Northern Territory, Australia, 700–900 million years old (approximate magnification × 2500). *E.* Tangled algal filaments and spores (approximate magnification × 800). *F, G.* Organisms of unknown affinities (approximate magnification × 2000). *H.* A single algal strand (approximate magnification × 2400). *E–H* from Gunflint Chert, Ontario, 1.9 billion years old. (Courtesy of E. S. Barghoorn.)

cherts of the Middle Huronian Gunflint Formation in Ontario, about 1.9 billion years old. Trapped by the silica surrounding these plant remains were also traces of eight amino acids. These are the oldest known multicellular fossils.

Still more recently, J. W. Schopf and E. S. Barghoorn have reported rod- and coccus-shaped bacteria (Fig. 18–2) from organic-rich black cherts of the Fig Tree Series of South Africa. These, more than 3 billion years old, are the oldest known fossils, and are accompanied by biological hydrocarbon compounds including phytane and pristane. Filaments of blue-green and green algae have been found in the Bitter Springs Formation

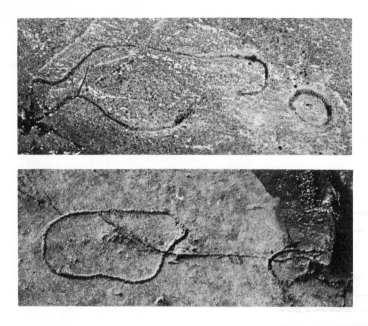

Fig. 18–3. *Corycium enigmaticum,* supposedly a Precambrian algal fossil. The saclike objects are outlined in graphite. (Courtesy of the Geological Survey of Finland.)

of late Precambrian age (700–900 million years old) from Australia (Fig. 18–2).

A saclike, probably algal object with graphitic walls, from rocks of the Bothnian Group in Finland, has been described by J. J. Sederholm as *Corycium enigmaticum* (Fig. 18–3), probably 2 billion years old. Within the last decade, algal spores have been found in Precambrian rocks of Siberia and North America; some of these spores, it has been claimed, may actually have been the product of terrestrial or semiterrestrial plants. Objects that have been interpreted as remains of vascular plants have been reported, with less assurance, from Siberia. Little doubt now remains that Precambrian bacteria, algae, and spores have been found in rocks that are billions of years old.

In recent years much has been discovered about Precambrian dinoflagellates, which at certain times in their individual development secrete siliceous tests known as hystricospheres. So abundant and varied are these microfossils that attempts have been made to correlate Precambrian deposits across continents. Whether these organisms are plants or animals is still debated, and the tendency today is to place them, together with all other unicellular organisms, in a separate kingdom, PROTISTA.

Animal Fossils

Precambrian radiolaria from Brittany and sponge spicules from the Grand Canyon are considered mythical today. *Brooksella,* also from the Grand Canyon, is interpreted, probably correctly, as the impression of the underside of a jellyfish, though it is not completely convincing and recalls desiccation cracks in sediments. Trails or burrows of crawling creatures have been collected from Proterozoic beds in the Grand Canyon, from the Belt Series, and from the late Precambrian Nama Group in South Africa. This poor assortment is practically all that is known from Precambrian rocks, except for the remarkable assemblage from the Ediacara Hills of South Australia, and similar, though far less abundant, forms from southwestern Africa, and from Leicestershire, England. The Ediacara fauna has been described by R. G. Sprigg and M. F. Glaessner. It contains several genera of medusae, two genera of pennatulids, two of annelids, and two genera which cannot be assigned to any known group of organisms, living or fossil (Fig. 18–4). These fossils were discovered on weathered surfaces of a quartzite occurring a few hundred feet below a horizon bearing a Lower Cambrian fauna that con-

Fig. 18–4. Late Precambrian fossils from Ediacara, South Australia. *A. Cyclomedusa,* a jellyfish. *B. Parvancoria,* of unknown affinities. *C. Spriggina,* a segmented worm. (Courtesy of M. F. Glaessner.)

A

B

C

tains archaeocyathids but no olenelline trilobites (the latter are unknown in Australia). Some have claimed that they should be called not Precambrian but Earliest Cambrian ("Eocambrian," according to some geologists). However, the occurrence of the same genera in undoubtedly Precambrian beds of southwestern Africa and England supports a similar age for the Ediacara quartzites.

The assiduous search for Precambrian fossils has resulted in many erroneous conclusions. Many of the so-called fossils are now considered to be of inorganic origin, as is the case with J. W. Dawson's *Eozoon canadense* (see Fig. 2–13), supposed by him to be a giant foraminifer but now considered to be the product of metamorphism of Grenville limestone.

CAMBRIAN LIFE

If the invertebrate phyla are arranged in order of their biological complexity, which would presumably be much the same as the order of their development from a simple ancestor, among those phyla persisting to the present we would expect the most primitive animals and plants to occur prominently in the Early Cambrian fauna. However, of the four most primitive phyla of animals— PROTOZOA, PORIFERA, ARCHAEOCYATHA, and COELENTERATA—only the archaeocyathids are common Early Cambrian fossils. The other three are present, but form an insignificant part of the whole fauna. Instead, the most abundant phylum is the ARTHROPODA, including the TRILOBITA, probably the most complex

Fig. 18–5. Middle Cambrian fossils from the Burgess Shale, British Columbia. *A, B. Wiwaxia* and *Canadia*, annelids. *C. Amiskwia*, a chaetopod worm (magnification × 3). *D. Mackenzia*, a shell-less hexacoral. *E. Aysheaia*, an onychophoran. All the fossils illustrated here are without hard parts, with the possible exception of the scales of *Wiwaxia*. (Courtesy of the Smithsonian Institution.)

Fig. 18–6. A Middle Cambrian habitat group, with a sampling of the flora and fauna of the Burgess Shale. *A. Marpolia,* a blue-green alga. *B, C. Choia* and *Vauxia,* siliceous sponges. *D.* A jellyfish. *E. Mackenzia,* a hexacoral. *F. Acrothele,* a small inarticulate brachiopod. *G. Worthenia,* an annelid worm. *H. Aysheaia,* an onychophoran. *I, J. Neolenus* and *Ogygopsis,* trilobites. *K, L. Sidneya* and *Marella,* trilobitoids. *M. Hymenocaris,* a crustacean of unknown affinities. (Courtesy of the Smithsonian Institution.)

of the invertebrate phyla, making up, according to V. J. Okulitch, 32 per cent of the known species. The balance includes archeocyathids (30 per cent), brachiopods (21 per cent), mollusks—mostly gastropods (10 per cent), annelids (3 per cent), and protozoans, sponges, coelenterates, echinoderms and *incertae sedis* (about 1 per cent each). Although the Early Cambrian fauna is diversified, there is a far greater abundance and variety of organisms in Middle Cambrian rocks, and by Late Cambrian time both abundance and variety had increased still more. The abnormal fauna and flora of the Burgess Shale member of the Middle Cambrian Stephen Formation reveal the advanced stage of evolution and the variety of organisms at that time (Figs. 18–5 and 18–14).

This remarkable fauna was preserved by exceptionally selective sedimentation. It is made up mostly of arthropods, but sponges, worms, and jellyfish are also present. Most of the 70-odd genera are unknown elsewhere. Here, then, in a limited area, is an incredibly lifelike assemblage of animals and plants that normally would never be preserved. It is as if we were given a momentary and tantalizing glance into the Middle Cambrian sea (Fig. 18–6), with a view of a more abundant and varied fauna and flora than is afforded by the rest of the fossil record.

Much has been written concerning the "sudden" appearance of the Cambrian fauna. A detailed analysis of the first occurrences shows rather that fossil groups appeared

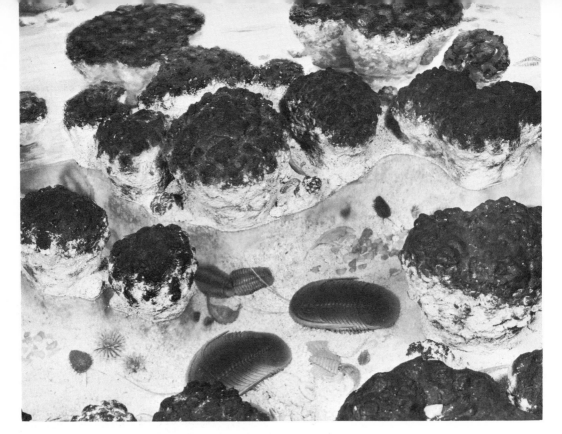

Fig. 18–7. *Cryptozoon,* a lime-trapping alga. The picture shows a Late Cambrian intertidal zone in the eastern flank of the Adirondacks with a *Cryptozoon* reef exposed at low tide. If planed off by erosion, the algal heads would show the characteristic concentric structure. In the channels there are trilobites—*Dikellocephalus* is the largest, *Saratogia* the smallest, and *Prosaukia* the intermediate one—together with a few other fossils and wave-broken fossil debris. (Courtesy of the New York State Museum.)

(Camb) plants = algae

gradually and successively (straggling in, as F. H. T. Rhodes has expressed it) during Early Cambrian time. Early Cambrian rocks are sparsely fossiliferous compared with Middle and Upper Cambrian strata, in which fossils become progressively more abundant. One reason for this difference may be that during the Early Cambrian Epoch the seas were restricted to geosynclines, notoriously poor milieus for the preservation of fossils, and that the spreading of the epeiric seas with widespread opportunities for abundant shallow-water life began in Middle Cambrian time and reached full flood in Late Cambrian time.

V. J. Okulitch has written, "We can therefore visualize the Lower Cambrian life as one in the early stages of colonization of the sea bottom. Small isolated [groups] were established here and there and only much later were these outposts of life knit together as populations grew."[*]

Plants

Cambrian plants are almost exclusively algae. Among the lime-trapping types are stromatolites called *Cryptozoon* (Fig. 18–7), which were more abundant in Lower Ordovician beds, but which built reefs in Cambrian time. Non-calcareous algae are known, but are poorly preserved except in the Burgess Shale, from which ten species of blue-green, one species of green, and two species of red algae have been described.

[*] V. J. Okulitch, "The Lower Cambrian Fauna," Royal Society of Canada Symposium, *Evolution: Its Science and Doctrine* (Toronto: The University of Toronto Press, 1960), p. 13.

In some of these fossils, e.g., *Marpolia* (Fig. 18–6), the most delicate strands are preserved.

Spores, presumably algal, have been reported from Cambrian rocks almost the world over. S. N. Naumova and A. N. Krystofovitch have reported Lower Cambrian spores of primitive land plants from the Baltic region and from Siberia.

Protozoa, Porifera, and Archaeocyatha

Both RADIOLARIA and FORAMINIFERA are present in the Cambrian fauna, though nowhere are they rock formers, nor do they provide usable index fossils. Some paleontologists doubt that the simple saclike objects assigned to these orders have been correctly identified.

Sponges have been reported from Lower, Middle, and Upper Cambrian beds. Two localities deserve special mention. First, the Burgess Shale of Middle Cambrian age has yielded exquisitely preserved complete sponges with the delicate spicules well shown (Fig. 18–6). Second, from supposedly Middle Cambrian black shales in Quebec, J. W. Dawson described several species of sponges, some of them showing the complete form of the individual (Fig. 18–8). Most of the other occurrences are of scattered siliceous spicules.

The archaeocyathids were conspicuous, distinctive, and among the most numerous constituents of Early and Middle Cambrian faunas. Although the skeleton of the animal resembled that of both the corals and the sponges, the group today is generally considered to be distinct from both those phyla and deserves to be elevated to the status of a phylum. Archaeocyathid fossils are cone-shaped and consist of inner and outer calcareous, porous walls separated by a series of radial septa (Fig. 18–9). The animals were gregarious and carpeted parts of the Early Cambrian sea floor, but nowhere built topographically prominent reefs. They were extremely abundant during the Early Cambrian Epoch, but were extinct by the end of Middle Cambrian time. They were the first sessile animals and, except for a few articulate

Fig. 18–8. Cambrian sponge fossils in which the spicules have been lightly picked out with white paint. *Top: Dictyospongia,* showing the network of fused spicules. *Bottom: Protospongia,* showing the form of the sponge together with the anchoring rods. (Courtesy of the Redpath Museum.)

brachiopods, were the first animals to build strong calcareous tests.

Coelenterata

The classes SCYPHOZOA and HYDROZOA are represented in rocks of Lower Cambrian and younger age by dozens of impressions of the undersides of jellyfish. *Brooksella* ranges from the Precambrian of the Grand Canyon through the Cambrian of North America and Europe. Within the scyphozoans are the CONULATA, rare in Cambrian beds but common in the later Paleozoic strata (see Fig. 19–1). Of the corals there is a soft-bodied, cylindrical form known as *Mackenzia* (Figs.

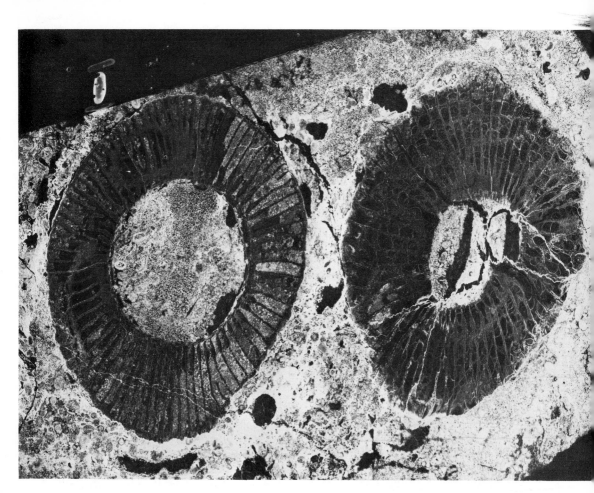

Fig. 18–9. Photomicrograph of a transverse thin section of two archaeocyathids, *Coscinocyathus (left)* and *Pycnoidocyathus (right)*. Note the inner and outer walls and the central cavity. (Courtesy of V. J. Okulitch.)

Inarticula

↓

articulat

Brachiopods

18–5 and 18–6), the discussion of which will be deferred to the description of corals of the Mesozoic Era (see p. 488 and Fig. 21–27); and a coral-like fossil is reported by M. A. Fritz from Upper Cambrian rocks of British Columbia.

Brachiopoda, Bryozoa, and Phoronida

The most abundant brachiopods of the Cambrian Period were the INARTICULATA. These primitive types secrete a pair of shells made up of layers of chitin and calcium phosphate and held together by muscles attached to the interior of each shell, but lack a mechanism to lock the valves together at a hinge line. The Cambrian inarticulates were mostly small, conical shells, now brown or black. After the Cambrian the inarticulates were rarely numerically important, but they have survived to the present day.

The articulate brachiopods appeared in Lower Cambrian strata with their inarticulate relatives, but did not become abundant until later in the period. This group secretes shells of calcium carbonate that have a strong hinge mechanism, involving teeth and sockets, to control the opening and closing of the valves. They were rare in the Early Cambrian Epoch, and did not become common until the succeeding Ordovician Period.

Bryozoa have been reported from Upper Cambrian beds of British Columbia. In some Upper Cambrian sandstones, vertical burrows known as *Scolithus* (see Fig. 2–8) are common. These burrows were probably made by either phoronids or worms.

Inarticulata

Gastropoda and Other Mollusca

Gastropods, among the most abundant of modern classes, began in the Lower Cambrian as small, depressed, conical shells; there are also primitively coiled spiral shells. By Late Cambrian time the spiral form was established, a form which has led to the abundant gastropod fauna of today. The earliest accepted cephalopod is a small, straight or slightly curved cone found in Upper Cambrian rocks. Pelecypods are not known certainly from Cambrian beds; most of the fossils claimed to be Cambrian pelecypods have been determined to be bivalved crustaceans.

Annelida

Irregular trails and castings presumably of annelid origin are known throughout the Cambrian (Fig. 18–10). Beautifully preserved, abundant worm fossils in the Burgess

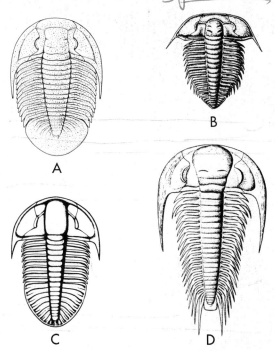

Fig. 18–11. Cambrian trilobites. A. Tellerina. B. Olenus. C. Ogygopsis. D. Paradoxides. A and B are Late Cambrian genera; C and D are Middle Cambrian. A and C belong in the Pacific cratonic realm; B and D in the Atlantic geosynclinal realm. (From *Treatise on Invertebrate Paleontology*, courtesy of the Geological Society of America and the University of Kansas Press.)

Shale fauna show the annulation of the body, the fine setae, and traces of the internal anatomy (Figs. 18–5 and 18–6). From this locality Walcott identified 12 genera and 20 species of annelids, only one of which occurs elsewhere.

Trilobita and Other Arthropoda

Trilobites < Arthropoda

The trilobites belong to an extinct class of the phylum Arthropoda and are characterized by a longitudinally three-lobed, transversely segmented, chitinous carapace (or dorsal shield). Although most of them ranged between 1 and 4 inches in length, they included the largest animals of the Cambrian Period, and specimens of the genus *Paradoxides* (Fig. 18–11) attain a length of 20 inches. In the Cambrian System trilobites make up about one-third of the number of species described. The earliest appearance

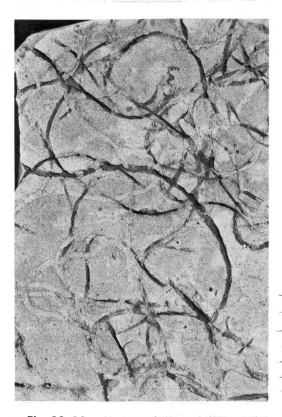

Fig. 18–10. Horizontal, curved burrows of an unknown small marine organism, Upper Cambrian of southern Quebec (about ¼ actual size).

of trilobites, especially *Olenellus* or its close relatives (Fig. 18–12), in the stratigraphic record is generally taken to mark the beginning of the Paleozoic Era, although in a few localities this event is marked by brachiopods and archaeocyathids. These first trilobites differed from most later ones in that the facial suture, along which the head shield split to allow an easy molting, followed the frontal margin and was therefore not visible from above. The central raised portion of their head shields, known as the glabella, was more extensively segmented than in later trilobites. There were as many as 45 body segments in some genera, whereas most later trilobites have about 10 or 12. This large number of segments has suggested to many paleontologists the possibility that trilobites, and therefore arthropods in general, are descended from multisegmented annelids. These early trilobites have been placed by some paleontologists in a suborder named the OLENELLINA after the most familiar genus of the group, *Olenellus*. This particular trilobite was blind. The frontal region of the glabella was bulbous and was flanked by long, curving ridges simulating eyes. The posterior corners of the head were elongated into spines, and the third segment of the thorax was similarly extended. *Olenellus* has been called the "spar-tailed trilobite" because its tail carried a long spike. Because the olenelline fauna is distinctive, restricted to the rocks of the Early Cambrian Epoch, and nearly world-wide in distribution, its presence makes recognition of Lower Cambrian beds relatively easy. Some of the member genera apparently preferred to live on the floors of the geosynclines, and others in the shelf seas. This division of trilobite faunas on the basis of preferred environment became pronounced later in Cambrian time. The earliest Paleozoic trilobites apparently crawled over the sea floor or swam for short distances in the shallow water. From this beginning the group diversified to become mud burrowers, active swimmers, passive floaters, and crawlers.

The Lower Cambrian fauna is found in so many parts of the world that it is referred to as a cosmopolitan fauna. Middle and Upper Cambrian trilobite faunas, however, may be divided into three groups, each characteristic of a certain geographic district. These faunal realms also have differences in other types of fossils. In each district the animal population has a certain unity and an over-all dissimilarity to that of neighboring realms. For example, present-day Africa and South America have similar climates and physiographic environments, but the faunas of these two continents have few species in common, and many families are confined to one or the other of them. The marine faunal realms of today are the Indian, Atlantic, and Pacific oceans.

Cambrian trilobites of North America and Europe occupy two faunal realms that correspond to the main tectonic divisions of the continents, the craton and the geosyncline; an intermediate realm may be recognized, but is not everywhere distinguishable. The trilobites of the geosynclinal realm lived on the margins of the continents, largely in eastern New England and the Acadian region of the Maritime Provinces, but also on the West Coast. They include mud-loving trilobites which flourished in the deeper waters of the geosynclinal tracts of both North America and Europe, and rarely invaded the interiors of the continents. In the Middle Cambrian Series, *Paradoxides* (Fig. 18–11) is a common trilobite in this realm, as is *Olenus* (Fig. 18–11) in the Upper Cambrian Series. The trilobites of the cratonic realm lived in shallow, clear, sandy or limy epeiric seas. During the Middle Cambrian Epoch, this fauna was characterized by *Albertella* and *Bathyuriscus* in the western interior, and by many large-tailed genera. They were replaced in Late Cambrian time by *Dikellocephalus* and *Crepicephalus*, and by a host of other trilobites (Fig. 18–11).

Trilobites are the best index fossils for the Cambrian Period because they evolved fairly rapidly and are abundant, diverse, large, and easily identified. The class reached its acme in Late Cambrian time (Fig. 18–13), failed to maintain it into the beginning of the Ordovician Period, and thereafter declined to ex-

Fig. 18–12. *Paedumias nevadensis,* an olenelline trilobite, closely related in form to *Olenellus.* (Courtesy of V. J. Okulitch.)

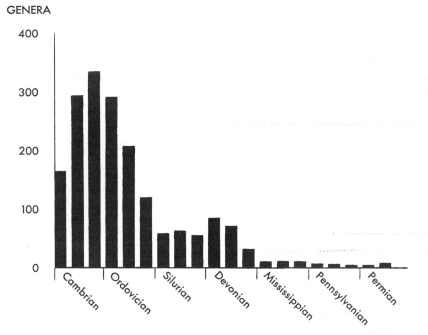

GENERA

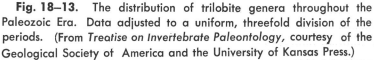

Fig. 18–13. The distribution of trilobite genera throughout the Paleozoic Era. Data adjusted to a uniform, threefold division of the periods. (From *Treatise on Invertebrate Paleontology,* courtesy of the Geological Society of America and the University of Kansas Press.)

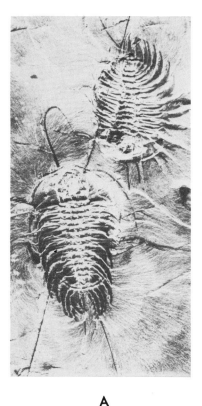

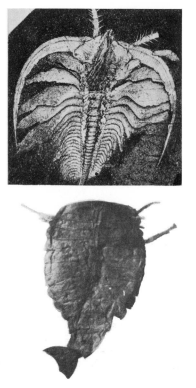

A
B

Fig. 18–14. Trilobites and trilobitoids from the Burgess Shale. A. The trilobite *Neolenus*, showing the exceedingly rare preservation of swimming appendages and antennae. B. The trilobitoids *Marella splendens*, *Sidneya inexpectans*, and *Wapta fieldensis*, all of which show the preservation of delicate gills, body appendages, or antennae. The last three are known only from the 7-foot bed in the Burgess Shale on Mount Wapta, British Columbia. (Courtesy of the Smithsonian Institution.)

tinction at the close of the Paleozoic Era.

Among Walcott's collection of fossils from the Burgess Shale, there are more than a score of species of crustaceans whose general aspects are those of trilobites but which, for various technical reasons, cannot be included in that class. They are usually referred to as the Trilobitoidea, which include only two species not in the Burgess Shale fauna. Some of these marvelously preserved fossils are presented in Fig. 18–14.

Among other crustaceans, only the ostracods occur in Cambrian rocks. A few of these small, bivalved animals belong in the Lower, Middle, and Upper Cambrian beds.

Echinodermata and Graptoloidea

Although these two groups began their history in Cambrian time, they were much more characteristic of Ordovician rocks, and their treatment will be given under that period.

QUESTIONS

Questions for the material in this chapter are included in the list at the end of Chapter 22.

REFERENCES AND SUGGESTED READINGS

References and suggested readings for the material in this chapter will be found at the end of Chapter 22.

19

Ordovician and Silurian Life

INTRODUCTION

By the end of Cambrian time, all the main zoological phyla had evolved, but invertebrates still represented the major portion of living organisms. Toward the end of Silurian time, however, both plants and vertebrates began to assume the importance they were to have during the remainder of the Paleozoic Era.

During the Cambrian Period, far more deposition of sediments took place in geosynclines than in shelf areas. The transgression of epeiric seas over North America which began at the end of Middle Cambrian time brought a significant increase in the number and varieties of organisms in the Late Cambrian Epoch. The increase in Middle Ordovician organisms may have been a response to the opening of new environments as the epeiric seas spread and to the changing environment of the Tippecanoe seas as their shorelines shifted. In adjusting to these new conditions, the invertebrates demonstrated a remarkable adaptive radiation (Fig. 19–1).

Ordovician and Silurian strata of the shelf environment are replete with fossils. Usually the state of preservation is good, and the wide development of various facies faunas, though of little importance until the Late Cambrian, gives added interest to the fossils of the Ordovician and Silurian. Black shale facies with graptolites and the contemporary shell-limestone facies with brachiopods and trilobites may have almost no fossils in common. The first true reef faunas are found in Ordovician rocks. Extensive epeiric seas provided a habitat in which invertebrates thrived and reached numbers never since attained. These situations and conditions recurred throughout geological time, but the conditions under which invertebrates first thickly populated the sea floors need to be specially emphasized. Those conditions that witnessed the establishment of vertebrate animals in fresh water and of vascular plants on land cannot at present be referred to any recognized environmental conditions.

Fig. 19–1. Ordovician habitat group. A large straight nautiloid lies on the sea floor with tentacles extended. A smaller one lurks among the algae, etc., in the left background, and a coiled nautiloid crawls along in the right foreground. Crinoids wave in the open water, and algae are bent over by a slight current. Bryozoan colonies, trilobites, cup corals, gastropods, brachiopods, and pelecypods are present. The knoll on the left is made up largely of colonial corals. The conical floating objects are conularids, organisms related to jellyfish. Suspended from the sea surface, probably by floats, is a colony of graptolites. Contrast this with the Middle Cambrian restoration in Fig. 18–6. Except for seaweeds and trilobites, there are no life forms common to the two periods. (Diorama by Paul Marchand, courtesy of the Redpath Museum.)

PLANT FOSSILS

Algae

Soft-bodied algae are known throughout the Ordovician and Silurian periods but are rare and never well preserved. In fact, they have often been mistaken for the fossils of animal burrows. *Cryptozoon* (see Fig. 18–7), a lime-trapping alga common to both Cambrian and Ordovician rocks, was an important rock builder throughout the Early Ordovician Epoch. A few lime-secreting algae of lesser importance (*Solenopora*) occur in both periods.

Vascular Plants

Reference has already been made to the possibility of land plants in Cambrian rocks. R. Kozlowski and P. Greguss have made a preliminary announcement of the discovery of land plants (*Musciphyton*) in Ordovician rocks of Poland. Few other occurrences have been reported from pre-Devonian strata. The Australian plant *Baragwanathia*, first credited to the Silurian Period, has recently been dated as Devonian.

ANIMAL FOSSILS

The Lower Invertebrates

RADIOLARIA and FORAMINIFERA are present in Ordovician and Silurian rocks but are rare and poorly preserved and are never rock builders. Because of their minute size and generally poor preservation, they are not used as index fossils.

Sponge fossils are usually preserved as isolated, or at least separated, spicules. They are sometimes strewn over a bedding plane or, more rarely, embedded in chert with the spicules more or less in the positions they occupied in the living animal. Some are distinctive index fossils for the Middle Silurian, but on the whole the phylum is of little geological importance.

Stony corals are first found as small reef-building forms in Middle Ordovician strata. These first corals were members of the TABULATA, colonial animals that secreted a skeleton composed of a series of closely appressed, simple tubes divided horizontally by transverse plates. At the end of the Ordovician Period, the tabulate corals underwent a rapid evolution and became the principal reef builders of Silurian time. The most abundant genera of this period were the honeycomb coral *Favosites* and the chain coral *Halysites* (Fig. 19–2). The tabulate corals reached their peak in the mid-Silurian reefs and declined slowly throughout the remainder of the Paleozoic Era.

The simple, horn-shaped corals, divided radially by a series of vertical septa, appeared only slightly later than the tabulates. In all simple Paleozoic corals, these radial septa have a fourfold arrangement that places them in the subdivision TETRACORALLIA. The most common Ordovician tetracoral is the horn-shaped genus *Streptelasma*, with tangled septa in the center forming a vesicular mass. Also common are colonial tetracorals with skeletons composed of hexagonal tubes, each divided by twelve septa. One of the best known of these is *Foerstephyllum* of the Middle and Upper Ordovician.

The STROMATOPOROIDEA were colonial organisms probably related to the hydroids or corals. They secreted a skeleton of thin layers of calcium carbonate separated by minute pillars. These lamellar structures encrusted other animals or grew into spherical, cabbage-like masses on the sea floor. The stromatoporoids were important reef builders throughout their existence from Ordovician to Late Devonian time.

The Silurian reefs of the Michigan basin have already been described. Among the most common corals composing these reefs were *Favosites*, *Halysites*, *Syringopora*, *Heliolites*, and various genera of stromatoporoids. From that time on, corals have been important reef builders.

Brachiopoda and Bryozoa

The climax of the brachiopods came in the Middle Paleozoic. The inarticulates reached

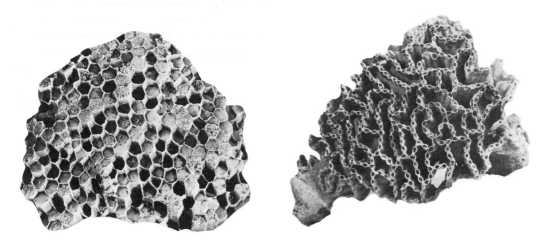

Fig. 19–2. Tabulate corals. *Left: Favosites* (Ordovician–Devonian). *Right: Halysites* (Ordovician–Silurian). These were the chief contributors to the Silurian reefs.

Fig. 19–3. *Lingula s.l.,* an inarticulate brachiopod in Lower Ordovician dolomite from Quebec.

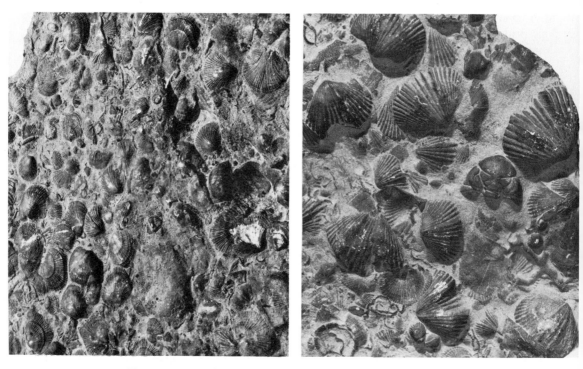

Fig. 19–4. Middle Ordovician articulate brachiopod assemblages from Montreal. *Left: Dalmanella* (Ordovician–Silurian). Just below the center is a pygidium of the trilobite *Calymene. Right: Platystrophia* (Ordovician–Silurian). *Dalmanella* and *Zygospira,* branching bryozoan colonies, and a head shield of the trilobite *Calyptaulax* are also present.

maximum diversification in the Ordovician, and at the end of Silurian time only the three families that exist today remained. One of the best known genera is *Lingula s.l.* (Ordovician–Recent), shown in Figs. 19–3 and 19–5. Because of its excessively long range, *Lingula* has no rival as a "living fossil" in the animal kingdom.

The articulates, represented by nine families in the Cambrian Period, burgeoned in Ordovician time to 54 families. During the Silurian this number was reduced to 38, but in species and individuals there was not much difference between the articulates of the two periods. In many rocks of these periods shells of articulates are the most abundant fossils (Fig. 19–4).

Many of the brachiopods were gregarious, and though they rarely make up whole beds like oysters, their shells form a great part of many limestones. Brachiopods are the most useful of all Paleozoic animal groups in providing index fossils because they are diverse and numerous and evolved rapidly.

Although no classification of brachiopods is universally accepted, the articulates fall into six fairly distinct categories (orders or suborders, according to the classification used). Of these groups the earliest is the ORTHIDA, which had shells with long, straight hinge lines and conspicuous radial ornamentation. *Platystrophia* and *Dalmanella* are two well-known genera (Figs. 19–4 and 19–5). The orthids began in the Cambrian, reached their height during the Ordovician, and declined gradually to extinction by the end of the Paleozoic. A second group, the STROPHOMENIDA, had shells that were generally concavo-convex with a straight hinge line and relatively weak radial ornamentation. *Rafinesquina* (Fig. 19–5) is one of the most abundant Ordovician genera. *Leptaena* was widespread from the Ordovician to the Mississippian periods. *Chonetes,* with spines restricted to the hinge line, was common from Middle Silurian to Permian. *Productus s.l.* (Devonian–Permian), a heavy-shelled form with spines distributed over both concave and convex shells, was particularly characteristic of the late Paleozoic (Fig. 19–5). *Gigantoproductus giganteus* is the largest brachiopod known, about 8 inches wide at the hinge line.

A third category, the PENTAMERIDA, had a short hinge line and relatively smooth, biconvex shells with a peculiar internal plate formation to accommodate the attachment of muscles. These brachiopods began in the Middle Cambrian but were not common until the Silurian and did not survive the Devonian. Some Silurian limestones are made up almost wholly of the large shells of the best known genus, *Pentamerus* (Fig. 19–5).

A fourth group, known as the SPIRIFERIDA, had a wide variety of shell forms, but all members had an internal, calcareous spiral structure for the support of the breathing apparatus (Fig. 19–5). Spiriferids appeared in the Ordovician, became very abundant in Devonian time, and lasted until the Jurassic. *Zygospira* (Ordovician) (Fig. 19–6), *Athyris* (Devonian), and *Spirifer s.l.* and closely related genera (Silurian–Permian) are characteristic genera. *Spirifer s.s.* is confined to the Mississippian.

The RHYNCHONELLIDA (Fig. 19–5) were short-hinged, radially plicate forms, biconvex in most genera. *Lepidocyclus* (Ordovician) and *Leiorhynchus* (Devonian) are characteristic genera. They were most abundant from the Ordovician to the Mississippian, and again in the Jurassic Period, after which they declined to the few genera that are alive today. The TEREBRATULIDA were a group of almost wholly smooth, short-hinged shells (Fig. 19–5) with the breathing apparatus carried on a calcareous loop. They began in the Silurian but never reached abundance during the Paleozoic Era. They are well represented in Jurassic beds, and comprise most of the brachiopods living today. *Cryptonella* is a characteristic Devonian genus.

Bryozoa are extraordinarily abundant in limestones of Ordovician and Silurian age (Fig. 19–7). Many of the rocks of those periods are composed largely of their fossils.

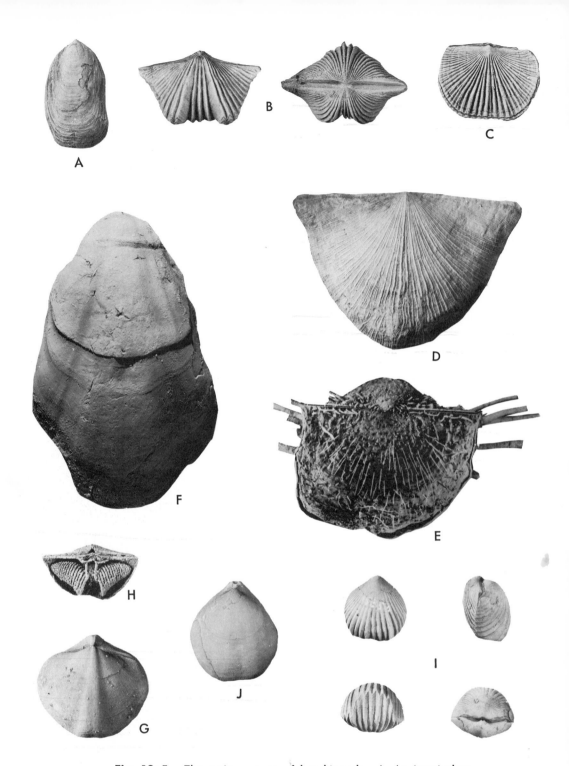

Fig. 19–5. The major groups of brachiopods. A. An inarticulate type, *Lingula*. B–I. Articulates: B, C. Orthids, *Platystrophia* and *Dinorthis*. D, E. Strophomenids, *Rafinesquina* and *Productus*. F. Pentamerids, *Pentamerus*. G, H. Spiriferids, *Eospirifer* and *Mucrospirifer*. I. Rhynchonellids, *Cassidirostrum*. J. Terebratulids, *Cranaena*. All of the above are from Ordovician or Silurian rocks except *Cranaena*, which is Lower Devonian. (Courtesy in part of the Smithsonian Institution, in part of the Redpath Museum.)

Fig. 19–6. *Zygospira.* An Ordovician spiriferid brachiopod. (Courtesy of the Smithsonian Institution.)

They were important contributors to some reefs. Bryozoa make excellent index fossils but must be identified from thin sections examined under the microscope (see Fig. A–14).

Mollusca

The cephalopods first appeared in the Late Cambrian. By Early Ordovician time they were common in the epeiric seas. Some were crawlers and others were swift swimmers. All were predatory and probably ate any animal not protected by a stony shell. All the early members of this class were nautiloids whose septa dividing the shell into chambers were simple saucer-like plates. The chambers were filled with gas and probably served to relieve the animal of much of the weight of its heavy shell. During the Early Ordovician Epoch, the complete range of shell forms existed—from straight to curved cones to loosely and tightly coiled shells. All these forms persisted for several periods and the last still exists today as the genus *Nautilus* (see Fig. A–18).

By the close of the Ordovician Period, all the major groups of nautiloids had appeared. Some secreted the largest invertebrate shells known, massive cones up to 17 feet long (Fig.

19–1). By Silurian time, however, nautiloids were less abundant (Fig. 19–8) and had begun the steady decline that continues to the present. The abundance, rapid evolution, and wide distribution of the nautiloids (which may have continued after death by the floating of their empty shells) make them good guide fossils. They were certainly the most powerful invertebrates during Ordovician and Early Silurian times, yielding to or possibly sharing dominance with the eurypterids in the Late Silurian.

Three times as many families of gastropods have been described from Ordovician rocks as from Cambrian. Most of the Early and Middle Ordovician gastropods were coiled in a plane, but those with a spire rapidly overshadowed the simpler types. In general shape there is not much difference between

A

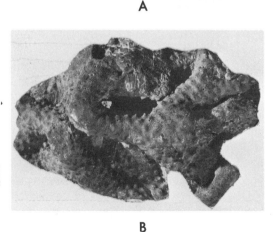

B

Fig. 19–7. Ordovician bryozoa. A. *Prasopora.* B. *Hallopora.* Both are common rock builders. (B. Courtesy of the Redpath Museum.)

Fig. 19–8. Rock garden on the Silurian sea floor. The assemblage of animals and plants in general resembles that of Fig. 19–1. The mound on the right is a reef which has been built up by compound corals (some individuals expanded), lacy bryozoan colonies, white algal growths, etc. Crinoid-like cystids wave on long stems above the reef, and crinoids are rooted both there and in the left foreground. Cephalopods and trilobites cruise over both reef and adjacent sea floor. Algae are present on the latter. (Diorama by George Marchand, courtesy of the Buffalo Museum of Science.)

the gastropods of Ordovician–Silurian time and those of today. Pelecypods (referred to as BIVALVIA by many modern writers) appear in Lower Ordovician beds but do not become common until the Upper Ordovician. They are rarely used as guide fossils for these two periods. Gastropods, however, have been found to be useful.

One difficulty in the study of molluscan fossils arises because these animals secrete a shell of aragonite rather than calcite. Their shells therefore are dissolved more easily, and usually only casts and molds remain to show where shells have been (see Fig. 2–5).

Arthropoda

At the beginning of the Ordovician, trilobites were somewhat less abundant than they had been at their climax in the Upper Cambrian, but by the middle of the Ordovician they were obviously on the downward path and continued to decline during the Silurian (see Fig. 18–13). The many varieties of form and "ornamentation" of the trilobites were without doubt adaptations to certain habitats: the mud burrowers, such as *Cryptolithus* (Fig. 19–9), lost their eyes and developed a broad frontal brim; the floaters,

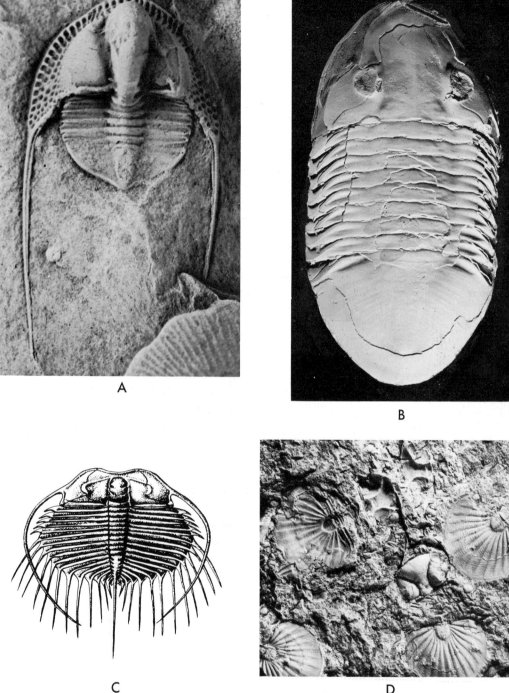

Fig. 19–9. Lower Paleozoic trilobites. *A. Cryptolithus* (Ordovician), a mud burrower. *B. Isotelus* (Ordovician), simple and unspecialized, a surface crawler. *C. Ctenopyge* (Cambrian), adapted for floating or swimming. *D. Scutellum* (Silurian), an assemblage of dissociated parts of dorsal shields. (*A.* Courtesy of the Smithsonian Institution. *B.* Courtesy of the Redpath Museum. *C.* From *Treatise on Invertebrate Paleontology,* courtesy of the Geological Society of America and the University of Kansas Press. *D.* Courtesy of the Geological Survey of Canada.)

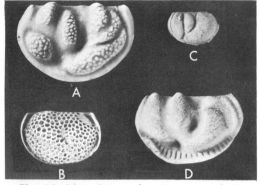

Fig. 19–10. Ostracods. Because of their small size (generally 1–2 mm long), they are usually called microfossils, and are of great value in correlation carried out by means of borehole cuttings. A, B, D. Silurian. C. Devonian. (Courtesy of R. V. Kesling.)

such as *Ctenopyge* (Fig. 19–9), became spiny and small, thereby increasing in surface area while remaining constant in weight; and the smooth type, such as *Isotelus* (Fig. 19–9), was well adapted to crawling over the sea floor. Other trilobites developed spines, probably for defense against nautiloids and primitive vertebrates. Many trilobites developed the ability to enroll—as does the only modern terrestrial crustacean, the pill-bug— doubtless a method of protecting their soft underbody. Whole trilobite fossils are comparatively rare. Upon molting the exoskeleton tended to fall apart, resulting in an assemblage of trilobite debris. See *Scutellum* in Fig. 19–9.

Because they had no biting mouth parts, it is supposed that trilobites fed on carrion, and they probably were largely responsible for keeping the early Paleozoic sea floor clean. In turn, they were most likely preyed upon by cephalopods, eurypterids, and fish, all of which contributed to their decline and probably to their extinction in Permian time.

Ostracods, first noted in Cambrian rocks, became abundant in Early Ordovician time and have remained so since. Some beds of Lower Ordovician limestone are almost completely composed of their tests. The majority of these early ostracods were smooth, such as *Leperditia*, but carapaces with nodes, ridges, furrows, frills, and other irregularities appeared before the Ordovician was over (Fig. 19–10). When they are abundant, they are useful to the petroleum geologist as index fossils because most of them are small enough to be brought intact to the surface in well cuttings.

The eurypterids were the largest arthropods of all time (Figs. 19–11 and 19–12). Because their long body clearly resembles that of a scorpion, they are sometimes called sea scorpions. Their five pairs of appendages included walking feet and swimming paddles; and a pair of pincers, always on the first set of appendages, made some of them the most powerful animals in the Silurian seas. Fragments of a specimen collected from Upper Silurian limestone near Buffalo, New York, suggest that that species grew to a length of 9 feet, but 9 inches was probably the average length. The earliest eurypterids are found in Lower Ordovician strata; their fossils, however, are common in North America only in the Upper Silurian argillaceous limestones of New York and Ontario.

Fig. 19–11. *Eurypterus lacustris,* Upper Silurian, Ontario. Like trilobites, eurypterid fossils are usually found only as fragments. Nearly complete ones such as this are rare. The appendages stemming from the head region are poorly shown. (Courtesy of the Geological Survey of Canada.)

eurypterids – Arthropods.
up-Sil.

Fig. 19–12. Late Silurian hypersaline environment. Two euryp-terids (*Carcinosoma*) on a sea floor devoid of organisms except for worms, gastropods, and algae. (Courtesy of the New York State Museum.)

The group persisted to the end of the Paleo-zoic Era, but specimens are rare in rocks younger than Devonian. Early eurypterids are found in rocks deposited in marine en-vironments (Fig. 19–12); by Silurian time they had taken to brackish water estuaries, and in Devonian and subsequent time they are found in sediments laid down in fresh-water environments. Eurypterids were car-nivorous and the larger ones almost certainly were predators.

Echinodermata

All major divisions of the echinoderms were present in Ordovician rocks. Only the cri-noids deserve more than casual mention. In both the Ordovician and Silurian they were abundant in places, and their small calcareous plates accumulated in such quantities that they formed thick "crinoidal limestones." Some Ordovician limestones composed en-tirely of cystid plates are difficult to distin-guish from these crinoidal limestones. Cri-noids increased in number throughout early Paleozoic time, reached a climax in the Mis-sissippian Period, and then declined.

Graptoloidea

Graptolites reached their climax in both abundance and variety during the Ordovi-cian Period, declined throughout the Silurian Period, and became extinct in Mississippian time. The primitive netlike or treelike den-droid forms with an indeterminate number of branches, such as *Dictyonema* (Fig. 19–13) and *Dendrograptus,* appeared in the Mid-dle Cambrian Epoch. From these forms the more advanced graptoloid stock evolved in Early Ordovician time by a process of stipe reduction, passing through stages of 64, 32, 16, 8, 4, and 2 terminal branches (Fig. 19–14). Colonies with four branches either hanging from a central disc (*Tetragraptus*) or united back-to-back along an axis (*Phyllo-graptus*) are common and characteristic of Lower Ordovician rocks. By late Early Or-dovician time the two-branched stage was reached. At first the branches were spread apart like wings (*Didymograptus*), but later they became fused back-to-back to form a biserial colony (*Diplograptus*). In Silurian time most of the graptoloids consisted of a

single branch (*Monograptus*); when this group became extinct early in the Devonian, graptoloid evolution came to an end. However, the simple netlike dendroid graptolites persisted until the Mississippian Period.

The graptolites probably floated free, or were suspended from floats or seaweed near the surface of the ocean, and were therefore distributed by winds and currents to all parts of the world. Because the group evolved rapidly and each new type spread quickly over a wide area, the graptolites make excellent index fossils wherever they are found for correlating rocks of Ordovician and Silurian ages. However, they were preserved almost solely in black shales, and so are of limited usefulness.

Fig. 19–13. *Dictyonema* (Cambrian–Mississippian), one of the longest-lived of graptolite genera. The specimen shown is an expanded colony from the Silurian of Ontario. (Courtesy of the Redpath Museum.)

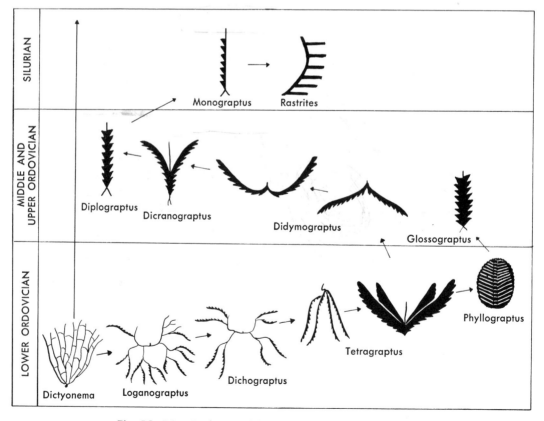

Fig. 19–14. Evolution of the form of the graptolite colony.

Fig. 19–15. Articulated plates of parts of the dorsal shield of *Astraspis desiderata* (approximate magnification × 2). All other Ordovician vertebrate fossils consist of separated plates. Photograph of a latex mold of the original in the Smithsonian Institution. (Courtesy of Tor Ørvig.)

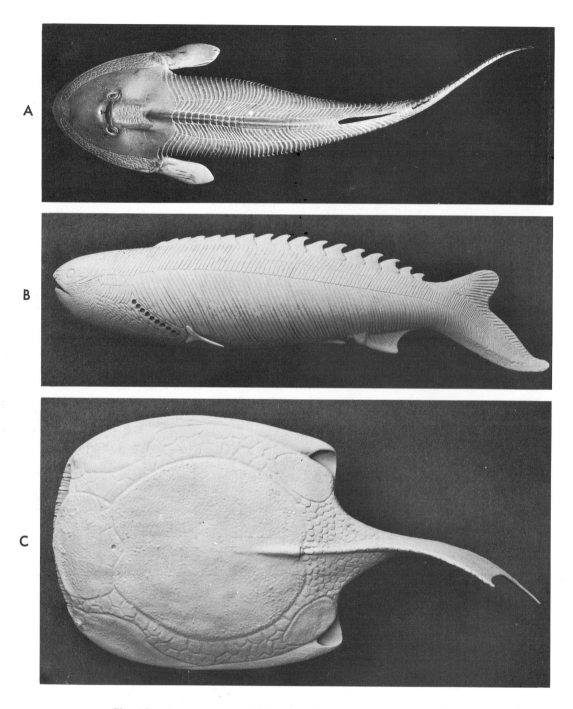

Fig. 19–16. Agnathous fish from Middle Paleozoic rocks. A. *Hemi-cyclaspis* (Late Silurian), a typical ostracoderm with rigid anterior and flexible, finely plated posterior. B. *Pterolepis* (Late Silurian), a finely plated member of the Agnatha. C. *Drepanaspis* (Early Devonian), with a turtle-like anterior and small, flexible tail. (Courtesy of the American Museum of Natural History.)

Vertebrata

Fragmentary remains of bony-plated fish have been found in Lower Ordovician rocks of the Baltic region and at several places in Middle Ordovician rocks in the eastern Cordillera. The bony plates are by no means primitive, suggesting that the animal which bore them had Cambrian, even possibly Precambrian, ancestors. The most nearly complete of these Ordovician fossils shows an extensive dorsal shield but gives little idea of the appearance of the living animal (Fig. 19–15). The oldest complete vertebrate specimens occur in the uppermost Silurian beds of England and Scandinavia. These early vertebrates belong to the class AGNATHA (Greek: without jaws), the largest subdivision of which contains the ostracoderms (Greek: plated skin). The ostracoderms possessed a notochord and gills but lacked a lower jaw. They were encased largely in bony plates that protected them from enemies but restricted their swimming activities. Most ostracoderms had flat, broad-brimmed heads with the jawless mouth on the underside. *Hemicyclaspis* (Fig. 19–16) is typical. Undoubtedly, they spent much of their time scavenging by filter-feeding on the muddy bottoms of streams and lakes. Other types of ostracoderms with more streamlined bodies, such as *Pterolepis* (Fig. 19–16), were adapted for active swimming, but none of them was as efficient a swimmer as the modern fish because their heavy plate covering restricted their movements.

Ostracoderms were plentiful and diversified in the Early Devonian Epoch. One of them, *Drepanaspis* (Fig. 19–16), was a very flat and broad lake-bottom feeder. They began to decline, however, with the development of more efficient fish known as placoderms, and by the end of the Devonian they had become extinct. Only the cyclostomes, a minor branch of the agnaths which did not develop armor, survive today as the lamprey and the hagfish.

The origin of the agnaths remains a mystery. No earlier fossils are known which can be termed intermediate between these first chordates and any group of invertebrates. Study of comparative anatomy and embryological development of living forms suggests that the chordates are most closely related to the echinoderms and developed quite apart from the advanced segmented invertebrates, the annelids and arthropods. It remains for future discoveries to settle this problem.

QUESTIONS

Questions for the material in this chapter are included in the list at the end of Chapter 22.

REFERENCES AND SUGGESTED READINGS

References and suggested readings for the material in this chapter will be found at the end of Chapter 22.

20

Late Paleozoic Life

INTRODUCTION

When the Silurian Period closed, the Paleozoic Era was half over. All the invertebrate phyla and nearly all the classes had evolved. Three classes were added during the later Paleozoic, after which diversification involved only orders or taxa of lesser value. Out of a total of 375 million years, 200 million years of the Paleozoic Era were occupied by the Cambrian (100), Ordovician (60), and Silurian (40) periods. The evolutionary advances made during that time were substantial, but compared with the evolutionary progress of the second half of the era they seem insignificant.

By the end of Silurian time plants had gained a foothold on land, though possibly only an insecure one. During the remainder of the Paleozoic much of the continental area became forested and all the major plant types except the flowering plants, evolved. Such an advance was great enough in itself, but its consequences in setting the stage for the coming of the land vertebrates were of even greater significance. From one type of Devonian fish the land vertebrates evolved rapidly through the amphibian stage and gave rise to the first animals independent of the water, the reptiles. The birds and the mammals arrived during the Mesozoic Era. The late Paleozoic was a time of fundamental and rapid change.

With the exception of nautiloid cephalopods and trilobites, all major subdivisions of invertebrates forged ahead in number and variety during this time. The trilobites died off in the Permian Period. Nautiloid cephalopods with straight or tightly coiled shells lived beyond the Permian, and of these only one genus of coiled nautiloids exists today.

PLANTS

During the Precambrian and Early Paleozoic, marine algae were abundant, and by Silurian time all the major divisions of the algae were in existence. Blue-green algae are the most conspicuous of algal fossils because they formed easily preserved, hemispherical masses called stromatolites. Because of their lack of hard parts the other seaweeds are in general poorly preserved in all systems, and practically the only records of their existence are vague branching or swirling impressions known as fucoids.

432

Fig. 20–1. Habitat group showing land plants along a Devonian shore. In the foreground is *Psilophyton* with its curled tips, accompanied by primitive low ferns. Large tree-sized ferns (*Aneurophyton*) are shown with their bulbous trunk bases. The apparently leafless trees on the left are lycopsids. (Mural by G. A. Reid, courtesy of the Royal Ontario Museum.)

Nevertheless, the sea floors presumably always had a quota of waving seaweeds, but only in rare deposits such as the Burgess Shale are these early algae preserved in any detail.

Until Early Devonian time the land was bare of vegetation, with the possible exception of the rock-clinging lichens and a few questionable terrestrial plants. Cambrian, Ordovician, and probably Silurian landscapes must have been as bleak as those of desert regions today.

From modest beginnings at the start of the Devonian Period, land plants underwent an impressive explosion in the Upper Devonian. The plants that provided much of the vegetation for the coal of the Pennsylvanian System evolved. As the Paleozoic Era came to an end, the coal-forming flora of the swamps declined and an upland flora appeared that ultimately was to cover the earth.

Nature rarely compartmentalizes her offspring, but the progress of plant life can be divided for convenience into a half-dozen stages (see illustrations on the front end papers):

1. Precambrian floras—bacteria and algae.

2. Emergence upon land, Devonian (possibly earlier)—*Psilophyton*, etc.

3. Terrestrial adaptive radiation, Upper Devonian to Pennsylvanian—lycopods, sphenopsids, ferns, seed ferns, cordaites, conifers.

4. Permian to Triassic depression—lycopsids and sphenopsids much reduced.

5. Mesozoic recovery—cycads and conifers in ascendancy, angiosperms appear.

6. Modern flora—ferns, conifers, and angiosperms dominate.

The *Psilophyton* Flora

In 1859, James W. Dawson recognized in Devonian sediments of the Gaspé Peninsula of Quebec a branching plant which he called *Psilophyton* and which he believed was the first land plant. Since Dawson's discovery, many similar fossil plants have been described from beds of Early to Late Devonian age, and have been assigned to the phylum PSILOPSIDA (Fig. 20–1).

The simplest, and possibly the most primitive, of the psilopsids is *Rhynia,* from the Middle Devonian of Scotland, which was found preserved in a silicified Devonian peat bog in complete anatomical detail, together with a few ticks and primitive spiders. The underground rootstock, or rhizome (see Fig. A–2), in well-preserved specimens is covered by many hairlike structures. The stems were at least 20 cm long and up to 6 mm thick, and were either naked or provided near the base with small protuberances considered by some to be the forerunners of leaves. The sporangia, or spore cases, were carried on the tips of the branches, and some have yielded well-preserved spores (asexual reproductive bodies). *Psilophyton* was a larger plant that grew from a horizontal rhizome to a height of 100 cm. The tips of some of the branches were coiled, and the spore cases were carried at the ends of the branches.

A more complicated and larger psilopsid is *Asteroxylon,* with both dichotomous and irregular branching. The lower parts of the stems, at least, are clothed with an abundance of spirally arranged leaflike structures, possibly the forerunners of the spiral leaves of some of the lycopsids. None of the psilopsids survived the Devonian Period, unless the modern *Psilotum* is included in the phylum.

The ancestry of the psilopsids is not known. Differentiation of the psilopsids produced three prominent members of the Devonian and later Paleozoic plant groups—the LYCOPSIDA, SPHENOPSIDA, and PTEROPSIDA. These persisted as abundant constituents of the world flora until the close of the Paleozoic Era, when the lycopsids and sphenopsids approached extinction. Only a handful of genera persist today. The pteropsids, on the other hand, have remained important members of the world flora until the present, and are considered to have given rise to the seed-bearing, and hence the flowering, plants of modern times.

Lycopsida

The lycopsids, sometimes called the scale trees, are a group represented today only by the common creeping ground pine, *Lyco-*

podium (see Fig. A–3), and two or three other genera. The earliest lycopsid, *Baragwanathia,* from the Devonian of Australia, was somewhat larger than *Lycopodium* but otherwise similar. Most Devonian lycopsids were of this type, but in the late Paleozoic coal swamps they developed into trees more than 100 feet high (Fig. 20–2). Most of them had straight, high trunks that were branched only near the top. The younger branches were thickly set with long, narrow leaves that reached lengths of 2 or 3 feet. The roots of the lycopsid trees were small compared with the bulk of the tree and spread laterally rather than downward. The tree reproduced by means of spores that were usually housed in cases at the ends of the branches. *Lepidodendron* grew to heights of about 100 feet and was extensively branched at the top (Figs. 20–2, 20–8 and 20–10). Leaves grew from the trunk and branches in spiral rows and left scars on the bark when they were shed, in a pattern similar to that of a snake's skin (Fig. 20–3). More than 100 species of *Lepidodendron* have been described, and they are among the most common impressions found in the Pennsylvanian coal measures. Another important lycopsid of this time was *Sigillaria* (Figs. 20–2, 20–3, 20–8, and 20–10). Its swordlike leaves, up to 3 feet long, grew in vertical rows from the trunk and left scars of octagonal outline resembling an old-fashioned letter seal (Latin: *sigillum*). The tree grew to heights comparable to that of *Lepidodendron* but was either unbranched or branched once near the top, where the leaves of the mature plant appeared.

Sphenopsida

The sphenopsids (or arthrophytes) are spore-bearing plants characterized by jointed stems. They are represented today by a single genus, *Equisetum,* the horsetail or scouring rush of railway embankments and swampy places (see Fig. A–4). The main stem of the sphenopsids is usually longitudinally ribbed and is divided into segments by joints, from which circlets of branches or leaves are given off. Spore cases are found

Fig. 20–2. Reconstruction of a Pennsylvanian coal forest. Tall, branched *Lepidodendron* trees dominate the scene. Unbranched *Sigillaria* trees with tulip-shaped crowns of leaves and *Calamites* with whorls of leaves surrounding the trunks and branches are prominent in the swamp. A dragonfly skims across the water, and an amphibian basks in the sun. (Mural by P. R. Haldorsen, courtesy of the National Museum of Canada.)

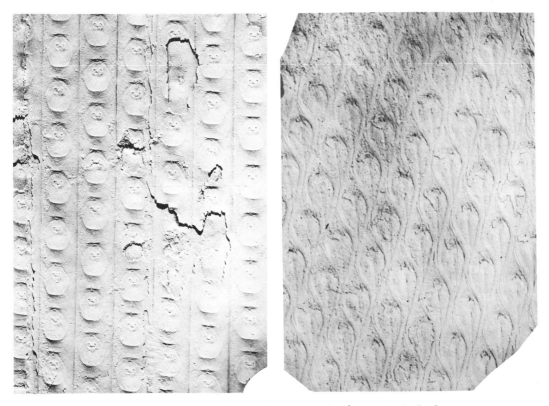

Fig. 20–3. Bark of lycopsid trees, with characteristic leaf-scar pattern. *Left: Sigillaria. Right: Lepidodendron.* (Courtesy of the Redpath Museum.)

Fig. 20–4. Portion of a *Calamites* stem showing the vertical fluting and annular constrictions. (Courtesy of the Field Museum of Natural History.)

Fig. 20–5. *Annularia,* whorls of leaves which have fallen away from the constrictions on branches of Calamites or other arthrophytes. (Courtesy of the Field Museum of Natural History.)

at the tips of the main branches. Although most of the modern horsetails are only a few feet high, their ancient representatives grew to heights of nearly 100 feet (Figs. 20–2, 20–4, and 20–8), and were minor contributors in the formation of coal. Their history begins with small fossils in the Rhynie Chert, but in the Pennsylvanian coal swamps the most important genus, *Calamites,* grew to be 80 feet tall. Most of the stem fossils are internal molds, to which coalified bark material sometimes adheres (Fig. 20–4). Like

their modern representatives, they were either hollow or filled with pith. The circlets of leaves were united at their bases into a continuous sheath surrounding the parent branch, from which they easily became separated. When only the leaves of *Calamites* are preserved, they are given names such as *Annularia* or *Asterophyllites* (Figs. 20–5 and 20–8).

Pteropsida

Pteropsids are the true ferns, so called to differentiate them from the seed ferns. True ferns reproduce by means of spores that are shed from spore cases on the undersides of the leaves. Some of the Devonian pteropsids were treelike plants (Fig. 20–1), but during the Pennsylvanian Period they probably constituted much of the underbrush of the coal swamps. Of the spore-bearing terrestrial plants, they are the only group to persist in abundance to the present.

Ferns are among the most common of Devonian plants. *Aneurophyton,* widely known by its earlier but misleading name, *Eospermatopteris,* grew to at least 40 feet in height (Fig. 20–1). Its remains were first found at Gilboa, New York, and it is sometimes referred to as the Gilboa tree. From

Fig. 20–6. *Archaeopteris, a low-growing Devonian fern.* (Courtesy of the Redpath Museum.)

the bulbous anchoring roots, up to 3 feet in diameter, numerous slender rootlets penetrated the soil. The trunk bore near its upper end a number of fernlike branches, many of which carried terminal spore cases. *Archaeopteris* was another Devonian fern, probably of treelike height (Fig. 20–6).

Pteridospermales

The pteridosperms, or seed ferns, were entirely fernlike in their leaves and stems, but, unlike any plant so far described, they reproduced by means of seeds and pollen. Although the seed ferns are now extinct, the more complex cycads and the angiosperms, which later came to dominate the flora, are believed to have evolved from them. Unless the seed-bearing organs are preserved, some fernlike fossils such as *Neuropteris* (Fig. 20–7) and *Pecopteris* (Fig. 20–8) cannot

usually be identified as either pteropsids or pteridosperms. *Glossopteris* (Fig. 20–9) is a well-known genus occurring only in the Southern Hemisphere. The *Glossopteris* flora is one of the evidences favoring the late Paleozoic union of South America, Africa, India, and Australia into a vast southern continent. Both the true ferns and the seed ferns grew in late Paleozoic time into trees 30 to 40 feet high, like the modern tree ferns of the tropics. The pteridosperms persisted into the Jurassic Period, but they were never a major constituent of the land flora after Pennsylvanian time.

Cordaitales

The CORDAITALES were a primitive order of treelike plants closely related to both the seed ferns and the conifers, and perhaps intermediate between the two groups. They had

Fig. 20–7. Reconstruction of the seed fern *Neuropteris*. Notice the fernlike foliage and the seeds depending from the tips of the branches. (Courtesy of the Field Museum of Natural History.)

Fig. 20–8. A corner of a Pennsylvanian forest. On the left a roachlike insect crawls up a *Lepidodendron* trunk. Left center is a fern with leaves resembling *Pecopteris*. The thick trunks on the right are sphenopsids whose small branches carry abundant whorls of leaves similar to *Annularia*. A huge dragonfly perches on an arthrophyte stump. *Sigillaria* trees can be seen in the left background. (Courtesy of the New York State Museum.)

Fig. 20–9. Leaves of *Glossopteris*, a member of the Pteropsida. (Courtesy of R. D. Gibbs.)

long, bladelike leaves and bore clusters of naked seeds. Most cordaitids were trees with wood like that of the conifers, but with a central core of pith. They appeared in the Pennsylvanian and Permian periods, when they were the most abundant of the seed-bearing plants. The earliest genus, *Callixylon*, from the Upper Devonian, is known to have been 5 feet in diameter. It probably stood several tens of feet high, although the longest trunk so far measured is only 9 feet. *Cordaites* grew to nearly 100 feet in the Pennsylvanian coal swamps. The upper part of its trunk was divided into several branches which bore leaves up to 4 inches wide and 3 feet long. Of all the plants so far mentioned, only pteropsids and cordaitids persisted in force through the Permian Period (Fig. 20–10), but these died out early in the Mesozoic Era. They are supposed to have given rise to the conifers during the Pennsylvanian Period.

Coniferales

The chief characteristics of the conifers are the bearing of naked seeds in cones and a trunk composed solidly of wood (see Fig.

A–6). In these two features they differ from the cordaitids. In the Pennsylvanian they became the dominant type of tree, yielding only during the Cenozoic to the spread of angiosperms and to destruction by man. *Walchia* (Fig. 20–10) is a genus of Permian time.

Ginkgoales

The ginkgoes form a small but interesting group of conifer-like trees first found in Lower Permian beds and persisting today as a single species. Fan-shaped leaves, more or less lobed, are characteristic of this group.

Résumé

The Devonian land flora consisted of primitive plants known as the psilopsids. By Upper Devonian time many higher plants evolved and took the place of the psilopsids. Three of these, the lycopsids, sphenopsids, and pteropsids—all spore-bearing—developed throughout the Mississippian and Pennsylvanian and were responsible for the greatest part of the plant remains making up Pennsylvanian coal. All survive to the present, but only the pteropsids are present in any

Fig. 20–10. Diorama of a water hole in an arid part of west Texas during Permian time. The large tree in the center foreground is *Cordaites*. Two tall *Sigillaria* trees grow nearby. At the extreme right is a tall *Lepidodendron* and a *Sigillaria* with divided top. Of intermediate heights are two tree ferns, and small bushlike ferns form a thicket nearby. Sphenopsids grow near the water. Finbacks *(Dimetrodon* at left, *Edaphosaurus* at right) and smaller reptiles are the only animals present. In the distance are primitive conifers, probably *Walchia.* (Courtesy of the New York State Museum.)

numbers. The disappearance of the swamps tolled the knell of most of the spore bearers, but the newly evolved seed plants were able to adjust to an upland situation. Unfortunately, their chances of being buried and preserved in that environment were slight. The seed ferns, conifers, and ginkgoes thrived under the new conditions and became the dominant types in the early part of the Mesozoic Era. Of these, the seed ferns have the distinction of giving rise to the higher seed-bearing plants, including cordaitids, conifers, and gingkoes.

INVERTEBRATES

The oldest fossils that can be assigned unequivocally to the FORAMINIFERA come from Lower Ordovician limestone. They are small tests composed of sand grains stuck together to make a covering for one-celled animals. Fossil forams are relatively rare in lower Paleozoic rocks. In the Devonian Period, some animals of this order secreted tests of calcium carbonate composed of a series of chambers coiled in one plane. Tests of this type, known as endothyroid, became abundant during the Mississippian Period and contributed to the limestones accumulating over North America at this time. Some granular limestones prove, on close examination, to be composed almost completely of these minute tests.

A family of forams called the fusulines evolved from the endothyroid stock at the beginning of the Pennsylvanian Period. The fusulines formed spindle-shaped tests composed of a wall coiled along the long axis of the spindle and enclosing a space divided from pole to pole by thin plates or septa

(Fig. 20–11). Most fusuline shells are about the size and shape of a grain of wheat, but some grew to almost an inch in length (Fig. 20–12). Throughout the Pennsylvanian and Permian periods, the fusulines evolved rapidly, multiplied astronomically, and spread globally. They are therefore the most satisfactory index fossils for dating beds of late Paleozoic time. The group underwent periods of accelerated evolution in the Middle Pennsylvanian and again in Early Permian time.

A remarkable local development took place among sponges in Late Devonian time (Fig. 20–13), when widespread colonies of glass sponges such as *Hydnoceras* (Fig. 20–14) spread across the eastern United States. Generally, sponges are unimportant Paleozoic fossils, but they seem to have played an important part in the building of the Permian reefs of western Texas. Both tabulate and rugose corals surpassed them in number in Silurian rocks, built extensive barrier and patch reefs until the Pennsylvanian Period,

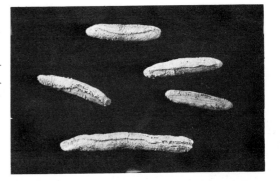

Fig. 20–12. Relatively gigantic examples of the fusuline foram *Parafusulina*, an index fossil for the Permian (actual size). (Courtesy of the Smithsonian Institution.)

and declined to extinction by the end of the Permian (Fig. 20–24).

Throughout this time, BRYOZOA were extraordinarily abundant; they have continued to act as rock builders to the present day. Of special interest is the FENESTELLIDA, a family in which the colony is built like the fabric of lace. *Fenestella* and *Archimedes* (Fig. 20–15) are well known and abundant genera. In *Archimedes*, the lacy network spiraled around a screwlike axis (possibly formed by a symbiotic alga), which is generally the only part of the organism to be preserved. *Archimedes* is abundant in Upper Mississippian rocks and is one of the most easily recognized index fossils. Nineteenth-century prospectors used it as a guide to the coal-bearing strata when they learned that coal seams are all stratigraphically above the "screw fossil."

Brachiopods flourished as never before throughout the Late Paleozoic (Fig. 20–16). Spiriferids were most abundant in the Devonian and lasted into the Mesozoic Era. One of the important events in the late Paleozoic evolution of invertebrates was the climb to dominance of the productids, which evolved from the *Rafinesquina* stock in Devonian time and rapidly became one of the most abundant of brachiopod families. Productids superficially resembled *Rafinesquina*, but their thin shells were produced along the anterior margin and were conspicuously bent

Fig. 20–11. Photomicrograph of Pennsylvanian limestone showing cross-sections of the fusuline foram *Triticites* (magnification × 10). (Courtesy of the Illinois Geological Survey.)

Fig. 20–13. The glass-sponge garden of western New York in Devonian time. More than a dozen kinds are shown in this seascape. The arthrodire *Dinichthys* chases a small, early bony fish. (Courtesy of the New York State Museum.)

Fig. 20–14. *Hydnoceras,* the sponge at the right in Fig. 20–13, as it appears as an actual fossil. In all three individuals the rectangular arrangement of the spicules can be seen. (Courtesy of the Redpath Museum.)

Fig. 20–15. The Mississippian bryozoan *Archimedes.* This specimen shows only the screwlike axis. On the sharp revolving edge the fragile, lacy fenestellid colony was attached. (Courtesy of the Redpath Museum.)

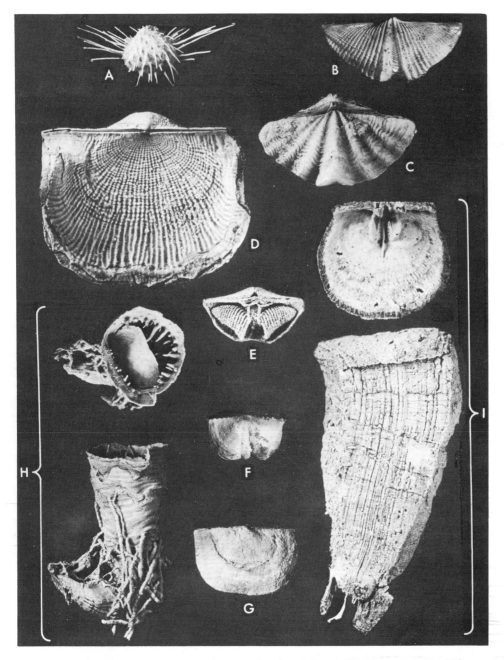

Fig. 20–16. Upper Paleozoic brachiopods. *A. Echinauris* (Permian), a productid, showing the large lateral anchoring spines. *B. Mucrospirifer* (Devonian), a spiriferid. *C.* Interior of the same, with laterally directed spirals. *D. Kozlowskiellina* (Devonian), a spiriferid. *E. Reticulata* (Permian), a productid. *F, G. Mesolobus* and *Chonetes,* Pennsylvanian productids. *H. Prorichthofenia* (Permian), top and side views of the hornlike pedicle valve and the caplike brachial valve. *I. Scacchinella* (Permian), the conical pedicle valve and the normal capping brachial valve. (*A, C, D, E, H, I.* Courtesy of the Smithsonian Institution. *B, F, G.* Courtesy of the Redpath Museum.)

Fig. 20–17. Mollusks of the Upper Paleozoic. *A. Shansiella,* a gastropod (Pennsylvanian, Texas). *B. Pseudopleurophorus,* a pelecypod (Devonian–Permian, North America). *C. Orthonota,* a pelecypod (Devonian, New York).

and covered with spines. These were adaptations to living on soft, muddy ocean floors. The productids failed to survive the Permian Period. Some of them became cemented to the sea floor by one valve which, as a result, grew larger and more irregular than the other. This trend in brachiopod evolution led, in the Permian Period, to such forms as *Richthofenia* and *Scacchinella,* so aberrant that they appeared more like corals than brachiopods (Figs. 20–16 and 20–24).

Mollusks continued to be important members of the marine fauna. Pelecypods were abundant in Devonian muds and sands (Fig. 20–17) and invaded fresh-water environments, where they have thrived ever since. Gastropod fossils record little except a general increase in variety. Among the cephalopods, however, there is a marked change. Ammonoids, which were to become of supreme importance during the Mesozoic Era, appeared in the Devonian Period but were never abundant in the late Paleozoic. The goniatites, with suture lines made up of simple angular lobes and saddles (Fig. 20–18), form the largest group of late Paleozoic cephalopods, and their coiled shells are common fossils in the black shales of this time. Because these animals were free swimmers and spread to all parts of the world, they make good index fossils. The ammonoid suture evolved (Fig. 20–19) into increasingly complex forms: from the broadly curving **goniatite** type to the **ceratite** type, with one side of the curves folded minutely, to the **ammonite** type, in which the entire suture is complicated by minute folds of several orders (see Fig. 21–20). Ammonoids of all three suture types appeared before the close of the Paleozoic Era, and the most advanced, the ammonite type, is found on many Permian shells. The intense folding of the sutures of Mesozoic ammonoids is foreshadowed by the Permian genus *Timorites* (Fig. 20–19).

Fig. 20–18. A late Paleozoic goniatite cephalopod, *Imitoceras* (Mississippian, North America), showing the characteristic suture pattern. (Courtesy of the Smithsonian Institution.)

Fig. 20–19. Permian ammonoids. *Left: Popanoceras* with a ceratite suture, from Texas. *Right: Timorites* with ammonite-type suture, from Timor. (Courtesy of A. K. Miller and W. M. Furnish.)

Fig. 20–20. A group of Devonian trilobites, *Phacops rana*. Notice that the dorsal shields are all complete; hence these are not fossilized molts. Compare with *Scutellum* (Fig. 19–9D). (Courtesy of the Smithsonian Institution.)

Trilobites continued their decline throughout the Upper Paleozoic. In Devonian time they were uncommon, though not rare (Figs. 20–20 and 20–21). By Mississippian time they were very scarce, and the last trilobite disappeared before the end of the Permian.

The late Paleozoic depression had a great effect on the ostracods: family after family failed to survive the Permian Period. However, enough taxa survived to carry on and are found in enormous numbers and great variety throughout the Mesozoic and Cenozoic eras.

Only two classes of the phylum ECHINODERMATA, the crinoids and the blastoids, are common as fossils in late Paleozoic rocks. Both classes began in Ordovician time and reached their peak during the Mississippian Period. The abundance of Mississippian crinoids (Fig. 20–22), attested by the great volume of crinoidal limestone of this age (Fig. 20–23), has already been discussed (see pp. 170–171). The calices of crinoids are generally rare fossils. At Crawfordsville, Indiana, great numbers of Mississippian crinoids have been collected from a single stratum of very fine-grained silt, which allowed an almost perfect preservation of every detail. A similar preservation of Mesozoic crinoids is shown in Fig. 21–26.

The budlike blastoids were rare before the Mississippian but reached their maximum

Fig. 20–21. Restoration of a reefy Devonian sea floor occupied largely by colonial corals, but also some very large horn corals. The spiny trilobite *Tretaspis* and the frilled nautiloid cephalopod *Gyroceras* feed on dead and live material respectively, while a straight nautiloid bides its time. Smaller trilobites and a few gastropods crawl about. A large, delicate crinoid is rooted in the foreground, and on the reef to the right is a colony of branching sponges. (Courtesy of the Smithsonian Institution.)

Fig. 20–22. A rich crinoid fauna growing on a Mississippian sea floor. (Courtesy of the Smithsonian Institution.)

late in that period, when the genus *Pentre-mites* became widespread and abundant. No blastoids are known from rocks of Late Pennsylvanian age, but the discovery of a rich blastoid fauna in Indonesia has extended the range of this class to the end of the Paleozoic. The history of the blastoids during Late Pennsylvanian time is a mystery, but a small group must have survived adverse conditions in some isolated corner of the world and found its way to Indonesia before extinction (Fig. A–26).

One of the most significant developments of this time was the adaptive radiation of marine animals into a fresh-water environment, and ultimately onto dry land. This radiation probably occurred in the Silurian Period, but not until late Paleozoic time did a diverse fauna become established in these environments. As far as we know, only two invertebrate phyla—the MOLLUSCA and the ARTHROPODA—were involved. Pelecypods were water-tied, and though they occur in fresh-water beds from Devonian time on, they never became terrestrial. Gastropods, however, were able to adapt their respiratory system to air breathing, and their first terrestrial representatives appeared in Pennsylvanian coal measures. Among the arthropods, centipedes and millipedes are recorded from Pennsylvanian and Devonian beds respectively. Winged insects first appear in Lower Pennsylvanian strata, but their ad-vanced state of evolution suggests that they began earlier, perhaps in the Mississippian, or even possibly in Devonian time. The coal forest supported an insect population composed largely of cricket-like insects, cockroaches, and an extinct order resembling the modern dragonfly of which more than 800 species have been described from the coal measures. So rapid was the diversification of the insects in late Paleozoic time (Fig. 20–25) that, apart from the development of the social insects, such as bees and ants, few changes in the class have taken place since. On the whole insects are extremely rare fossils, but they occur in abundance in Permian shales, particularly in Kansas. The scorpions were probably the earliest terrestrial arthropods and may have left the sea as early as Silurian time. In the Middle Devonian Rhynie Chert of Scotland, fossil ticks have been recognized, and questionable spiders have been reported from Devonian rocks. Spiders have been positively identified, however, from the Pennsylvanian Period.

VERTEBRATES

By Middle Silurian time vertebrates had been in existence for at least 60 million years but generally had not advanced past the stage of the weak-jawed agnaths. The development of an articulated lower jaw among vertebrates in Late Silurian time initiated

Fig. 20–23. Crinoidal limestone of Devonian age, New York. (Courtesy of the Redpath Museum.)

Fig. 20–24. Permian coral reef. Colonial corals provide the framework, with sponges, spiny and ribbed brachiopods (including productids, spiriferids, rhynchonellids, etc.). At least three kinds of cephalopods are active on both reef and sea floor. The peculiar objects in the center foreground are discarded shells of an aberrant brachiopod, *Leptodus.* (Courtesy of the Smithsonian Institution.)

such a burst of evolution that the Devonian Period has been called the "Golden Age of Fishes." The first fish to possess a lower jaw belonged to a group known as the PLACODERMI. The diversity of this group indicates either a long pre-Silurian history—for which no fossil evidence has been found—or one of the most rapid adaptive radiations in geological history in Late Silurian and Early Devonian time. The gills of the agnaths are separated and supported by compound cartilaginous structures known as gill arches, each shaped like a V on its side with the apex pointing back. In some gill arches there was considerable ossification, and the addition of teeth to such a structure hinged at the point of the V conforms to the shape and function of two jaws.

It is not known which of the agnaths gave rise to the jawed fish. Most agnaths had flattened bodies and fed on the sea bottom. *Birkenia*, however, a small animal a few inches long, had a narrow high body and was an active swimmer (Fig. 20–26). The mouth, which in most agnaths was round and opened on the underside, opened at the front as a horizontal slit. Whether the upper and lower parts moved relative to each other is not known. Spines like those of the most primitive jawed fish, the ACANTHODII, and a tail that was remarkably fishlike reinforce the impression that *Birkenia* was akin to the group of ostracoderms from which the jawed fish evolved. *Birkenia* itself, however, was too specialized to have given rise to the jawed vertebrates.

Fig. 20–25. Late Paleozoic insects. Both belong to extinct orders. *Top:* A distant relative of the modern stone-fly (Permian, Kansas). *Bottom:* Specimen from the Pennsylvanian of Illinois. (Courtesy of F. M. Carpenter.)

Fig. 20–26. Devonian anaspids (approximate magnification × 2). *Top: Birkenia* (Silurian–Lower Devonian). *Bottom: Pteraspis* (Lower Devonian). Anaspids did not survive the Devonian Period. [Photograph by C. W. Stearn, by permission of the Trustees of the British Museum (Natural History).]

The most important subdivisions of the placoderms include the Acanthodii, the Arthrodira, and the Antiarchi. The shark-like acanthodians had bony spines that supported the leading edges of their paired and unpaired fins. In the Devonian genus *Diplacanthus* (Fig. 20–27), the upper jaw was toothless and the lower jaw was provided with sharp teeth. Relatively small bony plates covered the head, and the rest of the body was encased in rhombic scales. Acanthodians reached their maximum development in Early Devonian time, and lingered into the Early Permian.

The arthrodires became the largest and probably the most voracious of Devonian vertebrates. The head and shoulder regions were encased in bony plates, and in early forms such plates also covered the tail region. In later arthrodires the tail was covered by flexible scales, a great advantage for active swimming. The mouth was equipped with large bony plates on both the upper and lower jaws that could shear any object upon which they closed. A ball-and-socket joint between the armor plates of the head and shoulder regions enabled the fish to raise its head and to open its mouth wider than earlier forms. This branch of the placoderms reached its acme in *Dinichthys* (Fig. 20–13), a 30-foot monster that must have been the terror of the Late Devonian seas. Its fossils are found in black shale around Cleveland, Ohio. A smaller form, *Coccosteus* (Figs. 20–27 and 20–29), must have been equally successful in hunting smaller prey. Other arthrodires were flat-bodied, bottom-living animals with teeth suitable for crushing and feeding on shelled invertebrates. Successful as the arthrodires appear to have been, they did not survive the Devonian Period.

In the group known as the antiarchs, the bottom surface was flat, the head and fore-part of the body were covered by a heavy bony shield, and the rest of the body was either naked or covered with small scales. Two jointed lateral appendages, not to be confused with fins, projected behind the head and were used for propulsion or for holding the body in place against a current. The antiarchs superficially resembled some of the ostracoderms, probably because both were adapted to feeding on the sea bottom. In some of the specimens of *Bothriolepis* (Fig. 20–28) from Scaumenac Bay in eastern Que-

bec, mud infiltrated the carcasses immediately upon the death of the animal, preserving some of the internal systems in full detail. These fish had functional lungs connected with the pharynx, but no trace of lungs has been found in any of the agnaths. *Pterichthyodes* is a common form with the posterior part of the body covered by scales (Fig. 20–28).

The placoderms were more efficient than the agnaths in movement and eating, but the swift sharks and bony fish that appeared in Devonian time soon overshadowed their placoderm competitors. A few forms survived into the Mississippian Period, but the majority were confined to the Devonian.

Cartilaginous Fish

From the Carboniferous Period on, the waters have been dominated by the two major groups of living fish, the CHONDRICHTHYES or cartilaginous fish, and the OSTEICHTHYES or bony fish. The living chondrich-

Fig. 20–27. *Coccosteus*, a Devonian arthrodire, seizes one of a school of the acanthodian *Diplacanthus*. The neck joint, which allowed all arthrodires to raise the skull, is well indicated. [Photograph by C. W. Stearn, by permission of the Trustees of the British Museum (Natural History).]

Fig. 20–28. Devonian antiarchs. *Top: Bothriolepis* (½ actual size). *Bottom: Pterichthyodes.* The head and anterior parts of both were covered by large plates. In *Bothriolepis* the posterior portion was naked; in *Pterichthyodes* it was covered with small scales. [Photograph by C. W. Stearn, by permission of the Trustees of the British Museum (Natural History).]

thyans, the sharks and their relatives, have a completely cartilaginous skeleton, which can be fossilized only if—as very rarely happened—it was strengthened by calcification. However, the teeth, which are covered with resistant enamel, the spines, which are similar to those of the acanthodians, and the scaly skin of some species are capable of preservation. In contrast to higher fish, sharks lack an air bladder. *Ctenacanthus* (Fig. 20–29) is a primitive shark 3 feet long that is found well preserved in Upper Devonian black shale near Cleveland, Ohio.

Sharks were plentiful throughout the late Paleozoic. A single group survived into the Triassic and diversified in the Mesozoic and Cenozoic eras into the fusiform modern sharks and the flattened skates and rays. Though apparently never numerous in post-Paleozoic seas, sharks were able to hold their own against competition from bony fish, marine reptiles, and marine mammals, and can be considered an eminently successful group today.

Bony Fish

The cartilaginous fish have been conspicuous members of the marine fauna since the Devonian, but they have always been vastly outnumbered by the bony fish, or OSTEICH-

THYES. In contrast to the sharks, these forms generally have a well-ossified skeleton and an air bladder. Primitive bony fish generally resembled the acanthodians: both had a fusiform body with the head and gill region covered by large bony plates and a complete covering of small scales in the posterior region.

Bony fish first appear in the fossil record in the Lower Devonian, already divided into two diverging stocks: the ACTINOPTERYGIA or ray-finned fish, with the fins supported by a number of nearly parallel bony rays and most of the controlling muscles located in the body wall, and the SARCOPTERYGIA or lobe-finned fish, whose fins are supported by a strong central axis of bone which is surrounded by muscles. In the ray-fins there was a girdle of bone around the anterior part of the body, attached to the skull in some species, which acted as a base for the articulation of the pectoral fins. The earliest of these fish, of which *Rhadinichthys* (Fig. 20–29) is a good example, appear in fresh-water sediments of

Middle Devonian age. From these have descended all the bony fishes of modern fresh-water and salt-water environments, except the sarcopterygians. In this evolution the scales progressed from heavy rhombic forms characteristic of the modern garpike and sturgeon, through intermediate forms, to thin, rounded, flexible scales like those of the salmon. The skeleton evolved from partly cartilaginous and bony to a completely bony condition. The pelvic fins, which were originally posterior in position, moved forward. In many modern ray-fins both pectoral and pelvic fins are located just behind the skull. In Paleozoic bony fish the lung functioned for breathing, but was later transformed into the swim bladder that controls the buoyancy of most modern fish.

From their beginning in the Early Devonian Epoch, the sarcopterygians diverged into two stocks, the lungfish or DIPNOI and the CROSSOPTERYGIA. The earliest lungfish found thus far were marine (Fig. 20–29), but by the Upper Devonian they had become

Fig. 20–29. Devonian seascape. A large primitive shark, *Ctenacanthus* (common in the Cleveland Shale), eyes a few primitive ray-fins of the genus *Rhadinichthys*. On the sea floor *Coccosteus* (at left) and the lungfish *Dipterus* (at right) react to danger by immobility and perhaps by a protective change of coloring. (Courtesy of the Buffalo Museum of Science.)

Fig. 20–30. On the margin of a Devonian fresh-water pond, the lobe-finned crossopterygian *Eusthenopteron* clambers up the bank with the help of its strong bony fins. (Courtesy of the American Museum of Natural History.)

specialized toward life in fresh water, where the constant threat of desiccation gave a distinct advantage to those forms that had developed lungs and were capable of utilizing atmospheric oxygen. A further early specialization of this group was the ability to aestivate. During times of partial or complete desiccation, some lungfish burrowed into the mud and remained inactive during dry spells, returning to the surface with the coming of rains. Evidence of this practice is recorded as far back as the Pennsylvanian. Burrowing lungfish are represented today by the African and the South American genera. The Australian lungfish does not aestivate.

Lungfish were numerous and diverse in the Devonian, but the group has gradually declined since then with little evolutionary change. In modern lungfish the extensive bone in the skull and vertebral column has been largely replaced by cartilage, and the scales have been reduced in thickness. The presence of lungs and muscular paired fins has suggested that the lungfish were related to the ancestors of the land vertebrates. However, their highly specialized dentition and inadequate ossification preclude this relationship.

The lateral fins of the crossopterygians were supported by bones similar to those of the limbs of the land vertebrates. The skeleton was well ossified, unlike that of the lungfish, and the pattern of skull bones closely resembled that of the early amphibians. Like all bony fish, they had a saclike extension of the gullet which served as a primitive lung and nostril passages leading from the exterior to the mouth cavity that enabled them to breathe with the mouth closed. So many resemblances between Devonian crossopterygians and primitive amphibians exist that paleontologists agree that the Late Devonian forms, such as *Eusthenopteron* (Fig. 20–30) probably gave rise to the first amphibians.

As the shallow-water pools in which they lived dried, these fish flopped about on land, breathing air until they found another pool. Under such conditions, those animals with strong fin lobes and lungs would have a great advantage over their less endowed relatives. The premium placed on walking fins and lung breathing by such intense environmental pressure promoted the emergence of land-walking amphibians from water-tied fish.

Lungfish and crossopterygians overcame in different ways dry periods in what was probably a semiarid climate. The lungfish remained dormant, that is, they reacted passively, and reverted in the ensuing wet season to gill breathing. The crossopterygians, on the other hand, reacted actively and left their stagnant or drying pool to seek a more favorable environment.

From Middle Devonian time the crossopterygians evolved along two lines into the marine COELACANTHINI and the fresh-water RHIPIDISTIA, which became extinct in the Permian. Man's ancestry can be traced through the latter. The coelacanths developed steadily and became most abundant in the middle of the Mesozoic, but they are not represented in the post-Cretaceous fossil record and were at first presumed to have become extinct. However, in 1938, a living coelacanth was dredged off the coast of South Africa and was given the name *Latimeria* (Fig. 20–31), in honor of the person responsible for its preservation. Since then a score of specimens have been found. The absence of coelacanths from the fossil record can be attributed to their shift early in the Cretaceous Period to a deep marine environment, from which normally few forms are found as fossils. Although not in direct line toward land vertebrates, these newly discovered fish are the only surviving examples of the crossopterygians.

Amphibians

One of the most dramatic events in the history of vertebrates was the invasion of land by the Paleozoic amphibians, which evolved from the fresh-water descendants of the crossopterygians, the rhipidistians. The shallow-water environment of the rhipidistians was probably subject to frequent desiccation. This gave an advantage to forms which could either aestivate, as did the lungfish, or move about on dry land for short periods. The rhipidistians were probably first forced onto land by the necessity of finding new pools as others dried up. Gradually, as natural selection chose those features useful on land, the rhipidistians became less at

Fig. 20–31. *Latimeria*, a modern coelacanth. This group was once believed to have become extinct in the Mesozoic Era, but has recently been found in the Indian Ocean. Notice the stout fin bases. (Courtesy of J. L. B. Smith.)

home in their original environment and more dependent on terrestrial adaptations. As terrestrial animals, however, they were still forced to return to the water to reproduce, because the developing eggs and young remained dependent on water for support, respiration, and protection from desiccation.

When the fish emerged onto land they had to achieve a permanent air-breathing capability. To support the animal's body against the force of gravity, the amphibian skeleton became more robust than that of its fish forebears. The vertebrae developed special articulating processes which strengthened the vertebral column; the lungs, already present, were supported by a rib cage; and the gills, which could not function without being continuously bathed in water, were lost. Tear ducts in the skull suggest that the eyes, no longer bathed by water, were kept moist by fluids from within the animal itself.

The fishlike scales of early amphibians helped to prevent desiccation, but they gradually lost their importance and disappeared in all descendants, lightening the body and improving movement on land. The loss of scales also permitted respiration through the body surface, a beneficial adaptation, since the lungs of most amphibians did not provide a wide enough surface area for efficient respiration. The auditory system of early amphibians was insufficiently developed for a land environment, for air is less dense than water and is therefore a poorer conductor of sound waves. However, the yoke between the skull and the upper jaw gradually evolved into an intermediary structure, the stapes, which improved hearing ability by directly linking the external eardrum to the brain case.

The earliest known amphibians come from Upper Devonian beds of Greenland. The striking similarity of their skeletal structure to that of Late Devonian lobe-finned fish leaves little doubt as to their ancestry. They are known as the LABYRINTHODONTIA because they, like the rhipidistians, possessed teeth with enamel folded in complicated patterns. Labyrinthodonts were generally sprawling, lazy, and probably stupid beasts that could

not stray far from the water in which their eggs were laid and their young were hatched. They reached their largest size in such broad-headed, squat creatures as the Permian genus *Eryops,* 5 to 6 feet long. The labyrinthodonts reached their greatest variety in Mississippian and Early Pennsylvanian times and became extinct late in the Late Triassic, at about which time some appear to have adapted to a marine habitat.

Reptiles

Vertebrate life took a great step forward when animals were emancipated from an aquatic life by the development of an egg that could be laid and hatched on land. This great evolutionary step marks the transition from amphibians to reptiles. The reptile has a great advantage over the amphibian in that its embryo is supported in a water-filled sac, the amnion (Greek: bowl), and is enclosed in a strong but permeable shell. These amniote eggs contained enough yolk to nourish the growing fetus internally and a sac for the waste products, which among amphibians were discharged directly into the water. The entire embryo was encased in a shell strong enough to resist destruction but porous enough to permit osmotic exchange of waste carbon dioxide for oxygen from the air. The oldest fossil egg comes from Lower Permian strata of Texas, but reptilian fossils can be identified on the basis of bone structure from strata as old as Early Pennsylvanian.

The most primitive reptiles are known as the COTYLOSAURIA, sometimes referred to as the stem reptiles. They form an almost perfect link between the amphibians and the more advanced reptiles. From cotylosaurs we can trace the ancestry of most, if not all, subsequent reptiles. Most cotylosaurs were small and rather lizard-like in general proportions, with a dentition indicative of a carnivorous habit.

A second reptilian stock, the SYNAPSIDA, apparently descended from very early cotylosaurs, for the earliest known members of both lineages are found in the same Lower Pennsylvanian beds. Primitive synapsids, the pelycosaurs, were the dominant reptiles of

the Late Pennsylvanian and Early Permian. Most pelycosaurs were lizard-like in appearance, but two genera, *Dimetrodon*, a carnivore, and *Edaphosaurus*, a herbivore, developed extremely long neural spines on the vertebrae which apparently supported a tall web of skin, or "sail." This has given the popular name of finbacks to these reptiles (Figs. 20–10 and 20–32). Whatever its primary selective advantage, such a web could be used as a heat absorber or dissipater. This suggests that mammalian temperature control existed even in these early reptilian predecessors. Tooth differentiation also first appears in early pelycosaurs, with the development of "canine" teeth between incipient incisors and cheek teeth.

In the Middle Permian, carnivorous pelycosaurs gave rise to a more advanced order of mammal-like reptiles, the THERAPSIDA. Although their skeletal structure was generally reptilian, they possessed all the morpholog- ical features of primitive mammals. For instance, they had a well-developed secondary palate which separated the nasal passage from the mouth and led to more efficient breathing, and dentition differentiated into incisor, canine, and cheek teeth. Instead of walking with their elbows and knees stuck out, in the sprawling, inefficient gait of the other reptiles, they were able to move with their legs directly under their bodies, a pattern of locomotion that supports the body more efficiently and is used by almost all four-legged mammals. Many therapsids were small, agile carnivores. The members of one subdivision, of which *Cynognathus* (see Fig. 21–19) is representative, may have crossed the line separating reptiles from mammals: they had many mammalian skeletal characteristics and may also have had hair and warm blood. The mammal-like reptiles flourished in Late Permian and Triassic times, especially in the Southern Hemisphere.

Fig. 20–32. A group of finback reptiles. The one in the left foreground with nubbly dorsal spines is *Edaphosaurus,* a herbivore. The other five belong to the carnivore genus *Dimetrodon*. This latter is the most common Permian reptilian fossil in North America. A group of small pelycosaurs is seen on the left; on the right the small amphibian *Diplocaulis* remains dependent on the water. (By Charles Knight, courtesy of the Field Museum of Natural History.)

THE PERMIAN ORGANIC CRISIS

At the end of the Paleozoic Era many types of marine invertebrates died out, but other groups continued unchanged into the Mesozoic Era. N. D. Newell has said that "the wholesale extinction of major groups at the close of the Permian period in some ways marks the most critical time in invertebrate history since the early Cambrian." The cause of these extinctions is one of the major problems of paleontology.

Many of the older invertebrate stocks were at a low ebb of vitality in late Paleozoic time. If the rates of evolution of invertebrate phyla and classes are plotted against geological time, a general decrease in the appearance of new animals is evident in the Pennsylvanian Period. However, the faunal population was not small at this time because the rates of extinction were also low. In other words, the Pennsylvanian fauna was more or less stable with respect to the appearance and disappearance of taxonomic groups.

The evolution of marine phyla illustrates how extensive the late Paleozoic crisis was. The corals underwent the most dramatic change, for at the end of the era the tetracorals became extinct and the tabulates were so reduced that paleontologists are not certain that they survived into the Triassic Period. Two of the four Paleozoic classes of the bryozoans died out at this time. Several of the superfamilies of the brachiopods (e.g., PRODUCTACEA, CHONETACEA, and DALMANELLACEA) became extinct. Two orders of the crinoids died out, and the rest showed a general decrease in numbers. The blastoids also died out in the Permian Period. The trilobites finally disappeared after a long decline that began early in the era, and the eurypterids did not survive the Pennsylvanian Period. On the other hand, groups such as the forams, ammonoid cephalopods, ostracods, and echinoids, and all fish except the acanthodians were apparently unaffected by the passing of the era.

Although the Great Permian Depression brought significant changes in marine forms, non-marine animals were little affected. Insects probably increased steadily from Pennsylvanian time to the present. Labyrinthodonts diverged into a number of strictly aquatic lineages in the Upper Permian, and several of these continued until the close of the Triassic before becoming extinct. The cotylosaurs were gradually replaced by more advanced reptiles throughout the Permian and Triassic, but without any dramatic extinctions. The pelycosaurs were succeeded by the therapsids in a similar fashion.

In the plant kingdom, the near extinction of the lycopsids, sphenopsids, pteridosperms, and cordaitids can properly be related to the disappearance of the Pennsylvanian swamps. The pteropsids, however, were able to adapt to the drier conditions and have survived to the present.

We shall never be sure why certain large groups of organisms become extinct at particular times in geological history because we cannot reconstruct the environments of the past in sufficient detail. Changes in the environment to which the animals and plants had become adapted may have been one major cause of extinctions. If a species or family has become highly specialized to a particular environment, and that environment is wiped out by earth movement or changes in sea level, climate, ocean currents, etc., the group will die unless further adaptation is possible. Less specialized animals or plants may be able to evolve in another direction and become adapted to the new situation, but highly specialized organisms rarely retain this evolutionary flexibility.

At the end of the Paleozoic Era the continents were uplifted, and the epeiric seas in which the invertebrates flourished were restricted. Competition among the marine organisms became greater as they were crowded for room and food, and those that were highly specialized for life in a particular habitat and could not adapt to changing conditions lost out in the struggle for existence. Only marine forms like *Lingula*, whose ecological niche has always existed, or forms that still retained the ability to evolve in harmony with the changing environment, were able to survive.

QUESTIONS

Questions for the material in this chapter are included in the list at the end of Chapter 22.

REFERENCES AND SUGGESTED READINGS

References and suggested readings for the material in this chapter will be found at the end of Chapter 22.

21

Life of the Mesozoic Era

The Paleozoic Era is often referred to as the age of invertebrates, the Mesozoic as the age of reptiles, and the Cenozoic as the age of mammals. In no other era was the dominance of a group of animals as clear as it was in the Mesozoic, during which the reptiles invaded land, sea, and air environments and became masters of each. Some reptiles grew to a size that has never been equaled by land animals; among them were the largest land predators that ever lived. Although reptiles of all kinds had been successful, they almost all succumbed to the drastic extinction that left but a few surviving into the Cenozoic.

The dramatic saga of the reptiles had its counterpart among the invertebrates in the rise of the ammonoids to pre-eminence, and the subsequent Late Cretaceous environmental crisis from which none survived. Among plants, the evolution of angiosperms late in the era initiated the change from conifer-dominated floras to the deciduous forests of today.

FISH AND AMPHIBIANS

Among the Mesozoic fish, the sharks and their relatives were present throughout the era but would probably have shrunk to an innocuous few had it not been for the increase of the actinopterygians during the Triassic and Jurassic periods, and particularly for their explosion in the Cretaceous. All sharks are carnivores and have probably always been at or near the apex of the food pyramid in the sea. Lungfish and crossopterygians, never numerous, are recorded throughout the Mesozoic Era. The actinopterygians became dominant, filling essentially all aquatic environments. Their evolution has been so complicated that they have been classified primarily on the basis of levels of development, measured in part by the following features: gradual thinning of the scales, increased ossification of the vertebrae, reduction in the gape of the mouth, modification of the lung into a swim bladder, forward movement of the pelvic fin to a position above the pectoral fin. Today they outnumber many times over all other vertebrates combined. No known niche in the sea is without its ray-finned inhabitants.

Amphibians continued the decline that set in toward the middle of the Permian Period. The last labyrinthodont disappeared in the Late Triassic. Frogs and sal-

461

amanders were left, surviving inconspicuously to the present. Neither group shows any sign of being headed for extinction.

By Triassic time the basic differentiation of reptiles had been completed. The classification of these animals is based primarily upon the structure of the skull, and in particular upon openings in the skull to accommodate expansion of the jaw muscles. The primitive condition, inherited from the amphibians, is a solidly roofed skull. Reptiles retaining this condition include the cotylosaurs and turtles. The latter appear in the Triassic. For practical purposes, however, we shall treat reptiles in accordance with their habitat—reptiles of the lands, the sea, and the air. In Paleozoic time most of the reptiles were terrestrial, and some possibly semiaquatic like crocodiles today; but one Permian group, known as the mesosaurs, was adapted to a completely aquatic life.

THECODONTS: PROTOTYPES OF THE RULING REPTILES

Some modern lizards, when pursued, abandon their normal four-footed gait and take to their hind feet, using their tail as a balance. The beginning of the Triassic Period saw the appearance of the thecodonts, reptiles that stood and walked normally on their hind feet rather than on all four. These are worthy of some attention because they were the ancestors of the great reptiles of later Mesozoic time, known as the archosaurs, or ruling reptiles.

Primitive thecodonts were small animals, 2 or 3 feet high, with strong hind legs upon which they walked. The weight of their body was supported at the hips and was balanced by a long, heavy tail. The placement of the whole weight of the body on the hips made a strengthening of this bony structure necessary, and as an accommodation, the junction of the hip bone with the vertebral column was extended to take in several vertebrae. Each half of the pelvic girdle, composed of three bones, assumed a triradiate form with one branch pointing downward and forward, another down and back, and the third nearly parallel to the backbone. With the change from the quadrupedal posture of their cotylosaur ancestors, the hind legs were lengthened and strengthened, and the forelegs, which tended to lose their function of supporting the body, were reduced. The hind limbs were moved directly under the body instead of being sprawled out as in the amphibians and most of the early reptiles, thus helping to support the greater weight. The skull was lightly constructed and was provided with two openings on each side of the bony framework which reduced its weight. All these changes were passed on by the thecodonts to their descendants, the dinosaurs (see Fig. 21–3).

Phytosaurs

Although the early thecodonts were small, agile, bipedal, running creatures, some of their heavier descendants reverted to a four-footed stance. Among these were the phytosaurs, carnivorous reptiles abundant in Late Triassic time. In exterior form the phytosaur was almost identical with the modern crocodile (Fig. 21–1). Undoubtedly the phytosaurs in Triassic time were similar in their habits to crocodiles or alligators today, floating or lying almost submerged in rivers and lakes, ready to devour passers-by. The phytosaurs are only distantly related to the crocodiles, however, and became extinct in Late Triassic time, just as the first crocodiles appeared. The similarity of the two groups is an example of the principle of **evolutionary convergence,** according to which animals of different lineages become adapted to the same habitat by developing at least superficial resemblances, even though their common ancestry may be remote. Among the differences between the two groups is the position of the nostrils, which are near the eyes in phytosaurs but at the end of the snout in crocodiles. Moreover, the crocodiles developed a secondary palate separating the nasal passage from the mouth, allowing breathing to take place while they are largely submerged.

DINOSAURS: MASTERS OF THE LAND

The suffix "-saur," common in scientific names of many reptiles, is derived from the

Fig. 21-1. The Triassic phytosaur *Rutiodon*. (Courtesy of the American Museum of Natural History.)   *Triassic phytosaur*

Greek word for lizard, *sauros;* the prefix "din-" comes from the Greek word *deinos,* meaning terrible. The term "dinosaur" was coined by Sir Richard Owen in 1841 for the giant reptiles of the Mesozoic Era which were then coming to the attention of the scientific world. When a fuller understanding of the nature of these remarkable fossils had been gained, paleontologists realized that these reptiles, which Owen had regarded as a single group, consisted of two distinct subdivisions, and the term "dinosaur," although still popularly used to include all huge Mesozoic land reptiles, has been discarded by some paleontologists as of little real taxonomic significance.

The separation of the dinosaurs is based on differences in the pelvic structure. The more primitive type of structure characterized the order known as the SAURISCHIA (reptile-hipped) and had a triradiate form like that of the thecodonts, from which the dinosaurs were derived early in the Triassic Period. The other order, the ORNITHISCHIA (bird-hipped), comprises reptiles with a hip structure like that of the birds. Figure 21-2 is a diagrammatic classification of the main sub-divisions of the dinosaurs showing their ranges and relationships.

Theropods   *reptile-hipped*

The first saurischians to appear were the carnivorous theropods of Upper Triassic time. A carnivorous way of life demands agility and speed, and they retained the thecodont's bipedal gait and many other features (Fig. 21-3). In fact, it is difficult to establish an exact separation between them and the thecodonts. Their forelimbs were small and probably served only for grasping food. The earliest lineage consisted of small, birdlike, lightly built, hollow-boned, small-headed forms, with three digits on fore and hind feet. A typical but late genus is *Ornithomimus* (Fig. 21-4), which probably fed on insects and other small animals. A second lineage of theropods evolved into giants. Their hind limbs were massive, their head was enormously enlarged, and their jaws took over the functions of grasping and tearing food. Their useless forelimbs were reduced to non-functional vestiges. *Antrodemus* (Upper Jurassic) and *Gorgosaurus* (Cretaceous) were capable of attacking the largest of their con-

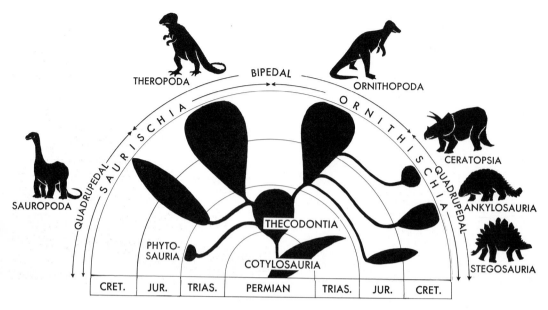

THEROPODA   BIPEDAL   ORNITHOPODA

S A U R I S C H I A   O R N I T H I S C H I A

QUADRUPEDAL   QUADRUPEDAL

SAUROPODA   CERATOPSIA

THECODONTIA   ANKYLOSAURIA

PHYTO-
SAURIA   STEGOSAURIA

COTYLOSAURIA

| CRET. | JUR. | TRIAS. | PERMIAN | TRIAS. | JUR. | CRET. |

Fig. 21–2. The relationships and ranges of the subdivisions of the dinosaurs.

Fig. 21–3. *Scleromochlus,* from the Triassic of Scotland. Long considered one of the thecodonts, which it resembles in many respects, it is now classified as a primitive saurischian dinosaur. The boundary between thecodonts and dinosaurs can be determined only with difficulty. [Courtesy of the British Museum (Natural History).]

Fig. 21–4. A Late Cretaceous landscape with several kinds of dinosaurs. On the left, *Trachodon*, a duck-billed wader, is alarmed by the proximity of *Tyrannosaurus*, whose attention is momentarily riveted on the armored dinosaur *Ankylosaurus* below him. In the middle distance a small carnivore, *Ornithomimus*, seizes a bird. Flowering plants abound to the near exclusion of earlier types. (Diorama by Mrs. Moray Maclaughlin, courtesy of the Redpath Museum.)

temporaries, even the 50-ton monsters described below. The largest theropod, a 45-foot reptile called *Tyrannosaurus*, appeared in Late Cretaceous time (Figs. 21–4 and 21–9). *Tyrannosaurus* held his massive head 20 feet above the ground and weighed 6–8 tons. He was the greatest land carnivore that the world has ever seen.

Sauropods

Except for the theropods all dinosaurs were herbivores, or eaters of vegetation. The sauropods were the vegetarian branch of the SAURISCHIA and possibly originated from the heavier quadrupedal thecodonts. They evolved into the largest land vertebrates that ever lived and have been exceeded in bulk among animals only by certain modern whales. Such Late Jurassic giants as *Brontosaurus* and *Diplodocus* reached lengths of 80 feet and weights of more than 50 tons. *Apatosaurus*, from Late Jurassic beds of western North America, was only 60 feet long and weighed merely 40 tons (Fig. 21–5). Sauro-

pods did not need speed or agility and developed solid, pillar-like legs to support their great bulk. The relative shortness of their forelimbs, a feature of all dinosaurs, was not marked. Their neck was long and their head comparatively small, not much larger than a horse's, with a small mouth equipped with peglike and flat teeth for cropping and crushing vegetation.

If these animals had been warm-blooded, they would have found it difficult to find enough food to sustain so massive a body; but, without the necessity of providing continuous body warmth, a moderate intake sufficed. The structure of the sauropod skeleton has led paleontologists to believe that they lived along the margins of lakes and rivers and spent much of the time in the water, where some of the weight of their bodies would be supported by its buoyancy. They could escape from predators by wading into deeps and keeping only their heads, on their long necks, above the surface of the water.

Fig. 21–5. *Apatosaurus,* a Jurassic sauropod from North America, similar in many respects to *Brontosaurus.* [Courtesy of the British Museum (Natural History).]

Fig. 21–6. A Late Cretaceous swamp scene with *Thespesius*, a duck-billed dinosaur. (Courtesy of the Geological Survey of Canada.)

Ornithopods - bird hipped.

Among the ornithischian dinosaurs, those that retained the two-footed stance of the thecodonts are grouped together as the ornithopods, although they are sometimes referred to as the duck-billed dinosaurs because the front part of their mouth lacked teeth and was modified into a beak or bill (Figs. 21–4 and 21–6). This curious adaptation to a vegetarian diet is common to all the ornithischians, but in the other groups the bill has a pointed, parrot-like beak and is not flattened like that of a duck. The ornithopods appeared in the Late Triassic, by which time they had diverged markedly from the thecodont pattern, but reached their greatest diversity in the Late Cretaceous Epoch, when advanced members of the group grew to lengths of 30 and 40 feet and weights of several tons (Fig. 21–4). Their duck bills and webbed feet show that they lived near the water and probably used it as a refuge when attacked (Fig. 21–6). Some Late Cretaceous ornithopods show peculiar extensions

of the nasal passages into hollow crests at the top of the skull; these have been interpreted as air reservoirs that allowed the animal to stay submerged for relatively long periods, or as resonance organs used by the animal to intensify its call.

One of the first dinosaurs described scientifically was the ornithopod *Iguanodon*. During the excavation of a Belgian coal mine, 29 of these individuals were found together as they had fallen into an ancient fissure in the coal measures which later filled with sediment in Cretaceous time. A remarkable feature of the anatomy of these dinosaurs was a horny spike that took the place of the thumb. It must have been a formidable weapon of defense. Three other separate lineages are recognized—the stegosaurs, ankylosaurs, and ceratopsians—all of which reverted to a quadrupedal stance.

Stegosaurs and Ankylosaurs

The stegosaurs and ankylosaurs were the plated and armored dinosaurs, respectively. The stegosaurs, typified by *Stegosaurus*, was a large, quadrupedal animal with a double row of upright, bony plates along its back and a short tail armed with several bony spikes (Fig. 21–7). The skull was small, and the brain was extremely small in relation to the size of the animal—far smaller, in fact, than the enlargement of the neural cord in the hip region that served to direct the operation of the hind limbs and tail. The stegosaurs were among the first ornithischians, appearing early in Jurassic time, but they were also the first major group of dinosaurs to become extinct.

The ankylosaurs were squat, slow-moving, primarily Cretaceous, armored reptiles. In *Ankylosaurus* the back was covered by thick, bony plates that gave protection as effective as that possessed by a turtle; in addition, along each flank was a row of bony spikes

(Fig. 21–4). The tail ended in a great knob of bone that could be swung as a bludgeon. The offensive use of the tail by animals that are armored for defense was adopted by such distantly related animals as the porcupines, the glyptodonts (Pleistocene inhabitants of the Americas), the ankylosaurs, and the stegosaurs. Both the plated and armored dinosaurs had small, weak teeth and must have fed upon soft plants. *Polacanthus* (Fig. 21–8) was an Early Cretaceous ankylosaur which depended for defense upon enormous, solid spines along the back and smaller plates along the tail.

Ceratopsians

The ceratopsians, or horned dinosaurs, were a highly specialized, Late Cretaceous suborder of the ornithischians. In habitat

Fig. 21–7. The Late Jurassic plated dinosaur *Stegosaurus*. The vegetation in the foreground and right middleground is made up of cycadeoids. (Courtesy of the Field Museum of Natural History.)

Fig. 21–8. *Polacanthus,* a bizarre ankylosaur from Lower Cretaceous beds of Great Britain. [Courtesy of the British Museum (Natural
History).]

and general appearance they were close to
the rhinoceroses of the present day. The
ceratopsians had a thickset, short, unarmored
body supported on pillar-like legs. The short
neck and massive head were covered by a
great, bony shield. This acted as a place of
attachment for large neck and jaw muscles,
and also as a protection for the vital neck
region. Most members of this group developed horns on the nose, above the eyes, and
around the edge of the frill. The largest of
the ceratopsians, *Triceratops,* appeared near
the end of the Cretaceous (Fig. 21–9). It
was 20 feet in length and had a long horn
above each eye and one on the nose.

One of the most important fossil discoveries of the present century was made by
Roy Chapman Andrews in the Mongolian
desert. Skeletons of the primitive ceratopsian *Protoceratops* were found associated
with clutches of eggs and immature specimens (Fig. 21–10). In some of the elongate

eggs, laid to hatch in the warmth of the sun
100 million years ago, the remains of embryonic dinosaurs could be detected. Although dinosaur eggs are among the rarest of
fossils, finds such as the Mongolian one leave
little doubt that dinosaurs reproduced in this
manner.

MARINE REPTILES

In mid-Paleozoic time, some vertebrate
animals left the water and began the con-
quest of the land. Their gills were eliminated as they developed lungs that enabled
them to breathe air; their fins changed to
feet; and they developed a complex egg to
protect their young. Yet the advantages of
life in the sea are so great that many groups
of both reptiles and mammals later forsook
their acquired land habitat and went back
to an aquatic life. Six groups of reptiles—
the mesosaurs, ichthyosaurs, plesiosaurs,

mosasaurs, crocodiles, and turtles—made this transition, the last two incompletely. Among the mammals, the seals and walruses, the whales and dolphins, and the sea cows returned to the sea. However, evolution cannot be set in reverse, and once these animals had become adapted to a life on land, they had to evolve still further in order to insure success in living in the sea. The limbs of all these animals were modified to finlike paddles; their breathing was restricted to times when they were at the surface; and they adopted habits to assure that their young did not drown when they were born.

Ichthyosaurs

Of all the marine reptiles, none adapted better to life in the sea or became more fishlike in form than the ichthyosaurs. The typical ichthyosaur had a streamlined body like that of a tuna or salmon, with a long jaw armed with many sharp teeth for catching fish (Fig. 21–11). The tail was fishlike in form and function and propelled the ichthyosaur by its lateral motion. The backbone was bent down into the lower lobe of the forked tail (Fig. 21–12), and the upper lobe was

supported by the skin. The limbs were modified to become balancing and steering fins, and the bones in them were reduced to small, close-fitting, polygonal plates (Fig. 21–12). Well preserved skeletons of ichthyosaurs with embryonic young within the body cavity suggest that these animals did not return to shore to lay eggs, as do marine turtles of the present day, but bore their young alive in the ocean as do the whales. They were doubtless as completely aquatic as are the sharks today; even temporary excursions on land must have been impossible. The largest ichthyosaurs grew to 30 feet, but many were only 5 or 6 feet long.

The ichthyosaurs appeared suddenly in mid-Triassic time, and no intermediate forms between them and their probable cotylosaur ancestors are known. They became extinct in the Late Cretaceous.

Plesiosaurs

The plesiosaurs were only distantly related to the ichthyosaurs and had a short, thick body with a relatively short tail. The limbs were modified into four long paddles by which the animal could row itself forward

Fig. 21–9. The largest land carnivore of all time, *Tyrannosaurus*, faces the huge horned dinosaur *Triceratops*. Both lived and became extinct toward the close of the Cretaceous Period. (Courtesy of the Field Museum of Natural History.)

or backward on the surface of the ocean (Fig. 21–13).

Most plesiosaurs had a long, flexible neck on which the small head could be maneuvered rapidly to catch fish or to fight. The largest of the plesiosaurs measured 50 feet in length. The neck of *Elasmosaurus* (Fig. 21–14), one of the largest, was twice the length of the body and contained 60 vertebrae. Ancestors of the plesiosaurs lived in the Triassic Period, but the group, in the strict sense, lived only during the Jurassic and Cretaceous periods.

Mosasaurs

The mosasaurs were members of the lizard clan that returned to the sea. In their long, streamlined body and tapering tail they resembled the sea serpents of mythology (Fig. 21–14). The head was elongated into a formidable jaw with many sharp teeth. As in the ichthyosaurs, the limbs were modified for balancing and steering, and the motion of the tail propelled the animal. The mosasaurs were confined to the Late Cretaceous seas and reached their greatest size in a 30-foot monster called *Tylosaurus*.

THE CONQUEST OF THE AIR

For 200 million years after the first animals climbed out on land from the lakes and streams, the air was populated only by the insects. The aerial environment was the last major one to be conquered by the vertebrates, because highly specialized animals had to evolve before the many problems of flight could be solved. A flying animal must have a strong skeleton to hold the enlarged muscles needed for flight, but its bones must be light so as not to be a burden. Both birds and reptiles solved this problem in part by developing hollow bones and a keeled breastbone for the attachment of the muscles that drove the wings. Furthermore, the limbs of a flying animal must be highly modified to bear it up in the air. The birds solved this problem by developing feathers to form wings; the reptiles and bats solved it by developing a membrane, stretched between the forelimb and the body, as a wing (Fig. 21–15). A flying animal must have a high rate of metabolism, so that it may maintain the strenuous actions of flying over a long period. The birds and the bats solved this problem

Fig. 21–10. *Protoceratops,* a small ceratopsian dinosaur, several clutches of whose eggs were found in Mongolia. (Courtesy of the American Museum of Natural History.)

Fig. 21–11. The ichthyosaur *Eurhinosaurus.* Air breathers, these animals had to come to the surface periodically; they probably resembled the modern porpoise in habits as well as in shape. (Reproduced from J. Augusta and Z. Burian, *Prehistoric Animals.* London: Spring Books, 1956.)

Fig. 21–12. Skeleton of an ichthyosaur showing the highly modified limbs with the finger bones reduced to small plates. Note the downward deflection of the tail. (Courtesy of the Redpath Museum.)

Fig. 21–13. The plesiosaur *Cryptodeidus*. Two of these animals are seen from above, swimming at the water's surface, where they used their strong paddles to propel themselves. (Reproduced from J. Augusta and Z. Burian, *Prehistoric Animals.* London: Spring Books, 1956.)

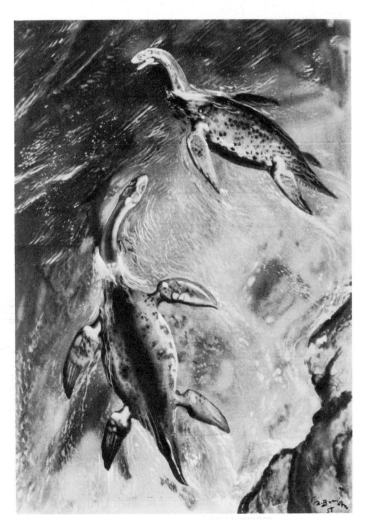

Fig. 21–14.   A Late Cretaceous seascape in western North America. The plesiosaur *Elasmosaurus* attempts to repel the attack of the fierce mosasaur *Tylosaurus*. Overhead, *Pteranodon*, the largest of the pterosaurs, glides on a 25-foot wing span. (Reproduced from J. Augusta and Z. Burian, *Prehistoric Animals:* London: Spring Books, 1956.)

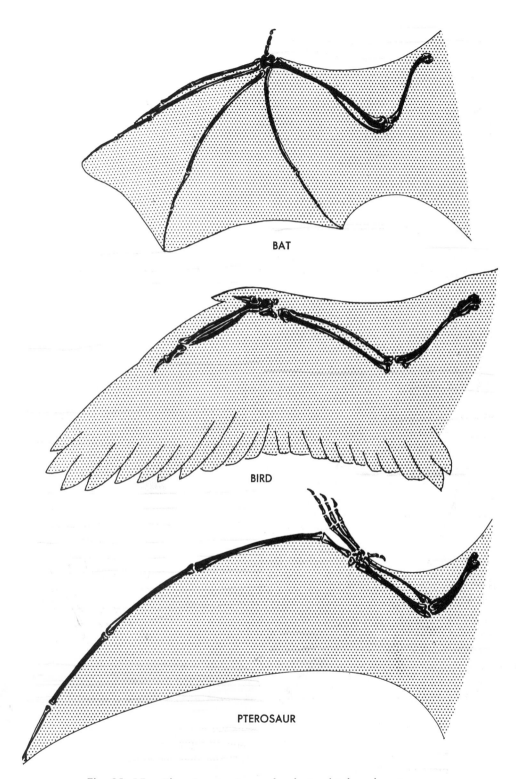

Fig. 21–15. The wing structures of a bat, a bird, and a pterosaur.

by a temperature control system that we call "warm blood." There has been some question as to whether flying reptiles could have had a sufficiently high metabolism to sustain flight. The development of a birdlike skeleton and brain, however, indicates that they were otherwise well adapted to flight. This has led some paleontologists to suspect that the flying reptiles may have attained a high, well-controlled body temperature, like the birds.

Pterosaurs

The flying reptiles of the Mesozoic Era are called pterosaurs. This highly specialized group arose presumably from thecodont stock at or before the beginning of the Jurassic Period, though its relationship to other archosaurs (the "ruling reptiles," including ORNITHISCHIA, SAURISCHIA, CROCODILIA, and PTEROSAURIA, biologically related by the structure of the skull) is not clear. They persisted until shortly before the end of the Cretaceous Period; their extinction may have been caused by unsuccessful competition with birds. The pterosaur wing was a membrane stretched between the enormously enlarged fourth finger and the body and hind legs of the animal (Fig. 21–15). The fifth finger was lost, and the other fingers at the front of the wing were modified for grasping cliffs and trees, from which the animal probably hung. The hind limbs were feeble and probably could not support the pterosaur efficiently on land. Some pterosaurs, such as *Rhamphorhynchus*, had a long trailing tail with a rudder-like enlargement; others, for example *Pterodactylus* (Fig. 21–16) and *Pteranodon* (Fig. 21–14), had none. *Pteranodon* was the largest of the flying reptiles and the largest animal, in span of wings, ever to fly. Although its body was only the size of a turkey, its wing span was more than 25 feet. It was probably incapable of flapping such a long fragile wing efficiently, but flew largely by gliding on upcurrents of air, just as eagles and hawks do today. The head was elongated in front into a long beak for catching fish and projected behind into a bladelike crest. Many pterosaurs are believed to have glided and swooped over the sea, looking for surface-swimming fish, but an animal like *Pteranodon* would have had great difficulty rising into the air again after making a catch.

LESSER REPTILES

Our attention is naturally drawn toward the ruling reptiles and the marine monsters of the Mesozoic Era. Without exception these became extinct by the close of the era. Several other kinds of reptiles are worthy of our attention, largely because these relatively insignificant groups have survived to the present day. Turtles appeared in the Upper Triassic and became increasingly common during the remainder of the Mesozoic Era. In the Cretaceous Period they invaded the sea, and both marine and terrestrial groups, if not actually advancing, were at least holding their own. Crocodiles first appeared in the Jurassic Period. They continued to be common throughout the rest of the Mesozoic, but were then long past their zenith. Lizards first appeared in the Upper Jurassic, increased throughout the Cretaceous Period, and are probably at their peak today. One marine branch, the Cretaceous mosasaurs, has already been described. Snakes, the last reptilian group to evolve, appeared later in the Cretaceous, and are rare as fossils. They are the most progressive group and have probably not yet reached their acme. The disaster to which the ruling reptiles and many other species succumbed at the end of the Mesozoic Era apparently did not overcome these relatively inconspicuous groups.

THE END OF REPTILIAN DOMINANCE

At the end of the Mesozoic Era, sweeping changes in the environment of the reptilian faunas of the world resulted in the wholesale extinction of the saurischian and ornithischian dinosaurs, the pterosaurs, the plesiosaurs, ichthyosaurs, and the mosasaurs after 100 million years of reptilian dominance of land, sea, and air. A change that would have affected the varied habitats occupied by the many reptiles listed above is difficult to

Fig. 21–16. *Pterodactylus,* a small pterosaur. Note the forward-pointing teeth, useful for impaling surface-swimming fish while the reptile was skimming over the sea. [Courtesy of the British Museum (Natural History).]

imagine. Swamp dweller and upland browser, carnivore and herbivore, sea serpent and flying reptile, biped and quadruped, armored and unarmored forms were among those that failed to survive the end of the Cretaceous Period. With the exception of the stegosaurs, the entire assemblage seems to have become extinct within a few million years. Yet some reptiles, such as the crocodiles, turtles, and lizards, which seem to have occupied environments similar to those of their extinct relatives, did survive to the present day. No single mechanism has been suggested that satisfactorily explains this phenomenon. Certainly no world-wide physical calamity was responsible. In western North America, deposition was continuous from the Late Cretaceous into the Paleocene Epoch. Dinosaur remains become rarer and rarer in the Upper Cretaceous rocks and near the end of the epoch vanish completely. Other surviving reptilian groups continue into the Cenozoic beds without interruption. Archosaur extinction can hardly have been a result of direct competition with mammals, for that group did not become dominant until after the archosaurs had disappeared.

Possible Causes of Extinction

We have seen that a cooling of the world's climate began at the end of the Cretaceous Period, continued through the Cenozoic Era, and eventually brought on the Ice Age. This climatic change and the general elevation of the continents at the end of the Mesozoic Era may have modified the vegetation on which the herbivorous dinosaurs fed and may have chilled the seas until they were no longer tolerable to the marine reptiles. However, no drastic changes in the vegetation, except the emergence of the angiosperms, took place within the Cretaceous, and the herbivorous dinosaurs appear to have satisfactorily adapted to this change. The survival of the Late Cretaceous crisis by the warm-blooded mammals and birds suggests that the crisis may have been a climatic one to which the reptiles would have been more sensitive. A similar evolutionary crisis of unknown origin marked the end of the Triassic Period, when six orders of reptiles, including the theco-

donts and mammal-like reptiles, became extinct. Both of these crises for the reptiles were also crises for the ammonoids, as we shall see below, but the connection between such remotely related animals is difficult to imagine.

If, as we suspect, the large herbivores—particularly the sauropods—were dependent on extensive areas of swamp and lake for support and food supplies, they would have been vulnerable to slight climatic or geological changes which might have drained these areas. Their extinction, which apparently did slightly precede that of the carnivorous forms, could have led to the death of the reptiles that preyed upon them. The extinction of such terrestrial herbivores as the ceratopsians, however, would seem to be an independent phenomenon, and the death of the totally marine plesiosaurs seems even less reasonably related.

Other suggestions as to the fate of the reptiles in late Mesozoic time have been made. A disease which attacked reptiles alone may have reduced the numbers of these animals on land, in the sea, and in the air. Once their numbers had been markedly reduced, the factor of mammalian competition, even if it were directed solely to the destruction of reptilian eggs, may have been important. There is no support for such concepts as racial senility, or loss of vigor, in leading to the extinction of any group. The extinction of the dinosaurs and other groups of reptiles remains as much a problem as the dying of many invertebrate stocks at the end of the Paleozoic Era. Both probably resulted from the failure of specialized animals to evolve rapidly enough to adapt to changes in their environments.

BIRDS

The reptilian ancestry of birds is revealed by features of their skeleton and by their egg-laying reproductive system. The fossil record of birds is poor, but specimens have been found that reveal a stage in the evolution of birds from reptiles.

For many years a fine, even-textured, cream-colored limestone has been quarried near Solenhofen, southeastern Germany, for use as lithographers' stone. The limestone was deposited in Upper Jurassic marine lagoons surrounded by coral and sponge reefs. In the course of these quarrying operations a beautifully preserved fossil fauna including more than 450 species of animals has been collected. Many of these specimens preserve impressions of certain soft, delicate parts that usually decay.

Among the most significant fossils recovered from the Solenhofen Limestone are two specimens of the first bird, *Archaeopteryx*, about the size of a crow (Figs. 21–17 and 21–18). The skeletons of these birds are typically reptilian; if the impressions of the feathers had not been preserved, they would have been classed as reptiles. The neck was long and flexible and supported a small head. The brain was more reptilian than like that of a modern bird. The beak was long, with numerous teeth, a feature not found in post-Mesozoic birds. The tail was long, composed of many vertebrae, and fringed by a row of long feathers on either side. The forelegs bore clawed digits of reptilian type.

No other birds are known from Jurassic rocks, but several from Cretaceous rocks resemble modern birds more than they do their Jurassic precursors. By Cretaceous time, the bones of the skull had coalesced, the long tail had been reduced, and the breastbone had been greatly enlarged and keeled for the attachment of the muscles that worked the wings. The teeth were reduced in number and there were no claws on the wings. The Cenozoic evolution of birds, however, cannot be traced in any detail because of the paucity of fossil specimens.

MAMMALS

Mammals did not appear until the Upper Triassic, but the group leading to mammals, the mammal-like reptiles, can be recognized as a separate lineage in rocks as old as Early Pennsylvanian. The primitive mammal-like reptiles, the pelycosaurs, are all clearly reptilian in morphology. Within the succeeding therapsid assemblage, between the Middle Permian and Late Triassic epochs, the transition to mammals was completed.

The therapsids are a diverse group, but their separate lineages developed a number of mammalian characteristics. Certainly the cynodonts, represented by the genus *Cynognathus* (Fig. 21–19), came the closest to a completely mammalian structure and probably gave rise to at least one branch of mammals; however, a polyphyletic origin of mammals from several therapsids is generally accepted. The various skeletal changes undergone by the therapsids include the modification of the pelvic and pectoral girdles and limbs so that they were brought in under the body for a more efficient gait, compared with the sprawling posture of the pelycosaurs and other primitive reptiles. Many of the bones in the lower jaw were lost or were transformed into mammalian ear ossicles, leaving only a single element. The brain case was remodeled from a small, poorly ossified tube lying inside the external skull bones to a bulbous structure utilizing the original skull walls. The teeth became further differentiated, and a secondary palate was developed to separate the nasal passage from the mouth. Although there is no fossil evidence, advanced mammal-like reptiles probably started to develop an apparatus for internal heat production and control.

Mammalian Characteristics

According to the fossil record mammals evolved from the mammal-like reptiles before the end of the Triassic Period. Mammals may have originated earlier, even as early as late in the Permian Period, but until the end of the Cretaceous Period they were relatively unimportant in the total biota. However, as the ruling reptiles were extinguished, the mammals began their period of dominance. What characteristics enabled these new forms to dominate their environment?

The mammals are characterized by a high rate of metabolism and a more or less uniform body temperature, higher than that of their environment. With two exceptions, modern mammals bear their young alive and nourish them through infancy with milk from the mother. Most mammals are insulated with a covering of hair; scales or plates are very rare. Although none of these fundamental

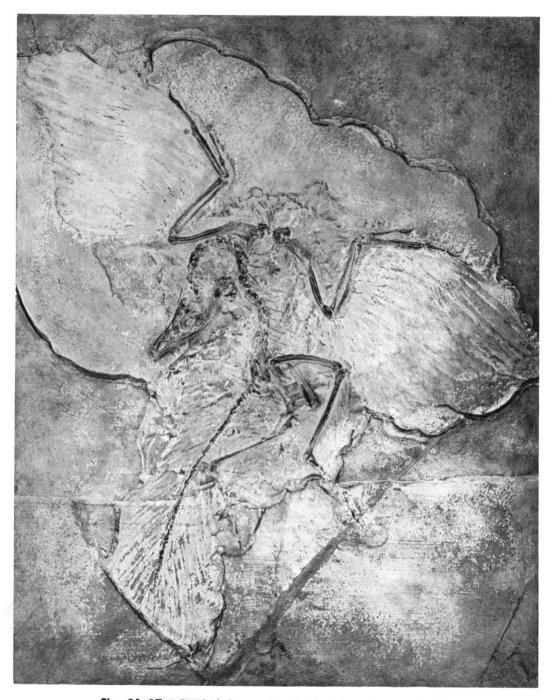

Fig. 21–17. Fossil skeleton of *Archaeopteryx*. Photograph of a cast of the original Berlin specimen, sometimes known as *Archaeornis*. (Courtesy of Ward's Natural Science Establishment, Inc., Rochester, N. Y.)

Fig. 21–18. Restoration of *Archaeopteryx*, made directly from the skeleton represented in Fig. 21–17. (Courtesy of the American Museum of Natural History.)

Fig. 21–19. Mammal-like reptiles from the Permian–Triassic boundary of Africa. Several carnivorous therapsids *(Cynognathus)* menace a plant-eating related form *(Kannemeyeria)*. These two genera were once considered to belong to the Permian Period, but are now generally recognized as having lived at the beginning of the Triassic. The bushes are primitive conifers. (Courtesy of the Field Museum of Natural History.)

features can be observed in fossil skeletons, many differences in bone structure serve to separate mammalian remains from those of other animals. Among these differences may be mentioned the double ball-and-socket joint by which the head connects with the neck; the single bone that forms the lower jaw on each side; the fusion of the three bones of the pelvis into one; the single opening in the skull for the nostrils; and the differentiation of the teeth into molars, premolars, canines, and incisors. No one of these features is restricted to mammals, for they were anticipated by different groups of the mammal-like reptiles.

Mesozoic Mammals

No complete skeletons of Jurassic mammals have been discovered, but their scattered bones occur in Jurassic sediments around the world. Many teeth and jaws and a few limb bones have been recovered from the Morrison Formation of the Rocky Mountain region (see Chapter 10). From these fragmentary fossil remains and from living species, mammals can be divided into several orders, of which the most important are as follows:

> Placentals
> Marsupials
> Monotremes
> Pantotheres
> Symmetrodonts
> Multituberculates
> Triconodonts

The triconodonts and symmetrodonts were restricted to the Middle and Late Jurassic epochs. The former died off without issue, but the symmetrodonts probably gave rise to the pantotheres. The triconodonts and symmetrodonts are known only from teeth and jaws, which show that most were the size of a rat but that some grew as large as a rabbit. The multituberculates were the most abundant and the largest of Mesozoic mammals; the largest was comparable in size to a woodchuck. They occur in Upper Jurassic beds and recur in Paleocene beds, becoming extinct in the Early Eocene. The pantotheres arose in the Middle Jurassic, became abundant in the Late Jurassic, and doubtless gave rise to both marsupials and placentals.

Of the living orders of mammals the monotremes are the most primitive. Their egg-laying habit and their many reptilian anatomical features suggest their closeness to the reptiles. No fossil monotremes older than the Pleistocene of Australia are known, but they must represent one of the earliest, and certainly the least progressive, mammalian developments from some group of Triassic mammal-like reptiles.

Marsupials and placentals first appear in Upper Cretaceous rocks. Both groups reached their greatest development in the Cenozoic Era and are described more fully in Chapter 22.

For the 110 million years of Jurassic and Cretaceous time, small ratlike mammals of all seven orders were dominated by reptilian predators and forced either to acquire nocturnal and arboreal habits or to retire into regions of high latitude or altitude, where the low temperatures would prevent pursuit by cold-blooded reptiles. Much evolution took place during the Mesozoic, but not until the beginning of the Cenozoic did the explosive radiation of the mammals begin.

MESOZOIC INVERTEBRATES

Reference has been made in Chapter 20 to the crisis in invertebrate life at the end of the Paleozoic Era. The extinction of many groups of animals at that time resulted in a generally different marine invertebrate population in Mesozoic and Cenozoic seas. Brachiopods that throng Paleozoic rocks are not important as fossils in later strata; the corals and bryozoans changed almost completely, and of the fossil invertebrates, mollusks became the most numerous and useful to paleontologists.

Ammonoids and Belemnites

By Permian time that branch of the cephalopods known as the ammonoids had evolved three basic suture patterns: goniatite, ceratite, and ammonite (Fig. 21–20). In Triassic time the ammonoids with a ceratite suture, in which only the side of the inflection that is convex posteriorly is intricately folded, replaced the goniatites as the dominant cephalopods. Although many Triassic ammonoids had the ceratite suture, some were characterized by the ammonite suture, which is complexly folded throughout its length.

At the end of the Triassic Period some drastic change in the marine environment resulted in the near extinction of the whole ammonoid race. Of the many families that lived in that period, only one (Phyllocerati-dae) survived the crisis, founding a new lineage in the Jurassic and Cretaceous periods.

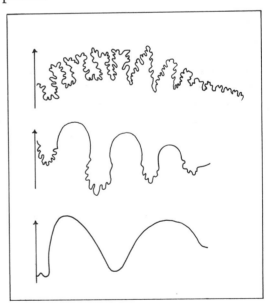

Fig. 21–20. The suture lines of three types of ammonoids seen as if straightened out. The arrow points forward on the outside edge of the last whorl of the shell. *Top:* The ammonite *Pompeckjites* (Triassic). *Middle:* The ceratite *Bulogites* (Triassic). *Bottom:* The goniatite *Muensteroceras* (Mississippian).

During the Jurassic Period the ammonites evolved rapidly to exploit the environments left vacant by the passing of the ceratites. They were swimming animals, independent of sea-floor sedimentary facies, and were carried by currents to all parts of the world. The rapidity of their evolution and dispersal makes the Jurassic ammonites ideal index fossils. Detailed collecting of ammonites from some European sedimentary successions has made possible the division of the strata into zones only a few inches thick. Fifty-eight ammonite zones in the Jurassic System are valid for correlation throughout the world.

Most ammonoids were coiled in one plane, like a watch spring. However, as early as Triassic time some grew into other forms, such as the trochoid spiral typical of gastropod shells. The number of these specialized ammonites increased into the Cretaceous Period, when straight, loosely coiled, hooked, and trochoid shells were not uncommon (Figs. 21–21 and 21–22). Some paleontologists have suggested that this widespread specialization prevented the ammonites from adapting to the changing marine conditions toward the end of the Cretaceous Period. However, the reason or reasons for the extinction of the ammonites at the end of the

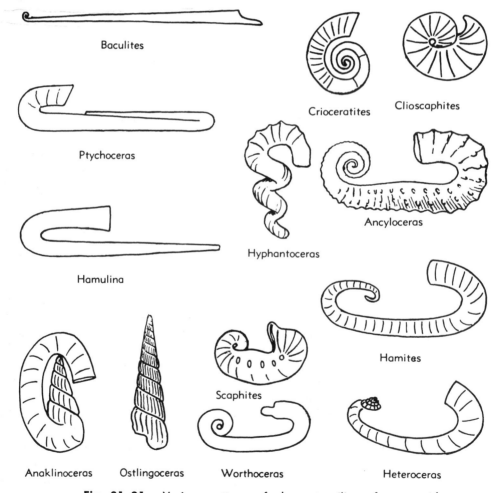

Baculites

Ptychoceras

Hamulina

Crioceratites

Clioscaphites

Hyphantoceras

Ancyloceras

Hamites

Anaklinoceras   Ostlingoceras   Worthoceras   Scaphites   Heteroceras

Fig. 21–21. Various patterns of aberrant coiling of ammonoid cephalopods. (From *Treatise on Invertebrate Paleontology*, courtesy of the Geological Society of America and the University of Kansas Press.)

Fig. 21–22. Late Cretaceous marine habitat group. On the right, the large coiled ammonite *Placenticeras;* in the left middleground, the loosely coiled ammonite *Helioceras* (among the seaweeds) and the straight-shelled ammonite *Baculites* in a swimming position. Note the initial coiled shell in the last. Above *Placenticeras* are two squidlike belemnites. (Courtesy of the University of Michigan Museum.)

Mesozoic Era are as mysterious as the cause of the passing of the ichthyosaurs, plesiosaurs, and mosasaurs.

The fossils of belemnites are sharp-pointed rods composed of solid calcite of the shape and size of cigars (Fig. A–19). . They occur abundantly in Mesozoic rocks (Figs. 21–22 and 21–23), and have been reported from late Paleozoic rocks. Fortunately, these strange fossils have occasionally been found associated with the impression of the soft parts of the animal that secreted them. From such specimens paleontologists have learned that the rod formed part of the internal skeleton of an elongate squidlike cephalopod. The belemnites, like the ammonoids, are good index fossils to Mesozoic rocks because they were fast swimmers and were quickly dispersed throughout the world.

Pelecypods

The most interesting path of evolution followed by the pelecypods during the Mesozoic Era began when they started to live with one valve resting on, or cemented to, the ocean floor (Fig. 21–24). The lower valve became enlarged, and the upper valve was reduced until it was merely a cap on the lower one. During the Jurassic Period one group of pelecypods evolved a massive lower valve that rested in the muddy sediment and became coiled at the beak in a plane perpendicular to that between the valves. These shells, known as *Gryphaea*, are abundant in argillaceous Jurassic rocks. Some Cretaceous pelecypods became coiled in a plane parallel to that between the valves; these are called *Exogyra*. In still another group, the lower valve was so thickened that it became conical and eventually horn-shaped. Such pelecypods resembled both the corals and some Permian brachiopods, which developed a similar form in response to a comparable sedentary way of life. These coral-like pelecypods, known as rudistids (Fig. 21–24), thrived in banks like oysters during the Cretaceous Period but became extinct at its end. A similar habitat is occupied by oysters of

Fig. 21–23. A slab of Jurassic limestone showing a great variety of invertebrate fossils. In the center and to the left are three belemnite guards. On the extreme left and to the right of the central belemnite are two kinds of gastropods. The long fossil in the upper right-hand corner is a pelecypod. Most of the other fossils are ammonites, of which at least four kinds are shown. Note the ammonite suture lines on the largest shell. (Courtesy of the Redpath Museum.)

the present day, but they do not show the extreme modification of the Mesozoic pelecypods. A common genus of normal pelecypods is *Trigonia*, extraordinarily abundant in certain Jurassic rocks (Fig. 21–25).

Echinoderms

Only one family of crinoids, so abundant in the late Paleozoic, survived that era; before becoming extinct at the end of the Triassic, it gave rise to an advanced group known as the ARTICULATA, the fossils of which are very common at a few horizons. One such stratum is the Niobrara Chalk of Upper Cretaceous age in western North America, where the stemless genus *Uintacrinus* profusely covers some bedding planes (Fig. 21–26). Asteroids and echinoids (see Figs. A–23 and A–27)

were never important in the Paleozoic, but both classes increased from their least distribution in the Permian to a maximum today.

Corals and Forams

The racial history of the corals is unique among the invertebrates. The tetracorals were abundant in certain parts of Permian seas but perished at the end of the period, and for all of the Early Triassic Epoch the corals left no record. In Middle Triassic time new corals, characterized by a sixfold symmetry of septa, appeared; this variety increased and diversified to form the hexacorals of the present day. No agreement has been reached on what was happening to the corals in Early Triassic time, but corals of some sort must have existed then. Possibly, ancestors

Fig. 21–24. Mesozoic pelecypods. *A. Exogyra*, view of one of the valves coiled at the beak in the plane of the valve. *B. Gryphaea*, side view of both valves. The lower valve is much larger than the nearly flat, upper valve and is coiled in a plane at right angles to that between the valves. *C. Inoceramus*, a group of specimens of this concentrically ribbed genus. *D. Hippurites*, a rudistid. The lower valve has grown to resemble conical corals. (Courtesy of the Redpath Museum.)

Fig. 21–25. *Trigonia*, a rock-building Mesozoic pelecypod. (Courtesy of the Redpath Museum.)

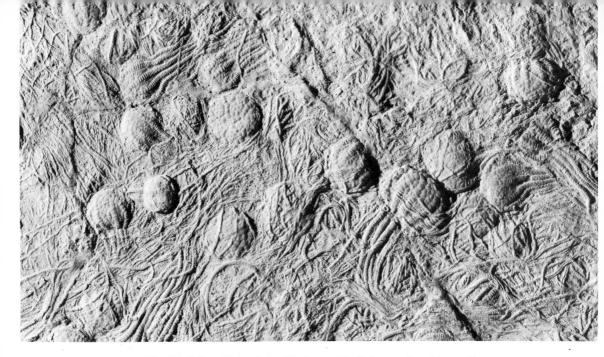

Fig. 21–26. Slab of the Niobrara Chalk Formation (Upper Cretaceous of Kansas) showing an abundance of heads and arms of the stemless crinoid *Uintacrinus socialis*. The preservation of crinoids in such a nearly perfect state is unusual. (Courtesy of the Royal Ontario Museum.)

Fig. 21–27. Possible relationship between *Mackenzia* (Middle Cambrian) and *Edwardsia* (living), involving the evolution of the hexacorals either from tetracorals or directly from Precambrian ancestors.

of the hexacorals with a sixfold symmetry lived during the Paleozoic Era, but did not secrete preservable hard parts until Triassic time. A clue to the solution of this problem is provided by *Mackenzia* (see p. 411), one of the remarkably preserved fossils from the Burgess Shale, which closely resembles a modern sea-anemone hexacoral without hard parts. A possible explanation of the difficulties is shown in Fig. 21–27, in which the tetracorals and hexacorals are shown as distinct subdivisions of coelenterates, with a common Precambrian ancestor. Another possibility is that the hexacorals arose from the tetracorals at the close of the Paleozoic Era, and transitional forms may yet be found in Lower Triassic rocks.

Another important group of invertebrates in Mesozoic rocks consists of the forams. After the fusulinids, which were so abun-

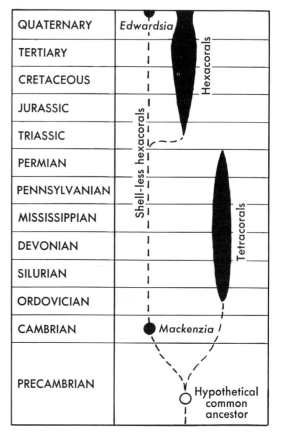

dant in the late Paleozoic, had disappeared, forams increased in numbers and varieties to reach what may have been their maximum in Cretaceous time, though they are scarcely less abundant today. In that period forams first became planktonic. Since then, foram shells such as *Globigerina* (Fig. 21–28) have been raining down on the ocean floor, building up oozes such as those which cover 51 million square miles today. Their tests also contributed to the Cretaceous chalk beds of northern Europe and western North America.

THE MESOZOIC FLORA

Cycads and Cycadeoids

At the close of the Paleozoic Era the terrestrial flora changed very little. Several Paleozoic plant groups, including the horsetails, the seed ferns, the ferns, and the conifers, persisted into the next era (Fig. 21–29). The trees petrified in the Chinle Formation of Arizona were redwood conifers not unlike those that grow in California and Oregon today.

The cycads and the cycadeoids were distinctive members of the Mesozoic flora. The former are still living and are commonly known as the sago palms, but the latter are extinct. Some of these plants were as tall as palms and had a circle of palmlike leaves 30 or 40 feet above the ground (see Fig. A–5), but many grew from a low, almost spherical, trunk close to the ground (Figs. 21–7 and 21–29). The cycads bear male and female cones, but the cycadeoids bore the first complex flowers. The cycads and cycadeoids reached their acme in Early Cretaceous time and were thereafter overshadowed by the fast-rising angiosperms.

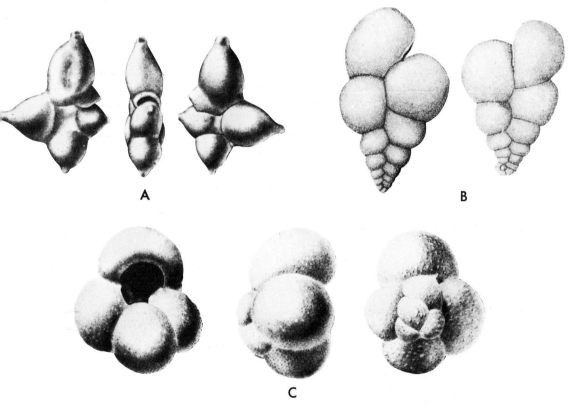

A

B

C

Fig. 21–28. Early planktonic forams. A. *Shackoina*, Cretaceous (magnification × 200). B. *Heterohelix*, Cretaceous (magnification × 100). C. *Globigerina*, Early Tertiary to Recent (magnification × 90). (From *Treatise on Invertebrate Paleontology*, courtesy of the Geological Society of America and the University of Kansas Press.)

Fig. 21–29. Early Mesozoic landscape showing some aspects of the flora. In the marshy foreground are several kinds of *Calamites* which had persisted from the Paleozoic Era. Ferns abound, and cycadeoids on bulbous and treelike stems were becoming abundant. In the distance are conifers. (Reproduced from J. Augusta and Z. Burian, *Prehistoric Animals.* London: Spring Books, 1956.)

Fig. 21–30. Leaf of *Liquidambar*, an angiosperm from Cretaceous rocks of western North America. (Courtesy of the Smithsonian Institution.)

Angiosperms

Although we do have microfossils of angiosperm pollen from Jurassic rocks, the explosive appearance of angiosperm macrofossils at the end of Early Cretaceous time was one of the most dramatic events in plant history. The angiosperms make up the greater part of the visible modern flora and are familiar to all as the flowering plants. The first angiosperms were remarkably modern in aspect, and many modern genera, such as birches, elms, and willows, may be recognized among Cretaceous plants (Fig. 21–30). Because they appeared all over the world at nearly the same time, we believe that the angiosperms must have originated considerably earlier, perhaps in the Jurassic Period, and must have been confined to the uplands during the first part of their evolution, where there would be little opportunity for them to be fossilized. Only when the environment became suitable for them to invade the lowlands were they preserved in the sedimentary record.

The problem of the origin of the angiosperms has concerned many paleobotanists. Some have suggested that they evolved from the cycadeoids, but this has not been proved. Until a fuller record of primitive angiosperms is found in pre-Cretaceous rocks, the problem will probably remain one of the many enigmas of the history of life on earth.

QUESTIONS

Questions for the material in this chapter are included in the list at the end of Chapter 22.

REFERENCES AND SUGGESTED READINGS

References and suggested readings for the material in this chapter will be found at the end of Chapter 22.

22

Life of the Cenozoic Era

The Cenozoic Era is often referred to as the Age of Mammals because of the dominant position members of that group achieved during the era. Nevertheless, there is a good fossil record of plants, invertebrates, and non-mammalian vertebrates. The main course of the Cenozoic evolution of these non-mammalian groups has been sketched in Chapter 21 and need not be repeated here. Except for the following brief note on birds, the present chapter will be concerned solely with the evolution of mammals.

BIRDS

Since their origin in Jurassic time, birds have increased in diversity and numbers and are probably at their maximum today. Because their fossils are scarce, little is known of the details of their Cenozoic evolution. One interesting development was the evolution of large, carnivorous, flightless birds chiefly in South America and Australia, where they did not need to compete with placental carnivores. Many, such as *Andalgalornis* (Fig. 22–1), had gigantic skulls set on an ostrich-like neck and body.

MAMMALS

As the Cenozoic Era began, the mammals were emerging from the dominance of the reptiles. For more than 100 million years they had lived the life of small, retiring, probably nocturnal and arboreal animals, few of them exceeding the size of a cat; they fed on insects, carrion, and vegetation and occupied much the same ecological niche as do the insectivores and small rodents today. With the disappearance of most of the reptiles, land, sea, and air environments were opened for the mammals to occupy. The resulting diversification and multiplication of the mammals to exploit these newly available habitats was one of the greatest evolutionary explosions on record.

Mammalian Characters

Elsewhere in this book some of the mammals of the early Cenozoic fauna are described as archaic, and certain features of their anatomy are said to be primitive. These statements imply that what are known as advanced mammals modified these features as they became adapted to certain ways of life.

Fig. 22—1. *Andalgalornis,* one of the many large, mostly flightless, Early Tertiary birds of South America (about one-twelfth actual size). (Courtesy of the Field Museum of Natural History.)

The most important of these features are body size, feet, teeth, and brain.

Size. Commonly, but not universally, early members of mammalian lineages were small creatures, and the later ones giants. The evolutionary trend toward increase in size can be detected again and again in the history of families and orders. An increase in size, unless so great that it strains muscle and bone, is advantageous to all herbivorous animals for they are thereby protected from smaller carnivores and they require less food in proportion to their size than do smaller animals. Decrease in size is a much less common evolutionary trend.

Feet. Primitive mammals had five clawed digits on both fore and hind feet, a condition still retained by man and by some other animals not specifically adapted for fast running. A few of the archaic groups dropped a finger or a toe, but most retained the conservative 5 digits. Running mammals modified the primitive claws to bony hooves, and achieved an advantage by rising up on the toes of their feet and thereby gaining a greater length of leg and stride. As this tendency to run on the toes became more pronounced, the outer toes were raised from the ground, and either degenerated to mere splints of bone or disappeared. The modern horse has reached a stage of evolution at which the foot is supported by the nail of the middle toe; the other toes have degenerated.

Teeth. Teeth are among the commonest mammalian fossils because they are the hardest and chemically the most stable parts of the skeleton. This is fortunate for they reveal much about the habits of the animal to which they belonged. The teeth of primitive placental mammals, including all of the archaic types, consisted of 3 incisors, 1 canine, 4 premolars, and 3 molars on each side of the jaws, or 44 teeth in all. Such a dental pattern is expressed as a formula thus:

$$\frac{3\text{-}1\text{-}4\text{-}3}{3\text{-}1\text{-}4\text{-}3}$$

According to this system man's dental formula would be:

$$\frac{2\text{-}1\text{-}2\text{-}3}{2\text{-}1\text{-}2\text{-}3}$$

(Check this for yourself, but remember that you have probably lost your third molar or wisdom teeth). The back teeth, which are used for chewing, were primitively short and had low, blunt cusps.

When the more advanced mammals specialized in their diet they refined the primitive tooth pattern by eliminating teeth that were not used for their particular food and modifying others, particularly the molars and premolars. Browsing animals that ate soft plants and tree leaves retained low unspecialized teeth (Fig. 22–2). The chewing molar teeth (Fig. 22–5) of the carnivores degenerated and almost disappeared, while their canines developed as stabbing or slashing teeth. One of the most remarkable dental adaptations was a direct result of the appearance and rapid spread in Miocene time of the grasses, and the change by many hoofed animals from a browsing to a grazing diet. To chew the hard, abrasive grasses, their teeth had to be still harder and capable of enduring a lifetime of wear. Grazers evolved high-crowned teeth in which the enamel was folded into the central part, giving the tooth added toughness (Fig. 22–2). Omnivores, such as pigs and primates, whose food includes both meat and plants, retained basically primitive teeth with low, simple cusps.

Brain. Increase in brain size accompanies increase in body size in most animals because a greater sensory apparatus is needed to control a greater bulk. Such a proportional increase does not indicate an increase in intelligence. The intelligent processing (memory, reasoning) of impressions received from the outside world is carried on within the cerebrum, or forebrain, and is associated with the increase of the surface area of the cortex, or outer layer, by complex infolding. The intelligence of an animal is proportional to the relative size of the cerebrum and the infolding of its surface. In the primates the cerebrum is so enlarged that it completely covers the cerebellum, which directs the automatic body processes.

The Paleocene Fauna

Of the mammals present in Jurassic time only the small ratlike multituberculates occurred in the Paleocene Epoch, and these became extinct early in the Cenozoic Era. The monotremes, of which there are no fossils older than the Pleistocene, were certainly present. They are now, and perhaps always have been, isolated in the Australasian region. They lay eggs, lack normal mammary glands, and have an irregular body temperature. Some biologists feel that they should be classified as surviving therapsid reptiles. Because no fossil monotremes are known prior to the Pleistocene, and because their teeth are either missing or too aberrant for comparison with either Mesozoic mammals or therapsids, their ancestry remains unknown.

The marsupials appeared in Late Cretaceous time and persist today as the opossum of the Americas and a host of animals in Australia. Only where the marsupials were isolated geographically from competition with the more intelligent placentals were they able to thrive and diversify. The isolation of Australia and South America in early Cenozoic time allowed the evolution of rich marsupial faunas on those continents. Most of the marsupials of South America became extinct at the end of the Pliocene Epoch, when they came into competition with advanced placental invaders from North America that had crossed the newly exposed Isthmus of Panama. In Australia, a radiation comparable to that of the placentals elsewhere established a varied marsupial fauna free from the menace of the superior placen-

Fig. 22–2. Teeth of mastodon and mammoth. *Top:* A side view of a mastodon's tooth showing the paired cusps useful for crushing foliage, typical of browsing animals. *Bottom:* A top view of a tooth of a mammoth or elephant showing the infolding of the enamel that strengthened the tooth for grazing. The scales are in centimeters. (Courtesy of the Redpath Museum.)

Fig. 22–3. Reconstruction of the Paleocene condylarth *Phenacodus.* (By Charles Knight, courtesy of the American Museum of Natural History.)

tals until, late in the era, man, dog, rat, and rabbit arrived to threaten their existence. The earliest marsupials differed only insignificantly from the living opossum. From this stock, at the close of the Cretaceous, the major groups of Cenozoic marsupials differentiated.

The basic placental stock consisted of small animals that probably lived in trees. They resembled living insectivores and are included in this order. As early as Cretaceous time, primitive members of the primate and hoofed herbivore groups of the placentals can also be distinguished, but the main placental radiation took place in Paleocene time, when 20 additional orders appeared. Most of these early placentals are similar, and the distinctive features of the orders are obvious only after the initial divergences.

A few orders present in the Paleocene Epoch are commonly referred to as **archaic** because their members retained generalized teeth and feet and a small, primitive brain. The term "archaic," one more of convenience than of scientific importance, is here used to include three orders—condylarths, amblypods, and creodonts—all of which became extinct early in the Cenozoic as a result of competition with orders having specialized teeth, feet, and brain.

The condylarths were primitive, hoofed mammals of latest Cretaceous, Paleocene and Eocene times, and were the ancestors of the perissodactyls and artiodactyls of the later Cenozoic. One of the last of the condylarths was *Phenacodus* (Fig. 22–3), an animal the size of a sheep, with a long skull, rather short legs, a long tail, and the general appearance of a carnivore. Its teeth, however, show that it was a herbivore.

The amblypods, or pantodonts, were another group of primitive, hoofed mammals;

unlike the lightly built condylarths, they were ponderous and slow-moving (Fig. 22–4). Their skeleton was very strong and must have supported a heavy body. Most of their teeth were of the unspecialized type, indicative of a browsing diet, but their canine teeth were enlarged, possibly as a weapon of defense. This group died out in North America in Eocene time but lived on elsewhere into the Oligocene Epoch.

The creodonts were primitive carnivores which were almost entirely replaced by the true carnivores at the end of the Eocene Epoch, although they persisted in diminishing numbers until the Pliocene Epoch. In early forms the body was small, long, and slender like that of a mink. The creodonts diversified rapidly in Eocene time and grew to such a size that one of them had a skull 3 feet in length. They retained relatively small brains and apparently were not as intelligent as the true carnivores. They progressively failed as the latter thrived. Only one group survived the Eocene; the last survivor is found in Lower Pliocene beds.

ADVANCED MAMMALS

The first insectivores are found in Upper Cretaceous rocks and their fossil record can be followed to the modern representatives, the shrews, moles, and hedgehogs. The molar teeth of the Cretaceous specimens are intermediate in structure between those of

Fig. 22–4. Reconstruction of the Paleocene amblypod *Coryphodon*. (By Charles Knight, courtesy of the American Museum of Natural History.)

pantotheres and those of advanced mammals. All insectivores have a small, simple brain. Their small size and timid, retiring mode of living have allowed them to survive.

The rodents have always been gnawing animals with the four front incisors developed into sharp, chisel-edged tools. The lateral incisors, the canines, and some cheek teeth were lost. Similar specialization for gnawing developed in some late therapsids, in the multituberculates, and even in early Cenozoic primates. By the end of the Eocene, all the niches occupied by the gnawing animals in these groups were taken over by the rodents. No rodents are known from Cretaceous rocks, but a primitive, squirrel-like fossil occurs in Paleocene beds. The group to which rats and mice belong is first represented in Oligocene beds, which also hold the earliest of the porcupine group. Man has more to fear from the rodents than from any other group of mammals. Rats have followed man all over the world, menacing his food supply and carrying disease, particularly bubonic plague, with them.

A discussion of the primates, another element of the Paleocene fauna, is reserved for a later part of this chapter.

LATER CENOZOIC MAMMALS

Although no sudden change in fauna occurred, many of the primitive orders and families of mammals were replaced by more advanced groups in Late Eocene and Oligocene time.

Carnivores

The successful predaceous carnivore must be agile and speedy, be able to outwit his prey with superior intelligence, and be provided with claws and sharp canine teeth for grasping and rending its prey. The dentition of carnivores has been modified by the loss of some of the chewing cheek teeth and the development of others into long, ridged teeth (carnassials) for breaking bones and shearing tough food (Fig. 22–5).

Small carnivores that were contemporaries of the early creodonts of Middle Paleocene time apparently evolved directly from insectivores through the development of a specialized dentition and a relatively large brain. They soon diversified into several groups of true terrestrial carnivores, the fissipedes, of which two major lines are recognized. One line led to the civets, hyenas, and cats; the other led to the dogs, raccoons, bears, and weasels. A distinct group of living carnivores, known as the pinnipedes, includes the marine seals and walruses. These evolved from early fissipedes, which were similar to the ancestors of the otter. The pinnipedes had lost most of their tail before becoming adapted to aquatic life, and now propel themselves by limbs that are modified into paddles.

The dog family (CANIDAE) is one of the oldest in the carnivore group, and is one of the few mammalian lineages in which increase in size to giantism has not occurred. Within the cat family (FELIDAE) there de-

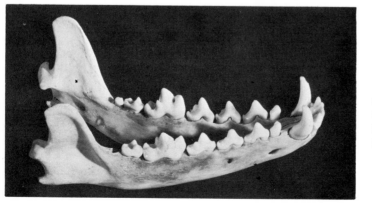

Fig. 22–5. Lower jaw of a fox, showing the cheek teeth for cutting flesh and the enlarged canines for seizing and tearing the prey.

Fig. 22–6. The saber-toothed cat *Smilodon*, Pleistocene of North America. The skull is about one-sixth actual size, the complete form about one-twelfth. (From *The Fossil Book*, by Carroll Lane Fenton and Mildred Adams Fenton. Copyright © 1958 by Carroll Lane Fenton and Mildred Adams Fenton. Reprinted by permission of Doubleday & Co., Inc.)

veloped the saber-toothed "tigers," whose upper canine teeth enlarged to dagger-like proportions and projected several inches below the lower jaw when the mouth was closed. The lower jaw opened the mouth wide on a special hinge to clear the stabbing teeth for killing large, thick-skinned prey (Fig. 22–6). The last and largest of the saber-toothed cats was the Late Pleistocene genus *Smilodon*. A great many skeletons of this tiger-sized cat have been excavated from an asphalt seep at Rancho la Brea, within the city of Los Angeles. The last saber-toothed cats died a few thousand years ago when the large Pleistocene mammals, such as mastodons and ground sloths, on which they preyed, became extinct. The earliest human invaders of North America probably contributed to their extinction in part by destroying their accustomed prey.

Odd-toed Hoofed Mammals

The mammals that developed hooves were herbivores of forest and plain that initially depended on running to evade their enemies. In the odd-toed branch of these animals, the perissodactyls, the axis of the foot along which the weight of the body was supported lay through the third, or middle, toe. The course of evolution of the foot of the odd-toed mammals may be understood by placing one's hand palm-down on a table, with all the fingers touching the surface. As the wrist is raised, to simulate the elevation of the foot for running on the toes, first the thumb leaves the table, then the fifth finger, and finally, if the weight is restricted to the third finger, the second and fourth cease to touch; in this way, toe reduction went irregularly through stages of five, three, and one.

The most primitive perissodactyl, *Hyracotherium*, appears just at the close of the Paleocene Epoch. It almost certainly evolved from among the condylarths. *Hyracotherium*, also called *Eohippus*, is closely related to the ancestry of the entire order, but is particularly thought of as the earliest member of the horse family (EQUIDAE). The evolution of this family is one of the best documented evolutionary sequences (Fig. 22–7). Between the Upper Paleocene and the present, this lineage evolved from small, running, forest-dwelling animals having four toes on the front feet and three on the hind feet, with

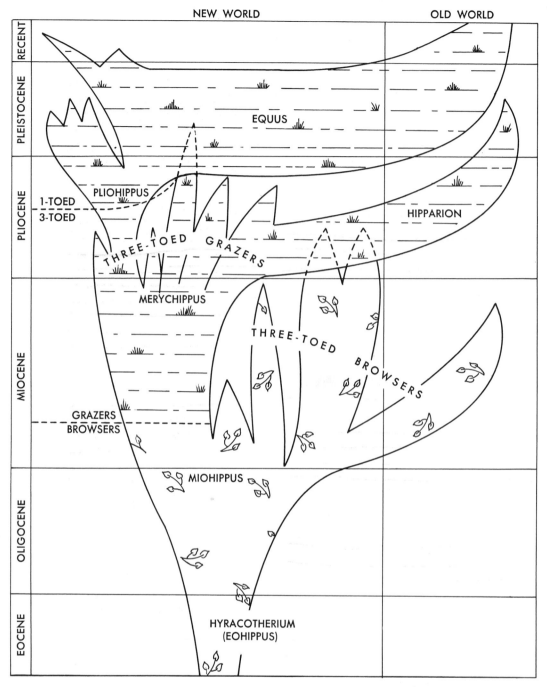

Fig. 22–7. The evolution of the horse family, the Equidae. The leaf and grass designs indicate browsing and grazing habits, respectively. (After G. G. Simpson.)

a dentition suitable for chewing only quite soft plant material, to large, galloping animals of the open plain capable of chewing and digesting one of the toughest foods, grass. The bones of the feet became elongated, the teeth increased in complexity, the digits were reduced to a single unit, and the brain increased in relative size and complexity. These changes did not, however, occur at a regular rate, nor did they all occur in the many separate lineages. During the Eocene, horses increased little from the terrier-like *Hyracotherium* (Fig. 22–8), but throughout the remainder of the Cenozoic,

Fig. 22–8. The earliest member of the horse family, *Hyracotherium,* sometimes called *Eohippus,* an animal about the size of a small dog. (Reproduced from J. Augusta and Z. Burian, *Prehistoric Animals.* London: Spring Books, 1956.)

their size increased gradually. The spread of grasslands in the middle Cenozoic provided an alternative diet, and the profound dental changes needed to accommodate it were initiated in a new lineage. The ancestors of the modern horse became grazers in Miocene time and evolved high-crowned teeth. The first of this advanced group that was adapted to life on the grassy plains, where the ability to run rapidly was a distinct advantage, was *Merychippus*, which walked on one toe and held the two shorter side toes off the ground. By the end of Miocene time one group of grazing horses (*Pliohippus*) had evolved to the single-toed stage. The modern horse (*Equus*) arose from *Pliohippus* during the Pliocene Epoch, by which time all the side branches of the family had become extinct, except *Hipparion*, which retained three toes into the Early Pleistocene.

The earliest horses were widespread in the Northern Hemisphere during the Eocene Epoch, but thereafter the family evolved in North America. Early in the Pleistocene, horses migrated across the Bering Strait and populated Asia, Africa, and Europe. By the end of the Pleistocene, all horses had died out in the New World. Our modern horses are all recent imports from Europe by man.

The modern African, Indian, and Indonesian rhinoceroses are remnants of a greater race that originated in Eocene time and for the rest of the Cenozoic were widespread across the northern continents. Many of the early forms were swift animals of the plains and did not have the horns that are so prominent on modern representatives of the group. At the end of Oligocene time this stock produced *Baluchitherium*, the largest land mammal that has ever lived, 25 feet in length and 18 feet high at the shoulders. Its long front legs and neck allowed it to browse where smaller beasts could not reach.

During the Miocene Epoch a fairly small rhinoceros named *Diceratherium* roamed the western plains in enormous herds. Their bones make up the bulk of the Agate Springs bone bed (Fig. 22–9), an accumulation of thousands of skeletons of animals probably drowned in a sudden flood. During the Ice

Fig. 22–9. A portion of the Agate Springs bone bed (Miocene of Nebraska). Most of the bones are of the rhinoceros *Diceratherium*, but a few are of *Dinohyus* and *Moropus* (see Fig. 22–12). (Courtesy of the Smithsonian Institution.)

Fig. 22–10.   Reconstruction of a group of titanotheres belonging to the genus *Megacerops* (Oligocene beds of Saskatchewan). (Painting by P. R. Haldorsen, courtesy of the Geological Survey of Canada.)

Age, woolly rhinoceroses roamed much of Europe and Asia. The nature of the fur of these extinct animals is known through a study of two specimens that were found preserved in a Polish oil seep, and also from drawings of the animals by prehistoric cave men.

The titanotheres (Fig. 22–10) were heavy, hoofed mammals with primitive teeth. This dominantly North American group appeared in Eocene time as contemporaries of the first horses, and lasted until Early Oligocene time. The race increased in size rapidly and developed various patterns of horns on their heads. The brain case remained small and primitive. The largest of the titanotheres, *Brontotherium*, had a thickset body supported by pillar-like legs and stood 8 feet high at the shoulder.

A peculiar development among the early perissodactyls led to the uintatheres (order Dinocerata), the largest land animals of Eocene time. *Uintatherium* (Fig. 22–11) was the size of a large rhinoceros and had a massive skull surmounted by six horns: two on the nose, two before the eyes, and two on the back of the head. The upper canine teeth were greatly enlarged into dagger-like blades, a strange feature for a herbivore. This group of mammals, sometimes included among the archaic mammals, became extinct early in the Oligocene Epoch.

The chalicotheres (Figs. 22–9 and 22–12), a long-ranging (Eocene–Pleistocene), superficially horselike group of perissodactyls, retained claws inherited from their condylarth ancestors but are classified with the hoofed mammals on the basis of other features of their skeletons. Their clawed feet appear to have been adapted to digging roots.

Mammals with Cloven Hooves

In this group of mammals, the artiodactyls, the weight of the animal was carried on the foot between the third and fourth toes. When they rose up on their toes, achieving greater speed, they first became four-toed and then two-toed. If the experiment with the hand is used to illustrate the evolution of this race, the thumb lifts from the table first and the second and fifth fingers next, leaving

Fig. 22–11. Restoration of the grotesque Eocene mammal *Uintatherium*, confined to North America. (By G. A. Reid, courtesy of the Royal Ontario Museum.)

the third and fourth to give the impression of a cloven hoof. These mammals make up a much larger group than the odd-toed hoofed mammals. They are divided into the SUINA, including pigs and hippopotamuses, and the RUMINANTIA, including camels, deer, giraffes, and cattle.

Pigs first appeared in Oligocene time and became one of the more successful of the mammalian races. They are highly intelligent animals adapted to a life in the forest and to an omnivorous diet, and tend to retain four digits. The hippopotamuses, which are a branch of the pig family adapted to a semi-

Fig. 22–12. In the foreground of this Miocene scene three entelodonts (*Dinohyus*) dig for roots. On the right are two chalicotheres (*Moropus*) with horselike bodies but clawed feet. A few three-toed horses (*Parahippus*) can be seen on the left. (Mural by Charles Knight, courtesy of the Field Museum of Natural History.)

aquatic life, did not appear until the Pliocene Epoch. An early offshoot comprised the entelodonts, sometimes referred to as the "giant pigs." The skull of *Dinohyus* (Figs. 22–9 and 22–12), the largest and the last, was nearly 3 feet in length.

The course of the evolution of the camels is almost as well known as that of the horses and is in many respects similar to it. The first camels were contemporaries of the first horses in the Eocene Epoch. By Oligocene time they had risen off their lateral toes and walked only on the third and fourth ones. In mid-Cenozoic time two branches of the camel family existed, the running camels and the giraffe camels. Typical of the latter group was *Alticamelus,* whose long neck supported its head 10 feet above the ground. North America was the home of the camel through most of the Cenozoic Era, but during the Pleistocene Epoch camels mysteriously died out here and are now found only in South America (llama) and in the Old World.

The oreodonts were middle and late Cenozoic ruminants closely related to the camels but sheeplike in form and of small size. Great numbers of their skeletons have been found in North America, indicating that they roamed the plains in large herds. They retained the four-toed foot.

The first members of the deer family appeared in Miocene time and have been predominantly an Old World group; today, this group includes a great variety of mammals, such as elk, moose, wapiti, and caribou. One of the most significant steps in the evolution of this family has been the acquisition of antlers that are discarded and regrown each year. The largest set of antlers unearthed was found in an Irish peat bog and was grown by the extinct "Irish elk" (actually a deer) of Late Pleistocene time. Giraffes, close relatives of the deer, began later in the Miocene but are unknown in North America.

Cattle, or bovoids, are characterized by long legs adapted to running, and horns, which are not shed, on both the male and female. Unlike the horse, camel, and rhinoc-

eros, the cattle are an Old World family which evolved in Europe and Asia late in Miocene time. Only a few members of this group, such as the bison, mountain sheep, and mountain goat, migrated to North America, and none reached South America.

Mammoths and Mastodons

The largest land animals now living are proboscidians, mammals whose nose forms a prehensile fifth limb called a trunk. The only living proboscidians are the Indian and African elephants, but they are survivors of a vigorous lineage that appeared in the Eocene Epoch. Advanced proboscidians are characterized by large, pillar-like legs, a massive body, and front incisor teeth enlarged to form tusks.

The first proboscidians were the size of a pig and had few elephantine features, but by middle Cenozoic time several typical lines had evolved. In some, both upper and lower incisor teeth were elongated, giving the animal four tusks; in others, the lower tusks were flattened, directed forward, and almost joined, forming a projection like a shovel in front of the mouth. Yet another branch, the dinotheres (Miocene–Pleistocene), had lower tusks which curved sharply backward toward the body. How the animal used such tusks is problematical, but it has been suggested that they were used in uprooting trees.

The jaws of early proboscidians were relatively long, compared with those of modern elephants, and contained many teeth bearing paired, blunt cusps. These animals are mastodons (Figs. 22–2 and 22–13). Their teeth indicate that they were browsers. They lived in North America until Pleistocene time but then became extinct. One group of the proboscidians, the elephants, branched from mastodon stock in Pliocene time and evolved a striking dental apparatus for chewing abrasive grasses. Their teeth became large and intricately infolded with resistant enamel (Fig. 22–2), but only one at a time was used on each side of the short jaw. This was probably the result of the mechanical necessity of bringing the heavy trunk and tusks

Fig. 22–13. Mastodons. In the center is a reconstruction of the Cohoes mastodon, flanked by two skeletons of other mastodon finds, all from New York State. The background represents the Catskill Mountains as they may have looked late in the Ice Age. (Courtesy of the New York State Museum.)

as close as possible to the burdened neck muscles. Less strain was placed on the neck muscles as the skull became progressively shorter, but no space was left for the second incisors, canines, or premolars. As each elephant tooth wears out, a new one grows to replace it. Although it has the equivalent of only four chewing teeth in its mouth at one time, the elephant uses the normal complement of 16 molar teeth in succession. The modern elephant dies of starvation or indigestion after he has worn out his four sets of molars. The largest of the elephants, the woolly mammoth that inhabited North America, Europe, and Asia during the Ice Age, was 13 to 14 feet high at the shoulder and was covered with shaggy reddish hair (Fig. 22–14). Almost as much is known about these extinct animals as if they still lived, because several specimens have been found frozen in the Siberian tundra in such good condition that the flesh was apparently still

edible. One of the major sources of ivory has been Siberian mammoths' tusks, which reach a length of 13 feet. These lumbering elephants were hunted by early European man, who painted their picture on the walls of his caves. Both mammoth and mastodon were common in North America up to the close of the Wisconsin glaciation. Closely related to the proboscidians is a group known as the sirenians, which, as early as the Eocene, adopted an aquatic life. Several lines of descent are known, but only one, including the manatee, has living representatives in North America.

Edentates

The edentates, an insignificant part of the modern fauna, include the anteaters, sloths, and armadillos. This race is worthy of mention here because two of its members were common during the Pleistocene Epoch in North America. One of these was the giant

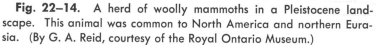

Fig. 22–14. A herd of woolly mammoths in a Pleistocene landscape. This animal was common to North America and northern Eurasia. (By G. A. Reid, courtesy of the Royal Ontario Museum.)

ground sloth, an extinct animal the size of an elephant (Fig. 22–15). The ground sloths were descended from the ancestors of the modern tree sloth, small South American mammals with feet adapted for hanging upside down from branches, and from them they inherited an awkward gait. The ground sloths walked on the sides of their feet rather than on the soles and must have been clumsy, slow-moving beasts. The ground sloths, such as *Megatherium*, were contemporaries of prehistoric man on this continent and became extinct only a few thousand years ago in both North and South America.

Fig. 22–15. Ground sloths originated in South America; this one (*Megatherium*) migrated to North America during Pleistocene time. (Painting by Charles Knight, courtesy of the Field Museum of Natural History.)

Fig. 22–16. The ground sloths were accompanied into North America by an armored relative, the armadillo *(Glyptodon)*. Compare the body and tail armor with that of *Ankylosaurus*, Fig. 21–4. (Painting by Charles Knight, courtesy of the Field Museum of Natural History.)

Another branch of the edentates, represented today by the armadillos, developed body armor. The armadillo's armor is segmented, but its Pleistocene relative, the glyptodont, like the turtle, had a rigid shield completely covering the body (Fig. 22–16). The glyptodont's tail was equipped with a spiked club of bone which, like the tail of the stegosaurs, was used defensively. Both the glyptodonts and the ground sloths crossed into North America via the Isthmus of Panama at the beginning of Pleistocene time. How they survived the northward migration, faced with the southward surge of advanced carnivorous mammals invading South America, is a mystery.

Cetaceans

A distinct group of marine mammals (CETACEA), the whales, porpoises, and dolphins, is descended from terrestrial carnivores. When their fossil record begins, in the Eocene, the postcranial skeleton is already highly specialized for swimming. The hind limbs were lost and the forelimbs were modified into paddles. The skull retains the dentition and brain case typical of the primitive creodonts. By the time they were first recorded, whales were divided into two groups, the toothed whales, including the dolphins, porpoises, and killer whales, and the baleen or whalebone whales. The latter group has lost all the teeth and developed a series of ridges of horny tissue extending down from the upper jaw. These ridges strain small organisms from the sea, on which the animals feed.

PRIMATES

The order of mammals to which man belongs (PRIMATES) arose from insectivore stock late in the Cretaceous Period, and insofar as they specialized at all, it was for an arboreal mode of life. Through the development of the following characteristics the primates became adapted to a life in the trees:

1. Improved, forward-looking eyes, binocular vision, and depth perception. The eyes became the principal sense organ, and the sense of smell was reduced.
2. A complex, large brain that facilitated clearer reasoning and quickened co-ordinating reactions, particularly in the cerebral hemispheres where the integration of sensory information takes place.
3. A thumb separate from and opposable to the rest of the digits, equipping the hand for grasping branches and, in connection with the improved brain, for the delicate and intelligent handling of objects; reduction of claws to nails.
4. Unspecialized teeth and skeletal elements that allowed a varied diet and habitat.

Tree Shrews, Lemurs, and Tarsiers

Although we are principally interested in the anthropoid, or manlike, branch of the primates, the order includes many less advanced animals. Among these are the tree shrews, once included among the insectivores but considered by some authorities to be the most primitive branch of the primates. They are small, arboreal creatures, large-brained, with an opposable thumb and big toe. They alone, among the primates, possess claws instead of nails. The lemurs, small, long-faced and long-tailed arboreal animals, appeared at the beginning of the Paleocene Epoch and their fossils are found in Paleocene and Eocene beds of North America and Europe. One of the best known is *Notharctus* (Eocene of North America), less than 1 foot in length. Thereafter, lemurs were practically confined to the island of Madagascar until the Pleistocene, during which interval that island was isolated from the mainland and was also nearly devoid of carnivores. They persist, showing little anatomical advance, as the bush-babies and aye-ayes of today. The wide-eyed, fragile tarsiers are another group of primates that appeared early; they are now restricted to the jungles of eastern Asia. Like the lemurs, they are not represented in middle or late Cenozoic rocks. Among their interesting features are their eyes, which are turned completely forward, their shortened nose, and their rounded face, which approximates that of the hominids. These and other features suggest that the line of descent was from the insectivores through the lemurs and the tarsioids to the hominids.

Monkeys and Apes

All other primates are included in the anthropoids, or manlike group, which contains Old World monkeys, New World monkeys, apes, and man. In this group the four adaptations listed above are brought to varying degrees of development. Monkeys are first found in Eocene strata of Asia. From this stem, in some manner not clearly understood, the New World monkeys migrated to South America by Miocene time and since then have developed independently of other primates. So far as is known, none reached North America. Apes first appeared in the Lower Oligocene, represented by *Propliopithecus,* and evolved through a Late Miocene–Early Pliocene form, *Proconsul,* to the living great apes, the gibbon, orangutan, chimpanzee, and gorilla. The fossil record of this evolution is maddeningly meager. The brain capacity and body size of the apes are greater than those of the early primates, but their teeth remained essentially primitive, suitable for a varied vegetarian diet. Too large to scamper along tree branches as monkeys do, they took to swinging from branch to branch and developed longer arms, facilitating this method of travel. The heavier apes, the chimpanzee and gorilla, found swinging through the trees difficult and spent much of the time walking along the ground.

Man

At about the Miocene–Pliocene boundary, one branch of the apes followed an evolutionary course that led to freedom from a life in the trees, perfection of the erect posture, and a two-legged walk. The brain of this new race developed gradually to greater and greater complexity, and ultimately to a size three times that of the most advanced ape. With an erect posture the forelimbs were free to handle objects, to make implements and weapons, and to investigate the world of nature. Because postnatal training of offspring was extended over a period of years, information and skill learned by one generation could be passed on to the next, and a body of knowledge could be accumulated in the rapidly developing cerebrum, the seat of memory. This branch of the primates developed a social organization into families, clans, tribes, and nations such as had never been approached by any animal before. They were so successful in their exploitation of many different environments that they extended their range to all parts of the world and became the most abundant of the species of higher vertebrates. These advanced primates were men.

MAN

Our information about prehistoric men is derived from two sources: their skeletons and the objects they fashioned to supplement their hands. The latter source leads to an understanding of man's social and industrial progress, whereas the former serves to place him in his proper niche among other animals. We shall first consider the skeletal evidence. In zoological classifications the family to which the human race belongs is known as the HOMINIDAE. The differences separating members of this family from those of the PONGIDAE, or ape family, are few but significant. Certain differences in brain structure are important. Modern man has an average cranial capacity of 1500 cc, whereas the largest of the apes has a capacity rarely exceeding 500 cc. More important than the size is the make-up of the brain. The frontal part of man's brain is larger than that of the ape's. The projection of the skull forward to accommodate the enlargement gives man a forehead and a nearly vertical face. Not all skulls of prehistoric men show a special development of that part of the brain and of the lower jaw that have to do with the faculty of

speech, yet in some specimens these modifications can be recognized.

The teeth are diagnostic. The line of the ape's teeth is a U-shape; man's is a curve, thus ⌣, with no parallelism between the molar regions (Fig. 22–17). Human canines barely project beyond the plane of the rest of the teeth; the ape's canines are always prominent, especially in the male. Differences in the mounting of the skull, the pelvis, and the leg and foot bones reflect the upright position of man's body and the stooped position of the ape's. These and many minor characteristics serve to set man apart from the ape morphologically. Socially, the difference between man and the apes is one of degree. Chimpanzees and gorillas are gregarious, with due regard to family ties and responsibilities. Culturally, there is a vast difference. Man is the only animal to make tools and to make use of fire.

Up to a century ago, no fossil remains of humans were accepted in scientific circles; but, beginning with the discovery of prehistoric skeletons in the Neander valley near

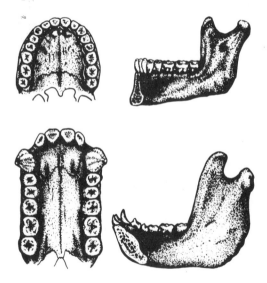

Fig. 22–17. Lower jaw of man *(top)* and gorilla *(bottom)*. On the left is the dental arch as seen from above; on the right, the inside of the right half of the jaw. (From *General College Geology*, courtesy of A. J. Eardley and Harper & Row.)

Düsseldorf, overwhelming evidence of a long prehistory of the human race has come to light. According to the fossil remains human prehistory can be divided into five parts, each of which is described below.

Ramapithecus

Ramapithecus, the earliest hominid fossil, is known from lower jaws found in the Upper Miocene and Lower Pliocene of Kenya, northern India, China, and possibly Europe. Both the diagnostic divergent lines of the molars and the relatively smaller incisors, canines, and premolars separate these jaws from those of fossil or modern apes. The weakness of the front teeth suggests an inability to use these teeth for stripping leaves from branches as do the apes today, and suggests therefore a greater dependence on the use of the hands. Unfortunately, only lower jaws have been found, and there are no artifacts associated with those jaws. No other Pliocene hominid fossils have so far been discovered.

The Australopithecines

For the past forty years, evidence from discoveries in South Africa has been building up to support the contention that a very primitive type of man lived there early in the Pleistocene Epoch. Although there have been several discoveries, and a variety of names applied to them, all may be grouped together as the australopithecines. These were rather short hominids with teeth, pelves, legs, hands, and feet closely approximating those of modern man. The brain, although considerably larger than that of any of the great apes, is smaller than that of any other hominid. Crudely shaped stone implements associated with the skeletons are conclusive evidence that the users belonged within the human family. That they were directly ancestral to modern man is unlikely, but no definite conclusions can yet be made. Nevertheless, at the beginning of the Pleistocene, and possibly late in the Pliocene, primitive, erect, tool-making hominids were already in existence (Fig. 22–18).

Homo erectus

Primates that can be recognized unequivocally as men have been found in Lower and Middle Pleistocene deposits in Java, China, and Germany. The Javanese specimens were found in 1892 by Eugene Dubois in beds of Early to Middle Pleistocene age. Dubois found a skull cap, a thigh bone, and several teeth associated with the remains of numerous mammals; since then other skulls and jaw parts have been unearthed. Dubois called this fossil *Pithecanthropus erectus* (erect ape-man).

The Chinese specimens were recovered from caves near Peking and were first called *Sinanthropus pekingensis*. The skeletons are so similar to those of the Java man that they are believed to have belonged to the same race, and their name was changed to *Pithecanthropus pekingensis*. The Peking fossils have a greater brain capacity, and, unlike the Javanese fossils, were accompanied by tools and evidences of fire.

A massive jaw found in gravels of Middle Pleistocene age near Heidelberg, Germany,

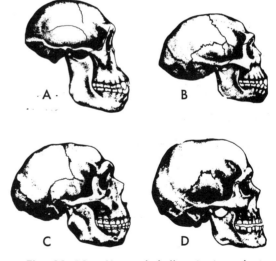

Fig. 22–18. Hominid skulls. A. *Australopithecus.* B. Peking man, *Homo erectus.* C. Neanderthal man, *Homo sapiens neanderthalensis.* D. Cro-Magnon man, *Homo sapiens sapiens.* (After Robinson, McGregor, and Weinert, from *Vertebrate Paleontology,* courtesy of A. S. Romer and the University of Chicago Press.)

may be a European representative of the Java race. It was first named *Homo heidelbergensis*. The jaw is considerably larger than that of any modern man, but its teeth are relatively small and modern looking. Although none of the skull or other bones have been discovered, it seems reasonable to suppose that this jaw belonged to a member of the same race as the Java and the Chinese men.

The Java and Peking men had many apelike features, but their brain capacity and use of tools and fire set them far above even the most advanced apes. They had heavy brow ridges above the eyes and a receding forehead that formed the front of a shallow brain pan. The nose was flat, the mouth thrust forward, and the chin non-existent (Fig. 22–18). They walked with the body erect or nearly so. Their brain capacity ranged between 900 and 1200 cc, compared with an average of 400 cc for the largest apes and 700 cc for the australopithecines. Modern man's capacity averages 1500 cc, and ranges between 1200 and 1800 cc. Because there is no valid reason for separating the Java and Peking men, both, together with Heidelberg man, are included within the species *Homo erectus* (see Fig. 22–19).

Homo sapiens neanderthalensis

The skeletons in the next stage in man's evolution as recorded by fossils are common and widely distributed, compared with those of the preceding races. The European representatives of this group are sometimes called *Homo sapiens neanderthalensis* because the first skull of this type was found at Neanderthal in Germany. Skeletal remains of the neanderthals have been found distributed over Europe, North Africa, and Palestine. Neanderthal man was distinctly brutish in appearance but had a brain large enough to indicate that he was an intelligent human. He was short and broad, and walked in a stooped position, with head thrust forward and knees probably slightly bent. His head was held low on his shoulders by a very short neck. His face retained, in the massive brow ridges, broad nose, protruding mouth, and lack of chin, the brutish features of the

Java race (Figs. 22–18 and 22–19). In the Third Interglacial Stage, men of this race probably lived in the open, but with the onset of the Fourth Glaciation, they adopted cave life, the rigors of which may have weakened them and contributed to their ultimate extinction.

Modern Man—Homo sapiens

Neanderthal man appears to have succumbed to the extreme climate of the Ice Age and to the invasion of his homeland by a more advanced race, the Cro-Magnons. These men were tall and perfectly erect. They had long heads, relatively high foreheads, and pointed chins. Although they retained a slight bony ridge over the eyes, it was not massive like that of their predecessors. Physically and probably mentally they were not inferior to modern Europeans. The origin of the Cro-Magnons is not known, but they were certainly not descended directly from the brutish Neanderthal race they displaced (Fig. 22–18).

Scanty skeletal evidence indicates that modern man lived before and during the period when the Neanderthal race was dominant. In Europe the Cro-Magnons persisted in a few scattered enclaves, but for the most part they either followed the receding continental glacier northward or intermingled with modern races of Asian origin that were invading Europe. These or other possibilities lie more in the domain of the anthropologist and the historian than of the geologist.

MAN THE TOOL MAKER

The second mode of approach to the prehistory of mankind is by way of the objects which he has used and made. Many animals, such as worms, insects, spiders, fish, and birds, manufacture things, but much of the process is instinctive. Man is the only animal whose artifacts are the result of the desire or the need of an individual, and his ability to make tools or other objects is never inherited.

Man may be defined as a maker of tools and a user of fire, for by the possession of these skills he is set apart from the rest of the animal kingdom. Primitive tools and charred

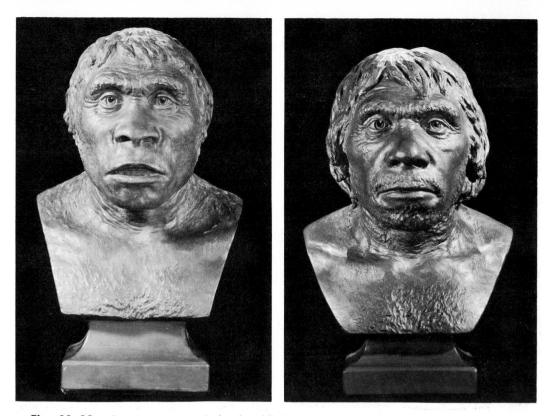

Fig. 22–19. Reconstructions of the heads of early man. *Left: Pithecanthropus (Homo erectus). Right: Homo sapiens neanderthalensis.* (By J. H. McGregor, courtesy of the American Museum of Natural History.)

wood and bone are found with some of the oldest fossil skeletons that can be recognized anatomically as those of men. Tools, weapons, and ornaments made by a primitive people, taken together, define the culture of that people and tell us a great deal more about the way the members lived than do the skeletal remains. The bones of prehistoric men are rare fossils, and most of the information about our ancestors of Pleistocene time has come from a study of the things they fashioned from stone and, to a lesser extent, from bone and wood. Because stone is the most resistant of such materials to weathering and decay, tools that were made of stone form the vast majority of those which have been preserved. Tools of wood, doubtless used by these men, soon rotted in the ground. Men who used stone in making their tools are said to have lived in the **Stone Age.** This period of time may be divided into Old, Middle, and New, or, in formal terms, Paleolithic, Mesolithic, and Neolithic periods (Fig. 22–20).

The methods by which early men fashioned their tools depended on the stage to which their skill had advanced in working the material, and on the type of work that the tool was required to do. Archeologists separate Stone Age tools into classes on the basis of their shape, the way they were made, and the uses to which they were presumably put, and give these traditions names that refer to the locality from which the tools were first described. Some of these toolmaking traditions may originally have been associated with a single group of primitive men, but such was the interchange of ideas, even in the earliest society, that one group undoubtedly borrowed techniques of toolmaking from others.

Charred wood and bones, and old hearths, tell something about early man's habits and accomplishments. Stone lamps attest his use of fire for lighting purposes.

Neither tools nor evidences of fire have been found associated with the remains of *Ramapithecus.* Pleistocene man used a variety of materials for tools, depending upon what was available in the region he inhabited.

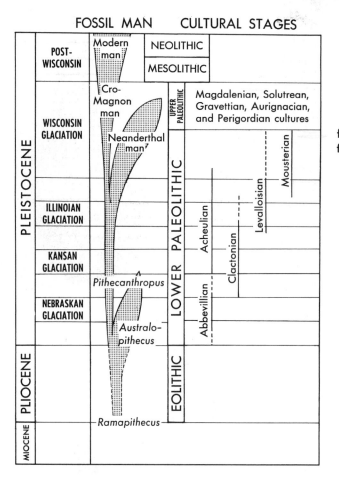

Fig. 22–20. Correlation between fossil men and the cultural stages defined on the basis of their implements.

The Africans used sharp-edged pebbles of lava and other materials, and may have discovered how to sharpen the edges by chipping. The East Asians used quartz and sandstone and developed what is called the chopper-tool tradition. These tools, with an edge trimmed like an adze, were found in the caves with the skeletons of Peking man. Man soon learned that the even, fine texture of flint and chert allows the stone to be broken along a curved plane in a direction determined by the angle of the blow. In the hands of a skilled artisan these materials can be worked to a strong, hard, and sharp edge. Prehistoric man took tens of thousands of years to perfect his technique of working flint until, at the end of the Stone Age, he was able to produce from these raw materials tools which were not only useful but also of great beauty.

Core and Flake Traditions

A flint tool may be made by reducing a nodule, or core, to the desired shape and discarding the chips, or by carefully striking off a flake from the nodule and discarding the core. These two methods of making tools can be recognized throughout the Old Stone Age and are called the **core** and **flake traditions,** respectively. The earliest stage of the core-tool tradition is termed **Abbevillian.** Abbevillian tools are nodules of flint crudely rounded at one end and chipped to a point at the other to form a pear-shaped instrument (Fig. 22–21). They are sometimes referred to as hand axes (*coups de poing*), but they were probably used for cutting and scraping as well as for chopping. Tools of the earliest flake tradition, called **Clactonian,** appear at about this time and may have been

Fig. 22–21. Primitive flint implements. *Left:* An eolith, a chipped flint nodule that may or may not have been worked by man. *Center:* An Abbevillian hand axe. *Right:* An Acheulian hand axe (approximately ½ actual size). (Courtesy of the McCord National Museum.)

made by a people different from the makers of the Abbevillian hand axes. The extreme rarity of skeletal fossils associated with these tools makes a positive statement on questions such as this impossible. The Clactonian flakes were trimmed around the thin edges somewhat to make a more efficient tool, but, if the flake had been struck off correctly, very little extra work was necessary to make a good cutting or scraping edge. Later workers of the hand axe tradition learned to flake the core with a wooden or bone hammer when trimming the rough tool, and in this way produced much smoother edges. This advanced hand axe tradition is called **Acheulian** (Fig. 22–21).

Several advances in the technique of shaping flint tools were made during the middle division of the Old Stone Age. The first of these was the careful preparation of a striking platform along the edge of the core. The flake was then detached with a bone or wooden punch hit with a mallet or hammer stone, and trimmed along the cutting edges if necessary. Flakes formed from such a core

Fig. 22–22. Flint tools from the later part of the Old Stone Age. *Lower left:* A large flake chipped around the edges in the Levalloisian manner. *Lower right:* A tool in the Mousterian tradition. *Top:* Tools of the blade traditions—*left,* a projectile point; *center,* a blade; *right,* a burin or graver. (Courtesy of the McCord National Museum.)

characterize the **Levalloisian** tradition of tool-making (Fig. 22–22). The people who worked flint in this way lived at the same time as those who made the Acheulian hand axes, and at some sites tools which embody these two traditions are found together. In addition to the above techniques, Neanderthal man made tools of the **Mousterian** tradition by striking small triangular flakes from a core and trimming them on one or both sides to produce slightly serrated cutting edges (Fig. 22–22). Different tools of this tradition were manufactured for specific tasks such as scraping, cutting, sawing, and chopping. Workmen of the Levalloisian and Mousterian traditions were the first to attach their points to shafts for use as spears, thus opening up a whole new arsenal of weapons for the prehistoric hunter.

At the beginning of the latest glacial advance of Pleistocene time, Neanderthal man was using a mixture of tools that had originated as separate traditions among different peoples. In Europe his tools were various blends of Acheulian, Mousterian, Levalloisian, and other traditions. The relationships between some of these traditions is illustrated in Fig. 22–20.

Blade Tradition

Flint working underwent a revolution during the latest glacial age, with the appearance of the blade traditions. Long, straight blades of flint were produced by carefully preparing the core and striking the desired flake from it with a bone or wood punch hit with a hammer stone. The flint artisans also developed a method of spalling off small flakes from the tool by applying pressure with the point of a hardened wooden or bone tool. This flaking gave a much finer edge and finish to tools than was possible to attain by percussion methods. Blade tools were modified for special uses (Fig. 22–22). Blades with a rounded back were used as knives, gravers, or burins and chisels; points with a projection or tang were fastened to spear or arrow shafts; and pointed, narrow blades were used for drilling. Men began to make smaller flint flakes, known as microliths, for fitting along the edges of bone harpoons and spears.

The great diversity of these Late Paleolithic tools reflects the many cultures that were developing at this time. Among the more important of these cultural groups were the Perigordians, Aurignacians, Gravettians, Solutreans, and Magdalenians. Flint flaking reached its highest stage in the tools of the Solutreans, who excelled in the art of pressure flaking. Some of their laurel-leaf points are so beautifully worked as to make one feel that they were created as works of art or for ceremonial use, although most appear to have been used as arrowheads. That Late Pleistocene man possessed considerable artistic ability is shown by decorations which the Aurignacians and Magdalenians worked on their weapons and tools, and by the marvelous paintings they executed in deep recesses of caves (Fig. 22–23).

EARLY MAN IN NORTH AMERICA

The primates had become extinct in North America shortly after the beginning of the Cenozoic Era, before they evolved, elsewhere, to the monkey stage. Prehistoric man did not appear in the Americas until late in the Wisconsin glaciation, near the end of the Old Stone Age. Late Paleolithic man apparently crossed to North America from Siberia over the Bering Strait, which, during the late stages of glaciation, had emerged from beneath the sea. As a result, the record of man on this continent shows none of the evolutionary and cultural steps that can be traced in Asia and Europe.

When the ancestors of the North American Indians came to this continent is not yet known. Except for the questionable evidence of charred mammoth bones in California yielding a radiocarbon age of 29,650 ± 2500 years, there is little reason to suppose that man crossed the Bering Strait before 15,000 years ago. The earliest traces of the human occupation of this continent come from numerous and widespread Folsom points (Fig. 22–24) associated with bones of extinct bison, for which radiocarbon dating gives an age of a little less than 10,000 years. Still older by an unknown amount, perhaps one or two thousand years, is the Llano cul-

Fig. 22–23. Cave painting of an aurochs (or bull) jumping and a group of horses, Lascaux, France. (Courtesy of the Caisse Nationale des Monuments Historiques.)

Fig. 22–24. Fluted points (Folsom type) from the Lindenmeier site, Colorado. (Courtesy of the Smithsonian Institution, Office of Anthropology.)

ture of the western United States. No bones of Folsom or Llano men have been found.

CIVILIZATION

Near the end of the Stone Age man slowly began to abandon a subsistence based on hunting and collecting fruits and roots, and turned to herding animals and, later, to agriculture. The development of agriculture was one of the major revolutions in man's history; before he could grow food, he had to give up his wandering in search of fruits and game and settle down to live in one place. Once held to a fixed location by the necessity of tending his fields, man built permanent houses, then villages and then cities. The revolution in man's life from hunting to farming began in the Near East about 6000 B.C. and spread outward, reaching Britain about 2500 B.C. These first farmers lived in the New Stone Age and finished their tools by pecking, grinding, and polishing them to a smooth surface.

Documenting the history of civilization is the task of the historian, not the geologist. The time when man changed from a primitive hunter, at the mercy of his environment, to a civilized creature able to mold his environment to his advantage seems a good time to close the account of the historical geology of North America, and to let the archeologists and historians continue the tale.

QUESTIONS

1. One often reads of the "sudden" appearance of fossils in Cambrian rocks and of the "sudden" disappearance of dinosaurs. Discuss the "suddenness" in these two cases.

2. The genus *Nautilus*, the coelacanth *Latimeria*, and the brachiopod *Lingula* have persisted long after the taxa to which they belong have almost disappeared. How can you explain such persistence?

3. There is good reason for assuming that plants descended according to the scheme algae→psilophytes→ferns→seed ferns. Through what taxa were modern flowering plants derived from seed ferns? When did the changes occur?

4. There are several debatable points concerning the history of life on this planet. Mention as many as possible, and give the two or more sides to each question.

5. Among land animals, amphibia were dominant during much of the late Paleozoic, reptiles during the remainder of the Paleozoic and the Mesozoic, and mammals during the Cenozoic. Is there reason to suppose that a fourth group will succeed mammals and become dominant? To appreciate the force of this question, put yourself in the place first of a Silurian fish, then of a Mississippian amphibian, and lastly of an early Cretaceous reptile.

6. On the end papers of this book several patterns of "life lines" are shown. Trilobites begin almost at their maximum and gradually die away. Tetracorals begin modestly and maintain a maximum until just before extinction. Crinoids and ammonoids show more than one maximum. How can you explain such apparent irregularities?

7. What is the evidence for concluding that mammals were descended from reptiles? Reptiles from amphibia? Amphibia from fish? Birds from reptiles? What taxon may have been ancestral to the chordates? What difficulties crop up in answering the last query?

8. What is the difference between microfossils and macrofossils? Name a few taxa made up of what are usually called microfossils. Would it be appropriate to call bryozoans and ostracods "semi-microfossils"?

9. Why are the following taxa poorly represented in rocks: pelecypods, birds, sponges, insects, jellyfish, worms?

10. Period by period, give the dominant (specify both the most powerful and the most abundant) type of marine invertebrate animal (e.g., Silurian—eurypterids, most powerful; brachiopods, most abundant).

11. Since living in the sea is "easy," why should organisms have invaded the land? Describe the transition in habitat and the possible advantages for plants and for animals.

12. Which of the main taxa of plants now existent were *not* represented in the flora that inhabited the Pennsylvanian coal swamps? When did these later taxa begin their history?

13. Why is paleoecology a far more difficult study than ecology?

14. Sketch briefly the contribution to historical geology made by Charles Darwin and William Smith.

15. Which phyla of organisms would you expect to be represented in Precambrian rocks? Which phyla are actually preserved as fossils in those rocks? If there is any discrepancy in your answers to these questions, how can you explain it?

16. Give several reasons for the relatively sudden appearance of fossils in Precambrian rocks and discuss the one you favor.

17. Name at least three taxa of fossils that have been successfully used as index fossils. In each case, give the characteristics which made such use successful.

18. Throughout post-Precambrian eras there have been times of evolutionary expansion and other times of evolutionary retreat. Give examples of each kind and relate them to contemporary ecological conditions.

19. What are the main differences between molecular evolution before the origin of life and subsequent organic evolution?

20. Why are reef structures favorable for the storage of petroleum? What phyla are chiefly concerned? What is the oldest reef known?

REFERENCES AND SUGGESTED READINGS

General

BEERBOWER, J. R. *Search for the Past*, 2d ed. Englewood Cliffs, N.J.: Prentice-Hall, Inc., 1968. A study of paleozoology, by phylum, with an evolutionary approach. Eight of the 21 chapters are concerned with general and special topics.

FENTON, C. L., and FENTON, M. A. *The Fossil Book*. Garden City, N.Y.: Doubleday and Co., Inc., 1958. An abundantly illustrated treatment of the nature, occurrence, and relationships of fossils, with much additional information not ordinarily found in textbooks.

GOLDRING, W. *Handbook of Paleontology for Beginners and Amateurs, Part 1*, New York State Museum Handbook 9, 2d ed. Albany, N.Y.: 1950. A textbook covering the principles of paleontology, paleobotany, and invertebrate and vertebrate paleontology.

SHIMER, H. W., and SHROCK, R. R. *Index Fossils of North America*. New York: John Wiley & Sons, 1944. Classification, descriptions, and illustrations of thousands of fossils.

STIRTON, R. A. *Time, Life and Man: The Fossil Record*. New York: John Wiley & Sons, Inc., 1959. A textbook of paleontology which first describes the life of each period and then discusses selected topics in the evolution of the invertebrates, vertebrates, and plants.

Invertebrates

EASTON, W. H. *Invertebrate Paleontology*. New York: Harper & Row, 1960. A standard, well-illustrated treatment . of invertebrates, phylum by phylum.

MOORE, R. C. (Ed.). *Treatise on Invertebrate Paleontology*. Lawrence: Geological Society of America and the University of Kansas Press, 24 parts, 16 published 1953–67. A stupendous compendium of invertebrate taxa arranged according to modern classifications down to the generic level. For most genera there are illustrations. Essential for specialists, helpful for others.

SHROCK, R. R., and TWENHOFEL, W. H. *Principles of Invertebrate Paleontology*, 2d ed. New York: McGraw-Hill Book Co., 1953. An advanced textbook in invertebrate paleontology which describes in detail the various invertebrate phyla in the fossil record.

Vertebrates

COLBERT, E. H. *The Dinosaur Book*. New York: McGraw-Hill Book Co., 1951. A very readable and authoritative treatment not only of dinosaurs but of many other reptiles.

COLBERT, E. H. *Evolution of the Vertebrates*. New York: John Wiley & Sons, Inc., 1955. A compact treatment. Not so full or up to date as Romer (1966), but should be used by every student of paleontology.

ROMER, A. S. *Man and the Vertebrates*. Baltimore: Pelican Books, 1954. A clearly written and well-illustrated textbook of vertebrate evolution.

ROMER, A. S. *Vertebrate Paleontology*, 3d ed. Chicago: University of Chicago Press, 1966. The bulk of this book consists of 26 chapters devoted to descriptions and discussions of vertebrate taxa. Three chapters treat vertebrate histories of the Paleozoic, Mesozoic, and Cenozoic eras. One long chapter is concerned with the classification of vertebrates, and is, in addition, a checklist of all known genera. An adequate bibliography according to taxa is included. Indispensable for any paleontologist primarily interested in vertebrates.

SIMPSON, G. G. *Horses*. New York: Oxford University Press, 1951. A thoroughly readable and reliable account of the history of the horse family.

WOODFORD, A. O. *Historical Geology*. San Francisco: W. H. Freeman and Co., 1965. A good treatment of fossil vertebrates.

Human Prehistory

OAKLEY, K. P. *Man, the Tool-maker*. London: British Museum, 1956. A fascinating booklet describing the tools of flint, bone, and wood that prehistoric man fashioned.

SIMONS, E. L. "The Early Relatives of Man," *Scientific American*, 211: 50–62, 1964. Discusses the newer evidences from Africa.

Special Topics

DARRAH, W. C. *Principles of Paleobotany*, 2d ed. New York: The Ronald Press Co., 1960. Embodies modern ideas concerning classification of fossil plants.

LADD, H. S. "Treatise on Marine Ecology and Paleoecology," *Geological Society of America Memoir 67*, vol. 2, "Paleoecology." Following a general consideration of various facets of paleoecology, the book treats more than a score of topics concerned with both temporal and spatial paleoecological situations in North America. The last third of the book is an annotated bibliography of marine paleoecology of plant and animal taxa.

RAYMOND, P. E. *Prehistoric Life*. Cambridge, Mass.: Harvard University Press, 1939. Not a textbook, this work consists of a compilation of chapters on selected features of the evolution of life.

RUSH, J. H. *The Dawn of Life*. Garden City, N.Y.: Doubleday and Co., Inc., 1962. (Paperback edition, Signet Science Library, 1962.) A clear exposition of the chemical evolution of organic molecules preceding the origin of living cells.

SIMPSON, G. G. "The History of Life," in *The Evolution of Life*, ed. Sol Tax. Chicago: University of Chicago Press, 1960. Largely concerned with vertebrates, Simpson's chapter is a philosophical and statistical account in which most of the data refer to mammals.

APPENDIXES

A

A Summary of the Plant and Animal Kingdoms

THE NAMES OF PLANTS AND ANIMALS

Before the sciences of botany and zoology were established, plants and animals were given names such as buttercup, dog, rose, or cat, which differed of course from language to language. As more of the world of nature was investigated, names were invented to designate types of organisms that were generally unknown to the common man. Had this scheme of naming continued, each language would have been burdened with myriads of names for the types of animals and plants that modern scientists have distinguished, and it would have been almost impossible for scholars of one language to have assimilated the names proposed by scholars of other languages.

Fortunately, in 1735, before this confusion was far advanced, a Swedish naturalist named Carl Linneus proposed that animals and plants be named in Latin, the scholarly language of the eighteenth century. He also proposed that each organism be given two names: the first to indicate the general group of animals or plants to which the organism belonged, and the second to distinguish the particular type of animal within that group. These two names correspond in a general way to our family name (Smith) and given name (William). Our family names are written last, and our given names (which modify our family names, like adjectives) are written first: William Smith. Because modifying adjectives follow nouns in Latin, however, the group names of organisms are written first and the specific names last. Thus cats of all kinds were called *Felis* (Latin for cat) by Linneus. Within this large group he designated several kinds of cats, such as *Felis domestica* (the domestic cat), *Felis leo* (the lion cat), and *Felis tigris* (the tiger cat). The first name of these cats is known as their generic name, and all cats are said to belong to the **genus** (plural, **genera**) *Felis*. The second name is their specific name and serves to distinguish the various types or **species** (plural, **species**) of cats within the genus *Felis*. Because of its simplicity and freedom from language barriers, Linneus' **binomial system of nomenclature** has been universally accepted. As a result, the names of animals and plants are the same in all languages, and to a large extent the relationships between organisms can be expressed by these names.

In this book the authors rarely refer to specific names, but the student should realize that every genus must have at least one species, and some have hundreds of species. As scientific investigation advances, a genus is sometimes found to be too inclusive, and the species in it are often regrouped within several newly defined genera. The original name is usually retained for one of the new and restricted genera. Thus, the genus *Spirifer*, named in the early days of paleontology, has in modern times been subdivided into scores of new genera and the name *Spirifer* has been retained for one of them. The new genera, which were once included in the old genus, may collectively be referred to as *Spirifer sensu lato* (in the wide sense), and the new restricted genus becomes *Spirifer sensu stricto* (in the restricted sense). These are usually abbreviated to *Spirifer s.l.* and *Spirifer s.s.*

The relationship between organisms is further elaborated in a system of classification in which the genera, such as *Felis,* are grouped together into **families,** the families into **orders,** the orders into **classes,** the classes into **phyla,** and the phyla into **kingdoms.** The family of cats, the FELIDAE, belongs to the order CARNIVORA, which also includes most other meat-eating mammals and some extinct groups. This order belongs to the class MAMMALIA, which includes all the four-footed, warm-blooded animals with hair. The mammals are a division of the phylum CHORDATA, which comprises all the animals with backbones; this phylum, together with all the invertebrate phyla, is included in the ANIMALIA or animal kingdom. The relationships between organisms is so complex that

many more categories than those mentioned above are necessary to express these relationships. Detailed classifications contain such categories as superfamilies, suborders, superorders, and infraclasses.

In some modern classifications three kingdoms are recognized—PLANTAE, ANIMALIA, and PROTISTA. The last includes all one-celled organisms. Because this refinement has no bearing upon any geological problems, however, it is not followed here. The classification used in Appendix B is much simplified because its purpose is to help the student with only little training in biology and paleontology to place in proper relationship the plants and animals mentioned in the main part of the text.

THE PLANT KINGDOM

Phylum Thallophyta

The thallophytes are a diverse group of primitive plants that are divided into several distinct phyla in modern detailed classifications, and include such forms as bacteria, slime molds, fungi, and seaweeds. Most of them have a negligible fossil record because they lack hard parts and disintegrate rapidly on death.

Bacteria. Bacteria, the smallest forms of living matter, occupy every environment in the modern world in astronomical numbers. Their paleontological record extends back to the Precambrian. Although bacteria are invisible to the naked eye, the chemical transformations they promote in their life processes are important in the formation of certain sedimentary rocks (see Fig. 18–2).

Diatoms. The diatoms (Fig. A–1) are microscopic plants that live in marine and fresh-water environments. Their tests, or shells, composed of opaline silica, may accumulate in great numbers to form a layer of siliceous sedimentary rock known as diatomite. Because the colloidal silica of their tests is easily dissolved by water percolating through sedimentary rocks, diatoms are generally not well enough preserved in older sedimentary series to be positively identified.

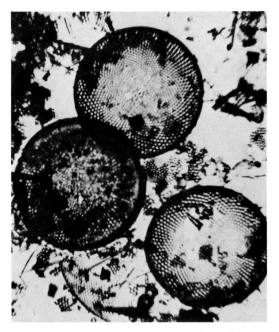

Fig. A–1. Recent diatom ooze from the Bering Sea (magnification × 1800). (Courtesy of Taro Kanaya.)

Algae. The most important thallophytes, as far as the paleontologist is concerned, are the algae or seaweeds. The algae that secrete calcium carbonate contribute extensively to the formation of limestones, particularly reef limestones. The blue-green algae form fine filaments of cells which may secrete calcium carbonate on their outer surfaces. These primitive plants are responsible for the formation of such simple fossils as *Collenia* of the Belt Group, the cryptozoans of Paleozoic strata, and the stromatolites of all periods. The green algae form mats of floating scum on bodies of fresh water; some of them also secrete lime and have been important contributors to fresh-water limestones. The red algae secrete a rigid, calcareous structure consisting of numerous regularly placed cells, and are the most important modern reef builders with a paleontological record extending back to the early part of the Paleozoic Era. The brown algae include the common seaweed washed up along the seashore by storm waves; most of these do not secrete hard parts and are represented in the fossil record only by swirling markings and impressions called fucoids (see Figs. 18–2, 18–3, 18–6, 18–7, 19–8, 19–12, and 21–22).

Phylum Bryophyta

The mosses and liverworts are grouped among the bryophytes. Although they are better adapted for life on land than the multicellular thallophytes, they are still in a very primitive stage of evolution and have not developed special vascular tissue for conducting fluids. Their fossil record is insignificant.

Phylum Psilopsida

Included in the psilopsids are the first land plants of Early Devonian time (Fig. A–2; see also Fig. 20–1). The psilopsids lacked true roots or leaves. From a horizontally creeping stalk, or rhizome, upright stems bearing small bracts branched off. Spore cases were carried at the tips of the stems. The psilopsids are represented today by a few remote relatives of the Paleozoic plants, chiefly *Psilotum*, that live in tropical and subtropical environments. For the most part these plants are small, but some reached heights of several feet.

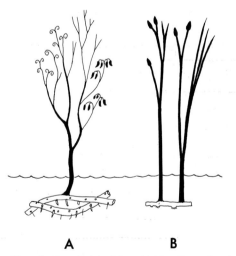

A   B

Fig. A–2. Psilopsids, primitive Devonian land plants. A. *Psilophyton princeps.* B. *Rhynia major.* The stems and spore cases are shown in solid black, the underwater creeping rootstocks in outline (approximately one-tenth actual size). (A. Modified from Dawson. B. Modified from Kidston and Lang.)

Phylum Lycopsida

The scale trees, or lycopsids, are another group of plants represented in the modern flora by a few small genera descended from their larger and more numerous Paleozoic ancestors. The modern lycopsids are commonly referred to as the club mosses. The most familiar of such plants is the ground pine, *Lycopodium*, a ground creeper of shady woodlands (Fig. A–3). The simple, vertical, bladelike leaves of the lycopsids are arranged in spiral rows on the stems. Reproduction is carried on by spores in small cases at the base of certain fertile leaves. These leaves usually grow together at the tips of the branches and form organs resembling the cones of pine trees (see Figs. 20–1 to 20–3, 20–8, and 20–10).

Fig. A–3. *Lycopodium,* a living lycopod with the spore cases in the axils of the leaves. (Courtesy of R. D. Gibbs.)

The lycopsids grew to heights of 50 to 100 feet in the coal forests of late Paleozoic time. When the leaves that emerged directly from the trunks were shed, they left scars on the bark that gave the lycopsids a scaly appearance. Some of the larger representatives of this group are described and illustrated in Chapter 20.

Phylum Sphenopsida (Arthrophyta)

Sphenopsids include the modern scouring rush and "horsetail fern" (Fig. A–4). They have a simple, longitudinally ribbed stem divided transversely by a series of joints. At these joints whorls of branches or leaves emerge. The spores are carried in cases at the tips of the stems. The late Paleozoic representatives of this phylum, *Calamites,* grew to treelike size in the coal swamps. *Calamites* had a hollow stem whose stump was commonly filled with sand or silt when the plant died. Many of the fossils of this plant are interior molds left when the surrounding parts of the plant decayed (see Figs. 20–2, 20–4, 20–5, 20–8, 20–10, and 21–29).

Phylum Pteropsida (Ferns)

Ferns reproduce by means of spores contained in small, dark cases that appear periodically, usually on the undersides of certain leaves. They have a well-developed vascular system of cells specialized for conducting sap through the stem. The ferns probably were derived from a psilopsid ancestor in Devonian time and have been abundant to the present day. During the late Paleozoic, many were tall enough to be called "tree ferns" (see Figs. 2–3, 20–1, 20–6, 20–8, 20–9, and 21–29).

Phylum Gymnospermae

Seed ferns (Pteridospermales). The foliage of the pteridosperms was similar to that of the ferns, but the plant produced seeds instead of spores. A spore is a single cell that is cast off by the plant and grows as it can, but a seed is fertilized and grows in the ovary for some time until, equipped with food, it is released to form a new plant. During Penn-

Fig. A–4. The modern arthrophyte *Equisetum*. *Left:* The typical habit of growth (one-tenth actual size). *Right:* Young shoots showing immature spore cases (½ actual size). (Courtesy of R. D. Gibbs.)

Fig. A–5. *Macrozamia*, a modern cycad about 15 feet high (Australia). The fruit is borne at the top of the trunk and is hidden in this photograph by the long leaf branches. (Courtesy of R. D. Gibbs.)

sylvanian time seed ferns grew to tree size, but in the Jurassic they became extinct. However, they gave rise to all the other seed-bearing plants (see Fig. 20–7).

Cycads and Cycadeoids. The cycads and cycadeoids bore naked seeds. They had long, unbranched trunks with a spread of palmlike leaves forming a crown. The cycads, which persist in the present as the sago palm, do not possess flowers (Fig. A–5). The cycadeoids, however, bore primitive flowers at the top of the trunk, and are believed to have given rise to the true flowering plants in the early Mesozoic Era.

Conifers. The conifers are a group of plants that bear unprotected seeds in cones and generally have bladelike or needle-like leaves, evergreen foliage, and a treelike form (Fig. A–6). Cordaitids and gingoes are primitive conifers, but each is assigned to a separate class by some paleobotanists. Cordaitids were late Paleozoic trees that had long, swordlike leaves up to 3 feet in length at the top of a high trunk. The ginkgoes are primitive conifers that are represented in the modern flora by a single species, the maidenhair tree. The peculiar fan-shaped leaves of these trees can be found in rocks as old as Permian, and are abundant in Mesozoic strata. True conifers appeared late in the Paleozoic Era and reached their evolutionary peak in the Mesozoic Era. Representatives of this group, such as the pine, hemlock, spruce, yew, and redwood, are common elements of the modern coniferous flora (see Fig. 20–10).

Phylum Angiospermae

The angiosperms, or true flowering plants, have been immensely successful since their first appearance in the Jurassic Period and are represented by a quarter of a million species in the modern world. The seeds of these plants are not naked like those of the more primitive seed-bearing plants, but are protected by a capsule. Their leaves are common in the sedimentary record from Cretaceous time on, and many of the modern genera, such as the willow, birch, and magnolia, can be easily recognized in Cretaceous

deposits. The angiosperms apparently developed from the cycadeoids and soon displaced them in the flora of late Mesozoic time. Today they include such diverse plants as the grasses, hardwood trees, most of our table vegetables, and all of our garden flowers (see Figs. 21–4 and 21–30).

THE ANIMAL KINGDOM

Phylum Protozoa

The simplest and most primitive animals include the protozoans. The phylum includes animals all of whose body functions—respiration, feeding, ejection of waste products, growth, and reproduction—are carried on within a single cell. Within this group is a host of largely microscopic animals, some of which are parasitic, some plantlike in their functions, some marine, some fresh-water, some colonial, some single, some with calcareous or siliceous shells, and some naked. Nearly all can reproduce asexually by splitting in two, but most turn to sexual reproduction at certain stages of their life histories. The study of this phylum is important in the search for an understanding of the origin of life because the simplest of these creatures must have been among the first living things. For the paleontologist, only those protozoans that secrete a preservable shell (generally called a test in this phylum) are of primary concern. Of these only two orders, the RADIOLARIA and the FORAMINIFERA, are represented by an adequate fossil record.

Most of the foraminifers, or forams, secrete a microscopic calcareous test composed of one or a series of chambers in a variety of patterns (Fig. A–7). Some forams secrete a test composed of sedimentary particles, largely sand grains, cemented together to form spheres, tubes, or groups of chambers. The first forams appear in the fossil record in Ordovician rocks and are of this type. The group as a whole has flourished throughout its geological history. In the late Paleozoic the FUSULINIDAE, which formed an internally complex test shaped like a grain of wheat, were the most important family. A signif-

Fig. A–6. A modern North American conifer, *Tsuga,* the hemlock fir, showing the characteristic foliage and cones (½ actual size). (Courtesy of R. D. Gibbs.)

Fig. A–7. A group of modern forams from the Gulf of Mexico showing various methods of growth (magnification ✕ 33). (Courtesy of F. B. Phleger.)

icant event in protozoan evolution was the appearance during the Cretaceous Period of the pelagic forams that floated on the surface of the ocean rather than living on the sea floor in shallow water, like most of the group. Early in the Cenozoic Era a tribe of forams called the nummulites grew to great size, comparatively speaking (about 1 inch across), and was so abundant in the rocks of the Mediterranean region that the Eocene Epoch is sometimes referred to as the nummulitic period in Europe. Great strides were made in the study of the forams when petroleum geologists found, in the early part of this century, that many of these fossils could be brought unharmed to the surface in the drill cores of oil wells. The forams were used for determining the horizons which the wells had reached and for correlating strata be-

tween wells (Fig. A–8; see also Figs. 2–17, 20–11, 20–12, and 21–28).

The other group of protozoans that secrete a test are the radiolarians. These microscopic animals construct a delicate framework of opaline silica in a variety of radiating patterns (Fig. A–9). However, such a fragile, open test composed of a relatively soluble substance, colloidal silica, is soon crushed or dissolved after it has been entombed in sediments. For this reason, most pre-Cenozoic radiolarian deposits have been converted into structureless chert or flint by solution and redeposition in percolating water.

Some chert nodules of Mesozoic and Paleozoic ages preserve vague radiolarian impressions, but in general the paleontological record of this group is poor.

Fig. A–8. A corner of the micropaleontological laboratory of Shell Canada Limited at Edmonton, Alberta. Here, after appropriate chemical and mechanical treatment, forams, hystrichospheres, pollen, spores, and other microfossils are prepared and examined in the search for and use of index fossils. (Courtesy of Shell Canada Limited.)

Phylum Porifera

The lowest grade of multicellular life includes animals grouped in this phylum, the PORIFERA, or sponges. In these and all higher animals the cells that make up the organism are specialized for certain purposes and cannot live independently like protozoan cells. In its simplest form the sponge is like a vase with porous walls (Fig. A–10). Water is drawn in through the pores in the wall of the "vase" by the action of cells equipped with small, whiplike appendages whose movement creates a current in the water. Microscopic plants and animals in the circulating water are caught on cells inside the body cavity and provide food for the whole animal. In more advanced sponges, the interior surface lined with these food-absorbing cells is intricately folded into the thickened wall, thus enlarging both the flagellate and the food-gathering surfaces.

The hard parts of the PORIFERA consist of calcareous or siliceous elements called spicules, which may be fused to form a continuous framework, or may be free in the soft

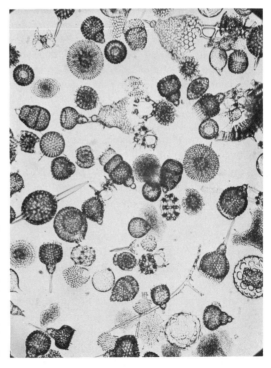

Fig. A–9. Radiolaria from Miocene beds, Philippine Islands (magnification × 70). (Courtesy of W. R. Riedel.)

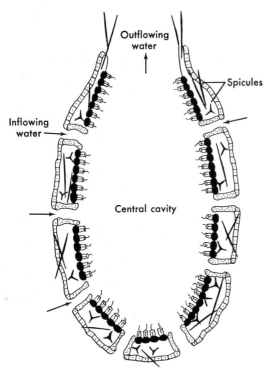

Outflowing
water

Spicules

Inflowing
water

Central cavity

Fig. A–10. Diagrammatic cross-section of a simple sponge showing the direction of flow of water through the pores and central cavity. The dark objects embedded in the tissue are spicules. The three layers of the body are shown: the ectoderm, or epidermis, on the outside; the endoderm lining the interior and, in some cases, the canals; and mesogloea filling the space between.

body of the sponge. If the spicules are unconnected, they are released when the organic tissues of the animal decay and are scattered by currents on the ocean floor. Some sponges have a rigid calcareous skeleton composed of irregular, interlocking spicules. Others, such as the glass sponges, have a skeleton composed of spicules of silica fused into a regular network. Still others are strengthened with spongin, a protein compound chemically similar to hair.

Isolated spicules of sponges are not uncommon fossils, but a fossil with spicules showing the outline of the whole animal (see Fig. 18–8) is a rare specimen. The history of the sponges can be traced back to the Cambrian Period. Except locally, at no time in their geological history have sponges been impor-

tant fossils for rock building or correlation (see Figs. 18–6, 18–8, 20–13, 20–14, 20–21, and 20–24).

Phylum Archaeocyatha

The archaeocyathids were animals that flourished in the Early Cambrian Epoch and lingered on into the Middle Cambrian. Their hard parts were vase-shaped, and resembled a sponge in general, but were composed of two solid calcareous walls separated by a set of radial partitions, or septa (see Fig. 18–9). The soft parts of the animal were apparently confined to the space between the two walls. They presumably fed by absorbing microorganisms through their walls from the circulating sea water, in much the same way as the sponges.

Phylum Coelenterata

This large and diverse group of animals is characterized by saclike bodies with tentacles around the mouth. Food, guided into a central opening of the body through the action of the tentacles, is digested by special cells on its inside surface. Waste products are ejected through the same opening. This phylum includes the hydroids, jellyfish, the various types of corals, and some extinct groups of doubtful affinities.

The HYDROZOA, simplest class of the coelenterates, have an unmodified saclike digestive system. Most of the members of this group are colonial animals in which each individual, or polyp, inhabits a small cup in a treelike colony. Some polyps have special beaklike organs that clean the colony; others are specialized for stinging, and others for reproduction. The reproductive polyps give off small jellyfish at certain times of the year which take part in a sexual reproductive process that results in a new colony of polyps. The hydrozoans are poorly represented in the fossil record, but the extinct stromatoporoids may belong to this class.

The STROMATOPOROIDEA were reef-building animals that constructed a calcareous skeleton of laminae spaced about 5 per mm, separated by short pillars generally positioned at right angles to the laminae. From this simple plan the stromatoporoids evolved into encrusting and cabbage-like forms of great internal structural complexity (Fig. A–11). They thrived in the reefs of Silurian and Devonian times and helped to build the resistant framework that withstood the waves. They became extinct suddenly at the end of the Devonian Period for a reason that is not yet known. Very little has been learned about their soft parts, but the similarity of their skeleton to that secreted by the modern hydrozoan *Hydractinia* has led to their placement in the same class.

Another group of coelenterates, the jellyfish, forms the class SCYPHOMEDUSAE. Since they have no hard parts, jellyfish are represented in the fossil record by only rare impressions of their lower surfaces on the soft mud of the ocean floor (see Figs. 18–4, 18–6, and 19–1).

Geologically, the corals, or ANTHOZOA, are the most important subdivision of the coelenterates. These animals can increase the area of the digestive surface on the interior of the body sac by folding the wall inward to form a series of radial partitions called mesenteries. The basal disc of the body is also folded radially so that the major ridges of the base alternate in position with the mesenteries (Fig. A–12). In most corals the cells on the basal exterior surface secrete calcium carbonate in the form of a plate or shallow cup surrounding the lower part of the body. Where the lime-secreting cells are folded inward at the base of the cup, they secrete a set of radial plates called septa. A cup, cone,

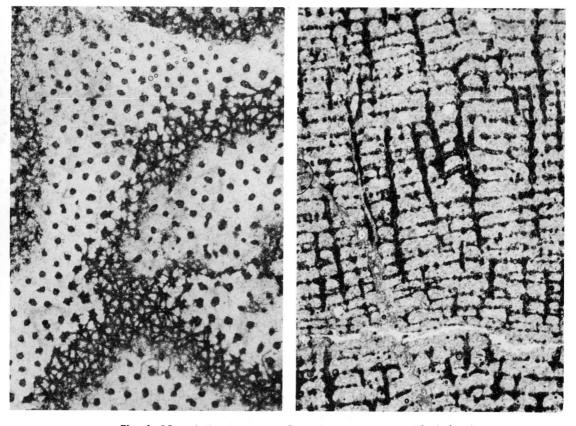

Fig. A–11. *Actinostroma,* a Devonian stromatoporoid. *Left:* A tangential section. *Right:* A longitudinal section showing pillars and laminae. From Evie Lake Reef, British Columbia (magnification × 40).

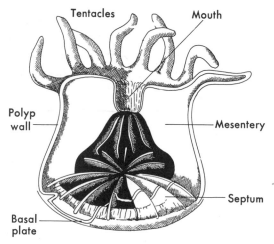

Fig. A–12. Cutaway drawing of a simple coral polyp, showing the digestive cavity divided radially by mesenteries, and the alternation of the mesenteries with septa in the basal part of the polyp.

or cylindrical structure, divided by radial partitions, is the typical fossil coral.

Some corals are colonial; others are single (see Fig. 20–21). The single coral secretes a cup which increases in diameter as the animal grows. In the process of growth the polyp periodically lifts itself upward in the cup and in many cases partitions off the abandoned part with a calcareous plate called a tabula. The early smaller parts of the skeleton are left behind as the animal builds itself a horn-shaped support which it occupies at the top, in a depression called the calyx. Many individuals unite to form the large structures built by the colonial corals. The individuals occupy parallel tubes packed closely together to form a hemispherical, encrusting, or branching colony.

Corals are classified on the basis of the nature and symmetry of their septa. The most common Paleozoic corals had septa arranged in fourfold symmetry and are called tetracorals, or sometimes the RUGOSA. Most post-Paleozoic corals have septa arranged in sixfold symmetry and are called hexacorals (ZOANTHARIA). In certain colonial Paleozoic corals the septa were reduced to spines and low ridges. Because the individual tubes were relatively free of septa but crossed by

prominent tabulae, these corals are called the tabulate corals (TABULATA). Geological ranges of these various groups of corals are shown in charts in the end papers at the front of this book (see Figs. 2–10, 18–5, 18–6, 19–1, 19–2, 19–8, 20–21, 20–24, and 21–27).

Phylum Bryozoa

Although the bryozoan polyp superficially resembles that of the coelenterates, it is more complex. Instead of a simple sac for digestion the bryozoan has a complete gut with separate mouth and anus. The individual is much smaller than the coral polyp and, with the exception of a single genus, always lives in colonies. The polyp of these colonies secretes a calcareous or chitinous "house" in the form of a box or a tube. The colony as a whole is made up of many such tubes or boxes and may be encrusting, branching, netlike, lacy, or hemispherical—or almost any shape (Fig. A–13). The internal structure of these colonies is often so complex that micro-

Fig. A–13. Small, twiglike bryozoa in Ordovician limestone from Montreal.

scopic examination of thin sections cut from them is required before they can be identified (Fig. A–14). Bryozoan colonies can generally be distinguished from colonial corals by the smallness of the cell and the absence of tabulae and septa. Since their beginning in the Ordovician Period, they have been exceedingly abundant and occasionally rock builders (see Figs. 2–1, 19–1, 19–4, 19–7, 19–8, and 20–15).

Phylum Brachiopoda

The soft parts of the brachiopods resemble those of the bryozoans, but the hard parts consist of two shells (or valves) secreted above and below the body. Although brachiopods can be gregarious, they never build colonial structures as do bryozoans. The brachiopod is attached to the sea floor by a muscular stalk or pedicle which emerges either between the valves or, more commonly, from a hole in one of them known as the pedicle valve (Fig. A–15). The animal has either a continuous or a blind gut, a complex muscular system for the control of the valves, and delicate "arms" called brachia whose functions are respiration and the guiding of food toward the mouth. The brachia of many of these animals are supported by calcareous ribbons in the form of loops or spirals, or by short structures projecting from the brachial valve.

Most brachiopods secrete a shell of calcite, but primitive ones (class INARTICULATA) secreted chitin and calcium phosphate, which are commonly carbonized during preservation and appear as dark films on the bedding planes of rocks. The shells of advanced brachiopods (class ARTICULATA) are hinged, and interlock by tooth-and-socket structures. The hinged valves open to allow the animal to feed and breathe. The beaked part of the shell in the middle of the hinge marks the position from which growth started. The valves of most brachiopods show concentric lines of growth and are either folded or ridged in a radial pattern, presumably to give strength. In some brachiopods the hinge line is long and straight; in others it is short and slightly curved (see Fig. 19–5). In many

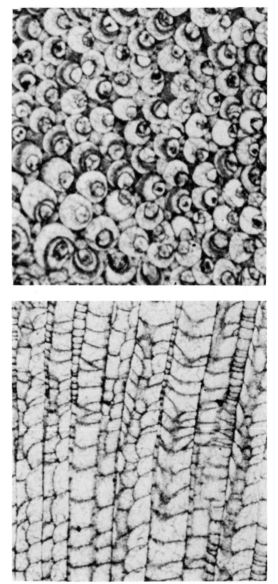

Fig. A–14. Transverse *(top)* and longitudinal *(bottom)* sections of *Prasopora*, a massive bryozoan colony, showing the complex internal structures of the fine tubes (magnification × 18). (Courtesy of M. A. Fritz.)

brachiopods, the hinge line is interrupted in the pedicle valve by the passage of the pedicle to the exterior. The interior surfaces of both valves are scarred where the muscles that drew the valves together or spread them apart were attached.

Both brachiopod shells may be convex, or one may be convex and the other flat or con-

Fig. A–15. Brachiopods. *Left:* View of the pedicle valve. *Center:* Side view of the same specimen of the living brachiopod *Magellania*. *Right:* Brachial valve of the Miocene brachiopod *Olenothyris*, with the beak of the pedicle valve showing the pedicle opening. (*Olenothyris* courtesy of Ward's Natural Science Establishment, Inc., Rochester, N. Y.)

cave. In all advanced and in most primitive brachiopods the valves are dissimilar because the larger one houses the pedicle opening; but each valve is symmetrical across an imaginary plane passing through the beaks perpendicular to one between the valves (Fig. A–15). Brachiopod shells may be distinguished from clam shells, which are mirror images of each other although neither is symmetrical. The great variety of shells secreted by brachiopods may be appreciated by an examination of Figs. 19–5 and 20–16. The brachiopods appeared in the Lower Cambrian Series, reached their acme in the middle and late part of the Paleozoic Era, and survive to the present day (see Figs. 2–1, 18–6, 19–1, 19–3 to 19–6, 20–16, and 20–24).

Phylum Mollusca

The MOLLUSCA are a diverse group of animals most of which secrete an external shell or shells of calcium carbonate. The phylum is divided into six classes, all of which have some fossil record; only three, however, the PELECYPODA, GASTROPODA, and CEPHALOPODA, are of primary importance to the paleontologist.

The pelecypods are commonly called the clams. They have highly organized soft parts which include a continuous gut, well-developed lamellar gills (hence their name LAM-

Fig. A–16. Interior and exterior of the two valves of the modern pelecypod *Venus*, showing the lack of symmetry of the individual valves, the teeth and sockets, and the hinge line.

ELLIBRANCHIA in British literature), and two tubes called siphons, which are essential for the feeding and respiration of the organism. Water filled with oxygen and minute food particles enters one of the siphons and leaves by the other bearing waste products. Many clams can move slowly by thrusting out a muscular extension of their body (called the "foot"), but many are anchored to rocks or foreign objects by cementation or by organic threads.

The body of the pelecypod is surrounded by a fleshy mantle that secretes the two valves of the shell (hence the recently proposed name of BIVALVIA for this class). These are located on either side of the body, not in an over-and-under position like those of the brachiopod. The two valves are mirror images of each other, but in general are not bilaterally symmetrical. Each valve projects backward into a beak and is crossed by growth lines concentric with the beak (Fig. A–16). The valves fit together with teeth and sockets along the hinge line, which prevents lateral slippage between the beaks. In most shells the hinge is equipped with an elastic, organic ligament that is tensed when the valves are closed and relaxed when they are open. Two large muscles passing from valve to valve control this movement.

The clam shell is composed of three layers. The outer layer is organic and prevents the inner layers of calcium carbonate from being dissolved in the surrounding sea or lake water. In fresh-water clams this layer is thick, but in marine clams it is thin and easily worn away. The main body of the shell is composed of calcite, but the inner part is lined with aragonite (another form of calcium carbonate) in the form of mother-of-pearl. Since aragonite is considerably more soluble than calcite, pelecypod shells in older rocks are generally less well preserved than those of the brachiopods, which secrete a shell entirely of calcite. The pelecypod shell may be ornamented with nodes, ridges, spines, and projecting growth lines. Pelecypods are first recorded in Ordovician rocks, and in general have been increasing in number and variety since (see Figs. 2–5, 19–1, 20–17, and 21–23 to 21–25).

The gastropods, or snails, have a single shell which is usually coiled like a circular staircase or corkscrew, although a few secrete a shell coiled in a single plane like a watch spring (Fig. A–17). The snails have a dis-

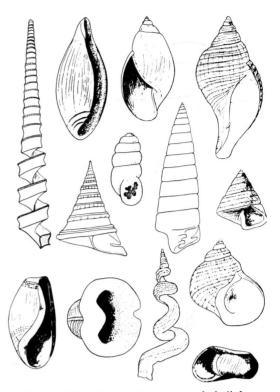

Fig. A–17. Variety in gastropod shell form. In all cases the spire, sometimes difficult to identify, points upward. Note that the mouth is usually on the right when facing the observer. From *Treatise on Invertebrate Paleontology,* courtesy of the Geological Society of America and the University of Kansas Press.)

tinct head equipped with tentacles, eyes, and a mouth. The animal creeps on a muscular lobe of the body called the foot and carries its twisted shell on its back. In times of danger the snail withdraws into its shell. Some have a horny or calcareous plate that acts as a trap door to close the shell aperture once the animal is inside. The shell is a simple coiled cone and is not divided into chambers. Gastropod shells may be ornamented in various ways with spines, nodes, and keels (Fig. A–17). In older sedimentary rocks they are poorly preserved because the shell substance is largely aragonite, and many of the earlier fossils are only molds or fillings of the interior. The gastropods appeared in the Cambrian Period and have been abundant in marine environments since that time. They have also been successful in invading fresh-water and terrestrial environments (see Figs. 2–5, 19–1, 19–12, 20–17, 20–21, and 21–23).

The cephalopods include such diverse animals of the modern oceans as the squid, nautilus, octopus, and cuttlefish. As the name cephalopod (Greek: head-foot) suggests, the head of these animals is surrounded by tentacles (a modified foot) which capture food. The cephalopod shell is fundamentally an external, chambered cone, but some of the members of this class secrete their shells within the soft body tissues. The modern pearly nautilus, the last of the great tribe of Paleozoic nautiloids, illustrates the main features of the shell structure (Fig. A–18). The shell is coiled in a single plane, and the outer whorl, in which the animal lives, covers all the earlier ones. The part of the shell not occupied by the animal is progressively partitioned off by concave, calcareous septa and the spaces so formed are filled with gas which

buoys the animal up in the water. The septa are pierced by a calcareous tube (the siphuncle) that carries an extension of the soft parts of the animal (the siphon) through the abandoned chambers. The line of contact between a septum and the inside surface of the exterior wall of the shell is called the suture. The earliest cephalopods had straight, conical shells in which the suture lines were simple and nearly circular. The cephalopods with simple septa are called nautiloids. They flourished from Late Cambrian to Silurian time but thereafter dwindled in numbers to the single genus of the modern oceans, *Nautilus* (see Figs. 19–1, 19–8, 20–21, and 20–24).

In Devonian time another type of cephalopod appeared in which the edges of the septa were crenulated, forming an undulating suture line. All the Paleozoic members of this advanced group, called the ammonoids, were coiled in a single plane, but aberrations appeared frequently in Mesozoic groups

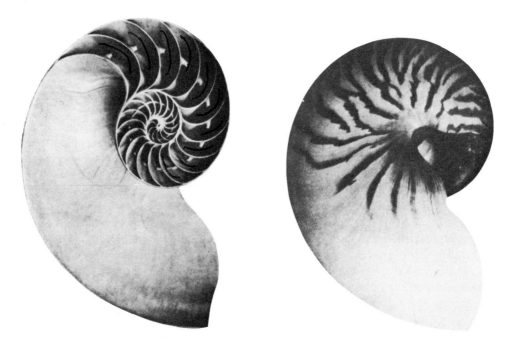

Fig. A–18. Exterior and longitudinal section of the modern pearly *Nautilus*. Notice the septa and their extension backward to form a discontinuous tube for the siphon (¼ actual size). (From *Treatise on Invertebrate Paleontology*, courtesy of the Geological Society of America and the University of Kansas Press.)

(see Fig. 21–2). The ammonoids evolved through a progressive complication of the suture line from the simplest type, with broad flowing curves (goniatites), through a type in which one side of the suture inflections was crinkled (ceratites), to a type in which the whole of the suture was intensely folded (ammonites) (see Figs. 20–18, 20–19, and 21–20). Ammonoids are among the most useful guide fossils for the Mesozoic Era (see Figs. 20–18, 20–19, 20–24, and 21–20 to 21–23).

The belemnites were squidlike cephalopods with an internal shell (phragmocone) similar in many ways to that of a straight nautiloid shell. The phragmocone was small, conical, and chambered and was encased posteriorly in a solid structure of calcite called a guard of approximately the size and shape of a cigar (Fig. A–19; see also Fig. 21–22). This guard is generally all that is preserved of the belemnite. From the front end of the phragmocone extended a rarely preserved, horny support for the front part of the body called a pen. The guards of belemnites are common fossils in Mesozoic sedimentary rocks and are used in correlation (see Figs. 21–22 and 21–23).

Fig. A–19. Belemnite guard and phragmocone. Half the guard is cut away to show the chambered phragmocone within.

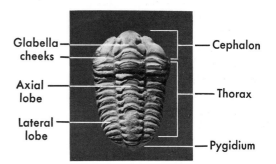

Fig. A–20. A typical trilobite, *Calymene*, showing the subdivision into cephalon, thorax, and pygidium, and other features.

Phyla Annelida and Onychophora

The annelids, or segmented worms, include the earthworms, sandworms, and leeches. They are poorly represented in the fossil record, but their hard siliceous mouth parts, known as scolecodonts, were occasionally preserved. The burrows of annelid worms are not uncommon in sandstone formations (see Figs. 2–8, 18–4, 18–5, 18–6, and 19–12).

The onychophores are caterpillar-like animals intermediate in character between the annelids and arthropods. The only living genus, *Peripatus*, has a wormlike body, a pair of antennae, and many paired, unjointed legs. One of the species found in the Middle Cambrian Burgess Shale is believed to belong to this phylum (see Figs. 18–5 and 18–6).

Phylum Arthropoda

The arthropods are complex invertebrates whose body is enclosed in a tough, chitinous, segmented exoskeleton. The limbs are jointed, allowing the animal to move freely, and from this feature the name ARTHROPODA (jointed legs) was derived. The arthropods have been among the most successful of all animals since their appearance in Cambrian time. They have diversified into marine, fresh-water, terrestrial, and aerial environments and include such different animals as the crabs, barnacles, trilobites, insects, spiders, and scorpions. Although nearly every order has some representation in the fossil record, only four have been preserved in any numbers: the TRILOBITA, INSECTA, OSTRACODA, and EURYPTERIDA.

The trilobites were a group of exclusively Paleozoic arthropods that were divided by two longitudinal grooves into an axial lobe and two lateral lobes (Fig. A–20). The upper surface of the trilobite was protected by a thickened chitinous carapace. The body was divided into a head (cephalon), thorax, and tail (pygidium). The thorax was

Fig. A–21. *Senoprosopis,* a fly from Oligocene beds at Florissant, Colorado. Note the preservation of the fine setae on the legs. (Courtesy of F. M. Carpenter.)

distinctly segmented, and each segment bore on the underside a pair of doubly branched limbs used in crawling or swimming. The segmentation of the head and tail was less obvious. The axial lobe of the head (glabella) was raised and bordered by lower areas called cheeks, on which multifaceted eyes were located. The grooves indenting the axial lobe marked the boundaries between the segments that had fused to form the head. The limbs of trilobites were apparently unsuitable for preservation, for they are among the rarest of fossils. Trilobites, like most other arthropods, grew by discarding or molting their exoskeleton and secreting a larger one. Many trilobite fossils are undoubtedly these discarded carapaces and not the actual remains of the animal (see Figs. 2–11, 18–6, 18–7, 18–11 to 18–14, 19–5, 19–8, 19–9, 20–20, and 20–21).

The insects are the most numerous and diverse group of arthropods. Like most animals living in terrestrial and aerial environ-

ments, however, their fossil record is unsatisfactory. Apart from a few exceptional sedimentary deposits which contain them in great numbers (Fig. A–21), the insects are practically unrepresented in most of the sedimentary sequence. They have three pairs of unbranched legs, a single pair of antennae, and, normally, a pair of wings (see Figs. 2–6, 20–2, 20–8, and 20–25).

The ostracods are members of the crustacean arthropods and are related to the crabs (see Fig. 19–10) and lobsters. They are small—in most cases minute—aquatic animals that secrete a double-valved shell carried on either side of the body and hinged at the top. Appendages projecting between the edges of the shell are used by the animal to swim. Only the shells of these animals are preserved as fossils, but they occur in great numbers in some beds. Because they are small enough to be brought intact to the surface in the cuttings from oil wells, these shells have been extensively used for correlation.

They may be smooth or complexly ornamented with ridges, spines, nodes, frills, and pits (see Fig. 19–10). Ostracods are abundant in marine and fresh-water sediments from Ordovician time on. Crabs and lobsters begin to be common at the end of the Mesozoic (Fig. A–22).

The eurypterids were a group of Paleozoic arthropods that resembled, and were closely related to, the scorpions. Unlike the scorpions, however, they were aquatic. The eurypterid body consisted of an apparently unsegmented head (on the underside of which the appendages were attached), a segmented abdomen, and a spikelike or buttonlike tail (see Figs. 19–11 and 19–12). In some eurypterids the appendages were modified for walking, swimming, or catching food. With the exception of a few of the nautiloids, the eurypterids were the largest and most powerful of Paleozoic invertebrates.

The spiders are close relatives of the eurypterids. Like the insects, they are poorly represented as fossils, but very primitive forms are known from rocks as old as mid-Devonian.

Phylum Echinodermata

Although echinoderms do not appear to be the most advanced of the invertebrates, most paleontologists believe that chordates and echinoderms sprang from a common ancestor early in the Paleozoic or late in the Precambrian. Echinoderms have a complex system of tubes for carrying water through the body and a test composed of calcite plates transversed by multitudes of fine canals. Each of the plates is a single calcite crystal. Most echinoderms have a fivefold symmetry (Fig. A–23) superposed on a bilateral symmetry. Some are sedentary, rooted by a stem to the ocean floor throughout their adult life.

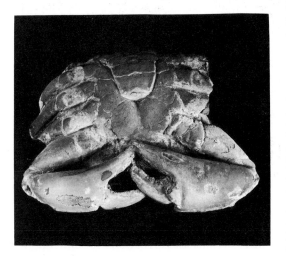

Fig. A–22. A Miocene crustacean, the crab *Archaeogeryon*, from South America. (Courtesy of the Smithsonian Institution.)

Fig. A–23. Illustrations of the pentameral symmetry of the echinoderms. *Left:* Upper surface of topmost disk of the stem of the crinoid *Apiocrinus*. *Center:* The irregular echinoid *Micraster*. *Right:* The modern sea star. (Courtesy of the Redpath Museum.)

Fig. A–24. The carpoid *Enoploura showing* upper and lower surfaces. One "arm" is missing, one is broken. The resemblance to cystids (Fig. A–25) is marked, but the two groups are separated by important morphological differences. (Courtesy of K. E. Caster.)

The mouths of these animals open upward, and the stems that connect them to the substratum are on the opposite side. Free echinoderms, such as the sea stars and sea urchins, have no stems and the mouths open downward.

The body of the anchored echinoderms is housed in a small sac of plates called the calyx. The calyx is attached to a column of centrally perforated, disclike plates resembling beads on a necklace. They are held together by a strand of muscular tissue that passes through the openings. The mouth is generally surrounded by branched arms arranged in fivefold symmetry. Food particles trapped by the arms pass along food grooves to the mouth.

The carpoids form what is probably the most primitive group of echinoderms. Their bilateral symmetry is supposedly characteristic of the ancestral echinoderm and they lack a water-vascular system (Fig. A–24).

The cystids are primitive anchored echinoderms with fivefold symmetry generally poorly developed (Fig. A–25). In some cystoids the food-gathering arms are absent and the food grooves are confined to the surface of the calyx; in others one or two arms may be present. Their plates are perforated by pores arranged in a variety of patterns (see Fig. 19–8).

The blastoids were a group of Paleozoic echinoderms that had calices composed of 13 plates (Fig. A–26). Five food grooves extended downward over the sides of the calyx and were bordered by rows of small platelets. Each groove was lined with small arms which guided the food into the mouth.

The crinoids have been the most successful of the attached echinoderms since their appearance in Lower Ordovician time (see Fig. 20–22). The crinoid calyx is composed of symmetrically arranged plates. The numerous arms occur in multiples of five and are branched many times. The plates of crinoids, like those of most attached echinoderms, tend to fall apart after the animal dies and are deposited by the waves as crinoidal limestones (see Fig. 20–23). Some crinoids shed their stems when they are mature and float free in the open ocean (see Figs. 19–1, 19–8, and 20–21).

The only abundant free echinoderms are the asteroids (sea stars) and the echinoids (sea urchins). The asteroids are usually shaped like a short-armed, five-pointed star.

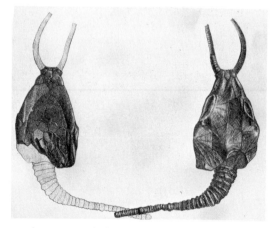

Fig. A–25. *Pleurocystites,* an Ordovician cystid somewhat resembling the carpoids in the flattened form, arrangement of plates, arms, and stem. However, many cystids lacked one or more of these features. (Courtesy of the Geological Survey of Canada.)

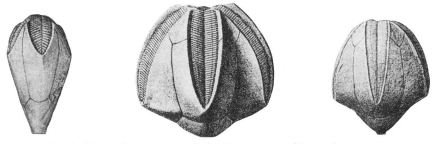

Fig. A–26. Three species of the Mississippian blastoid *Pentremites*. The stem and the many arms are rarely preserved. (From J. J. Galloway and H. V. Kaska, courtesy of J. J. Galloway.)

The food grooves along the underside of the arms converge on the central mouth. The groove of each arm is lined with minute tube feet which, controlled by the interior water-circulatory system, move the animal over the ocean floor.

The soft parts of the echinoids are enclosed in globular to discoidal shells that are covered with movable spines. Each spine projects from a protuberance on the plates (Fig. A–27), which are arranged in ten compound zones around the animal from "pole to pole." Alternate zones are perforated with double pores for the extension of the tube feet. The animal progresses by the movement of the spines and tube feet on its lower

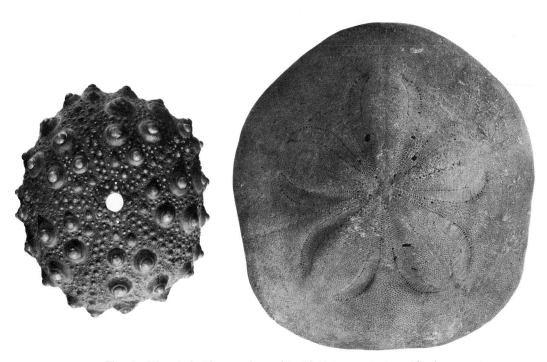

Fig. A–27. *Left:* The regular echinoid *Heterocentrotus.* The large tubercles bear spines as long as the diameter of the test; the anal opening is at the top. *Right:* The irregular echinoid *Clypeaster* with five petalloid areas; the anal opening on the underside is not visible. (Courtesy of the Redpath Museum.)

surface. In primitive, radially symmetrical echinoids, the mouth is at the center of this lower surface and the anus is diametrically opposite at the top. In the advanced types, the mouth evolved to a forward position—in the direction of movement—and the anus moved backward, destroying the radial symmetry and leading to heart-shaped echinoids with mouth and anus at opposite sides of the lower surface. In such asymmetrical echinoids the plates bearing the pores are commonly arranged in a petal-shaped pattern on the upper surface.

Phylum Chordata,
Subphylum Hemichordata

The hemichordates do not have a true backbone like the vertebrates, but a cartilaginous rod for support called a notochord.

Class Graptolithina. The graptolites are an extinct group of colonial organisms apparently, though obscurely, related to the hemichordates. All graptolites secreted colonial structures of chitin that are generally preserved as carbonized films on the bedding planes of black shales. The colonies are composed of a number of minute cups, each of which housed a polyp-like individual. The first graptolites built netlike structures in which the individuals occupied cups on branches of the net. More advanced graptolite colonies consisted of one or a few branches with cups arranged in a single or double row (see Figs. 2–4, 19–1, 19–13, and 19–14). The graptolites apparently floated, attached either to seaweed or to floats of their own making. They are excellent index fossils in rocks of Ordovician and Silurian ages.

Phylum Chordata,
Subphylum Vertebrata

The vertebrates are chordates possessing a backbone, and are grouped into five familiar divisions: fish, amphibians, reptiles, birds, and mammals. The fish include such a diversity of primitive vertebrates that in most classifications they are represented by four classes: AGNATHA, PLACODERMI, CHONDRICHTHYES, and OSTEICHTHYES.

Agnatha. The most primitive of the vertebrates, the agnaths, lack a jaw. Their mouths are merely holes on the undersides of their heads. This group is represented today by the lampreys, which are parasites of larger fish. Lampreys have a circular, rasping mouth by which they attach themselves to other fish and eat their flesh and suck their blood. During Ordovician and most of Silurian time, the only fish of which we have a record belong to this jawless class, but they were much different from their modern parasitic descendants.

Most of the early agnaths were characterized by a covering of bony plates and hence were called ostracoderms (armored skin) by paleontologists (see Figs. 19–15 and 19–16). The head was encased by a solid shield of bone above and by a mosaic of smaller plates below in which the mouth and gill openings were located. Behind this rigid head the flexible body was covered with smaller plates (see Fig. 20–26). The body and tail propelled the fish through the water. A few of the agnaths had lateral fins for balance and guidance, but some had spines which probably served the same purpose although inefficiently. With their heavy armor they must have been poor swimmers and probably lived much of their lives groveling on the sea floor in search of organic debris.

The fossil record of the agnaths begins in the Middle Ordovician Series, but only in rocks of Late Silurian and Devonian age was a record of the diversity and number of this race preserved. None of these later ostracoderms was ancestral to the higher fishes; most of them were specialized creatures incapable of giving rise to another race. The more advanced vertebrates must have branched off from an ancestor of the agnaths, perhaps as early as the Cambrian Period.

Placodermi. The placoderms were the first of the jawed vertebrates. They flourished during Late Silurian and Devonian times, dwindled to insignificance by late Paleozoic time (when the bony fish replaced them), and became extinct before the close of the era. They are a diverse class whose subdivisions have little in common.

One group of the placoderms has been called the spiny sharks but is better known by its scientific name, ACANTHODII. These animals were not armored but were covered with small diamond-shaped scales. Unlike the ostracoderms, they had paired fins that made them stable swimmers. Most acanthodians were equipped with many of these fins, not just two pairs like the more advanced fish. Each fin was supported along its leading edge by a strong spine which in some genera was longer than the height of the fin it supported (see Fig. 20–27).

Another group of the placoderms had heavy bony armor on the front part of the body like that characteristic of the ostracoderms. This group, known as the ARTHRODIRA, also had a ball-and-socket joint at the back of the neck. The head shield was joined to the body shield at this point in an arrangement that allowed the animal to tilt its head back and open wide its jaws. The fast-swimming arthrodires with gaping jaws, sharp teeth, and lengths up to 30 feet must have been fearsome predators in the Devonian seas (see Figs. 20–13, 20–27, and 20–29).

In a third group of the placoderms, the ANTIARCHI, the individuals were similar to ostracoderms in body armor but differed from them in that they possessed a jaw and long, jointed appendages that acted as fins at the sides of the boxlike body (see Fig. 20–28). These animals were adapted to scavenging the bottoms of lakes and streams like their relatives, the agnaths.

Chondrichthyes. The CHONDRICHTHYES, or sharks have an almost entirely cartilaginous skeleton, and as a consequence have a poor fossil record. They lack an air bladder, or lung, which is common in other fish. The sharks have been a successful branch of the vertebrates ever since they first appeared in the Devonian Period (see Fig. 20–29).

Osteichthyes. Nearly all the fish of the modern fauna belong to the class OSTEICHTHYES, commonly referred to as the bony fish. These animals have a strong internal skeleton, a rigid skull composed of many bones, and

two pairs of efficient paired fins that guide and balance the fish in the water. The divisions of the osteichthyans are particularly significant for the paleontologist: one comprises the ray-finned fish (ACTINOPTERYGII), and the other, lobe-finned fish (SARCOPTERYGII).

The first of the ray-finned fish appeared in the Devonian Period and were apparently very well adapted to fast swimming, for they soon replaced the competing placoderms as masters of the sea. Early members of this lineage had thick, shiny, diamond-shaped scales, and lungs that later evolved into the swim-bladder that controls the buoyancy of modern fish.

From the standpoint of evolution, the sarcopterygians, with internal nostril openings, are the more important order of the bony fish. The fins of these fish, unlike those of the ray-fins, are supported by a framework of bone with elements homologous to those of the limbs of the early land animals. Some of the sarcopterygians retained functional lungs; in other primitive fish these were converted into a swim-bladder. Two branches of this group diverged early in the Devonian Period from a common ancestral placoderm: the lungfish, which never attained a strong internal skeleton, and the crossopterygians, which developed a rigid internal skeleton and eventually gave rise to the land vertebrates. Three species of lungfish have survived to the present day, but they are only remnants of a race that was more abundant in the Mesozoic Era. A branch of the crossopterygians, not ancestral to the higher vertebrates, persists to the present day and is represented by a few specimens named *Latimeria*, first caught in 1939 off the coast of Madagascar. Skeletal comparisons of the Devonian crossopterygians with latest Devonian amphibians leave little doubt that one evolved from the other (see Figs. 20–29 to 20–31).

Amphibia. The amphibians are the most primitive of the land vertebrates. Their eggs are laid in water, and their young, after being hatched from the egg, live in the water. Young amphibians breathe by gills and later undergo a metamorphosis during which they develop lungs and legs, enabling them to live on land. The amphibians have not been entirely freed from dependence on water, and few of them can live far from it. The frog is the most familiar of modern amphibians. After being hatched, frogs pass through a tadpole stage before developing into animals capable of living on land.

The most primitive amphibians yet found come from beds of latest Devonian age. Nearly all the Paleozoic amphibians were low, squat creatures whose weight was supported by legs that emerged from the sides of their bodies rather than beneath them. They walked with their elbows and knees held outward in a slow, sprawling, wallowing gait. During most of Carboniferous time, the amphibians were unchallenged as rulers of the land. When the reptiles developed late in the Paleozoic Era, however, the amphibians were relegated gradually to the insignificant role they play in the fauna of the modern world.

One of the most important groups of amphibians of late Paleozoic time was the labyrinthodonts. These animals are so named because the enamel of their conical teeth is infolded to make a labyrinthine pattern in cross-section. In most respects these teeth were similar to those of their crossopterygian ancestors (see Figs. 2–7, 20–2, and 20–32).

Reptilia. The reptiles achieved freedom from the water because ther eggs were encased in a protective shell which prevented the eggs from drying out as they developed. This great step forward in adaptation to land life is difficult to place in time, for eggs are rarely preserved in accumulating sediments. The oldest known egg (Early Permian) postdates the oldest reptilian skeleton (Early Pennsylvanian). Reptiles quite probably evolved from amphibians during the Mississippian Period.

The most primitive order of reptiles, from which all others appear to have arisen, is called the Cotylosauria, sometimes known as the stem reptiles. The diversification of the reptiles into many different environments hitherto unoccupied by vertebrates gave rise to an evolutionary "explosion" in Pennsylvanian time. Some of the reptiles took to the sea (mesosaurs) and are thought to have been the earliest ancestors of most of the marine reptiles of the Mesozoic Era. By Late Permian time all five subclasses of reptiles are represented in the fossil record: the stem reptiles and turtles (Anapsida), the mammal-like reptiles (Synapsida), the ichthyosaurs (Parapsida), the plesiosaurs and their relatives (Euryapsida), and a large group (Diapsida) that includes the dinosaurs and their ancestors the thecodonts, and the snakes, lizards, and crocodiles. The relationships between these various reptiles and their geological histories are more fully treated in Chapters 20 and 21, which deal with the late Paleozoic and Mesozoic eras (see Figs. 20–10, 20–32, 21–1 to 21–16, and 21–19).

Aves. The birds are warm-blooded flying animals characterized by various structural adaptations to flight—such as wings, feathers, and hollow bones. The first birds, found in Upper Jurassic rocks, show many of the characteristics of the reptilian skeleton, and they obviously were descended from the branch of the reptiles that included the dinosaurs. The birds evolved rapidly through late Mesozoic and Cenozoic times, and their ability to fly was slowly perfected by a reduction in the length of tail, an enlargement of the breastbone (anchoring the flight muscles), the fusing of the bones of the hand (giving support to the wing), and many other structural changes. The fossil record of the birds is meager, for animals living in the aerial environment have little chance of being preserved in the sedimentary record (see Figs. 21–4, 21–15, 21–17, 21–18, and 22–1).

Mammalia. Some time prior to the end of the Triassic Period, the first mammals emerged from the stock of the mammal-like reptiles. Most of the mammalian skeletal characteristics, such as differentiated teeth, single jaw bone, double ball-and-socket arrangement at the back of the head, and solid palate, had been attained or approached by various members of the mammal-like reptiles. The basic mammalian features of reproduction, live birth, and suckling cannot be found in the fossil record; nor normally can the hairy covering, which is another feature of nearly all mammals.

The primitive Mesozoic mammals have been divided into several subclasses. However, only the pantotheres are of evolutionary importance, for this group gave rise to the higher mammals at the beginning of the Cretaceous Period. The advanced mammals constitute two numerically unequal groups: the marsupials, whose young are born in an underdeveloped state and must live for some time in their mother's pouch before becoming independent, and the placentals, which retain their young inside the body until they can live outside the mother. The radiation of the placental mammals at the beginning of the Cenozoic Era has been described in Chapter 22. A simple classification of this group is given in Appendix B (see Figs. 2–2 and 22–2 to 22–24).

B

A Simplified Classification
of Plants and Animals

The classification presented in this appendix has been considerably simplified from several sources. Many lesser groups that have a poor fossil record and little evolutionary significance have been omitted so that the student will not be burdened with unnecessary names. By reference to the classification of the plant and animal kingdoms, the student should be able to place the various groups of organisms mentioned throughout the book in their proper relationship to one another.

THE PLANT KINGDOM

Phylum Thallophyta. Bacteria, fungi, seaweeds

Phylum Bryophyta. Mosses, liverworts

Phylum Psilopsida. First land plants, e.g., *Psilophyton*

Phylum Lycopsida. Club mosses and scale trees

Phylum Sphenopsida. Horsetail rushes and related plants

Phylum Pteropsida. Ferns

Phylum Gymnospermae. Plants with naked seeds

  Class Pteridospermales. Seed ferns

  Class Cycadeoidea. Cycadeoids

  Class Cycadales. Cycads

  Class Cordaitales. Cordaitids

  Class Ginkgoales. Ginkgoes

  Class Coniferales. Conifers

Phylum Angiospermae. Flowering plants with enclosed seeds.

  Class Monocotyledonae. Seed possesses one cotyledon (first leaf). Lily, orchid, grasses

  Class Dicotyledonae. Seed possesses two cotyledons. Oaks, rose, beans, and melons

549

THE ANIMAL KINGDOM

Phylum Protozoa. Unicellular animals
  Class Sarcodina. Protozoans with pseudopodia for catching food
    Order Foraminifera. Test usually calcareous
    Order Radiolaria. Test usually siliceous
Phylum Porifera. Sponges
Phylum Archaeocyatha
Phylum Coelenterata. Saclike animals without continuous gut
  Class Hydrozoa. Hydrozoans
  Class Stromatoporoidea. Extinct reef builders of uncertain affinities
  Class Scyphozoa. Jellyfish
  Class Anthozoa. Corals
    Subclass Zoantharia. Hexacorals of modern seas
    Subclass Rugosa. Paleozoic tetracorals
    Subclass Tabulata. Tabulate corals of the Paleozoic
Phylum Ctenophora. Comb jellies, not known as fossils
Phylum Vermes. Zoologists now recognize nine phyla in this group of wormlike organisms, but as their fossil record is scant, they are of little interest to the paleontologist; see Annelida (below)
Phylum Bryozoa. Bryozoans
Phylum Brachiopoda. Brachiopods
  Class Inarticulata. Primitive phosphatic or chitinous brachiopods without hinges
  Class Articulata. Advanced calcareous brachiopods with hinges
Phylum Mollusca. Mollusks
  Class Pelecypoda (Bivalvia). Clams
  Class Gastropoda. Snails
  Class Cephalopoda. Cephalopods
    Order Nautiloidea. Nautiloids, suture lines simple
    Order Ammonoidea. Ammonoids, suture lines complex and folded
    Order Belemnoidea. Belemnites
    Order Sepioidea. Cuttlefish
    Order Teuthoidea. Squids
    Order Octopoda. Octopuses

Phylum Annelida. Segmented worms
Phylum Onychophora. Animals intermediate between annelids and arthropods
Phylum Arthropoda. Invertebrates with jointed legs
  Class Crustacea. Crabs, barnacles, ostracods
  Class Arachnoidea. Relatives of the spiders
    Order Xiphosura. King crabs
    Order Eurypterida. Eurypterids
    Order Scorpionida. Scorpions
    Order Araneida. Spiders
  Class Trilobita. Trilobites
  Class Myriapoda. Centipedes
  Class Insecta. Insects
Phylum Echinodermata
  Class Cystoidea. Cystids
  Class Blastoidea. Blastoids
  Class Crinoidea. Sea lilies
  Class Asteroidea. Sea stars
  Class Echinoidea. Sea urchins
Phylum Chordata. Animals with a notochord
  Subphylum Hemichordata. Notochord restricted to preoral region
    Class Graptolithina. Graptolites
  Subphylum Vertebrata. Animals with a vertebral column
    Class Agnatha. Primitive ostracoderms without jaws
    Class Placodermi. Placoderms, first fish with jaws
      Order Acanthodii. Spiny sharks
      Order Arthrodira. Joint-necked fish such as *Dinichthys*
      Order Antiarchi. Armored, bottom-dwelling fish with appendages
    Class Chondrichthyes. Sharks
    Class Osteichthyes. Bony fish
      Subclass Actinopterygii. Ray-finned fish
      Subclass Sarcopterygii. Fins supported by basal bony structure
        Order Dipnoi. Lungfish

Order Crossopterygii. Lobe-finned fish
  Suborder Rhipidistia. Ancestors of the Amphibia
  Suborder Coelacanthini. Coelacanths, e.g., *Latimeria*

Class Amphibia. Amphibians
  Subclass Aspidospondyli. Vertebrae preformed in cartilage
    Superorder Labyrinthodontia. Large, solid-skulled amphibians
    Superorder Salientia. Frogs and toads
  Subclass Lepospondyli. Vertebrae not preformed in cartilage

Class Reptilia. Reptiles
  Subclass Anapsida. No opening in roof of skull
    Order Cotylosauria. Stem reptiles
    Order Chelonia. Turtles
  Subclass Synapsida. Mammal-like reptiles
    Order Pelycosauria Fin-backed reptiles
    Order Therapsida. Ancestors of the mammals
    Order Mesosauria. Mesosaurs, primitive aquatic reptiles
  Subclass Parapsida
    Order Ichthyosauria. Ichthyosaurs
  Subclass Euryapsida. Plesiosaurs and their relatives
  Subclass Diapsida. Reptiles with two skull openings behind the eyes
    Superorder Lepidosauria. Lizards, snakes, primitive reptiles
    Superorder Archosauria. Dominant reptiles of Mesozoic time
      Order Thecondontia. Thecodonts and their relatives, the phytosaurs
      Order Crocodilia Crocodiles
      Order Pterosauria. Flying reptiles
      Order Saurischia. Reptile-hipped dinosaurs
      Order Ornithischia. Bird-hipped dinosaurs

Class Aves. Birds
Class Mammalia. Mammals
  Subclass Prototheria. Egg-laying mammals
    Order Monotremata. Monotremes, e.g., *Platypus*
  Subclass Allotheria
    Order Multituberculata
    Order Triconodonta (possibly not in this subclass
  Subclass Theria
    Infraclass Pantotheria. Jurassic mammals
      Order Pantotheria. Pantotheres
      Order Symmetrodonta. Symmetrodonts
    Infraclass Metatheria
      Order Marsupialia. Marsupials
    Infraclass Eutheria. Placental mammals
      Order Insectivores. Shrews, moles, etc.
      Order Chiroptera. Bats
      Order Primates
        Suborder Tupaioidea. Tree shrews
        Suborder Lemuroidea. Lemurs
        Suborder Tarsioidea. Tarsiers
        Suborder Anthropoidea. Monkeys, apes, and men
      Order Edentata. Anteaters, sloths
      Order Rodentia. Rats, squirrels
      Order Lagomorpha. Rabbits and hares
      Order Cetacea. Porpoises and whales
      Order Carnivora. Carnivores
        Suborder Creodonta. Extinct, early Cenozoic carnivores
        Suborder Fissipedia. Modern land carnivores, dogs, cats, etc.
        Suborder Pinnipedia. Seals and walruses.
      Order Condylartha. Condylarths, ancestral hoofed animals

Order Litopterna ⎫
Order Notoungulata ⎬ South American hoofed mammals
Order Astrapotheria ⎭

(*Class Mammalia—Continued*)

Order Pantodonta. Amblypods of early Cenozoic Era

Order Dinocerata. Uintatheres

Order Proboscidea. Elephant-like animals, mammoths, mastodons

Order Sirenia. Sea cows

Order Perissodactyla. Odd-toed hoofed mammals

Suborder Hippomorpha. Horses, titanotheres, etc.

Superfamily Equoidea. Horses

Superfamily Brontotheroidea. Titanotheres and chalicotheres

Suborder Ceratomorpha. Rhinoceroses and tapirs

Order Artiodactyla. Even-toed hoofed mammals

Suborder Suina. Pigs, hippopotamuses, oreodonts

Suborder Tylopoda. Camels and relatives

Suborder Ruminantia. Ruminating mammals, including deer, giraffes, cattle, and antelopes

Index

Numbers in *italic* type refer to pages showing pertinent illustrations. Numbers followed by an asterisk refer to pages on which the term is defined and appears in boldface type. The names in Appendix B have not been indexed.

$4.80
$
00

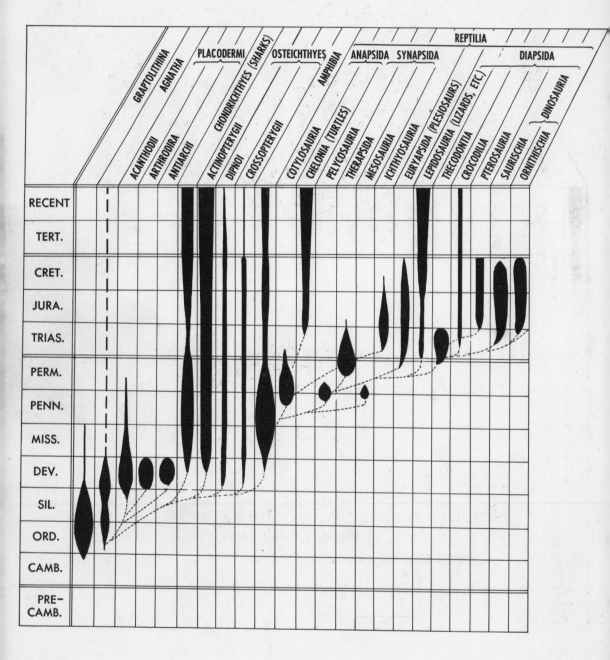